WHO'S WHO IN
ORNITHOLOGY

FIRST EDITION

WHO'S WHO IN ORNITHOLOGY

FIRST EDITION

Edited by John E Pemberton

BUCKINGHAM PRESS

Published in 1997 by
Buckingham Press
25 Manor Park
Maids Moreton
Buckingham MK18 1QX
England

Buckingham 01280 813931
International +44 (0)1280 813931

© Buckingham Press 1997

ISBN 0 9514965 8 1

Printed and bound in Great Britain by
Biddles Ltd
Guildford and King's Lynn

CONTENTS

PREFACE   5

INTRODUCTION   11

ABBREVIATIONS   13

BIOGRAPHIES   17

PREFACE

It will help in understanding the purpose and nature of this book to know something of its history. The early stages are described in an article I wrote in 1993 and which appeared in the following year's edition of *The Birdwatcher's Yearbook*. It went as follows:

> *Once it was known that Buckingham Press intended to publish a* Who's Who in Ornithology, *letters of encouragement quickly began to arrive. Some who wrote said they had thought of doing the same thing themselves but, for one reason or another, had never actually got round to it. The interesting thing was that among the many correspondents only one asked what purpose such a publication would serve and posed the basic question of whether it was really necessary. For me, as clearly it was for most others, its* raison d'être *was self-evident - and it remains so. While one generally picks up a who's who to check some fact about a person, it is the curiosity this kind of reference book stimulates that makes it so difficult to stop turning the pages and put it down again. The simple truth is that people not only need information about other individuals in the conduct of their affairs, they are also interested in them* as people.
>
> *This is borne out to some extent by the fact that there are scores of books in print either with the words* Who's Who *in their title or some other name like* Men of Achievement *or* Women in Politics. *The one which has the*

widest appeal of all is Who's Who *itself, the fat red annual publication with some 28,000 entries that range across the whole spectrum of human activity. You would think that having gone through successive editions since its inception in 1849, and become one of the most-thumbed volumes of all, its mission would be understood by everyone and its selection criteria unquestioned. The editors, however, still find it necessary to remind us in their preface that an invitation to appear should not be thought of as conferring distinction: "that", they say, "is the last thing it can do." So how are invitees selected, and how much is published about them? In the absence of any guidance on the matter, commentators are understandably puzzled as to why Graham Gooch should be included and not Gary Lineker, why Martyn Lewis and not Trevor MacDonald; and having counted the 15 lines for John Major they point quizzically to the 199 lines for Dame Barbara Cartland* (Daily Mail, *18 June 1993*).

My sympathies lie equally with the editors and the commentators. As far as Who's Who in Ornithology *is concerned I can at least explain the route to its publication and say why it took this turn and not that - subject to the caveat that there are doubtless still some roadworks ahead to be negotiated.*

The first task was to draw up a list of prospective invitees, the "guest list", and it seemed reasonable to start with names from The Birdwatcher's Yearbook. *After all, one* British Birds *reviewer had already dubbed it "a veritable Who's Who of ornithology". The only problem was that I had no way of telling whether some of the people - secretaries of natural history societies for example - were ornithologically biased or not. There was, of course, another way in which the yearbook could be of value. Each year a large mailing goes out for the purpose of updating entries in its various directory sections, and this was used in 1992 to circulate a form on which people could make nominations for the who's who, along with a brief indication of their reasons. The response was extremely good. Naturally there were duplications, but these in a way were helpful as they could be seen as mutually validating.*

I next enlisted the co-operation of the editors of appropriate magazines and journals, all of whom published notices about Who's Who in Ornithology *and extended my invitation to their readers to send in nominations, again with reasons. This help was invaluable in spreading word of the publication and helping to ensure that no-one who merited inclusion would fail to receive an invitation. "Now", wrote the editor of* Birdwatch Magazine, *"there's a chance for the many unsung heroes of amateur ornithology (and all the professionals too) to have their achievements documented in print."*

Respondents were not slow to voice their opinions as to what they expected of Who's Who in Ornithology. *The words of one, that it should include "the best of the other ranks and NCOs as well as the officers, and there are many of them" found persistent echoes. One of Scotland's most active ornithologists, for example, wrote: "There's an awful lot which simply would not happen were it not for the willingness of some fieldworkers - amateurs in particular".*

The larger national organisations were each invited to recommend categories of people within their staff and membership whom they felt ought to be included. Where this gave rise to internal discussions, the question of what criteria to apply was manifestly the issue that caused most difficulty. What prevailed was a desire to help. Their responses, and the reasoning that lay behind them, were of immense practical benefit. In one case, that of the British Ornithologists' Union, my only action was to add from their membership the names not already on my list.

There followed a lengthy period of desk research, involving library visits, to collect the names of authors of articles in the main journals, those which also gave addresses being the most helpful. However, experience with The Birdwatcher's Yearbook *over fourteen years has shown that people do tend to move about. So I carried out a mailing to a sample which included names collected in this way and others which had come in as recommendations, so as to verify their addresses before sending out invitations. Though the number of envelopes returned by the Royal Mail was quite small in percentage terms, some of the people concerned were "musts" for the who's who on any reckoning. For now they had to be marked on my records as "Address unknown", for attention later.*

There are many who oil the wheels of ornithology. A well known name urged the inclusion of the natural history editors of publishers of important book series. A director of a county wildlife trust, and himself a major contributor to ornithology, supported the case for key names from the world of bird hospitals. The curator of one of the largest museum bird collections in the UK offered to supply the names and addresses of the keepers in charge of the other important collections. The sheer number of recommendations received for leading bird photographers and artists made them essential categories. Throughout the list-building exercise one of the aims has been to encompass all aspects of the subject, and feedback has served both to support this principle and facilitate its achievement.

What all this was leading up to was the mailing of invitations to prospective biographees. Careful attention would have to be paid to the wording of the invitation itself. Given that it would be sent to people with greatly varying amounts to say about themselves, and that it would have to be meaningful to individuals drawn from a wide range of ornithology-related interests, the idea of designing a fill-in form was soon discarded. Nothing, I felt, would do more to diminish the confidence of recipients than to confront them with a set of boxes most of which they would have to leave blank simply because they did not apply in their own case. The alternative was to provide a list of headings with explantory notes and ask them to use these in compiling their responses. At a fairly early stage I sent out a pilot mailing to test how effective this would be: how useful each person found the headings and notes, and to elicit suggestions on how they might be improved. As a result the number of headings was reduced from twenty-nine to twenty and some of the notes modified. The revised invitation was then sent to a further sample and elicited information in the form required without any adverse comment.

Along with the mailing of data forms to bird recorders, clubs and wildlife trusts in 1993 for the next edition of The Birdwatcher's Yearbook, *the opportunity was taken to circulate county lists of prospective invitees for* Who's Who in Ornithology *as they then stood. This had a three-fold purpose - to allow me to thank those who had sent in nominations earlier; to show them that their recommendations had been added; and to let them see whether there were any gaps still to be be filled. For the reasons already stated I knew the lists must have contained the names of people who would themselves lay no claim to recognition as ornithologists, but I was not prepared for the strength of the blast that now hit me. "This list is simply incredible. I have been fully involved in the local ornithological scene for 50 years - have been bird recorder and editor of the annual report for the last 30 years - yet have never heard of the names marked with a question mark." That was just the start. Others came back with comments against nominees that ranged from "Dragonfly person" to "Nationally infamous as a stringer". However, despite these shocks to the system the respondents went on to reply in a constructive way by providing "good" names. They must have understood that I couldn't possibly know everyone personally. For my part I should have given them sight of the draft invitation, where it states: "The initial list of invitees has been compiled from a wide range of sources and many nominations have been received anonymously, sometimes with only sketchy reasons given. In extending this invitation we must therefore stress that receipt of information does not guarantee publication of an entry."*

One thing that characterises this organisational phase of the project to produce a Who's Who in Ornithology *is the abundant goodwill shown by those best able to contribute to its success. There is plentiful evidence of conscious effort and much time spent by individuals and groups in seeing to it that the initiative should not founder or fail to reach its full potential for want of their support. There are also promising signs that the converse will hold true: that those who may be invited without substantiated good reason will decline. My optimism in this respect stems from the replies received from several people of uncertain credentials who were included in the second sample mailing. In declining, some have even been kind enough to be almost apologetic for not being ornithologists.*

A rather more difficult category of invitee is that comprising what pollsters would call the "don't knows", except that here it is those who

don't know if they are "good enough" to appear. Self-assessment is
something on which little guidance can be given, but perhaps a careful
reading of this article will help them to decide. If I may coin a phrase,
modesty never made a good who's who. *I should also mention that there*
will be no "ghosting" of entries; in other words they will be compiled solely
from the information individuals supply about themselves. The
information may be edited, but biographees have the reassurance that they
will be sent proofs for checking.

It is planned to have the book out in time for Christmas 1994, though at
this stage it is not possible give a firm date. Returns from the preliminary
mailings of invitations have been excellent and embrace all sectors: local
stalwarts in the field to directors of national organisations - from A for
artists to Z for zoologists in fact, and everything in between. This does not
mean that entries will be grouped by topic; they will appear in one
alphabetical sequence of names.

To achieve the provisional publication target further distributions of
invitations will be phased, as will the return-by dates. The last mailing is
scheduled to take place by the end of 1993, with an ultimate return date of
31 March 1994. Within this time-frame further nominations can still be
considered.

For some biographees inclusion will be an accolade. This will not derive
from any editorial judgement but will be deduced from the published
account. For others, recognition of early accomplishments will be a spur to
further achievement. In any sphere the genuine greats, whether
professional or amateur, have always respected the maxim that is
sometimes expressed as noblesse oblige. *Their presence sets the standard*
for the aspirants on whom the future depends. The record of commitment
and achievement in every sector of our subject will ensure that the outside
world - and, indeed, posterity - perceives a true image of the vibrant state of
ornithology in the British Isles today.

Has anything changed meanwhile? As it transpired, the period of gestation
was longer than I had anticipated. This was not only unavoidable, it was in
one particular respect a considerable cause of regret. I refer to the people
who died either before I had the chance even to send them an invitation or
before I could send them a proof of their draft entry. However, in cases
where proofs did go out and were received back signed, the entries have
been included, along with an appropriate annotation. Conversely, the delay
has been quite beneficial to many people. They have had more work
published, gained promotion, completed projects or started new ones,
received awards - all enhancing their entries.

Instances of change of address have had mixed fortunes. Indeed some
individuals moved more than once during the period, but while most were

traced others remained elusive. Nothing, of course, could be done about invitees who *chose* not to reply; some expected names will be looked for in vain. The concept of completeness does not in any case apply to a work of this kind, not least because the sheer diversity of its potential constituency defies the application of strict criteria for inclusion. In this regard, a shift that did occur over the intervening period concerns geographical coverage. The original intention was to keep to the British Isles (including persons born abroad who had settled here), but exceptions were made first for some well known people who had gone to live abroad, then for one or two foreign nationals on whose behalf there was persuasive advocacy, and again for names (especially European) which had become familiar through work published here.

So it is fair to say that the book has grown organically. The governing imperative has been to represent all aspects of the subject and to include people of all 'ranks', as was emphatically requested by correspondents from the outset. I only hope that those who have had to be left out will not be offended or discouraged. The ultimate determinant has been space, and omission should not be construed as rejection.

With over one thousand entries this first edition of *Who's Who in Ornithology* presents the 'big picture' at a given moment in time. Embracing the achievements of individuals whose active participation in the development of ornithology spans most decades of this century it also chronicles the way in which the subject has evolved over the years and offers glimpses of how it could develop in the future.

I extend my sincere thanks to all who have contributed to the creation of this book, be it by making nominations, publicising the project, assisting with proof reading or in any other way. Most importantly I record my gratitude to the biographees themselves, not just for taking the time and trouble to compile their responses but also for staying the course and revising their proofs as the passage of time required.

If others learn as much from *Who's Who in Ornithology* as I have done in producing it, the effort will have been worthwhile.

John E Pemberton
16 December 1996

INTRODUCTION

Information about the biographees follows a general pattern, starting with the name and brief personal particulars, then detailing ornithological contributions, noting other interests and recreations, and concluding with means of contact. The following points should, however, be made. They are listed under headings for ease of reference.

Order of entries
Entries are arranged alphabetically by surnames. Where surnames are the same, the order is determined by forenames. Where surnames and forenames are identical the order is determined by dates of birth.

Names
If the first forename is not the one generally used by the biographee, or if a nickname is used, the chosen forename or the nickname is added in parentheses.

Dates
The convention has been adopted whereby an open-ended period of time is denoted by the start date followed by a hyphen; thus '1991-' means from 1991 onwards.

Degrees
For first degrees neither 'Hons' nor the class of degree is indicated, only the subject. Where the awarding institution is a university, only the place is given (eg 'Manchester' means Manchester University) otherwise a more specific name is used (eg 'Liverpool Polytechnic').

Quotations
Direct quotations from information supplied by biographees are enclosed within quotation marks. They may be used, for example, to preserve a flavour, record a claim or even, in one case, to share some lines of verse.

Memberships
Mention of societies to which biographees belong has been limited to those relating to overseas (eg Oriental Bird Club) and to species or categories of birds (eg Wader Study Group), thereby avoiding repetitious listing of the larger bodies such as BTO and RSPB.

Literature citations

Books. For most books the author/editor, title, edition and date are given, ie sufficient to enable them to be sought in libraries or ordered from booksellers.

priv print = item printed/published by the author.

Some abbreviated forms of titles have been used:

BTO Breeding Atlas = *The Atlas of Breeding Birds in Britain and Ireland* compiled by J T R Sharrock (Poyser, 1976)

BTO New Breeding Atlas = *The New Atlas of Breeding Birds in Britain and Ireland: 1988-1991* compiled by David Wingfield Gibbons *et al* (Poyser, 1993)

BTO Winter Atlas = *The Atlas of Wintering Birds in Britain and Ireland* compiled by Peter Lack (Poyser, 1986)

BWP = *Handbook of the Birds of Europe, the Middle East and North Africa: the Birds of the Western Palearctic* edited by S Cramp *et al* (Oxford University Press, 9 vols, 1977-94)

Concise BWP = two-volume edition of *BWP* (in press)

HBW = *Handbook of the Birds of the World* edited by Josep del Hoyo *et al* (Barcelona, Lynx Edicions, Vol 1 1992 - in progress)

Journals. Where journal titles have been abbreviated the full form should be recognised without difficulty. Examples of individual words are *Biol* (*Biological/Biology*), *Bull* (*Bulletin*), *Cons* (*Conservation*), *J* (*Journal*), *Proc* (*Proceedings*), *Soc* (*Society*), *Trans* (*Transactions*). Titles producing rather more cryptic abbreviations are *Biological Journal of the Linnean Society* (*Biol J Linn Soc*), *Bulletin of the British Ornithologists' Club* (*Bull BOC*), *Journal für Ornithologie* (*J für Orn*), *Journal of Applied Ecology* (*J Appl Ecol*), *Journal of Experimental Biology* (*J Exp Biol*), *Journal of Theoretical Biology* (*J Theor Biol*), *Philosophical Transactions of the Royal Society of Edinburgh* (*Phil Trans Roy Soc Edin*).

ABBREVIATIONS

This list contains abbreviations used in the biographical entries. It is not intended to be a general list of abbreviations used in ornithology. Where the meaning of a particular abbreviation can readily be deduced from its context it may not be listed here. See also 'Literature citations' in the Introduction.

AACCA Associate of the Association of Certified and Corporate Accountants
ABA American Birding Association
ABC African Bird Club
ABWS Army Bird Watching Society
ACA Associate of the Institute of Chartered Accountants
ACIB Associate of the Chartered Institute of Bankers
ACII Associate of the Chartered Insurance Institute
ACIS Associate of the Chartered Institute of Secretaries
ADAS Agricultural Development Advisory Service
AIEEM Associate of the Institute of Ecology and Environmental Management
AIInfSc Associate of the Institute of Information Scientists
ALA Associate of the Library Association
AMA Associate of the Museums Association
AMICE Associate Member of the Institution of Civil Engineers
AMIEE Associate Member of the Institution of Electrical Engineers
ANF Artists for Nature Foundation
AONB Area of Outstanding Natural Beauty
AOS Army Ornithological Society
AOU American Ornithologists' Union
ARCS Associate of the Royal College of Science
ARICS Associate of the Royal Institution of Chartered Surveyors
ARPS Associate of the Royal Photographic Society
ASAB Association for the Study of Animal Behaviour

ATD Art Teachers' Diploma
AWB Asian Wetland Bureau

BA Bachelor of Arts
BAOR British Army of the Rhine
BAS British Antarctic Survey
BASC British Association for Shooting and Conservation
BChir Bachelor of Surgery
BCL Bachelor of Civil Law
BDS Bachelor of Dental Surgery
BEng Bachelor of Engineering
BES British Ecological Society
BIPP British Institute of Professional Photographers
BLI BirdLife International
BM Bachelor of Medicine
BOC British Ornithologists' Club
BoEE Birds of Estuaries Enquiry
BOU British Ornithologists' Union
BS Bachelor of Surgery
BSc Bachelor of Science
BTCV British Trust for Conservation Volunteers
BTEC Business and Technology Education Council
BTO British Trust for Ornithology
BVetMed Bachelor of Veterinary Medicine
BVMS Bachelor of Veterinary Medicine and Surgery
BWP See 'Literature citations' in Introduction

CA Chartered Accountant
CB Companion of (the Order of) the Bath
CBC Common Birds Census
CBE Commander of (the Order of) the British Empire

CBiol Chartered Biologist
CCW Countryside Council for Wales
CEGB Central Electricity Generating Board
CEMPA Centro Estudos Migraçãoes e Proteção das Aves
CEng Chartered Engineer
ChB Bachelor of Surgery
CITES Convention on International Trade in Endangered Species
CMG Companion of (the Order of) St Michael and St George
CPhys Chartered Physicist
CPRE Council for the Protection of Rural England
CVO Commander of the (Royal) Victorian Order

DBV Deutscher Bund für Vogelschutz
DCH Doctor of Surgery
DFC Distinguished Flying Cross
DHKD Doğal Hayati Koruma Derneği
DIC Diploma of Imperial College
Dip BA Diploma in Business Administration
DL Deputy Lieutenant
DM Doctor of Medicine
DObstRCOG see DRCOG
DoE Department of the Environment
DoE(NI) Department of the Environment (Northern Ireland)
DOG (DO-G) Deutsche Ornithologen-Gesellschaft
DPhil Doctor of Philosophy
DRCOG Diploma of the Royal College of Obstetricians and Gynaecologists

EANHS East Africa Natural History Society
EAOS East African Ornithological Society
EAW(L)S East African Wildlife Society
EC European Community
ed edition; editor
EGI Edward Grey Institute of Field Ornithology (Univ Oxford)
EN English Nature
ESA Environmentally Sensitive Area
et al and others
et seq and the following
EU European Union
EURING European Union for Bird Ringing
EWNHS Ethiopian Wildlife and Natural History Society

FAO Food and Agriculture Organisation (United Nations)
FBCO Fellow of the British College of Optometrists

FBCS Fellow of the British Computer Society
FCA Fellow of the Institute of Chartered Accountants
FCII Fellow of the Chartered Insurance Institute
FCIS Fellow of the Chartered Institute of Secretaries
FCIWEM Fellow of the Chartered Institution of Water and Environmental Management
FCMA Fellow of the Chartered Institute of Management Accountants
FFCM Fellow of the Faculty of Community Medicine
FFOM Fellow of the Faculty of Occupational Medicine
FFPHM Fellow of the Faculty of Public Health Medicine
FFPS Fauna and Flora Preservation Society
FIBiol Fellow of the Institute of Biology
FIBMS Fellow of the Institute of Biomedical Sciences
FIMechE Fellow of the Institution of Mechanical Engineers
FInstP Fellow of the Institute of Physics
FIScT Fellow of the Institute of Science and Technology
FLA Fellow of the Library Association
FLS Fellow of the Linnean Society
FMA Fellow of the Museums Association
FRAI Fellow of the Royal Anthropological Institute
FRASE Fellow of the Royal Agricultural Society of England
FRCGP Fellow of the Royal College of General Practitioners
FRCP Fellow of the Royal College of Physicians
FRCR Fellow of the Royal College of Radiologists
FRCS Fellow of the Royal College of Surgeons
FRES Fellow of the Royal Entomological Society
FRGS Fellow of the Royal Geographical Society
FRICS Fellow of the Royal Institution of Chartered Surveyors
FRPS Fellow of the Royal Photographic Society
FRS Fellow of the Royal Society
FRSE Fellow of the Royal Society of Edinburgh
FSS Fellow of the Royal Statistical Society
FWAG Farming and Wildlife Advisory Group

FZS Fellow of the Zoological Society

GCT Game Conservancy Trust

HASA Holarctic Avian Speciation Atlas
HBW See 'Literature citations' in Introduction
HND Higher National Diploma
HRD Human Resource(s) Development

IASA International Association of Sound (and Audiovisual) Archives
IBA Important Bird Area
ICAO International Civil Aviation Organization
ICBP International Council for Bird Preservation
ICE Institution of Civil Engineers
IEEM Institute of Ecology and Environmental Management
IFAW International Fund for Animal Welfare
IOC International Ornithological Committee
ITE Institute of Terrestrial Ecology
IUCN International Union for the Conservation of Nature and Natural Resources
IWC Irish Wildbird Conservancy
IWRB International Waterfowl and Wetlands Research Bureau

JNCC Joint Nature Conservation Committee
JP Justice of the Peace

KCMG Knight Commander of (the Order of) St Michael and St George
KCVO Knight Commander of the (Royal) Victorian Order

LDS Licentiate of Dental Surgery
LEA Local Education Authority
LIBiol Licentiate of the Institute of Biology
LIEnvSc Licentiate of the Institute of Environmental Sciences
LIPU Lega Italiana Protezione Uccelli
Lit Hum *Litterae Humaniores*
LLB Bachelor of Laws
LLD Doctor of Laws
LNR Local Nature Reserve
LPO Ligue (Française) pour la Protection des Oiseaux
LRCP Licentiate of the Royal College of Physicians

MA Master of Arts
MAFF Ministry of Agriculture Fisheries and Food

MB Bachelor of Medicine
MBA Master of Business Administration
MBE Member of (the Order of) the British Empire
MC Military Cross
MCIB Member of the Chartered Institute of Bankers
MCIBS Member of the Chartered Institute of Bankers of Scotland
MCIEH Member of the Chartered Institute of Environmental Health
MCIWEM Member of the Chartered Institution of Water and Environmental Management
MIBiol Member of the Institute of Biology
MIBS Member of the Institute of Broadcast Sound
MICE Member of the Institution of Civil Engineers
MIEE Member of the Institution of Electrical Engineers
MIEEM Member of the Institute of Ecology and Environmental Management
MIEI Member of the Institution of Engineers of Ireland
MIHort Member of the Institute of Horticulture
MIMgt Member of the Institute of Management
MInstP Member of the Institute of Physics
MIStructE Member of the Institution of Structural Engineers
MME Magyar Madártani és Természetvédelmi Egyesület
MOD Ministry of Defence
MRCGP Member of the Royal College of General Practitioners
MRCP Member of the Royal College of Physicians
MRCS Member of the Royal College of Surgeons
MRCVS Member of the Royal College of Veterinary Surgeons
MRSC Member of the Royal Society of Chemistry
MRTPI Member of the Royal Town Planning Institute
MSA Master of Science and Agriculture
MSc Master of Science
MSIAD Member of the Society of Industrial Artists and Designers
MVB Bachelor of Veterinary Medicine

NABC North American Bird Club
NBC Neotropical Bird Club

NCC Nature Conservancy Council
NERC Natural Environment Research Council
NHS Natural History Society
NIBA Northern Ireland Birdwatchers' Association
NIOC Northern Ireland Ornithologists' Club
NODA National Operatic and Dramatic Association
NNR National Nature Reserve
NRA National Rivers Authority
NWC National Wildfowl Counts

OBC Oriental Bird Club
OIR Other interests and recreations
OSME Ornithological Society of the Middle East

PCB polychlorinated biphenyl
PGCE Post Graduate Certificate of Education
PhD Doctor of Philosophy
PIIA Practitioner of the Institute of Internal Auditors
priv print See 'Literature citations' in Introduction

QUB Queen's University Belfast

RA Royal Academy (Academician)
RAFOS Royal Air Force Ornithological Society
RAOU Royal Australasian Ornithologists' Union
RCS Royal College of Surgeons
RD Reserve Decoration
RGS Royal Geographical Society
RIBA Royal Institute of British Architects
RICS Royal Institution of Chartered Surveyors
RM Royal Marines
RMA Royal Military Academy
RNBWS Royal Naval Birdwatching Society
RNVR Royal Naval Volunteer Reserve
RPS Royal Photographic Society
RSA Republic of South Africa; Royal Society of Arts
RSE Royal Society of Edinburgh
RSNC Royal Society for Nature Conservation
RSPB Royal Society for the Protection of Birds

SAOS Southern African Ornithological Society
SAST Seabirds at Sea Team
ScD Doctor of Science
SEO Sociedad Española de Ornitología
SEOF Société d'Etudes Ornithologiques de France
SNH Scottish Natural Heritage
SOC Scottish Ornithologists' Club
SOTEAG Shetland Oil Terminal Environmental Advisory Group
SPA Special Protection Area
SPEA Sociedade Portuguesa para o Estudo das Aves
SPNR Society for the Promotion of Nature Reserves
SRC Science Research Council
SSC Species Survival Commission (of IUCN)
SSSI Site of Special Scientific Interest
SWLA Society of Wildlife Artists

TD Territorial Decoration
TNC Trust for Nature Conservation
TRAFFIC Trade Records Analysis of Flora and Fauna In Commerce

UEA University of East Anglia
UNDP United Nations Development Programme
UNEP United Nations Environment Programme

VC vice-county

WAGBI Wildfowlers' Association of Great Britain and Ireland
WAOS West African Ornithological Society
WBS Waterways Bird Survey
WEA Workers' Educational Association
WeBS Wetland Bird Survey
WIWO Werkgroep Internationaal Wad- en Watervogel Onderzoek
WOAD Welsh Office Agricultural Department
WPA World Pheasant Association
WSG Wader Study Group
WSRS Wildlife Sound Recording Society
WT Wildlife Trust
WWF World Wide Fund for Nature
WWT Wildfowl & Wetlands Trust

YHA Youth Hostels Association
YOC Young Ornithologists' Club

BIOGRAPHIES

ABBOTT, Stephen (Steve); *b:* 3 May 1952 in Eye, Suffolk. BSc Zoology with Botany (London, 1974). Biological science teacher. Chairman Surrey Bird Club 1989-92; Committee and Records Committee 1987-. Founder-member Berkshire Atlas Group and organiser of tetrad survey for *The Birds of Berkshire* 1987-89. BTO 'A' ringer since 1980 and trainer. Local organiser for BTO surveys. Special interest in birds of dry acid heathland eg Nightjar, Woodlark, Stonechat, Dartford Warbler. Illus talks to bird clubs. 27 Bosman Drive, Windlesham, Surrey GU20 6JN. 01276 475792.

ABRAHAM, Edward John (Ted); *b:* 26 January 1941 in Great Crosby, Lancs; *w:* Kathleen. BSc Chemistry with Physics (Manchester, 1962), PGCE (Liverpool, 1963). Retired schoolmaster. Founder and partner Birdline North West and Birdline Wales, both Oct 1989-. Hilbre Bird Obs Committee and Ringing Sec, and Cheshire Rarities Committee 1970-80. Tutor WEA and Liverpool Univ Dept of Extra Mural Studies 1975-89. RSPB/schools liaison (Wirral, Merseyside) from 1990. Special interests: migrants, rarities, waders, warblers, offshore islands. Travel to Caribbean birding locations. Editor *North West Bird Report* 1990-95. OIR: Manchester United FC. 20 Arden Drive, Neston, Cheshire L64 0SJ. 0151 353 0761.

ADCOCK, Maurice Albert; *b:* 30 Nov 1929 in Great Wakering, Essex; *w:* Beryl (deceased). Municipal College, Southend-on-Sea. Retired after 35 years in MOD. Chairman Foulness Wildfowl and Wader Count Group 1975-91. Committee MOD Conservation Group (Shoeburyness) 1975-91, 1993-. Sec Essex Birdwatching Soc 1989-. BTO Regional Development Officer Essex and Regional Representative Essex (South) Sept 1992-. BTO 'A' ringer since 1974. Monitoring Little Tern population on Foulness and Maplin Bank since early 1970s, based on ringing of pulli (produced first two recoveries on wintering grounds in W Africa and longevity record). Two Constant Effort Site plots on MOD property 1988-. Devised artificial nesting platforms for Herons to replace traditional sites in dead trees. Author of paper 'The Birds of the Foulness Area' (for MOD) and article in *Essex Bird Report* 1992 on the Foulness hailstorm which killed over 3,000 birds. Occasional TV appearances. Collector of books on ornithology. BTO Bernard Tucker Medal 1994, for outstanding service to the Trust. Member: Seabird Group, Wader Study Group. OIR: jazz (esp West Coast), playing piano and tenor saxophone, watching all sport. The Saltings, 53 Victoria Drive, Great Wakering, Southend-on-Sea SS3 0AT. 01702 219437.

AEBISCHER, Nicholas John; *b:* 9 March 1957 in Switzerland. Lic ès Sc Math (Lausanne, 1980), PhD Mathematical Ecology (Durham, 1985). Head of Biometrics, Game Conservancy Trust since Feb 1990. Prev: Research Asst/Senior Research Asst, Univ Durham 1984-87; Biometrician, Game Conservancy Trust 1987-90. Integrated Population Monitoring Working Group (BTO/JNCC) Sept 1990-. Scientific Advisory Committee WWT 1992-94. IUCN/SSC Specialist Group for the Sustainable Use of Wild Species Feb 1992-. Committee IUCN/SSC Partridge, Quail and Francolin Specialist Group Dec 1992-. Editorial panel *Gibier Faune Sauvage* Dec 1993-. BOU Council 1996-. Special interests: seabirds and their environment; gamebirds and their environment; population dynamics; population modelling; statistical methods in ornithology (esp population parameters, ringing recoveries, habitat use); sustainable exploitation of birds. Studies: population dynamics of Shag and Kittiwake in relation to the marine environment, and of Grey Partridge and Corn Bunting in relation to the agricultural environment; statistical methods for analysis of survival and habitat use. Bird-related travel to countries in Europe, Africa and N America. Scientific papers in *Acta Ornithologica, Bird Study, Ibis, J Field Ornithol, Ringing & Migration.* Joint editor of proceedings of Perdix VI, First International Symposium on Partridges, Quails and Francolins, held Sept 1991; joint editor of procs of Corn Bunting Workshop, held March 1995; joint editor of procs of Perdix VII, International Symposium on Partridges, Quails and Pheasants, held Oct 1995. Member: Société Romande pour la Protection des Oiseaux. The Game Conservancy Trust, Fordingbridge, Hants SP6 1EF. 01425 652381.

ALEXANDER, Gregory (Greg); *b:* 15 July 1955 in Southampton; *w:* Hilary. Environmental Science course (Romsey Further Education Centre, 1985). Shipping agent. BTO 'A' ringer since 1992. Secretary Lower Test Ringing Group 1988-; ringer in charge 1994-; compiler *LTRG Annual Report.* Contributor to BTO Nest Record Scheme 1985- (esp Swallow, Ringed Plover). Fieldwork in 1980s for Hampshire Ornithological Society tetrad atlas (*Birds of Hampshire,* 1993). Voluntary warden Lower Test Marsh 1986-87 and member Reserve Management Team. Studies include mortality and migration. Regular birding trips to Spey Valley and twice to California and Yosemite National Park. Articles and notes in *Annual Report of Southampton NHS, British Birds, BTO News* and local press. Prepared conservation submission against Fawley B Power Station (1989). Assisted in editing commercial video *Recognising Birds in Gardens* (prod by Ted Channell). Regular talks to schools and societies on bird behaviour and survival techniques 1983-86. Work in the Port of Southampton has stimulated ornithological interest in others (eg has been handed dead birds found on ships, inc Lanceolated Warbler and Black-eared Wheatear - sent to British Museum). Lobbies MP on conservation issues. Local Councillor 1983-86. OIR: popular music, satirical comedy, swimming, badminton. 6 Arliss Road, Maybush, Southampton SO1 6DG. 01703 773116.

ALEXANDER, Robert McNeill (Neill); *b:* 7 July 1934 in Lisburn, N Ireland; *w:* Ann. MA Zoology (Cambridge, 1959), PhD Zoology (Cambridge, 1958), DSc (Wales, 1969). FIBiol 1969, FRS 1987. Professor of Zoology, Univ Leeds since 1969. Prev: Lecturer in Zoology, Univ Coll N Wales 1959-69. Secretary Zoological Society of London 1992-. Special interests: biomechanics of animal (inc bird) movement, esp terrestrial locomotion. Author of eg *Animal Mechanics* (2nd ed 1983), *Elastic Mechanisms in Animal Movement* (1988), *Animals* (1990), *Exploring Biomechanics: Animals in Motion* (1992); some 200 scientific papers. Scientific Medal, Zoological Soc of London 1969; Linnean Medal for Zoology, Linnean Soc of London 1979; Muybridge Medal, International Soc for Biomechanics 1991. Dept of Biology, University of Leeds, Leeds LS2 9JT. 0113 233 2911.

ALLARD, Peter; *b:* 6 January 1947 in Great Yarmouth, Norfolk; *w:* Susan Ann. Aircraft handler. Norfolk County Bird Recorder 1977-94, later County Archivist. Editorial asst *Norfolk Bird Report* 1964-. Founder-member and Secretary Great Yarmouth Bird Club 1989-. Voluntary warden Breydon Water LNR 1969-. Seasonal warden Winterton Dunes NNR 1967-69. BoEE count organiser Breydon Water. BTO 'C' ringer since 1977. Special interests: identification, conservation, local migration studies. Established Common Tern nesting platforms at Breydon Water and Broadland. Responsible for establishment of Great Yarmouth Little Tern colony on the North Beach in 1986. Author *The Birds of Great Yarmouth* (1990); *Breydon Water and its Wildlife* and *Natural History of Great Yarmouth* (in prep); regular contributor to *Bird Watching* (1987-), local papers and magazines. 'Very conservation minded, but proud to have added eight species to the Norfolk list', inc Red-breasted Goose in 1962 when only 14 and Britain's first live Isabelline Wheatear in 1977; has also found no fewer than 18 Broad-billed Sandpipers at Breydon Water since 1961. OIR: local history; collecting stamps, old postcards and bottles; writing book on local maritime studies. 39 Mallard Way, Bradwell, Great Yarmouth, Norfolk NR31 8JY. 01493 657798.

ALLEN, Richard William; *b:* 2 November 1964 in Newbury, Berks. BA Graphic Design (Illustration) (Kingston Polytechnic, 1987). Freelance illustrator. Published work inc illustrations for *Where to Watch Birds in Hampshire, Dorset and the Isle of Wight* by George Green and Martin Cade (1989), *Essex Bird Report* 1988-94, BTO New Breeding Atlas, and *A Guide to the Sunbirds and Flowerpeckers of the World* (in prep); also illustrations (identification) for *Birdwatch* magazine and cover pictures for *British Birds, Birding World*. Exhibitions include SWLA (Mall Galleries) 1992-95; Wildlife Art Gallery, Lavenham, Suffolk. Bird Illustrator of the Year (*British Birds*) 1993. 3 Dudley Road, Fingringhoe, Essex CO5 7DS. 01206 729807.

ALLISON, Richard Iain; *b:* 8 March 1962 in Birmingham. BSc Geology (Plymouth, 1984). Area sales manager. Cambridgeshire County Bird Recorder 1993-. County Records Committee 1992-. Council Cambridge Bird Club 1993-. Special interests: gulls and wildfowl. Birding trips to The Gambia, USA, Israel, Costa Rica, Kenya, Morocco, Malaysia, South Africa and several countries in Europe. Occasional note in *British Birds*, regular county round-up in *Bird Watching*, and article on Fen Drayton Gravel Pits in *Cambridge Bird Report* 1990. Member: ABC. OIR: dragonflies, damselflies, butterflies, botany, geology, cricket. 29 Bagot Place, King's Hedges, Cambridge CB4 2UL. 01223 367392; mobile 0836 767360.

ALLSOP, Jake; *b:* 5 June 1936 in Hadley, Shropshire. MA Modern History (St John's College, Oxford, 1957), PGCE (Liverpool, 1959). Author and consultant in HRD. BTO 'A' ringer since 1972. Ringing Secretary, Christchurch Harbour Ringing Station 1974-83. Secretary Golden Oriole Group 1988-. Project co-ordinator 'Concern for Swifts' campaign 1996-. Special interests: Barn Owl, Golden Oriole, conservation of birds in Anatolian Turkey, population studies in local Cambs area through ringing. Co-author (with wildlife photographer Mike Read) *The Robin* (1992), *The Barn Owl* (1994). Member: as above, also Hawk and Owl Trust, Turkish Society for the Protection of Nature (DHKD). OIR: music (esp jazz), foreign languages. 5 Bury Lane, Haddenham, Ely, Cambs CB6 3PR. 01353 740540.

ALLSOPP, Keith; *b:* 21 June 1935 in Wolverhampton, West Midlands. BSc Mathematical Physics (Birmingham, 1956). FRMetSoc 1987. Senior Research Scientist, Cranfield University. Committee Leicestershire and Rutland Ornithological Society 1965-75. County Bird Recorder for Leics 1968-75. Special interests: migration; flight orientation and navigation; flight mechanics; weather and geomagnetic factors in relation to these topics. Author of monthly 'Field Notes' (LROS) 1968-75. Joint author of

'Monthly Reports', 'Seasonal Reports' and 'Yearly Summaries' for *British Birds* since 1976. OIR: photography. 137 Redbridge, Stantonbury, Milton Keynes MK14 6DL. 01908 315896.

ALSOP, Derek; *b:* 8 November 1930 in Whaley Bridge, Cheshire; *w:* Wendy. Decorator. Committee Derbyshire Ornithological Society 1964-79 and its representative on Peak Park Wildlife Group 1983-90. Warden of wildlife reserve at Taxal, Whaley Bridge from 1985. Special interest: moorland birds. Co-ordinated DOS Dipper survey 1993 for NW of county. Surveyed and published report on Ring Ouzel population of Derbyshire in 1974. Records of birds in local area of the Peak District kept since 1946, noting declines in many species and extinction of some. Many lectures on birds and habitats. Over twenty years photographing birds and flowers in the Peak District and abroad. 103 Macclesfield Road, Whaley Bridge, Stockport, Cheshire SK12 7DH. 01663 732744.

ALSTRÖM, Per Johan; *b:* 9 April 1961 in Sweden; *w:* Ulrica. Studies in Medicine and Biology at Univ Gothenburg. Freelance ornithologist. Swedish West Coast Records Committee mid 1970s-early 1980s (inc Chairman). Swedish Rarities Committee 1981-90. Identification consultant for *Birding World* 1988- and *Limicola* 1992-. Swedish representative of OBC since foundation in 1985. IOC's English Names Committee (Palearctic Sub-committee) since formation in 1996. Special interests: identification and taxonomy. Major projects are taxonomic reviews of various warbler genera (with Urban Olsson) and Holarctic larks, pipits and wagtails (with Krister Mild and Bill Zetterström). Travelled widely in Holarctic region, mainly in Asia (some 3 years total, approx one year in China). Much tape recording when travelling. Author (with Peter Colston and Ian Lewington) of *A Field Guide to the Rare Birds of Britain and Europe* (1991). Co-author and co-artist of handbook of Holarctic larks, pipits and wagtails (in prep). Some 60 papers and notes in eg *Birding World, British Birds, Bull BOC, Dutch Birding, Forktail, Ibis, J Bombay NHS, Limicola, Sandgrouse, Strix, Vår Fågelvärld*; also Editorial Board *Vår Fågelvärld*. Illustrations for several of own identification papers, also cover pictures for *Birding World, OBC Bull* and *Vår Fågelvärld*. Paintings exhibited at galleries in Sweden and Britain. Winner 'Bird Artist of the Year' competition in Sweden 1992. Swedish Ornithological Society's 'Ornithological Research Award' 1995. Member: OBC, Swedish Orn Soc. OIR: mammals, reptiles, amphibians, botany. Kungsgatan 3, 462 33 Vänersborg, Sweden. +46 (0)521 66291.

ANDREW, Dougal Graham; *b:* 19 May 1926 in Elgin, Morayshire; *w:* Gratian. Uppingham School. MA Law (Cambridge, 1949), LLB (Edinburgh, 1952). Writer to the Signet. SOC Council c1957-86. Scottish Birds Records Committee, latterly Chairman, c1957-71. Hon Member SOC, 1985. BOU Records Committee 1961-68. Trustee Fair Isle Bird Observatory Trust c1957-89. Founding editor *Edinburgh Bird Bulletin*, 1950 ('Britain's first bi-monthly local bird journal?'). Founding asst editor *Scottish Birds*, 1958-73. Mainly 'local patch' work and Scottish islands; also Arctic (Spitsbergen 1955, NE Greenland 1983). OIR: classical music, reading, golf. Muirfield Gate, Gullane, E Lothian EH31 2EG. 01620 843307.

ANDREWS, Ian John; *b:* 19 April 1958 in Rochester, Kent; *w:* Jill. BSc Geology (Hull, 1979), MSc Petroleum exploration studies (Aberdeen, 1981). Senior Geologist with the British Geological Survey, Edinburgh. Bird Recorder Lothian Region since 1992; prev Midlothian, W Lothian and Edinburgh Districts, and Forth islands 1986-89. BoEE organiser Outer Forth south 1984-89. Committee SOC Lothian Branch 1985-88, 1993-. *British Birds* correspondent for Jordan 1989-92. Special interests: birds of the Lothian Region, Jordan and Middle East; identification; photography; travel. Author *Birds of the Lothians* (1985), *Birdwatching Sites in the Lothians* (1989), *Birds of the Hashemite Kingdom of Jordan* (priv print, 1995). Editor *Lothian Bird Report* 1986-88; editor's assistant *Scottish Bird News* 1987-89, asst editor *Sandgrouse* 1995-. Papers and articles on Lothian Region (local rarities, skua passage, Scandinavian Rock Pipits, Shelduck census, Musselburgh list, Barns Ness list, birdwatching sites) in *Lothian Bird Report*; and on Jordan (black morph of Mourning Wheatear, raptor passage, Azraq oasis, Blue Tits) in *Sandgrouse*. Member: OSME. 39 Clayknowes Drive, Musselburgh, Midlothian EH21 6UW. 0131 665 0236.

APPLETON, Timothy Paul (Tim); *b:* 6 June 1947 in Tunbridge Wells, Kent; *w:* Yanina. Wells Cathedral School. Manager Rutland Nature Reserve since 1975. Prev: Deputy Curator Slimbridge Wildfowl Trust 1970-75. Leicestershire Rarities Committee 1990-. President Oakham School Orn Soc 1992-. Committee RSNC Conservation Policy and Technical Advisory Group 1996-. Tutor WEA evening classes and Nottingham Univ Adult Education Dept 1976-; lectures to wide variety of societies. BTO 'A' ringer since 1971. Special interests: waterfowl management and showing birds to people. Expedition leader to Svalbard to ring Barnacle Geese and to Papua New Guinea to study Salvador's Teal. Organiser of Rutland Water Ringing Group and all surveys on reservoir, ie waterfowl counts etc. Author

Rutland Water Nature Reserve: concept, design and management (1982) and *The Management of Rutland Water Reservoir for Wildlife* (1982). Editor *Birds of Rutland Water* (annual report) 1975-. Articles in eg *Bird Watching, Birdwatcher's Yearbook, Natural World, Wildfowl* and local society magazines. Photographs published in various magazines and books. Regular local TV and radio broadcasts. Joint organiser of the British Birdwatching Fair (started as the Wildfowl Bonanza, a local event, but realised the potential of a national event which has now become an international venue for birdwatchers, raising awareness and funds for international conservation projects). Leader of birdwatching tours to Africa, India, Latin and N America, Australia and Europe. Fishponds Cottage, Stamford Road, Oakham, Leics LE15 8AB. 01572 770651.

ap RHEINALLT, Tristan; *b:* 12 May 1956 in Denbigh, Clwyd; *w:* Isabel. BA Applied Biology (Cambridge, 1978), MA (Cambridge, 1982), PhD Marine Zoology (Wales, 1983). Self-employed biologist and writer. Argyll Bird Recorder since 1993. Committee Argyll Bird Club 1993-. Bird Recorder Arran NHS 1991-93. BoEE co-ordinator Arran 1991-93. NWC goose count organiser Arran 1991-93. Special interests: seabirds, identification. Widely travelled in Europe and N America (lived over two years in Canada), also Middle East and Far East. Editor *Arran Bird Report* 1992 (joint editor 1990, 1991). OIR: botany, entomology (hoverflies, moths), walking. 19 Shore Street, Port Wemyss, Isle of Islay, Argyll PA47 7ST. 01496 860361; fax 01496 860374.

ARCHIBALD, Myles; *b:* 24 April 1962 in London; *w:* Dr Kate Cabot. BSc Zoology (Bristol, 1983). Head of Collins Natural History Department since 1992. Special interests: population ecology of wildfowl and gamebirds, migration, behaviour. Member: ABC. OIR: sailing, East Anglia, Adnams. Collins Natural History, HarperCollins, 77-85 Fulham Palace Road, London W6 8JB. 0181 307 4225; fax 0181 307 4037; home 0181 995 3843.

ARLOTT, Norman Arthur; *b:* 15 November 1947 in Reading, Berks; *w:* Marie. Freelance artist. Illustrations for over seventy books inc *BWP, Collins Complete Guide to British Wildlife* and other field guides; also in many wildlife magazines. Designs for special bird stamp issues inc Jamaica, Bahamas, Seychelles, British Virgin Islands, The Gambia, Malawi, Christmas Island. Special interests: African ornithology, esp E Africa; leading tours to E Africa (Papyrus Tours). Bird Illustrator of the Year (*British Birds*) 1980 and 1981. Member: EAOS, EAWS, SWLA. OIR: golf, motor racing, football, food. Hill House, School Road, Tilney Saint Lawrence, Norfolk PE34 4RB. 01945 880543.

ARMSTRONG, Anthony (Tony); *b:* 28 November 1946 in Newcastle upon Tyne; *w:* Sandra. Dip Town Planning (Leeds School of Town Planning, 1969), MSc Urban Science (Birmingham, 1970). Principal planning officer. Committee Durham Bird Club 1981-. County Bird Recorder 1988-. Chairman County Rarities Sub-committee 1988-. County Wildlife Liaison Committee 1994-. Special interests: foreign birding and moorland birds. Instrumental in establishing Durham Upland Bird Study Group (Secretary) in Jan 1992: brings together local amateurs, university researchers, English Nature and RSPB staff; the first such group in England and the model for similar county study groups. Co-ordinating a study of the colonisation of county by Buzzard. Designed Whitburn Bird Observatory (seawatching) built by South Tyneside Council in 1989. Editor *Birds in Durham* (annual report) 1988-. Member: ABC. OIR: family, cooking, DIY. 39 Western Hill, Durham City DH1 4RJ. 0191 386 1519.

ARNOLD, Douglas Neil; MBE 1986; *b:* 17 February 1939 in Ilford, Essex. Teacher's Cert Geography (London, 1962), BEd Environmental Science (Southampton, 1977). CBiol, MIBiol 1980; FRES 1986. Bird tour leader since 1992 and consultant in environmental education since 1993. Prev: primary school teacher 1962-93; part-time lecturer in ecological studies, Bournemouth Polytechnic 1984-87. Committee Portland Bird Observatory and Field Centre 1969-94. Committee Dorset Bird Club 1969-83. Wildfowl and BoEE count organiser Dorset 1970-88. Founder and manager Radipole School local nature reserve 1968-. Holiday leader YOC 1970-93. Leader of Bird Group, Weymouth Youth Activities Centre 1969-79. Birdwatching leader Weymouth Adult Education Centre 1981-93. Special interests: environmental education and conservation, esp with young people. Author *Wildlife Conservation by Young People* (1976), *The Young Naturalist's Guide to Conservation* (1978), *The Young Ecologist* (1981), *The Young Naturalist* (1983), *Dorset Naturally* (1993). Co-author (with Alan Holiday) *Wytch Farm Oilfield: educational resource* (1992); contributor to *The Birds of Dorset* by E D V Prendergast and J V Boys (1983); local booklets on birds and insects, inc study methods. Sub-editor *Dorset Bird Report* 1970-79; articles in educational journals and in Dorset newspapers and magazines. RSPB President's Award 1988. OIR: watercolour painting, photography, listening to classical music. 14 Spa Road, Weymouth, Dorset DT3 5EL. 01305 770312.

ARNOLD, Maurice Arthur; *b:* 20 September 1925 in Wilnecote, Warks (now Staffs). Wilnecote High School, Tamworth. Retired. Wildfowl Count organiser for Staffs, Warks, W Midlands and Worcs 1978-. Compiled

Alvecote Pools Nature Reserve Annual Reports with late brother George Albert Arnold 1959-84. Many notes and articles, mainly in *West Midland Bird Club Annual Report* and *Bulletin*. Special interest: birds of W Midlands. Queen's Silver Jubilee Medal 1977 (for nature conservation and education); Countryside Award 1970 (European Conservation Year, for improvements to Alvecote Pools Nature Reserve). OIR: inc wild flowers, woodlands and wetlands, butterflies. 58 Overwoods Road, Hockley, Tamworth, Staffs B77 5LZ.

ARNOTT, John Michael Stewart; *b:* 12 June 1933; *w:* Lynne. BA Law (Peterhouse, Cambridge, 1957). Producer BBC radio wildlife programmes 1968-82, retired. Chairman Isle of May Bird Observatory 1980-86 (Secretary 1974-80). Chairman Fair Isle Bird Observatory Trust 1983-85 (Asst Sec 1974-83). President SOC 1984-87. Nature Conservancy Committee for Scotland 1986-91. NCC Advisory Committee on Birds 1990-91. NCC Scotland (later SNH) South East Regional Board 1991-95. Vice Chairman Countryside Commission for Scotland 1986-92 (member from 1982). Council member and Chairman Lothians Branch Scottish WT 1995-. Special interests: migration, Arctic birds, photography. East Redford House, 133 Redford Road, Edinburgh EH13 0AS. 0131 441 3567.

ASH, John Sidney; *b:* 26 May 1925 in Gosforth, Northumberland; *w:* Jonquil. BSc Entomology (Durham, 1945), DIC Entomology (1948), PhD Ecology of bird ectoparasites (London, 1952). Retired. Prev: ICI Game Research Station, Ecologist 1951-60; Game Research Assocn, Research Director 1960-69; Head, Medical Ecology Division, US Naval Medical Research Unit, Ethiopia 1969-77; Ornithologist, United Nations (FAO), Somalia 1978-82; Consultant, United Nations (UNEP, UNDP, FAO), Uganda, S Yemen, Maldives, etc 1983-84. During the 1950s and 1960s on BTO Council, Scientific Advisory Committee, Bird Observatories Committee, Bird Ringing Committee; Chairman BOU Records Committee (1969); Joint Committee of BTO/RSPB/GRA on Toxic Chemicals (1961-69); Research Committee on Toxic Chemicals: Working Party on Pesticides and Birds and Mammals; Wildlife Research Committee of Assocn of British Manufacturers of Agricultural Chemicals; Portland Bird Observatory Committee (1951-69). Also served on Committee on Bird-strike Hazards to Aircraft (Ethiopia 1974-77) and Board of Rachel Carson Trust for the Living Environment (USA 1963-96). Research Associate (honorary) Smithsonian Institution (USA 1973-96). Special interests: gamebirds, migration, African rainforests, bird pests, ecology, distribution, ringing (over 100,000 birds ringed 1940-94), pesticide/wildlife problems, pollen contamination of birds, ectoparasites, haemoparasites, particular species (inc Partridge, Red-legged Partridge, Red-backed Shrike, Stone Curlew, *Picathartes*). Many expeditions throughout Ethiopia, Somalia, Uganda, Nigeria; also to Indonesia, Indian Ocean islands, Bushmanland, Lake Chad (BOU Exped 1967), Azraq, Jordan (Internat Biological Programme Exped 1966); migration surveys in SE Morocco (1963, 1965), Indonesia (1982, 1990), Sudan (1986), Oman (1992, 1993), Red Sea (1994), Ethiopia/Somalia (1995), Saudi Arabia (1996), etc. Major schemes established in 1961 with Game Research Association: initiation of the first field surveys in UK of game and wildlife mortality associated with agricultural pesticides, the National Game Census which collected game bags and population data from 1.5 million acres of lowland Britain, and the National Game Marking Scheme through which 200,000 gamebirds were soon being marked annually. Project for the establishment of the Bird Distribution Atlas for Ethiopia was started in 1969, and for Somalia in 1978. Over 350 scientific papers, articles, reports, and a book (with J E Miskell) *Birds of Somalia* (in press). Editor *Game Research Association Annual Report* (1961-69). Radio and TV programmes in UK and abroad. BTO Tucker Medal 1967. Member: Bali Bird Club, Bustard Group, OBC, OSME, WAOS. OIR: country pursuits; association with inhabitants of deserts, rainforests and 'undeveloped' areas of the world; philately (early GB). Godshill Wood, Fordingbridge, Hants SP6 2LR. 01425 653375.

ASHWORTH, John Edward; *b:* 29 July 1937 in Southport, Lancs (now Merseyside). King George V Grammar School and Southport School of Art. Retired. Freelance lecturer and tour guide. Ornithology tutor for WEA since 1965 (32 centres in NW England). Part-time ornithology tutor Lancs Educ Auth 1966-75, Sefton Educ Auth 1967-74, Liverpool Univ Continuing Educ Dept 1974-76. Lectures to bird clubs, county wildlife trusts, schools, etc. Voluntary warden Mere Sands Wood Nature Reserve 1984-. Founding leader of Southport RSPB Members' Group 1977. President Merseyside Naturalists' Assocn (Chairman 1981-91). Past President Lancs and Cheshire Fauna Soc. Council Lancs WT 1973-. Special interests: population changes in British birds (fieldwork for BTO Breeding Atlas); waders (worked with Prof W Hale on his Redshank studies on Banks Marsh, Ribble Marshes NNR); upland birds of northern Britain, esp in Forest of Bowland AONB. Leader of bird tours inc several to Mallorca and Corfu. Author of sections on Merseyside and Greater Manchester for Pan/Ordnance Survey *Nature Atlas of Great Britain* (1989); short paper on egg-carrying by Blackbird in *British Birds* (1965). Contributed to BBC programme on threat of proposed Mersey Barrage to estuary birds (threat no longer exists). Large collection of ornithological and natural history books. OIR: British mammals and plants, fell and long distance walking, active member of YHA. 134 Fylde Road, Marshside, Southport, Merseyside PR9 9XL.

ATKINSON, Kim; *b:* 26 April 1962 in Bath, Somerset. MA Natural History Illustration (Royal College of Art, 1987). Freelance artist, esp ornithological subjects. Illustrations in *Bardsey Bird Observatory Report* since 1986; *Gwynedd Bird Report* 1991, 1992; *Birdwatcher's Yearbook* 1992; *Portrait of a Living Marsh* (1993); *Birds in Wales* by R Lovegrove *et al* (1994); *Artists for Nature in Extremadura* (1995). Worldwide exhibitions 1992,94,95 following Artists for Nature Foundation expeditions to Poland, Spain, Ireland and the Loire (France). Exhibits annually at SWLA (Mall Galleries). Also one-person and mixed exhibitions. One of several European artists in residence at Les Ecrins National Park, French Alps 1995 and 1996. *Natural World* Art Award 1993. Member: SWLA. OIR: walking, gardening, travel, general natural history. Ty'n Gamdda, Uwchmynydd, Aberdaron, Pwllheli, Gwynedd LL53 8DA. 01758 760257.

AVENT, Cyril Frederick Sale; *b:* 20 September 1937 in Tetney, Lincs. St Luke's College of Education, Exeter. Teacher, retired. Tutor in birdwatching and ecology at schools in Somerset 1957-91. Survey work for WWT on Shelduck 1987, and for RSPB on breeding waders on the Somerset levels 1992, 1994. Voluntary warden at Bridgwater Bay NNR since c1974. Chairman Mid-Somerset Naturalists' Soc 1968-85. Somerset TNC's Sedgemoor Area Committee c1971-86. Management Committee for Screech Owl Ponds LNR 1975-80. Special interests: birds of the Somerset levels, migration routes of birds in Somerset. Bird-related visits to Europe and the Arctic. Author of ornithological section of Somerset TNC report on the development of local brick pits as nature reserves (1978); contributor to local bird reports, newsletters and newspapers. OIR: amateur stage (awarded NODA long service medal and bars). 22 Provident Place, Bridgwater, Somerset TA6 7DT. 01278 459859.

AVERY, Mark Ian; *b:* 29 March 1958; *w:* Rosemary Cockerill. Bristol Grammar School. BA Applied Biology (Downing College, Cambridge, 1979), MA (Cambridge, 1981), PhD Winter activity of pipistrelle bats (Aberdeen, 1983). Head of Conservation Science RSPB since 1992. Prev: Research Biologist, then Senior RB, RSPB 1986-91; Contract Scientific Officer, Forestry Commission 1986; NERC Research Fellow, EGI Oxford 1984-85; Research Asst Animal Behaviour Research Group, Dept of

Zoology, Oxford 1979-80. Warden, St Cyrus NNR (summer 1976). Special interests: ecology, conservation, behaviour, red data books. Co-author (with R Leslie) *Birds and Forestry* (1990), and (with S J Petty) *Forest Bird Communities in Relation to Silvicultural Practices in the British Uplands* (1990). Over thirty scientific papers in eg *Ibis*, *J Animal Ecol*, *J Appl Ecol*, *Nature*; many articles in magazines eg *Ecos*, *New Scientist*. Broadcasts on national and local radio. OIR: National Hunt racing, opera, food, drink. Research Dept, RSPB, The Lodge, Sandy, Beds SG19 2DL. 01767 680551.

AXELL, Herbert Ernest (Bert); MBE 1965; *b:* 1 July 1915 in Rye, E Sussex; *w:* Joan. Independent consultant on bird habitats, planning reserves, etc. Retired in 1951 through ill health from Postal Services Operations Branch, GPO HQ (same job and office as Anthony Trollope). Founder-warden Dungeness Bird Observatory 1952. Warden RSPB Dungeness Reserve 1952-59. Senior Warden RSPB Minsmere Reserve 1959-75. RSPB Land Use Adviser 1975-80. President Suffolk Ornithologists' Group 1982-95 and Landguard Bird Observatory 1983. Egg-collector 1920; ringer since 1929 (before BTO founded). Special interests: migration; habitat engineering, esp for endangered species. Seven-year study of nocturnal migrant birds at lighthouses, inc work on floodlighting to prevent collisions; first ringing of birds on lightship, during migration study on Smith's Knoll LV in 1953; invented 'Dungeness' bird ringing pliers in 1954, later adopted by BTO; made original study of tarsi thicknesses on thousands of live birds of a hundred species to enable better-fitting rings. Reserve planning for many bodies in UK and abroad, eg Doñana, Spain; Mai Po Wetlands, Hong Kong. Extensive overseas travel for inspection of wildlife sites and lectures, inc three world tours. Winston Churchill Fellowship 1975 to study management of habitats for endangered birds in New Zealand and USA. Author *Minsmere: Portrait of a Bird Reserve* (foreword by HRH Duke of Edinburgh) (1977, Japanese ed 1995); *The Birds of Britain* (1978); *Birdwatch Round Britain* (with Robert Dougall) (1980); contributor to *Joyce, by Herself and her Friends* (1980); *Of Birds and Men*, autobiography (1992, Japanese ed in prep); since 1935 many papers and articles in popular and scientific journals. Since 1953 many radio and TV broadcasts in UK and overseas. MBE awarded for ground-breaking work on reserve development for birds *and birdwatchers*, inc pioneering 'scrape technology', vegetation control, gull control, first facilities for wheelchaired bird-watchers, etc. RSPB Bronze Medal 1960, for original work on predator control and protection of nesting birds at Dungeness, 1960. OIR: travel, nature photography, giving illustrated talks. Suffolk Punch Cottage, Bakers Lane, Westleton, Saxmundham, Suffolk IP17 3AZ. 01728 648331.

BAILLIE, Stephen Robert; *b:* 11 April 1953 in Liverpool; *w:* Dr Helen Smith. Leighton Park School, Reading 1966-71. Ewell County Tech Coll 1971-72. BSc Zoology (Aberdeen, 1976), PhD (Aberdeen, 1981) Population dynamics of the Eider in NE Scotland (Culterty Field Station 1976-79). Director of Populations Research, BTO since 1987. Prev BTO: Senior Research Officer (1983-87); Research Officer (1980-83). BTO 'A' ringer since 1971. Secretary Wader Study Group 1984-88. Chairman Wash Wader Ringing Group Scientific Committee 1983-88. WWT Scientific Advisory Committee 1992-96. Special interests: avian population dynamics and its application to the identification and solution of conservation problems; long-term monitoring of bird populations, including their breeding success and survival rates; population modelling; computerisation and statistical analysis of extensive ornithological datasets; interests in particular species include Eider Duck and Song Thrush. Some fifty scientific papers in eg *Acta Ornithologica, Bird Study, Ibis, J Appl Ecol, Nature, Ornis Scandinavica, Ringing & Migration, Seabird, Die Vogelwelt*; numerous semi-popular articles esp in *BTO News*; book chapters and research reports. Member: ASAB, BES, WSG. OIR: other aspects of natural history and conservation; gardening. BTO, The Nunnery, Thetford, Norfolk IP24 2PU. 01842 750050.

BAIN, Clifton George; *b:* 1 July 1961 in Edinburgh; *w:* Gillian. BSc Zoology (Aberdeen, 1983). Head of Conservation Policy, RSPB Scotland since 1995. Prev: Peatlands Policy Officer, RSPB 1993-95; Conservation Officer, RSPB E Midlands 1988-93; contract researcher, RSPB 1984-88. Special interests: conservation of bird habitats in UK; breeding waders in upland areas; behavioural ecology; wildlife legislation. Joint author of articles on bird conservation issues in eg *Bird Study* and *Thorne and Hatfield Moors Papers*. OIR: hill walking, gardening, real ale, folk music. RSPB, 17 Regent Terrace, Edinburgh EH7 5BN. 0131 557 3136.

BAINBRIDGE, Ian Paul; *b:* 11 July 1954 in Derby; *w:* Carole. BSc Biological Sciences (Wolverhampton Polytechnic, 1975), PhD Waders on the Ribble (Liverpool Polytechnic, 1982). Head of Scottish Research, RSPB since 1996. Prev: Senior Research Biologist, Scotland, RSPB 1993-96; Reserves Ecologist, Scotland, RSPB 1990-93; Conservation Planning, RSPB 1984-90; Conservation Officer, Northumberland WT 1979-84. SOC Council 1994-. BTO Research and Surveys Committee 1994-. Chairman Wash Wader Ringing Group Scientific Committee 1994-. Chairman BTCV NE England Committee 1982-84. BTO 'A' Ringer since 1970. Special interests: conservation management, waders. Articles on Curlew, forestry and birds, conservation management in eg *Bird Study*, *Britain's Birds*, *RSPB Conservation Review*. OIR: rock gardening. 3 Woodhouselee, Easter Howgate, Midlothian EH26 0PG. 0131 445 3268.

BAKER, Ernest William (Bill); *b:* 31 January 1913 in Unburton, Yorks; *w:* May. Anglo-Egyptian Schools, Cairo. Diploma in W Asiatic and Egyptian Archaeology (London, 1959). FRAI 1961. Tutor in Ancient Middle East Studies, Univ Nottingham and WEA. Voluntary warden Gibraltar Point 1968-71. Oiled Seabird Watch 1979-91. Special interests: birds of the Middle East, Arctic and Antarctic; seabirds and waders; migration. Contributed to EGI investigation on breeding biology of the Woodpigeon 1947. Species checks in Egypt 1984, 1987, 1991. Representations (with others) to Government on impact of shooting in sensitive areas produced positive personal response from Governor. Member: OSME, Seabird Group. OIR: railway history, aviation. 10 Rose Grove, Roman Bank, Skegness, Lincs PE25 1SN.

BAKER, Helen; *b:* 1 May 1944 in Hillingdon, Middx. Brondesbury and Kilburn High School. BA Science, inc Ecology, Evolution (Open Univ, 1982). Civil Servant. Secretary Ornithology Research Committee, London NHS 1980-95; Chairman Ornithology Section, LNHS 1993-. Waterways Bird Survey on stretch of Grand Union Canal 1979-. Organiser LNHS Canada Goose Survey 1983-84 and Survey of Birds of Small Open Spaces in Inner London 1987-88. Greater London organiser for BTO/WWT Mute Swan Survey 1990, and WWT Survey of Introduced Geese 1991. Organiser LNHS House Sparrow monitoring scheme. Reports of surveys in *London Bird Report*. OIR: gardening, classical music, medieval history, family history. 22 Townfield, Rickmansworth, Herts WD3 2DD. 01923 772441.

BALCHIN, Christopher Stephen (Chris); *b:* 8 August 1959 in Amersham, Bucks. Electronics engineer. Annual personal expeditions to tropics since 1982. Secretary and co-founder Neotropical Bird Club. Contributor to Avifaunal Survey of Tai National Park (*ICBP Study Report* 39) and Ecuadorian Dry Forest Project (*ICBP Study Report* 49). Participant in various BTO surveys. Parrots in Peril Expedition to SE Ecuador, winter 1994/95. Contributor to books: *Shorebirds* by Marchant and Prater (1986), *Birds to Watch* by N Collar *et al* (1994), *Threatened Birds of the Americas* by N Collar *et al* (1992), *Putting Biodiversity on the Map* by C Bibby *et al* (1992), *Key Areas for Threatened Birds in the Neotropics* by Wege and Long (1995); photographs published in *Hamlyn Photographic Guide to the Waders of the World* by Rosair and Cottridge (1995); articles in *Birding World*, *Malimbus*.

Member: ABC, NBC, OBC, WAOS. OIR: general natural history, music, live entertainment. 24 Juniper Close, Towcester, Northants NN12 6XP.

BALL, Alan Geoffrey; *b:* 4 February 1957 in Wisbech, Cambs; *w:* Jo. HND Civil Engineering (Trent Polytechnic, 1978). AMICE 1986. Engineer (Lincs CC Highways). Founder-member Lincolnshire Bird Club 1979, Committee 1981-88. Founder-member Boston RSPB Members' Group 1987, Committee 1987-90. Lincs County Ringing Recorder 1983-86. Lincs County Bird Recorder 1987-88. BTO 'A' ringer since 1977, member of Sponsors Panel since 1983. Special interests: ringing studies, esp species for which the Wash is important and particularly those not studied by others, such as gulls and various passerines eg Twite, Skylark and Lapland Bunting (study of latter proved wintering Wash birds to be Norwegian); keen photographer. Amateur local ornithological consultant since 1988 to Anglian Water in project to develop Marston Sewage Treatment Works as one of county's premier bird sites. Overseas travel for birds inc N & S America, N, W & E Africa, Israel, Thailand. Compiled and wrote *Lincolnshire Bird Report* 1987 and 1988. Regular illustrated talks to local groups. 101 Eastgate, Sleaford, Lincs NG34 7EE. 01529 307942.

BALLANCE, David Kenneth; *b:* 27 August 1934 in Hitchin, Herts. Oundle School. BA English (Corpus Christi College, Cambridge, 1958), Cert Ed (1959), MA (Cambridge, 1962). Retired schoolmaster. President Cambridge Bird Club 1957-58. Editorial Committee and contributor *Somerset Birds* (annual report) 1963-. Vice President Somerset Ornithological Society 1974-. Co-author (with Eileen M Palmer) *The Birds of Somerset* (1968); major contributor to *Birds of Somerset* published by Somerset Ornithological Society (1988). OIR: buildings, mountain walking. Flat Two, Dunboyne, Bratton Lane, Minehead, Somerset TA24 8SQ. 01643 706820.

BAMFORD, Roy; *b:* 27 June 1949 in Heanor, Derbys; *w:* Victoria. Self-employed educational/environmental contractor. Wildfowl and wader surveys for CCW 1993-94. Prev: wardening on several RSPB reserves 1975-78; conservation ranger Mid and W Wales. BTO 'C' ringer since 1988. Fieldworker and member Kite Committee 1981-91. Leader local YOC group. Organiser ornithological courses at National Centre for Alternative Technology 1994. Hon warden West Wales WT Cwm Cletwr LNR. Member Ceredigion Forest District Environment Panel. Special interests: comparative studies of effects of recent afforestation and replanting on birds; use of nestboxes in forestry. Articles on this and the importance for birds of broadleaved edges in forestry plantations in *Nature in Wales* and *Quarterly Journal of Forestry*; regular 'Country Diary' column in *Cambrian News* up to 1995. OIR: mountain walking, photography, coaching under 15s football team. Felin-y-Cwm, Ffwrnais, Machynlleth, Powys SY20 8TE. 01654 781343.

BARBER OF TEWKESBURY, Baron (Derek Coates Barber); Life Peer 1992; Kt 1984. Royal Agricultural College (MRAC), Hon DSc (Bradford, 1986), Hon FRASE 1986. Farmer and company director. Prev: Chairman Countryside Commission 1981-91. Founder-member Farming and Wildlife Advisory Group 1969. RSPB: Council 1970-75, Chairman 1976-81, President 1991-92; Vice President 1982-. Council BTO 1987-90. Vice President OSME 1987-. President Hawk and Owl Trust 1992-96. President Gloucestershire Naturalists' Society 1981-. Special interests: conservation, identification, wetland management. Editor *Farming with Wildlife* (1971) and occasional contributor to *British Birds*. RSPB Gold Medal 1982, for services to bird protection. Chough House, Gotherington, Cheltenham, Glos GL52 4QU. 01242 673908.

BARBER, Stephen Colin (Steve); *b:* 4 December 1950; *w:* Gill. An honorary warden at Rostherne Mere NNR since 1986. Cheshire and Wirral Ornithological Society: Editorial and Records Sub-Committee 1988-; Projects Sub-Committee 1988- (main achievement of which was publishing *The Breeding Bird Atlas of Cheshire and Wirral*, 1992), Vice Chairman 1994-. Adult education tutor. Special interest: collecting everything written about ornithology in Cheshire (inc its social history). Author (with Ron Harrison) *A Checklist of the Birds of Cheshire and Wirral* (1987); joint compiler *Cheshire and Wirral Bird Report* (prev *Ches Bird Rep*) 1984-, also editor of the Systematic List 1987-; compiler *Rostherne Mere NNR Report* 1986-; monthly Rostherne reports (with wife Gill) in *Bird Watching*. OIR: supporter of Manchester City FC, fantasy books, music by Neil Young, watching son Paul play soccer. 14 Thornfield Grove, Cheadle Hulme, Stockport, Cheshire SK8 6AZ. 0161 485 6571.

BARNES, Gordon John; *b:* 12 May 1934 in Birmingham; *w:* Perry. Hotelier (resident owner). BTO 'A' ringer 1960-85. Lived on Fair Isle 1960-75, sometime Asst Warden, then helping at the observatory with identification, recording migrants, training ringers; kept Great Bustard caught on the island throughout winter, bird then flown to Salisbury Plain by BEA to join captive breeding and reintroduction programme (BBC radio talk on this, 1970). Training ringers in Wales and Devon 1975-85. Special interests: gulls and terns; managing own SSSI, inc long-term study of birds and advising English Nature. OIR: butterflies, glow worms, clay tobacco pipes, local tree warden. Kingaroy, 1A Highcliffe Road, Swanage, Dorset BH19 1LW. 01929 426427.

BARNES, John; *b:* 9 April 1936 in Long Eaton, Derbys; *w:* Jan. Long Eaton Grammar School. BA French (Hull, 1958), Grad Cert Ed (Hull, 1959). Head of modern languages in secondary school, retired. BTO Regional Representative Caernarvonshire since 1987, organising and co-ordinating all surveys. Extensive fieldwork for BTO Breeding Atlas, Winter Atlas and New Breeding Atlas, and *An Atlas of the Breeding Birds of Shropshire* by P Deans *et al* (1992). Council Welsh Ornithological Society since 1993. Council North Wales WT for many years. Committee Cambrian Ornithological Society and Editor *COS Bulletin* 1982-. County Bird Recorder Caernarvonshire 1993-. Special interests: woodland and forest species (esp, in Britain, Crossbill and Hawfinch), raptors, photography. Bird-related trips to Israel, Canada, S Senegal, Costa Rica, etc (followed by illustrated lectures to societies). Writing *The Birds of Caernarfonshire*. Wide knowledge and collection of ornithological books, more recently bird postcards. OIR: hill walking, foreign languages, collecting fountain pens. Fach Goch, Waunfawr, Caernarvon, Gwynedd LL55 4YS. 01286 650362.

BARRITT, Michael Kenneth; Capt RN; *b:* 26 April 1948 in Paisley, Renfrewshire; *w:* Rosanne. Glasgow Academy. MA Modern History (Pembroke College, Oxford, 1967). Fellow of the Nautical Institute 1993. Royal Navy, Charge Hydrographic Surveyor. Numerous sea-going hydrographic appointments with responsibility for environmental obser- vations; commanded HM Surveying Ships 'Echo', 'Bulldog', 'Hecate'. Chairman Royal Naval Birdwatching Society since 1988. Special interests: seabirds. Numerous articles and bird reports in *Sea Swallow*, inc major sources on seabirds around the Fiji Archipelago, isolated Pacific and Southern Ocean islands, and the tropical South Atlantic. Member: Seabird Group. OIR: lay reader, naval history research, observations of natural phenomena from ships at sea, books, travel, sailing, music. 1 Boyle Close, Uxbridge, Middx UB10 0XB. 01895 810092.

BARTHEL, Peter H; *b:* 22 August 1955 in Hildesheim, Germany; *w:* Christine. Forestry, History and Biology at Univ Göttingen 1974-87, thesis on biometry and moult of Little Ringed Plover at Zoological Institute Göttingen 1987. Dip Biol. Editor *Limicola - Zeitschrift für Feldornithologie* since 1987. Chairman German Rarities Committee 1988-. Chairman

Standing Committee on German Bird Names 1994-. Secretary Association of European Rarities Committees 1991-95. Special interests: identification, waders, Eastern Palearctic birds. Author of several German books and booklets on birds and nature, inc official checklist of the birds of Germany (1993) and the forthcoming *Encyclopedia of the Birds of Europe* (5 vols). Adaptations and revisions of German editions of several Swedish and English books eg *Photographic Guide to Birds of Britain and Europe* by Delin and Svensson (1989), *Birds of Britain and Europe* by Bruun, Delin and Svensson (1990), *Macmillan Field Guide to Bird Identification* by Harris, Tucker and Vinicombe (1991), *Illustrated Encyclopedia of Birds* by Perrins (1992) and *Birds of Europe* by Jonsson (1992). Editor *Faunistische Mitteilungen aus Süd-Niedersachsen* 1978-86. Editor *Naturschutz in Niedersachsen* 1984-86. Co-editor *Ornithologen-Kalender* 1991-93. Identification consultant *Birding World* 1991-. Editorial consultant *Dutch Birding* 1992-. Some 300 articles since 1973 on identification, occurrence, biology, rarities and general aspects of ornithology and birdwatching in eg *Dutch Birding, J für Orn, Limicola, Ornis, Ornithos, Vogelwelt*. Member: Deutsche Ornithologen-Gesellschaft. Über dem Salzgraben 11, D-37574 Einbeck-Drüber, Germany. +49 (0)5561 82224; fax +49 (0)5561 82289.

BATTEN, Leo Adrian; *b:* 29 October 1944 in London; *w:* Angela. Finchley Grammar School. Regent Street Polytechnic. BSc Zoology (London, 1966), PhD Population studies and energetics of Blackbirds (London, 1977). Biodiversity Co-ordinator, English Nature since 1994. Prev: Head of Species, Sites and Urban Policy Branch, English Nature 1991-94; NCC Ornithological Advisor 1978-91; BTO Populations Section 1967-77. Rare Breeding Birds Panel 1978-. Board of International Waterfowl and Wetlands Research Bureau 1978-91. Evening class lecturer for Oxford and Cambridge, and London Univ Extra Mural Depts 1969-79. BTO 'A' ringer since 1962. Special interests: conservation management, population studies. Co-author *The Birdwatcher's Year* (1973) and *Red Data Birds in Britain* (1990); papers on population studies in *Bird Study, British Birds, Oryx, Scottish Birds*, etc; proceedings of conferences and several overseas publications; articles in popular magazines. OIR: classical music, natural history photography. 41 Turpins Chase, Oaklands, Welwyn, Herts AL6 0RP. 01438 716312.

BATTY, Leslie (Les); *b:* 24 July 1948 in Kingston upon Hull; *w:* Wendy. Hull Grammar School 1959-66. BSc Zoology (Wales, Bangor, 1970), MPhil thesis based on wader studies in Portugal (Wales, Bangor, 1992), MSc Estuarine & Coastal Science and Management (Hull, 1993). Lecturer in

Ornithology and Zoology at Bishop Burton College, Beverley 1994-. Prev: contract work (inc ornithological surveys) Institute of Estuarine & Coastal Studies, Univ Hull, 1991-93; Lecturer in Ornithology and Ecology, Universidade do Algarve, Faro, Portugal, 1985-91; A Rocha Bird Observatory and Field Study Centre (co-founder), Mexilhoeira, Portugal 1983-85; Head of Field Studies, Medina Valley Centre for Outdoor Education, Newport, Isle of Wight 1977-81; Asst Warden, Sayers Croft Field Study Centre, Ewhurst, Surrey 1971-74. Founder/Leader NE Hampshire RSPB Members' Group 1975-76 and of Isle of Wight RSPB Members' Group 1979-80. BoEE count organiser Medina estuary and Ryde Sands, Isle of Wight 1977-83. Adult education tutor in ornithology, Univ Hull 1991-95. Special interests: waders and seabirds; selection and management of bird reserves and habitats. Initiated international project on seabird/squid interactions as part of EC-funded project on squid in NE Atlantic, leading to Univ Glasgow/Univ do Algarve expedition to the Azores to study diet of Cory's Shearwater (Sept 1990); study of the distribution at sea of Cory's Shearwater in the Azores archipelago (Aug 1991); assessment of important areas for birds in the Algarve for the Liga para a Proteção da Natureza 1991. Articles in *Biologist*, *Isle of Wight Birds*, *Wader Study Group Bulletin* and Portuguese publicatons. Member: Estuarine and Coastal Sciences Assocn, European Union for Coastal Conservation, Portuguese Society for the Study of Birds (SPEA), Seabird Group, Wader Study Group. OIR: active member Beverley Minster church, walking, listening to folk music. 110 Norwood Grove, Beverley HU17 9JP. 01482 871140.

BAYLDON, John Michael (Mike); *b:* 20 June 1935 in Hull; *w:* Dorothy. Insurance manager. Prev: Royal Navy 1951-59. BTO 'A' ringer up to 1980. With Mike Bell negotiated to build Heligoland trap on private land and hence founded Bamburgh Ringing Station (1964, still operational). Bird-related travel and photography in N America, W Palearctic, Africa, Australia, Far East. Illustrated lectures to bird clubs in Yorks and NE England. Author *A Guide to the Birds of the Bamburgh Area* (1970). Member: ABA. OIR: history (inc visiting historical sites, family history). 9 Birchen Close, Bessacarr, Doncaster, S Yorks DN4 7JU. 01302 537234.

BEALEY, Clive Edward; *b:* 26 May 1956 in Sanderstead, Surrey; *w:* Sarah. Purley High School for Boys. BSc Biological Science (Westfield College, London, 1977), MSc Ecology (Univ Coll N Wales, Bangor, 1981). Environmental Change Network Officer, PLSD, Porton Down, Salisbury on secondment from English Nature. Prev: research contracts and consultancies inc NCC Wales Moorland Bird Survey 1981, 1983; Sussex WT/RSPB Sussex Woodland Survey 1982-93; RSPB Woodland Survey Northants 1984; Game Conservancy Pheasants and Woodlands Project 1987-89; Importance of R Avon (Hants) Flood Plain for Breeding Waders 1990; Assessment of Gravel Extraction Complex in Berks 1990-92; MAFF/ADAS Baseline Survey of Breeding Waders on the R Avon (Hants) ESA 1992; Conservation Officer/Asst CO, Somerset Levels and Moors, and Bridgwater Bay, English Nature 1992-94. Voluntary wardening stints for RSPB at Loch of Strathbeg, Arne, Dinas. Tutor/lecturer on various adult evening courses (eg City of London Univ, extra-mural courses in ecology); illustrated talks to bird groups. Leader of bird tours in Western Isles; visits to Cevennes and Camargue to assess feasibility of study holidays. Ringing asst with several groups 1970s-90s. Special interests: habitat selection and feeding ecology of Willow Warbler in S Britain; ecological interactions in flycatchers and warblers in N Wales. Led ornithological expedition to W Mongolia wetlands with endangered species; research on Malaysian Peacock Pheasant in Peninsular Malaysia 1989, 1991; joined expedition at Parc National des Oiseaux du Djoudj, W Senegal 1993. Joint contribution (with P A Robertson) on coppice management for Pheasants to *Ecology and Management of Coppice Woodlands* ed by G P Buckley (1992); articles and papers in bird reports and journals; various research reports. Interviews on local radio and participation in TV series *Bellamy's Bird's-eye View* (1989). Member: OBC. OIR: playing cricket, squash, tennis, good red wine, real ale, listening to flamenco guitar music. 2 St George's Cottages, South End, Damerham, Fordingbridge, Hants SP6 3HW. 01725 518420.

BEAMAN, Mark Andrew Saltford; *b:* 26 July 1951 in Bushey, Herts; *w:* Maire Elizabeth Morton. Uppingham School. MA Natural Sciences (Churchill College, Cambridge, 1973). Managing Director and Proprietor, Birdquest Ltd since 1981. Prev: Director, Sunbird Holidays 1978-81. Council (also report editor) Ornithological Society of Turkey c1971-77 and successor OSME c1977-79. Special interests: distribution and taxonomy of Palearctic avifauna, field identification of Palearctic birds, migration (esp raptors). Long-term studies of raptor migration through the Maltese islands (1967-70) and the Bosphorus (1971-72). Discovered the massive raptor migration through the Pontic Mountains (1976, with further studies 1977-81). Leader Cambridge Ornithological Expedition to Himalayas 1973. Extensive bird-related travels throughout Palearctic since 1981. Author: *A Guide to the Birds of Malta* (1975), *Palearctic Birds: a checklist* (1994), *Birds of Europe and the Western Palearctic: an identification guide* (1996). Editor

Turkish Bird Report 3 (1970/73) and 4 (1974/75). Various papers and articles in journals and magazines eg *British Birds, Dutch Birding, Ibis*. Member: ABA, ABC, Bombay NHS, Hong Kong Birdwatching Society, NBC, OBC, OSME. OIR: scuba diving. Two Jays, Kemple End, Birdy Brow, Stonyhurst, Lancs BB7 9QY. 01254 826317; fax 01254 826780.

BECK, John Roger; *b:* 1 December 1939 in Northampton; *w:* Doreen. Northampton Grammar School. BA Zoology (Hertford College, Oxford, 1961), MA (Oxford, 1970), PGCE 1976. Head of biology in secondary school. Prev: Asst Lecturer Zoology, Univ Southampton 1964-65; Research Biologist British Antarctic Survey 1965-70 (seabird ecology, Signy Island). Special interests: photography (stills and super-8 cine), recording for film soundtracks, breeding biology and distribution of Antarctic petrels. Summer expeditions 1959, 1960, 1993, 1994 to study status and breeding distribution of birds in Finnmark, N Norway. Contribution on breeding seasons and moult in some smaller Antarctic petrels in *Antarctic Ecology* ed by M W Holdgate (1970); author (with D W Brown) *The Biology of Wilson's Storm-petrel at Signy Island, South Orkney Islands* in Brit Antarctic Survey Report 69 (1972); papers on Antarctic birds in *BAS Bulletin, Ibis*. OIR: alpine gardening. Tokio Cottage, Bull's Hill, Walford, Ross-on-Wye, Herefs HR9 5RH. 01989 763114.

BELL, David Graham; *b:* 27 August 1934 in Manchester; *w:* Susan. Manchester Grammar School. BA French (Durham, 1956), Dip Ed (Durham, 1957). Head of languages in secondary school, retired. Adult evening class lecturer in ornithology, Northumberland CC 1987-91. British Birds Rarities Committee 1962-76. County Recorder for Northumberland 1961-66, Durham 1961-69, Cleveland (prev Teesmouth) 1958-68. Founder-chairman North Northumberland Bird Club 1984-. Joint Founder Teesmouth Bird Club 1960, later Chairman, member Records Committee 1960-. Committee Berwick Swan and Wildlife Trust 1993-95. RSPB Council 1994-. Founder-member WWF Guisborough Branch 1966. Committee Alnwick NHS 1980s. Ornithological consultant to Tees Valley Water Board 1970-78 and warden for their Scaling Dam Bird Reserve. Ornithological consultant to Border Forestry 1990-. Voluntary warden for Teesmouth Bird Club. Special Constable (bird protection) Durham Police 1960s. Special interests: identification, conservation, Arctic and Siberia. Extensive travel for birds in all continents. Lecturer and excursion leader at home and abroad. Former YOC Leader. Led team to former Yugoslavia to establish bird reserves 1986. Ecotourism projects in Greece 1992-. Editor of county bird reports Northumberland and Durham 1961-66, Durham 1967-69,

Cleveland 1975-; weekly columnist on birds for local papers 1987-; identification articles in *Birdwatch*, etc. Weekly broadcasts on birds on local radio (Borders) since 1995. Member: LIPU, LPO. OIR: table tennis (ETTA Club Coach). Farne View, The Wynding, Bamburgh, Northumberland NE69 7DD. 01668 214232.

BELL, Michael Vernon (Mike); *b:* 12 June 1951 in Ilkley, W Yorks. BSc Biochemistry (Leeds, 1972), PhD Biochemistry (Leeds, 1975). Biochemist with Natural Environment Research Council. Recorder NE Scotland and Editor *North-East Scotland Bird Report* 1981-86. Co-founder Central Scotland Goose Group (1988) and joint editor *CSGG Newsletter*. Regional co-ordinator for Grey Goose Counts (Central Region and Perth & Kinross District). Participation in many national surveys inc National Wildfowl Counts, Grey Goose Counts, Birds of Estuaries Enquiry Counts, raptor monitoring; also for BTO Breeding Atlas, Winter Atlas, New Breeding Atlas and North-East Scotland Atlas. Special interests: wintering Pink-footed and Greylag Geese; breeding and wintering wildfowl, waders and raptors, with emphasis on population monitoring in relation to land use. Joint editor *The Birds of North-East Scotland* (1990); several papers on above interests in eg *The Naturalist, Scottish Birds, Wildfowl*; many articles in *NE Scotland Bird Report*. Member: CSGG (above), Tayside Raptor Group. OIR: butterflies, dragonflies, photography, gardening. 48 Newton Crescent, Dunblane, Perthshire FK15 0DZ. 01786 822153.

BERROW, Simon David; *b:* 16 April 1964 in Hagley, W Midlands. BSc Applied Biology (Liverpool Polytechnic, 1987), PhD Zoology (Cork, 1991). Research biologist. Employed as a vertebrate ecologist with British Antarctic Survey at Bird Island, South Georgia studying Wandering Albatross, White-chinned Petrel and penguins until 1998. Fieldwork for 1992 Irish Chough Survey (IWC) and for BTO New Breeding Atlas; also short-term research asst WWT at Slimbridge and Caerlaverock. Special interests: monitoring and survey work; impact of fisheries on seabirds. Member Aberdeen University Expedition to Riglos, N Spain to study avifauna of the area (1985). Publications: contribution to *The Ecology of Lough Hyne* ed by A A Myers *et al* (1991); papers and short communications in journals inc *Bird Study, Irish Birds, Irish Naturalists' Journal*. OIR: cetaceans, sharks. British Antarctic Survey, High Cross, Madingley Road, Cambridge CB3 0ET. 01223 251400; fax 01223 62616.

BERRY, John; CBE 1968; *b:* 5 August 1907 in Edinburgh; *w:* The Hon Bride (Faith Louisa) Freemantle. Eton. BA Natural Sciences (Trinity

College, Cambridge, 1929), MA (Cambridge, 1930), PhD (St Andrews, 1935), Hon DSc (St Andrews, 1991), Hon LLD (Dundee, 1970). FRSE 1936. DL (Fife, 1969). Consultant ecologist. Prev posts inc Director of Nature Conservation in Scotland 1949-67; Commission on Ecology, IUCN (various offices inc President 1954-56); UK Rep on Exec Board, IWRB 1963-72; Vice Pres and Council, WWT 1969-. Special interests: behaviour, distribution, sub-speciation, taxonomy of wild geese; breeding in feral flocks of most species of 'true geese'; ducks and swans to a lesser degree; photography of wild geese. Author *The Status and Distribution of Wild Geese and Wild Duck in Scotland* (1939); contributions to books by other authors; many papers and articles in journals and conference proceedings. OIR: general natural history; specialist UK and overseas on pollution of water, land, atmosphere; water-use development, irrigation; breeding insects (esp Lepidoptera and Phasmida in insect house at Tayfield); environmental conservation; music. The Garden House, Tayfield, Newport-on-Tay, Fife DD6 8HA. 01382 543118.

BETTON, Keith Findlay; *b:* 29 June 1960 in Hammersmith, London; *w:* Esther. Thames Valley Grammar School 1971-76. Richmond-upon-Thames College 1976-78. N London Polytechnic 1978-80. Head of Corporate Affairs, Association of British Travel Agents. Dept of Environment Committee on Bird Sanctuaries in Royal Parks, Official Bird Observer Bushy Park 1973-79. Founder/Leader Richmond & Twickenham RSPB Group 1978-85. Committee (Chairman 1984-92) London NHS Ornithology Section 1978-. BTO Regional Representative Greater London 1981-93. President London NHS 1982-84; Chairman 1937 Bird Club 1986-87. BTO Winter Atlas Working Group 1982-85. Council London WT 1982-85. Ornithology tutor, City Literary Institute 1984-88. Committee BOC 1985-86. Council BTO 1987-91. Council Surrey WT 1987-92 and Chairman Marketing Committee 1989-93. Chairman London NHS Research Committee 1988-94. Co-ordinator London Breeding Bird Atlas, 1988-92. Recorder Surrey-in-London 1992-93. London co-ordinator WWT 1993-96. Asst recorder Hampshire Ornithological Society 1995-. Special interest: sound recording (large collection of own recordings from UK). Extensive bird-related travel in five continents. Editor *Atlas of Breeding Birds in the London Area* (1996). Editor *London NHS Newsletter* 1984-87 and *Ornithological Bulletin* 1987-93. Editor *Hants/Surrey Border Bird Report* 1993-. Articles (esp sound recording, birds in London and travel) in eg *Bird Watching, Birdwatch, Birdwatcher's Yearbook, BTO News, Country Life, Daily Telegraph*; contributor to *Birds of Hampshire* (1993). Member: ABC, Malta Orn Soc (Life Member), NBC, OBC, OSME. OIR: rugby league, Halifax supporter. 8 Dukes Close, Folly Hill, Farnham, Surrey GU9 0DR. 01252 724068; fax 0171 637 5626; mobile 0850 781057.

BHATIA, Zul; *b:* 12 February 1950 in Dar es Salaam, Tanzania; *w:* Jennifer. Project Co-ordinator, Forest Conservation Programme, Tanzania. Prev: RSPB Warden Insh Marshes 1982-95; contract warden/staff asst warden Dungeness, Havergate Island, Arne, Loch Garten, Minsmere. Special interests: E African (esp Tanzanian) avifauna; management of northern poor fen and census techniques for breeding wildfowl and waders. Member ICBP (Danish Section) expedition to coastal forests of SE Tanzania 1990 (paper on findings to Pan-African Orn Congress in Burundi 1992) and assisted with ringing in some of the Tanzanian coastal forests. Member RSPB/Vogelbescherming team investigating status of Fischer's Lovebird and the Tanzanian wild bird trade 1991 (senior author of report). Tour leader Kenya, Tanzania. Large collection of published and 'grey' literature on E African natural history. Many contacts in Tanzania and speaker of Kiswahili, Kaatchi, Gujerati etc. Contributor to *Tanzania Bird Atlas* (in prep) and *East African Bird Report*. Member: ABC, African Wildlife Foundation, EANHS, EAWLS, Wildlife Cons Soc of Tanzania. OIR: seeking alpine plants in wild and growing alpines. c/o RSPB, The Lodge, Sandy, Beds SG19 2DL. 01767 680551.

BIRCHAM, Peter Michael Miles; *b:* 30 September 1947 in Cambridge. Perse School Cambridge. Research Technician, Physiological Lab, Univ Cambridge. Part-time tutor in ornithology for Board of Education, Univ Cambridge. Cambridge Bird Club: Council 1976-80, 1987-92; Chairman Research Committee 1976-83, Ringing Sec 1976-80, Research Officer 1987-. Council and Conservation Committee Cambs WT (now Beds and Cambs WT) 1987-93. Wildfowl Counts organiser for Cambs. BTO 'A' ringer since c1972. Wicken Fen Ringing Group 1969-. Special interests: status of birds in Cambs; population and community studies. Author *The Birds of Cambridgeshire* (1989), contributor to *Cambridge Encyclopedia of Ornithology* (1992). Co-author (with J C A Rathmell and W J Jordan) *Atlas of Breeding Birds in Cambridgeshire* (1994). Editor *Cambridgeshire Bird Report* 1989-90, 1994-95; articles in *Cambridgeshire Bird Report, Nature in Cambridgeshire, Wicken Fen Group Report*. 14 Baldock Way, Cambridge CB1 4UX. 01223 211936.

BIRD, Stanley Eric (Eric); *b:* 17 May 1925 in Ashington, Northumberland; *w:* Lena. Morpeth Grammar School. LDS (Durham, 1948). ARPS 1990. Dental surgeon, retired. WEA lecturer on birdwatching over twenty years;

wildlife photographic seminars at Country Parks 1989-96. Council Northumberland WT 1974-89 and Chairman of its Wansbeck Group. Member Druridge Bay Reserves Committee since formation in 1990. Special interest: bird photography (over thirty years, at first 16mm cine now 35mm). First colour footage of Barn Owl nest. Worked on films for National Trust, inc Goosander and Little Tern. Expeditions to Bharatpur, India to film Siberian Cranes (1978); Arun Valley, Himalayas with film company to monitor bird migration (1981); Varangar peninsula for Arctic birds; Ecuador and the Amazon basin (1991); sub-Antarctic Islands of New Zealand and Macquarie Island, Australia (1994). Tour leader, with many visits to north, central and South Africa, USA and Canada, Europe and Middle East. Lectured throughout the country on ornithological travels. Much film used by BBC and independent TV in natural history programmes. Winner of 'Birds and Man' cine competition sponsored by RSPB and British Petroleum to mark European Conservation Year 1970. Involved with Northumbria Ringing Group from 1970s. Concerned with oiled seabirds in the early days of developing cleaning techniques. OIR: playing tenor saxophone, listening to jazz, cooking, travel to the world's wild places, five birdwatching grandchildren. Glen-Eildon, Thorp Avenue, Morpeth, Northumberland NE61 1JT. 01670 512432.

BIRKHEAD, Timothy Robert (Tim); *b:* 28 February 1950 in Leeds; *w:* Miriam. Leeds Grammar School 1958-69. BSc Zoology (Newcastle, 1972), DPhil (Wolfson College, Oxford & Edward Grey Institute, Oxford, 1976), DSc (Newcastle, 1989). Nuffield Fellow 1991-92; Leverhulme Research Fellow 1995-96. Professor of Behavioural Ecology, Univ Sheffield since 1976. Prev: Lecturer, Senior Lecturer, Reader at Univ Sheffield. Council BOU 1981-85. Council Association for Study of Animal Behaviour 1981-87. Seabird Group: Hon Sec 1979-83, Chairman 1987-91. President International Society for Behavioural Ecology 1996-98. Special interests: interface between behavioural ecology and reproductive physiology and behaviour, esp sperm competition; species studied in detail: Magpie, Zebra Finch, Common Guillemot. Long-term population studies (notably of Guillemots on Skomer Island since 1972 and Magpies around Sheffield). Studies of Zebra Finches in Australia, Yellow-billed Magpies in California, Buffalo Weavers in Namibia, Brünnich's and Common Guillemots in the Canadian Arctic. Author *The Magpies* (1991), *Great Auk Islands* (1993). Co-editor *Cambridge Encyclopedia of Ornithology* (1991) and *The Atlantic Alcidae* (1985). Co-author *Avian Ecology* (1983), *The Survival Factor* (1989), *Sperm Competition in Birds* (1992). Editor *Seabird* 1979-83; Consulting Editor (1993-94) then Editor *Animal Behaviour*

1994-95. Over 150 scientific and popular scientific articles in *BBC Wildlife*, *Natural History*, *New Scientist*. Member: AOU, ASAB, BES. OIR: three children, two dogs, painting and music. Dept of Animal and Plant Sciences, PO Box 601, University of Sheffield S10 2TN. 0114 282 4622.

BISHOP, David Raymond (Dave); *b:* 3 February 1955 in Birmingham; *w:* Doreen. Peter Symonds Grammar School, Winchester, Hants. ARICS 1983. Quantity surveyor. Special interest: Southern African birds. Botswana Bird Club: various posts inc Chairman. IWRB African Waterfowl Census co-ordinator for Botswana 1991-. Southern African Bird Atlas Project joint co-ordinator (with wife) 1991-. African Bird Club co-ordinator for Botswana Nov 1993-. Botswana co-ordinator and contributor to *Top Birding Spots in Southern Africa* compiled by Hugh Chittenden (1992). Contributor to *The Babbler* (Botswana Bird Club). OIR: bowling. UK: c/o 20 Litchfield Road, Midanbury, Southampton SO18 2BL. 01703 360887. Botswana: c/o McIntosh Latilla, PO Box 808, Gaborone. +267 326589.

BLACKBURN, Adrian Charles; *b:* 19 October 1946 in Spilsby, Lincs; *w:* Frances. Cert Ed (Birmingham Institute, 1969). Tutor in ornithology, Adult Continuing Education Dept, Univ Sheffield 1992-. BTO 'A' Ringer since 1965 and member of Sponsors Panel. Tutor/leader for ringing training courses in North Notts and Spurn Bird Observatory. Leader of seabird ringing and censusing visits to Sule Skerry, Orkney nine years between 1975 and 1996. Seabird Group Executive Committee 1984-88. E of England co-ordinator for Seabird Colony Register (Humber-Thames) 1985-87. Long-term studies inc ringing at reedbed/scrub site in N Notts (1972-), seabirds on Sule Skerry (1975-), breeding Barn Owls in E Lincs (1992-) and Wigeon wintering in N Notts (1992-). Member of expeditions to Mallorca to study the importance of the Albufera Marshes for breeding and migrating birds (1983, 1985) and the 1991 expedition to Senegal to study European migrant birds in their winter quarters. Articles on visits to Sule Skerry in seabird journals and newsletters; occasional interviews for local radio and TV on bird studies. Member: Seabird Group. Suleska, 1 Richmond Road, Retford, Notts DN22 6SJ. 01777 706516.

BLAKER, George Blaker; CMG 1963; *b:* 30 September 1912 in India; *w:* Richenda Dorothy (deceased). Eton. BA Modern Languages and History (Trinity College, Cambridge). Civil Servant, retired. Prev: Under-Secretary, HM Treasury and Dept of Education, 1957-71. Organised first national survey of Barn Owls 1932-33. Founder/Manager Vann Lake

Nature Reserve, Surrey 1964-86 (kept bird records 1964-93). President Surrey WT 1969-80. Publications: *Barn Owl Survey* (RSPB, 1934); summaries and comments of survey in *The Barn Owl in the British Isles* by Colin R Shawyer (1987) and in *The Birds of the British Isles*, Vol 4 by David A Bannerman (1955). Gold Medal of the RSPB 1934. Duke of Edinburgh's Countryside Award 1970. Member: Hawk and Owl Trust. OIR: travelling, mainly in Asia and Africa. Lake House, Ockley, Dorking, Surrey RH5 5NS. 01306 711268.

BLICK, Martin Allen; *b:* 4 March 1954 in Billingham, Co Durham; *w:* Marian. Special interest: birds of Cleveland. Cleveland WT Ornithologist 1986-88. Teesmouth Bird Club Records Committee 1972-. Organiser Teesmouth Birds of Estuaries Enquiry 1974-92. Author *Birds of Teesside 1968-73* (1978) and *Birds of Cleveland County* (1996). Joint compiler *County of Cleveland Bird Report* 1975-. 'Holder of highest number of birds seen in Cleveland, 315 out of 342 on county list.' 31 Clevegate, Nunthorpe, Middlesbrough TS7 0JH. 01642 326715.

BLINCOW, Jeffrey Ian (Jeff); *b:* 18 July 1957 in Northampton. Cert Ed Environmental Science (1978), Computing (1982). Teacher. Member of launch committee, Neotropical Bird Club (1993). Special interests: photography, distribution and identification. Bird-related travels in W Palearctic, N & S America, Africa, Australasia and SE Asia. Lectures on these given to bird and other clubs. Author *The Birds of Northamptonshire* (priv print, 1988). Illustrations in *Northamptonshire Bird Report* and *British Birds*. Member: ABC, NBC. OIR: hill walking, sailing, various sports. 1 Main Road, New Hackleton, Hackleton, Northants NN7 2DH.

BOAG, David; *b:* 8 March 1948; *w:* Janet. Freelance wildlife photographer, author and lecturer since 1988. Prev: agriculture. Long-term interest in Kingfishers; some of first photographs of them flying and diving, courtship, underwater, underground. Author/photographer *The Kingfisher* (1982), *The Atlantic Puffin* (1986), *The Living River* (1990), *The Living Woodland* (1992); also series 'The Spirit of Nature'. 1 Badbury Drive, Blandford, Dorset DT11 7UJ. 01258 451545.

BODDY, Michael (Mike); *b:* 20 January 1939 in London; *w:* Frances. Intermediate BSc Eng (Nottingham, 1958). Retired. Founder and organiser Redpoll Study Group 1978-80. BTO Ringing and Migration Committee 1979-86. Initiator and voluntary organiser of BTO's Constant Effort Sites ringing scheme 1981-85; contributor for two sites since 1981.

Chairman Lincolnshire Bird Club 1992-93. BTO 'A' ringer since 1959. Special interests: research based on ringing studies; migration of passerine species; survival and 'return rates' for passerines; passerine moult, esp juveniles; use of cloacal and brood patch examination to investigate timing and extent of breeding in passerine communities; fruit-eating by passerines; population studies of passerine communities, inc use of CBC and point-counts; study species: Woodpigeon, Dunnock, Lesser White-throat, Whitethroat, Redpoll, Greenfinch, Corn Bunting. Travel for birds inc Spain, Greece, Poland, Morocco, The Gambia, USA. Papers published in eg *Bird Study, British Birds, Lincolnshire Bird Report, Ornis Scandinavica, Ringing & Migration*. BTO's Bernard Tucker Medal 1986. OIR: fishing, watching sport on TV, book collecting, reading, gardening. Ashlea Cottage, Brickyard Lane, Theddlethorpe St Helen, Mablethorpe, Lincs LN12 1NR. 01507 338354.

BOLTON, Mark; *b:* 21 April 1964 in Beckenham, Kent. BA Natural Sciences (Cambridge, 1985), PhD Zoology (Glasgow, 1991). Director of A Rocha Bird Observatory, Portugal since 1994 (member of its Scientific Committee since 1988). Honorary Lecturer, Glasgow Univ 1995-. Prev: Research Fellow, Glasgow Univ 1991-94; Asst Warden A Rocha Bird Observatory 1985-88. Special interest: proximate control of avian egg production and clutch size (stimulated by three years research on Lesser Black-backed Gulls on Flat Holm in the Bristol Channel); energy requirements and reproduction of British Storm Petrels (Shetland). Author *An Atlas of Wintering Birds in the Western Algarve* (1987); scientific papers on breeding biology in eg *Canadian J Zool, Ibis, J Animal Ecol, Ornis Scandinavica, Proc Roy Soc*. Member: BES. A Rocha Bird Observatory, Cruzinha, Apt 41, 8500 Mexilhoeira Grande, Portugal.

BOND, Christopher (Chris); *b:* 28 February 1951 in Crayford, Kent; *w:* Margaret. Voluntary asst warden at Bough Beech Reservoir, Kent since 1984. Special interests: migration, photography. Articles in *Kent Ornithological Society Bulletin*; photographs in *Birding World, Birdwatch, Bird Watching*. Compiler and editor *Bough Beech Bulletin* monthly since 1989. OIR: contemporary music, playing pool. 11 Platt House Lane, Fairseat, Sevenoaks, Kent TN15 7LX. 01732 822523.

BOND, Gregory Charles (Greg); *b:* 24 July 1951 in London; *w:* Valerie. Alleyns College, Dulwich, London. ACII 1974. Insurance broker and risk manager. Essex Birdwatching Society: Executive Committee since 1986, Recording Committee and Rarities Panel since 1994. Special interests:

migration in Essex, identification (esp passerines). Sub-editor and author of passerine section *Essex Bird Report* 1988-90; author of annual summary *Essex Bird Report* 1989-. OIR: dragonflies, butterflies and moths, orchids, rugby, football. 11 Hearsall Avenue, Broomfield, Chelmsford, Essex CM1 5DD. 01245 441599.

BOND, Terence Edgar (Terry); *b:* 25 April 1945 in Barnstaple, Devon; *w:* Joy Penelope. Barnstaple Grammar School. ACIS 1973, FCIB 1975. Lending Services Director, Barclays Bank. Chairman/Group Leader Barclays Bank Bird Watching Society 1973-85. Committee and Field Leader Bristol RSPB Members' Group 1970s and 1980s. Special interest: wildlife photography (25 years). Extensive bird-related travel in northern hemisphere from N America to most European countries, Israel and Morocco. Birdwatching lectures (20 years) in England and Wales; on RSPB approved list of speakers. Long-term survey since 1980 of the birds, their trends and patterns, at the Barrow Gurney reservoirs near Bristol. Articles in eg *Bristol Ornithology* (behavioural patterns of Peregrines), publications of the Devon Birdwatching and Preservation Society, and *British Birds* (identification of Baird's Sandpiper). OIR: tennis, literature, music. 20 Ham Close, Charlton Kings, Cheltenham, Glos GL52 6NP. 01242 510452.

BONHAM, Gwendoline (Gwen); *b:* 22 November 1943 in Tring, Herts; Membership Secretary BTO 1964-87; Administrative Secretary BOU 1987-. OIR: theatre, sport, gardening, walking. Natural History Museum, Sub-Dept of Ornithology, Tring, Herts HP23 6AP. 01441 890080.

BONHAM, Patrick Francis (Pat); *b:* 4 August 1942 in Waltham Abbey, Essex; *w:* Mary. BSc Mathematics (London, 1963). Freelance editor. Bedfordshire Bird Recorder and tetrad survey organiser 1972-74. Treasurer Friends of Rye Harbour Nature Reserve 1980-87. Local organiser in Sussex of numerous species surveys, BTO New Breeding Atlas and Sussex Tetrad Atlas, also WWT waterfowl counter 1974-91. Council Sussex Ornithological Society 1986-91. Special interests: identification, migration and vagrancy of marsh and woodland birds; breeding and wintering distribution surveys and range changes; Grey and Yellow Wagtails, Reed and Sedge Warblers, Corn Bunting, Golden Plover. Travel for birds inc Canada, Israel, E Europe, Tunisia. Asst Editor *British Birds* 1970-73, then Executive Editor to August 1975. Author *Bedfordshire Bird Report* 1972-74. Editor *Sussex Ornithological Society Newsletter* 1976-80 and *Sussex Bird Report* 1986-91. *British Birds* studies of Choughs, Orioles, Cetti's Warbler expansion, etc. Species accounts in *Birds of the World* (partwork, 1969-71), etc. OIR: butterflies, walking, camping, hostelling, family activities, domestic architecture. Woodland View, Dixon Road, North Walsham, Norfolk NR28 9EA. 01692 403917.

BOOBYER, Mark George Gareth (George); *b:* 17 July 1963 in Lee, London. Colfe's School 1972-81. BSc Zoology and Botany (Swansea, 1984), MSc Ornithology (Cape Town, 1988). Head of Data Analysis Unit, Ecology and Conservation Branch, JNCC. Prev: Field Researcher National Avian Research Centre Abu Dhabi 1991; Data Asst (Ornithology) NCC 1991; Head of Raptor Breeding Centre, Capetown 1989-90; Researcher Percy FitzPatrick Institute of African Ornithology 1986-89. Special interests: Otitidae, Karoo bird/shrub steppe relationships, African raptors, Golden Plover; developing information systems to support national statutory and international conservation of birds and other vertebrates. Organised ornithological trips to Okavango Swamps, Botswana; Kosi Bay, Zululand; Malawi 1985-91. Author *Population Trends of the Golden Plover in Britain and Ireland* (JNCC, 1992); contributor (Golden Plover) to BTO New Breeding Atlas; articles in eg *Cons Biol*, *Ostrich*. Scientific Adviser to BBC *Natural World* series for *The Great Karoo: a secret Africa* (1991) and *The North York Moors* (1992). JNCC, Monkstone House, City Road, Peterborough PE1 2QG. 01733 62626.

BOOTH, Christopher John (Chris); *b:* 29 June 1932 in Aldridge, Staffs; *w:* Jean. Penzance Grammar School. BDS (Guy's Hospital Dental School, London Univ, 1955), LDS, RCS 1955. Retired Chief Administrative Dental Officer, Orkney Health Board. Temporary asst warden Skokholm Bird Observatory Aug 1953 and Lundy Bird Observatory Nov 1957. Dungeness Bird Observatory Committee 1959-61. BTO Representative Orkney 1976-86. Bird Recorder for Orkney 1980-. BTO 'A' Ringer since 1957. Special interests: study of the Raven in Orkney; also interested in Red-throated Diver, Peregrine, Great Skua. Author *The Birds of Orkney* (1984). Editor *Orkney Bird Report* 1980-. Papers in *Bird Study*, *Scottish Birds*; notes in *British Birds*, *Scottish Birds*. OIR: all forms of natural history (Orkney recorder for cetaceans, amphibians and reptiles), hill walking, sea kayaking, horse riding, photography, visiting islands. Ronas, 34 High Street, Kirkwall Orkney KW15 1AZ. 01856 872883.

BORROW, Nicholas (Nik); *b:* 5 August 1956 in London. BA Fine Art Painting (Wimbledon School of Art, 1978), PGCE (Avery Hill College, 1980). Freelance bird artist and illustrator since 1990. Birdquest staff leader since 1993. Special interests: birds of the Afrotropics. Drawings and paintings published eg in BTO Winter Atlas and New Breeding Atlas, *Birding World, Birds, British Birds*; also plates for field guide to the birds of W Africa (in prep). Member: ABC, OBC. Flat 5, 63/67 St George's Drive, Pimlico, London SW1V 4DD. 0171 834 6619.

BORTON, David George (Dave); *b:* 5 January 1942 in Headcorn, Ashford, Kent. Semi-retired. Voluntary warden at RSPB Loch Garten reserve for several periods in 1970s. Asst warden Fair Isle Bird Observatory 1981-83. Warden Cape Clear Bird Observatory 1984-88. Ringing Secretary Tipperary Ringing Group 1991-. Committee IWC Limerick Branch 1992-. BTO 'A' Ringer since 1979. Author 'The breeding passerines of Cape Clear Island 1986' in *Cape Clear Bird Observatory Report* 19, 1985/86. 40 Caragh Avenue, Caherdavin Park, Limerick, Ireland. +353 (0)61 452213.

BOSWALL, Jeffery Hugh Richard; *b:* 20 March 1931 in Brighton, Sussex; *w:* Pamela. Taunton House School and Montpelier College, Brighton. ARPS 1969. Senior Lecturer in Biological Imaging, Univ Derby since 1992. Prev: Head of Film and Video, RSPB, 1987-92; producer, BBC Natural History Unit, 1958-87; freelance TV and radio programme work for BBC Nat Hist Unit, 1954-; Asst to Director of Watchers and Sanctuaries, RSPB, 1951-54. Asst warden Skokholm Bird Observatory autumn 1951. Committee BOC 1973-75. BOU Council 1991-93. Chairman of First Wildlife Film-makers' Seminar Nov 1973 and of First International Symposium for Wildlife Film-makers Feb 1976 (also later ones). President Wildlife Trust Bristol Bath Avon 1988-. Trustee Wildlife Recording Trust of the National Sound Archive, 1989-. Special interests: visible migration, seabird ecology, penguins, tool-using, bird song, discography of published bird voice, Chinese ornithology, human mimicry of bird voice. Leader or lecturer on natural history tours to many countries. Joint editor 'Current Notes and Notices' in *Ibis*, Oct 1985-Oct 1987; c125 contributions to scientific journals 1947-; annual update on ornithology for *Encyclopedia Britannica*; co-author *Peterson Field Guide to Bird Songs of Europe* (16 audio cassettes). Radio productions inc *Birds of the Air, The Naturalist, Nature News*; writer/introducer of *Naturalist* and *Living World* programmes. TV productions inc *Look* series (introduced by Peter Scott) 1963-69. Wrote and produced award-winning *Private Life of the Kingfisher*. Many other productions including *Birds for all Seasons* 1986. Medal of Junior Recorders' Club of RSPB 1948. Haile Selassie I gold medal for services to the Ethiopian people 1971. Cherry Kearton Medal 1977 by the Royal Geographical Society for contributions to wildlife film-making and the preservation and publication of wildlife sound recordings. The Society of Authors/Pye Radio Award for *Pop of the (Tree) Tops: the 20 most musical British bird songsters*. Fellowship of the British Kinematograph, Sound and Television Society 1982 and President's Award from the Society for services to international wildlife film-making 1986. Scientific Fellow of the Zoological Society of London. Field collaborator, Laboratory of Ornithology, Cornell University, USA. Co-founder British Library of Wildlife Sounds (1968). Member: International Crane Foundation, OSME. OIR: avoiding gardening, political interests. Birdswell, Wraxall, Bristol BS19 1JZ. 0117 985 3418.

BOURNE, William Richmond Postle (Bill); *b:* 11 March 1930 in Bedford; *w:* Sheila. Brighton College. BA (Natural Sciences; Medical Preclinical Studies, third year Zoology, 1951), MB, BChir (Christ's College, Cambridge and St Bartholomew's Hospital, London, 1954), MA (Cambridge, 1959). Medical practitioner, first in geriatrics, then Ship's Surgeon, Royal Fleet Auxiliaries 1983-91, retired. Field asst Edward Grey Institute, Oxford 1958-61, investigating bird migration with radar in Aberdeenshire. Research Fellow Zoology Dept, Aberdeen Univ 1970-75, investigating distribution of seabirds at sea; Senior Research Fellow there 1978-79, investigating occurrence of birds at North Sea oil installations; Honorary Research Fellow there since then. Secretary Cambridge Bird Club 1949-51. Co-founder and first Recorder, Cyprus Ornithological Society 1957-58. Scientific Adviser, Royal Naval Birdwatching Society since 1957 (also for a time Army and RAF Ornithological Societies). BTO: Populations and Surveys Committee 1964-68, Chairman 1968-70, Council BTO 1964-68, 1970-74. BOU: Records Committee 1967-69, Council 1969-72, 1992-95. Founder and first Secretary Seabird Group 1966-78. British Section, ICBP. First Secretary, Seabird Committee, International Ornithological Congress 1966-80. Various other committees. Special interests: petrels and other seabirds, birds of oceanic islands, evolution, migration, zoogeography, history, conservation, pollution. Bird interests pursued in (among other places) Bermuda 1940-44, central Scandinavia 1949, Pyrenees 1950, Cape Verde Islands 1951, Madeira 1951 etc, National Service in RAF Malta, Cyprus, Jordan during Suez Affair, Iraq 1956-58, Greece, Crete, Italy, Finland 1958, Iceland 1962, 1983, USA 1962 etc, Gibraltar 1964 etc, Scandinavia and Bear Island 1973, Australia, New Zealand and Chatham Island 1974, Washington 1975, Alaska 1978, South Africa and Gough Island 1979, Newfoundland, Chile and Juan Fernandez 1983; as ship's doctor Ascension, Falklands and South Georgia five times, Persian Gulf twice 1983-91. Co-author (with S Cramp and D Saunders) *Seabirds of Britain and Ireland* (1974); several hundred smaller publications; edited *Cambridge Bird Report* for 1950, first *Cyprus Bird Reports* for 1957-59, *Seabird Bulletins* 1-3 1966-69, *Seabird Report* 2 1971; Editorial Board *Marine Pollution Bulletin* 1974-92; number of radio and TV appearances. Corresponding Fellow AOU 1968; Stamford Raffles Award, Zoological Society of London 1993. Involved in recognition of three new seabird species, description of three new races, and rediscovery of several lost species; rediscovered one insular landbird. Successful defence of Aldabra against development as a military base, Foulness as Third London Airport, Loch of Strathbeg (now an RSPB reserve) as largest North Sea gas terminal, and Henderson Island (now a World Heritage Site) against acquisition as a private estate. Helped with report on birds killed by oil from the *Torrey Canyon*, Irish Sea bird-kill 1969 (leading to controls on PCB pollution), and worldwide marine oil, toxic chemical and garbage pollution. OIR: metaphorically throwing stones at stained glass windows, walking, art (brother Bob an artist, daughter Mary a sculptor), talking, family, friends. 3 Contlaw Place, Milltimber, Aberdeen AB13 0DS. 01224 732348; fax 01224 272396.

BOWDEN, Christopher George Russell (Chris); *b:* 25 May 1960 in Felixstowe, Suffolk. BSc Ecology (Loughborough, 1982). Research biologist for RSPB/BirdLife International Bald Ibis conservation project in Morocco since 1995. Prev: project co-ordinator on BirdLife International's Mount Kupe Forest Project in Cameroon 1990-94; research biologist for RSPB studying habitat requirements and management for Woodlark and Nightjar on restocked Forestry Commission plantations 1986-90. Other projects inc breeding bird survey work in Egypt 1981; Dominica research team studying endemic parrots 1982 and 1983; RSPB research asst studying Snipe breeding requirements 1983; ICBP Cameroon Montane Forest Birds Survey Team 1983-84; research asst for Univ Orono, Maine, USA, studies of eg Black Duck, American Woodcock 1984; RSPB research asst studying Stone Curlew in Breckland 1985. Special interest in conservation and management of threatened species; also tropical forest birds. Member of Univ East Anglia expedition to Nepal surveying grassland habitat for rare mammals and birds 1978-79; OSME Yemen Expedition 1985. Also bird-related visits to Belize, Ecuador, Guatemala, Thailand, Morocco. BTO 'A' ringer since 1980. Chairman OSME Conservation Research Committee 1987-90. Committee Suffolk Ornithological Records Committee 1987-90. Papers in various journals inc *British Birds, Bull ABC, Bull BOC, J Appl Ecol, RSPB Conservation Review, Sandgrouse*; also short papers on ectoparasites and mammals in *Bull Brit Mus (NH), Entomologists' Gazette, Mammalia*. Member: ABC, OBC,

OSME, WAOS. OIR: travel, African music. c/o Field House, Thedwastre Road, Thurston, Bury St Edmunds, Suffolk IP31 3QY. 01359 270084.

BOWEY, Keith; *b:* 22 February 1961 in South Shields, Tyne & Wear; *p:* Julie Simpson. BSc Zoology (Newcastle, 1982). Senior Countryside Warden, Dept of Leisure Services, Gateshead MBC since 1986. Prev: Countryside Warden, Shibdon Pond Nature Reserve 1983-85. Treasurer Durham Ringing Group 1986-. Durham Bird Club: Committee 1989-, Projects and Surveys Committee 1991-, Chairman 1995-. Hawk and Owl Trust's Barn Owl Conservation Network Adviser for Durham 1992-. Co-ordinator of Durham Barn Owl Enquiry 1992, and of Coastal Migrant Watch 1992-96. Council Durham WT 1992-95. YOC Leader 1985-. BTO 'A' ringer since 1990. Special interests: bird ringing, upland birds, Barn Owl conservation, gull identification, Fair Isle Bird Observatory (regular visitor since 1985, some wardening, talks on its work), habitat management. Research on Sedge Warblers utilising rape crops, based at Durham Univ. Ringing expeditions to Noss, Shetland 1989, Portugal 1989, Senegal 1991, Mallorca 1992; asst scientist with several Earthwatch expeditions based at Albufera, Mallorca. Other bird-related visits in Mediterranean basin, Morocco and Egypt. Author *Where to Watch Birds in Durham* (1992). Co-author *Birds of Gateshead* (1993). *Birds in Durham* (annual report): species compiler and author of papers. Articles and notes in *Bird Watching, Birdwatch, British Birds, BTO News, Durham Wildlife, The Peregrine.* Paper on twelve-year study of Mute Swans at a single site published in *The Vasculum* 1995. Member: BES, Durham Upland Bird Study Group, Hawk and Owl Trust, LIPU. OIR: general natural history, literature, music and the cinema. 3 Alloy Terrace, Highfield, Rowlands Gill, Tyne & Wear NE39 2ND. 01207 545427.

BOWLER, Jonathan Mark (John); *b:* 23 February 1963 in Chiswick, London; *p:* Janet Hunter. BSc Ecology (East Anglia, 1984), PGCE (Bath, 1987). Research Officer for WWT since 1989. Prev: research asst for RSPB 1988; field surveyor for Interwader (now Asian Wetland Bureau) in Malaysia, Thailand and Singapore 1984-85; also voluntary wardening at RSPB Titchwell reserve. Special interests: ecology of Bewick's and Whooper Swans, avian research and conservation in SE Asia, and threatened waterfowl species. Contributed species status data for ICBP world checklist of threatened birds, and species distribution data to BirdLife International Endemic Bird Areas project (for Malaysia and Indonesia); also data to CITES-UK on field and trade status of the Salmon-crested Cockatoo to help upgrade the species to Category 1 of CITES.

Treasurer on Univ East Anglia/ICBP Arabuko-Sokoke Forest Expedition studying Red Data Book bird species in relict coastal forest in Kenya; field surveyor on UEA/ICBP Indonesian Water-birds Expedition surveying birds on the N Javan coast (esp Milky Stork) 1984; project leader in charge of ornithological research on Operation Raleigh Expedition to Seram, Maluku, Indonesia 1987; WWT expedition to Iceland investigating ecology of staging and nesting Whooper Swans 1992; member WWT/Russian/Dutch/Danish expeditions investigating summer ecology of Bewick's Swan in the Nenetski State Game Reserve, Russia 1992,93,94,95; co-leader of expedition to study feeding ecology of Flying Steamer Ducks in Alsen province, Chile 1995. Other ornithological experience in France, Spain, Mallorca, Switzerland, Greece, Turkey, USA, Venezuela, Sumatra, Australia, Hawaii. Joint author of chapter on the avifauna of Seram in *Natural History of Seram, Maluku, Indonesia* (1993). Author of many scientific reports and papers in eg *Ardea*, *Irish Birds*, *Kukila*, *Wildfowl*. Several radio and TV interviews and items on Bewick's Swans. Member: Indonesian Orn Soc, OBC. OIR: five-a-side football, cricket, squash, swimming, travelling, walking, real ale. Research Dept, WWT, Slimbridge, Gloucester GL2 7BT. 01453 890333.

BOYD, Hugh James; *b:* 12 May 1925 in Bristol; *w:* Gillian. Emeritus Research Scientist, Canadian Wildlife Service, Environment Canada, Ottawa since 1991. Prev CWS posts: Chief of Migratory Bird Research Division 1987-91; Acting Director, Ontario Region 1985-87; Senior Policy Advisor 1981-85; Director Migratory Birds Branch 1975-81; Research Supervisor Migratory Birds, Eastern Region 1967-75. In UK: seconded to Nature Conservancy Scotland 1965-67; Biologist Severn Wildfowl Trust, then Senior Biologist Wildfowl Trust 1949-1967; Warden Lundy Bird Observatory 1948-49. Served on Bird Observatories and Ringing Committees of BTO; President, Ornithological Section, Bristol Naturalists' Society 1964-65; a British delegate to the International Waterfowl Research Bureau. In Canada: member of Canadian Section, International Biological Programme; Inter-departmental Committee on Bird Hazards to Aircraft; Canadian delegate to IWRB. Special interests: behavioural ecology of geese, Arctic ecology, effects of climate on birds, international and national wildlife conservation policy. Co-author (with Peter Scott) *A Coloured Key to the Wildfowl of the World* (1950, 1961, 1968) and *Wildfowl of the British Isles* (1957); sections or chapters in several other books; author of over 150 papers in scientific journals from *The Auk* to *Wildfowl*. Chairman, Publications Advisory Committee, Canadian Wildlife Service. Awarded first Sir Peter Scott Medal 'for exceptional contributions to wildfowl and wetland conservation' by WWT, 1996. Member: AOU, Long Point Bird Observatory, Wader Study Group. 1032 Pinewood Crescent, Ottawa, Ontario, Canada K2B 5Y5. +1 613 8287886. Office: National Wildlife Research Centre, Canadian Wildlife Service, Environment Canada, Ottawa, Ontario, Canada K1A 0H3. +1 819 9976130; fax +1 819 9536612.

BOYER, Trevor; *b:* 11 November 1948 in Castleford, W Yorks. Cert in Graphics (Wakefield College of Art, 1966). Special interests: raptors and raptor migration. Extensive bird-related travels in Europe, N America, Mexico, Asia. Books illustrated wholly or in part: *Penguins* by B Stonehouse (1978), *Field Guide to the Birds of Britain* by P Burton and T Parmeter (1981), *Birdwatchers Britain* ed by J Parslow (1983), *Ducks of Britain & the Northern Hemisphere* by J Gooders (1986), *The Complete Book of British Birds* by R Hume (1988), *Birds of Prey of the World* by P Burton (1989), *Owls of the World* by R Hume (1991), *BWP* Vol 9 (1994). Monedula, Estcourt Road, Darrington, W Yorkshire WF8 3AJ. 01977 780065.

BOYS, John Vernon; *b:* 24 June 1934 in London; *w:* Katharine. Marlborough College (scholar) 1948-52. BA, MA Mathematics (Trinity College, Cambridge, 1958). Retired schoolmaster. Committee Dorset Bird Club since 1958, inc spells as Chairman and editor of bird report (contributor of records since age c10). Special interests: bird distribution, tetrad work; co-ordinator of BTO Atlas work in Dorset 1968-72. Member Cambridge North Borneo Expedition 1956. Widely travelled for birds in Europe, also S Africa. Co-author (with E D V Prendergast) *Birds of Dorset* (1983), compiler *Check-list of Dorset Birds* (1972); many minor articles in various publications. OIR: real tennis, choral singing, genealogy, the family. 21 Moor Road, Broadstone, Dorset BH18 8BA. 01202 692500.

BRACKENRIDGE, William (Bill); *b:* 1 April 1952 in Ayr. MA Geography, Archaeology etc (Glasgow, 1973); Teaching Cert 1974; BSc Biology, Ecology, Environment (Open Univ, 1993). Ecological and environmental consultant and RSPB summer warden, Inversnaid. Prev: Urban Wildlife Ranger Scottish WT 1991-94; Countryside Ranger, Stirling DC 1979-91. Council SOC c1975-78. Deputy County Recorder Forth Area. Bird-related travel in Europe, Israel, USA, Costa Rica, Brazil. Talks/slide shows. Publications: some short articles (eg orienteering and breeding birds in Loch Ard Forest, 1988); some illustrations for *Scottish Birds* in 1970s. Specialist in vocalisations and bird whistle imitations: various private (and some public) performances. Member: NBC. OIR: drawing wildlife. 7 The Square, Ashfield, Dunblane, Perthshire FK15 0JN. 01786 823021.

BRADLEY. Peter; *b:* 23 August 1960 in Lincoln. BA Social Sciences (Kent, 1981). Warden RSPB Surlingham and Rockland Reserves 1992-. Prev: Asst Warden RSPB Rye House Marsh 1991-92; contract warden at other RSPB reserves. Special interests: fen/wet meadow restoration; interpretation on bird reserves. Edited RSPB's *Water Project* (education guide). OIR: writing, walking. 25 The Green, Surlingham, Norfolk NR14 7AG. 01508 538661.

BRADSHAW, Christopher Gordon; *b:* 1 July 1969 in Farnborough, Kent. Rainham Mark Grammar School. Computer analyst/programmer. Recorder for North Sheppey and Swale (Kent) and member of Editorial and Records Committee Kent Ornithological Society since 1989. Organiser and participant in various surveys and censuses in Kent; 10km square steward for TQ95. Special interests: identification, migration, rarities. Participant in WIWO/DHKD bird survey of the Kizilirmak Delta, Turkey 1992; OSME expedition to southern Yemen (jointly responsible for collecting data on Important Bird Areas for BirdLife International book on IBAs in the Middle East). Extensive travel in Europe, N America, India, Thailand, China, Kenya, Hong Kong etc, to study identification of potential vagrants to Britain. Articles in *Kent Bird Report* and *OSME Bulletin*; co-author of paper on wetlands in Turkey, also contribution to *Turkey Bird Report 1987-91* (by Martins and Kirwan, in press) and co-author of paper in *Sandgrouse*. Photographs published in *Birdwatch* and *Dutch Birding*. Member: ABA, ABC, NBC, OBC, OSME. OIR: moths, butterflies, dragonflies, cricket, football, music, current affairs. 6 Collet Walk, Parkwood, Gillingham, Kent ME8 9QL. 01634 230590; work 01622 696686.

BRADSHAW, Colin; *b:* 24 February 1954 in Wallasey, Merseyside; *p:* Celia Bryce. St Anselm's College, Birkenhead 1965-72. MB, ChB (Sheffield, 1977), MRCP 1980, MRCGP 1982, FRCGP 1991. General medical practitioner. Committee Tyneside (later Northumberland & Tyneside) Bird Club in 1980s and Records Committe 1989-93. British Birds Rarities Committee 1992-. Special interest: identification, esp buntings, flycatchers, warblers. Travels to former USSR, China, USA, Canada - each several times. Extensive photographic collection. Numerous identification articles in *British Birds, Birding World, Birdwatch, Dutch Birding, Ontario Birds*; travel articles in *Birdwatch*; member *British Birds* Identification Notes Panel 1992-. Regular correspondent to Latvian Rarities Committee. Member: Beidaihe Bird Club, OBC. OIR: playing cricket and football 'with undiminished ferocity despite age'; playing guitar in a rock band and a country band; supporting Tranmere Rovers. 9 Tynemouth Place, North Shields, Tyne & Wear NE30 4BJ. 0191 257 2389.

BRAIN, Laurence Thomas Alfred; *b:* 21 October 1946 in Bedford; *w:* Sally. BVMS (Royal Veterinary College, Edinburgh, 1970), MRCVS 1970. Partner in mixed veterinary practice. Committee Aberdeen and District RSPB Members' Group since 1985, Chairman since 1991. Scottish Advisory Committee, RSPB 1989-92. Regular voluntary warden RSPB Loch of Strathbeg. Special interests: identification, raptors, care of injured birds esp raptors and owls. OIR: all natural history. Iona, 40 High Street, Turriff, Aberdeenshire AB53 6SX. 01771 644489.

BRAITHWAITE, Victoria Anne; *b:* 19 July 1967 in Bradford, W Yorkshire; *h:* Dr Andrew Read. BA Zoology (Oxford, 1988), Christopher Welch Scholarship Oxford Univ 1989-92, DPhil Visual landmarks and pigeon homing (Oxford, 1993). Lecturer Univ Edinburgh since 1995. Prev: post-doctoral research asst, Glasgow Univ 1993-95. Special interests: spatial memory and behaviour in several bird species, inc homing behaviour, migration and food storing. Scientific papers published in *Anim Behav, Ethology, J Navigation, Proc Roy Soc London (B)*. Member: ASAB. OIR: travelling, expeditions, diving (esp on coral reefs). ICAPB, University of Edinburgh, Ashworth Laboratories, The King's Buildings, Edinburgh EH9 3JT.

BRAZIER, Hugh; *b:* 17 November 1953 in Bristol; *w:* Caroline. BA English (Sidney Sussex College, Cambridge 1976), MA (Cambridge, 1980), Diploma in Library & Information Studies (London, 1978), MA (London, 1979). ALA 1979. Librarian. IWC: Council 1982-90, Hon Sec 1987-89, Chairman 1989-90. BTO: Ringing Committee 1983-87. Adult education lecturer in ornithology Univ College Dublin since 1982. BTO 'A' ringer since 1977 and member of Sponsors Panel. Special interests: ringing, Irish seabirds (Blasket Islands and other Kerry islands). Editor *Irish Birds* since 1985. Editor *IWC News* 1981-85. Editor *Irish Ringers' Bulletin* 1980-85. 5 St Fintan's Crescent, Sutton, Dublin 13, Ireland. +353 (0)1 8322479.

BRAZIL, Mark Andrew; *b:* 8 June 1955 in Redditch, Worcs. BA Biology and English Literature (Keele, 1978), PhD Behavioural ecology of the Whooper Swan (Stirling, 1981). Consultant and author; freelance photographer, lecturer and guide. Conservation Officer and co-ordinator of the Barn Owl Conservation Network, The Hawk Trust, 1988-89. Editor, United Nations University 1986-87. Lecturer Rakuno Gakuen Univ Hokkaido 1983-85. Bird tour guide for several companies. Travelled widely in Europe, Asia and South America. Research oriented consultancies for eg ITE, Wild Bird Society of Japan, TRAFFIC, WWF Japan, WWF

International. Special interests: the Japanese and E Asian avifaunas; particular species (*Cygnus cygnus, Haliaetus pelagicus, Larus saundersi, Ketupa blakistoni, Rallus okinawae*). Member of editorial committee of *Tori* (journal of Orn Soc of Japan) 1983-92, of *Journal of the Yamashina Institute for Ornithology* 1986-92, of *Japan Environment Review* 1986-, and *Journal of the Mammalogical Society of Japan* 1991-. Author *An Illustrated Guide to the Commoner Birds of the Ballestas Islands, Peru* (Lima, 1982), *Finding Birds in Japan: the Tokyo area* (Hokkaido, 1984), *Finding Birds in Japan: Honshu* (Hokkaido, 1985), *The Birds of Japan: a checklist* (Hokkaido, 1985), *Today Birds, Tomorrow Men: Suntory's 'Save the Birds!'* *Campaign* (Tokyo, 1985), *Washington Convention Data Book* Vols 1-3 (Tokyo, 1986), *A Birdwatcher's Guide to Japan* (Tokyo, 1987), *Nest Boxes for Barn Owls* (1988), *The Barn Owl: the farmer's friend needs a helping hand* with C R Shawyer (1989), *The Birds of Japan* (1991). Columnist for *The Japan Times* 1982-, *The Eco Times* 1993-95, *Kagaku Asahi* 1993-94. Author (and photographer) of numerous articles in national newspapers, popular and specialist ornithological and other journals in the UK, Japan and elsewhere. Regular consultant to NHK TV (Japanese Broadcasting Corporation) 1989-; also work for other TV companies in the production of natural history programmes, inc the 1986 Wildscreen Award winner 'Lords of Hokkaido'. OIR: mountain hiking, travelling, mammalian biology, other branches of natural history. UK contact address: Bredon Croft, Aqueduct Lane, Alvechurch, Birmingham B48 7BS. Tel/fax 0121 445 1603.

BRENCHLEY, Anne; *b:* 13 April 1956 in Pembury, Kent. Maidstone Grammar School for Girls. BSc Zoology (Aberdeen, 1979), PhD Regional variations in the breeding distribution of the Rook in relation to differing agricultural regimes within Great Britain (Aberdeen, 1984). Scientist with NCC/English Nature since 1985. Prev: contract research officer British Columbia Ministry of Agriculture (Canada) studying effects of Raven predation on new born lambs. Chairman Suffolk Ornithological Records Committee 1994-95; Committee SOC Aberdeen Branch 1990; YOC Leader Lowestoft, Aberdeen, Bury St Edmunds 1986-. Voluntary wardening at Dungeness Bird Observatory 1973-80. BTO 'A' ringer since 1982; joint founder Lackford Ringing Group (Constant Effort Site there since 1992); member Grampian RG; voluntary bird bander Canadian Wildlife Service at Qualicum, British Columbia 1984-85. Special interests: corvids, census and atlas work, moulting strategies. Studied moult in Ghana with Aberdeen Univ expedition 1978. Travel for birds inc Morocco, Denmark, the Alps, S Spain and Portugal, France (Camargue), Central Greece. Author of chapter on the use of birds as indicators of change in agriculture in *Agriculture and the Environment* ed by D Jenkins (1984); paper on Rook distribution and abundance in *J Zool* 1986; Rook species account in BTO Winter Atlas. OIR: organic gardening, wholefood cookery, listening to classical and Gaelic folk rock music, travel, plant photography, playing classical guitar, reading crime novels, aerobics, hill walking. English Nature, Norman Tower House, 1-2 Crown Street, Bury St Edmunds, Suffolk IP33 1QX. 01284 762218.

BRENNAN, Philip Anthony (Phil); *b:* 1 October 1950 in Ennis, Co Clare, Ireland; *w:* Noreen. Teacher. Ornithological consultant Shannon Airport 1985-86, 1989-94, and Galway Airport 1994. BTO 'A' ringer since 1978. IWC North Munster Branch (various offices) 1975-92. Chairman IWC Clare Branch 1992-94. Council IWC three years in late 1970s. Irish Ringing Committee 1985-86. Secretary Shannon Wader Ringing Group 1979-94. Organiser IWC/BTO Conference 1981. Organiser Loop Head Bird Observatory 1985-94. Special interests: Sedge Warbler study at Shannon Lagoon 1977-93 (over 6,000 ringed, 55 recovered abroad); Shannon Wader Ringing Group effort since 1974 with special emphasis on Dunlin, Curlew, Redshank, Whimbrel; bird illustration and painting. Senegal Expedition, one month winter 1991-92 and Thunder Cape, Canada 1993. Co-editor *Birds of North Munster* (1981); compiler *Loop Head Report* 1985-; illustrator *Birds of Killarney Woodlands* (1993) and *Birds of Clare and Limerick* (1994); wide variety of articles in IWC newsletters and local journals. Four one-man shows with high proportion on bird and wildlife paintings in 1980s, also participation in group art shows; large public bird display boards 1991-93. OIR: painting, traditional (mainly Irish) music, history (mainly local), creating 'garden' out of rock, canoeing. The Crag, Stonehall, Newmarket-on-Fergus, Co Clare, Ireland. +353 (0)61 472924.

BRITTON, Stuart Anthony; *b:* 17 May 1948 in Spilsby, Lincs; *w:* Janet. King Edward VI Grammar School, Spilsby. Police constable. Voluntary warden Linwood Warren Reserve, Lincs since 1983. BTO 'A' ringer since 1987 and member of Sponsors Panel. Special interests: ringing and training ringers. Secretary Mid-Lincs Ringing Group since 1989; Constant Effort Site organiser since 1988. Editor *Mid-Lincs Ringing Report* 1983-95. Area Wildlife Liaison Officer with Lincolnshire police, with special responsibility for investigation of offences relating to wild birds and their eggs. OIR: all forms of sport and avid follower of Leicester Tigers RUFC. 4 Anglian Way, Market Rasen, Lincs LN8 3RP. 01673 842899.

BRODIE GOOD, John Christopher; *b:* 19 March 1958 in London; *p:* Gayle Harris. Latymer Upper School, West London. Founder and Managing Director of Wildwings from 1990. Special interests: identification, migration. Extensive travels inc Europe, Kenya, Seychelles, Middle East, India, Nepal, Borneo, Antarctica and the Falklands, and North, Central and South America. Finder of Britain's first Philadelphia Vireo (Scilly). International House, Bank Road, Bristol BS15 2LX. 0117 984 8040.

BROOME, Anthony Michael (Tony); *b:* 5 April 1956 in Hazel Grove, Stockport, Cheshire. Marple Hall Grammar School. Electrical engineer with NORWEB. Bird Recorder for Cheshire and Wirral since 1987. Special interests: identification, migration, photography. Bird-related travel in Europe, N Africa, N America, and Near, Middle and Far East; detailed trip reports with maps for Israel, Turkey, Morocco, N India. One of several compilers of *Cheshire and Wirral Bird Report* 1984-; joint sub-editor of county newsletter 1989-. Joint author (with N Riddiford) of identification article on Pallas's Reed Bunting and a note on Pomarine Skuas in *British Birds*. Illustrations for *Cheshire and Wirral Breeding Bird Atlas* (1992). OIR: entomology, producing high quality plastic MV traps. Sibirica, 9 Vicarage Lane, Poynton, Cheshire SK12 1BG. 01625 878384.

BROWN, Alan; *b:* 9 May 1947 in Methil, Fife. Civil Servant. Recorder for East Lothian 1983-89. Lothian Records Committee 1983-96. Scottish Birds Records Committee 1984-94 (Secretary 1984-86). SOC Council 1986-90. British Birds Rarities Committee 1987-95. Special interest: identification of Western Palearctic species. OSME expedition to Yemen 1993. Widely travelled in W Palearctic; also former USSR, China, Hong Kong, Kenya, Uganda, USA, Venezuela. Identification articles in *British Birds* and *Scottish Birds*; compiler *Scottish Bird Report* 1976-85 and *Lothian Bird Report* 1983-91. Member: ABC, NBC, OBC, OSME. 23 King's Court, Longniddry, E Lothian EH32 0QP. 01875 852413.

BROWN, Andrew; *b:* 11 February 1960 in St Anne's on Sea, Lancs; *w:* Sue. BSc Zoology (Liverpool, 1981), PhD Parasite population ecology (Liverpool, 1984). Head of Ornithology, English Nature since 1992. Prev: Moorland Bird Study Team Leader, NCC then JNCC 1989-91. Special interests: bird conservation, upland birds, Twite, birds in Norfolk. Over twenty scientific papers in eg *Bird Study, Biol Cons, Freshwater Biol*; many NCC, JNCC and English Nature reports; several articles for Norfolk Bird Club. Member: ABC, NBC. OIR: world birding, eating. English Nature, Northminster House, Peterborough PE1 1UA. 01733 318362.

BROWN, Brian John; *b:* 17 September 1941 in Barnby, Suffolk; *w:* Christine. Lowestoft Technical College. Local Government Officer. Voluntary work for many years at RSPB Minsmere during H E Axell's wardenship and involved in development of the 'scrape'. BTO Regional Representative Suffolk 1980-84. WEA tutor on ornithology since 1987. Committee Lowestoft Field Club since 1962 (Chairman 1966). Suffolk Ornithological Records Committee 1987-93 (Chairman 1988-89). Lecturer on natural history subjects to local societies. Special interests: identification (esp gulls), migration, monitoring and studying the Lowestoft breeding Kittiwake colony, natural history photography (esp birds). Editor *Lowestoft Field Club Annual Bird Report* 1967-95; contributor to *The Birds of Suffolk* ed by W H Payn (2nd ed 1978) and to *Easy Birdwatching* (guide to birdwatching in Suffolk for the disabled) by S Piotrowski *et al* (1990); articles in *British Birds* and *Suffolk Birds*; many short notes, papers, photographs and drawings in books, periodicals and newspapers. Interviews on radio and TV. OIR: natural history in general (esp ferns and fungi), taxidermy, travel in Britain, modern cinema, local history. 24 Clifton Road, Lowestoft, Suffolk NR33 0HF. 01502 567727.

BROWN, Douglas William; *b:* 22 December 1942 in Brompton-on-Swale, North Riding of Yorkshire; *w:* Carolina. BSc Chemistry (Leeds, 1964). FRGS. Retired international executive. Voluntary wardening at Osprey site Loch Garten and ringing Storm and Leach's Petrels on St Kilda (National Trust for Scotland) in 1960s. Special interests: breeding biology, migration, raptors, UK bird observatories, Outer Hebrides. Overseas: Antarctica (British Antarctic Survey 1966-69); Cape May (New Jersey, USA) Raptor Banding Project annually since 1982. Co-author of article in *Ibis* on breeding biology of the Black-bellied Storm Petrel, and of BAS Scientific Report on biology of Wilson's Storm Petrel at Signy Island, South Orkney. Member: The Antarctic Club, American Birds and Hawk Migration Assocn of North America (USA), CEMPA (Portugal). Holder of BTO, Portuguese and USA ringing permits. OIR: photography (to published standard), cross-country skiing, antiques, classical music. 10 Leinster Mews, London W2 3EY. 0171 262 5247.

BROWN, Duncan; *b:* 11 February 1948 in Buxton, Derbyshire; *w:* Gillian. BA Art (Norwich School of Art, 1971), Art Teachers Cert (Univ Wales, Cardiff, 1972), Dip in Field Biology (London, 1982). Head Warden, N Gwynedd, NCC/CCW since 1984. Prev: NCC Warden, Rhinog, Morfa Harlech, Morfa Dyffryn, Cader Idris 1976-84. BTO Regional Representative Meirionnydd 1977-84. Heronries Census organiser Caernarfon since

1984. Wales Raptor Study Group Committee since 1991. Special interests: the Barn Owl in Wales, Pied Flycatcher, Herons. Numerous articles on birds and wildlife in various Welsh and English language journals inc *Bird Study*, *Cynefin*, *Dan Haul*, *Y Faner*, *Gwaith Maes*, *Nature in Wales*. Frequent broadcaster on wildlife topics in Welsh for Radio Cymru and in English for Radio Wales, also TV. Chairman: Cymdeithas Edward Llwyd (society for the promotion of conservation through the Welsh language), Cymdeithas Gwaith Maes (society for the promotion of environmental education in Welsh), Mammal Society. OIR: poetry, history of art, gardening, cookery, the Celtic world. Gwelfor, Ffordd Ceunant, Waunfawr, Caernarfon, Gwynedd LL55 4RY. 01286 650547.

BROWN, Robert Adrian (Bob); *b:* 19 August 1950 in London. BSc Zoology (Queen's Univ Belfast, 1973), PhD Marine Biology (QUB, 1976). RSPB Regional Officer for N Ireland since 1991. Prev: Head Warden National Trust Strangford Lough Wildlife Scheme 1981-91; earlier bivalve research included predator/prey relationship between cockles and overwintering Oystercatchers. Council Ulster WT 1983-91; Council Marine Conservation Society 1988-93, National Trust Strangford Lough Committee 1991-94, Strangford Lough Management Committee 1992-, N Ireland Environment Link Management Committee 1991-, RSPB representative Irish Sea Forum Steering Committee 1993-. Special interests: marine and coastal birds; ecology (esp breeding, feeding and migration, inc overwintering movements); marine conservation issues and coastal zone management. Extensive travel in S America, collecting material for talks and slide shows. Author *Strangford Lough: the wildlife of an Irish Sea lough* (1990); papers in biological and conservation journals inc *Irish Birds*, *J Marine Biol Assocn*, *J Zool*; articles on wildlife in magazines and local newspapers. Regularly interviewed on national and local radio and TV on conservation in N Ireland. Member: Marine Biological Association, Marine Conservation Society. OIR: sailing, hill walking, folk music, 'making wine and consuming the disastrous consequences', travel esp in S America and Caribbean. 1 Bishopscourt Road, Kilclief, Strangford, Co Down, N Ireland BT30 7NU. Work 01232 491547; fax 01232 491669.

BROWNETT, Anthony (Tony); *b:* 14 May 1941 in Banbury, Oxfordshire; *w:* Gillian. Banbury Grammar School. BSc Zoology (Univ College London, 1963). Civil Servant (DHSS) since 1972. Prev: Research Asst Biophysics Research Unit Loughborough Univ 1969-70, Field Asst Edward Grey Institute of Field Ornithology Univ Oxford 1966-69. Banbury Ornithological Society: recorder 1962-71, field organiser since 1985. Special interests:

breeding bird surveys. Particularly associated with the annual breeding season survey, an in-depth single-species survey repeated in rotation over a 25-year cycle (1961-); pioneer work on the Willow Tit (1964-65); originator of the random 1km square survey (1971). Author *A Study of Birds in the South Midlands* (1974), *The Birds of the Slade Nature Reserve Bloxham* (1992); numerous articles in *Annual Report of the Banbury Orn Soc*, and editor 1962-71; formerly contributor of *Ibis* abstracts. OIR: dragonflies. 28 Colesbourne Road, Brookside, Bloxham, Banbury, Oxon OX15 4TB.

BRUCKER, John Whitlock; *b:* 1 June 1929 in Oxford; *w:* Vivienne. Retired head teacher. Bird Recorder for Oxfordshire 1962-66, 1970-73, 1980-93. BTO Regional Representative South Oxfordshire 1974-80. President Oxford Ornithological Society 1973-76. Special interests: systems of record keeping for conservation purposes; organising local surveys; achieving co-operation between local interest groups and individuals. Author of *Crows, Ducks, Finches, Titmice* (1977). Co-author (with J M Campbell) *Birds of Blenheim Park* (1975) and *Birds of Blenheim Palace* (1987). Co-author (with A G Gosler and A Heryet) *Birds of Oxfordshire* (1992). Editor *Birds of Oxfordshire* (annual report) 1962-73, 1981-93 and editor of Oxford Orn Soc monthly bulletin 1980-93. Several broadcasts on Radio Oxford. OIR: music (choral singing), travel, gardening. 65 Yarnton Road, Kidlington, Oxon OX5 1AT. 01865 372845.

BRYAN, Maurice William; *b:* 3 May 1929 in Dublin, Ireland; *w:* Bernadette (Bobbie). The High School Dublin. BSc Experimental Science (Trinity College Dublin, 1951). CEng 1992, MIEI 1992. Chairman, Norton Associates. Proprietor, Kingfisher Technology. IWC: Chairman 1985-89, Hon Sec 1991-92, Council 1984-89, 1991-94. Chairman IWC Dublin (South) Branch 1983-88, Hon Sec 1989-. Tour guide 1991-. Special interests: bird conservation, general and specific (esp Corncrake, Brent Goose, raptors); behaviour (esp Brent Goose); photography; lecturing using own slides; bird painting; bird-related tourism. Travel inc eight months in Republic of S Africa 1980-81, Mallorca, USA. Numerous articles in newspapers and magazines. Broadcast short talks and panel discussions, weekly slot on CKRadio 1990-92. Fieldwork for Winter Bird Survey 1981-84, Winter Wetland Survey 1982-86, Breeding Bird Survey 1989-91. Under umbrella of Irish Section of ICBP, led successful campaign to have strychnine sales outlawed in R of Ireland; also major part in saving wetland feeding grounds of Dublin Bay through active opposition to road scheme. OIR: restoration and riding of veteran and vintage motorcycles. Bealac na Finnise, 22 Butterfield Park, Rathfarnham, Dublin 14, Ireland. +353 (0)1 4931877.

BRYANT, David Murray; *b:* 24 September 1945 in Norwich, Norfolk; *w:* Victoria. Greshams School, Holt. BSc Zoology (Imperial College London, 1966), PhD (Imperial College, Silwood Park, London, 1971). ARCS 1966. DIC 1972. Professor of Biology University of Stirling since 1990. Assistant on Skokholm 1963. SOC: Council 1976-78, Secretary Stirling Branch 1970-76. BoEE/WeBS co-ordinator for Forth Estuary since 1974. BTO: Research Committee 1992-96, Council 1994-. Special interests: ecology, behaviour and physiology of birds, esp hirundines, shorebirds, freshwater species. Many scientific articles inc *The Auk, Bird Study, Condor, Ibis, J Animal Ecol, J Zool, Wildfowl.* OIR: walking, skiing, theatre. Avian Ecology Unit, Dept of Biological Sciences, University of Stirling, Stirling FK9 4LA. 01786 467755/6.

BRYANT, Edward Alan (Alan); *b:* 4 July 1922 in Aberdare, Mid Glamorgan; *w:* Jean. Cathedral School Hereford. BSc (Eng) (Univ College Wales, 1942). CEng, MICE 1949. Retired civil engineer. Participant in Beached Bird Survey since its inception. Operator (with wife) of New Quay Bird and Wildlife Hospital since 1971 (esp oiled seabirds and seals). Author *Second Chance* (1981); weekly column in local newspaper; regular items on radio and TV, mostly in Wales. Prince of Wales Award 1975; Lord Erskine Award 1993. OIR: photography, music. Penfoel, Cross Inn, Llandysul, Dyfed SA44 6NR. 01545 560462.

BUCKLAND, Stephen Terrence (Steve); *b:* 28 July 1955 in Dorchester, Dorset; *w:* Pat. BSc Mathematics (Southampton, 1976), MSc Statistics (Edinburgh, 1977), PhD Statistics (Aberdeen, 1983). Professor of Statistics, University of St Andrews. Co-ordinator North-East Scotland Ornithological Atlas 1981-84. Statistical consultant to various ornithologists and societies. Special interests: survey design and analysis, line and point transect surveys, mark-recapture studies. Co-author *Distance Sampling: estimating abundance of biological populations* (1993); co-editor (with M V Bell and N Picozzi) *The Birds of North-East Scotland* (1990). Member: BES. OIR: walking, reading. Dept of Mathematical and Computational Sciences, University of St Andrews, North Haugh, St Andrews KY16 9SS. 01334 463787.

BUCKNELL, Neil John; *b:* 18 March 1956 in Reading, Berks. Theale Green School. MA Law (Selwyn College Cambridge, 1977). Solicitor. WeBS organiser for Berkshire since 1981. Committee (various posts) Reading Ornithological Club 1981-87, Chairman 1994-97. Evening class lecturer Univ Reading 1983-87. Berkshire Atlas Group (co-ordinated tetrad atlas survey and county avifauna) 1987-. BOU Ornithological Affairs Committee 1994-. Special interests: inland water birds (esp river birds) and encouraging local fieldwork; participant in BTO's Waterways Bird Survey since 1979. Co-editor (with Peter Standley *et al*) and contributor *The Birds of Berkshire* (1996). OIR: travel, motoring, general countryside matters, classical music. 10 Cleeve Court, Streatley, Reading RG8 9PS. 01491 873836.

BUDWORTH, David (Dave); *b:* 14 September 1943 in Creswell, Derbyshire; *w:* Madeline. BSc Electrical Eng (Loughborough, 1967), MSc Control Eng (Loughborough, 1970). AMIEE 1967. Electrical engineer. BTO Regional Representative Derbyshire 1975-79, for S Derbys 1993-. BTO 'A' ringer since 1969. Committee Derbyshire Ornithological Society since 1975, and Ringing Secretary since c1980. Ringing Secretary of both S Derbys Ringing Group and Sule Skerry RG since 1990. Committee Seabird Group 1990-91. Tutor for local ornithological classes 1972-92. Special interests: ringing, population studies. Organised twelve visits to Sule Skerry, Orkney 1975-93 to monitor seabird populations esp Puffin; similar expedition to N Rona 1984. Participant in seabird study on St Kilda, ringing studies in Mallorca and Portugal, and migration study in Senegal. Ringing on the Wash since 1972 and a number of local Common Birds Census studies. Several accounts of surveys of Sule Skerry birds lodged with BTO, SOC and RSPB, and one published in *Seabird* (1975). Actively involved with reserve management as chairman of local group committee and member of County Conservation Committee. OIR: Sec of Derbyshire Entomological Soc 1989-, specialism Heteroptera. 121 Wood Lane, Newhall, Swadlincote, Derbys DE11 0LX. 01283 215188.

BUISSON, Roger Simon Keith; *b:* 1 April 1960 in Bushey, Herts; *w:* Rebecca Mary. BSc Agricultural Chemistry (Wye College, London, 1981), DIC Civil Engineering 1986, PhD Behaviour of chlorinated organic micropollutants (Imperial College, London, 1986). MCIWEM 1990. Head of Conservation Management Advice, RSPB since 1996. Prev: Water Policy Officer, RSPB 1989-96; Scientific Officer, Upland Bird Survey Team (Wales), NCC. BTO 'A' ringer since 1986 and trainer. Records and Research Committee, Bedfordshire Bird Club 1993-. Treasurer, Madagascar Environmental Research Group 1988-. Committee Ornithology Section London NHS 1984-85. Committee Wye Ornithologists' Club (Kent) 1978-80. Voluntary warden Weston Turville Reservoir Nature Reserve 1975-78. Special interest: passerine population and distribution studies through field surveys and ringing. Articles on wetland conservation in eg *Birdwatcher's Yearbook*, *Ecos*, *RSPB Conservation Review*. Conference papers for eg

MAFF River and Coastal Engineers, Chartered Institution of Water and Environmental Management. Winner Keith Ellenton Photographic Prize (YOC) 1975. OIR: natural history photography. 25 Village Road, Cockayne Hatley, Sandy, Beds SG19 2EE. 01767 631583. RSPB 01767 680551.

BULLOCK, Robert Ward (Bob); *b:* 7 October 1950 in Northampton; *w:* Sue. BSc (Leicester, 1971), PGCE (Leicester, 1972). Teacher. Co-director, Birdline Midlands. Northamptonshire Bird Recorder since 1982. Founder-member Northants Bird Club 1973, Treasurer 1973-76, Secretary 1978-83. Special interests: waders, British and world lists, photography. Bird-related visits to 43 countries in six continents. Co-author of chapter on birds in *The Nature of Northamptonshire* by Colston and Perring (1989). Editor *Northamptonshire Bird Report* since 1982 and compiler or part compiler since 1974. Assisted in Northants section of *Where to Watch Birds in the East Midlands* by G Catley (1996). Reporter for *Bird Watching*. OIR: carp fishing, sport. 81 Cavendish Drive, Northampton NN3 3HL. 01604 27262.

BUNDY, Graham; *b:* 17 October 1936 in Southampton; *w:* Patricia Roden. Itchen Grammar School. Semi-retired. Fieldworker, SOTEAG (Univ Aberdeen) diver study Shetland 1989. Scientific officer NCC: Caithness 1987, Shetland 1986. Research biologist RSPB: Black-throated Diver study, Scotland 1977; Red-throated Diver study, Shetland 1976; (temp) Unst survey, Shetland 1974. Consultant for *BWP* on Libya and Middle East. Special interests: identification, zoogeography and species distribution, taxonomy, Arctic birds, desert ecology, seabirds, photography. Author *Birds of Eastern Province of Saudi Arabia* (1989), *Birds of Libya* (BOU Check-list No 1, 1976). Main articles in *Bird Study*, *British Birds*, *Bull BOC*, *Sandgrouse*, *Scottish Birds*. Member: OSME. OIR: travel (sixty countries), walking and exploring wilderness, driving, football, books, collecting jazz history on CD. 7 Culver, Ingleside, Netley Abbey, Southampton SO3 5GJ. 01703 456583.

BUNN, Howard John; *b:* 19 April 1958 in Grimsby; *w:* Jenny. County Bird Recorder for Lincolnshire and S Humberside since 1993. Lincolnshire Records Committee since 1984. 16 Vivian Avenue, Grimsby, S Humberside DN32 8QF. 01472 600268.

BURGESS, Neil David; *b:* 24 February 1962 in Hertford; *w:* Rosalyn. Richard Hale School, Hertford. BSc Botany (Bristol, 1983), PhD Fossils (Cardiff, 1987). Africa Officer, International Department RSPB since

1991. Prev: RSPB Advisory Department 1989-91 and contract ecologist 1987-88; scientific researcher, Natural History Museum 1983-87. Special interests: biodiversity of bird species in African forests, esp coastal and mountain forests of Tanzania; management of British habitats, esp wetland and heathland, with emphasis on *British Red Data Book* bird species; ornithological censusing techniques. Founder-member Institute of Ecologists and Environmental Managers. Co-author *Bird Census Techniques* (1992); articles in eg *Biol Cons, J Environmental Management, RSPB Conservation Review, Scopus*; papers in proceedings of Eighth Pan-African Ornithological Congress, African Biodiversity Conference. RSPB, The Lodge, Sandy, Beds SG19 2DL. 01767 680551.

BURNS, David William (Dave); *b:* 21 March 1950 in West Bromwich, West Midlands; *w:* Belinda. Carpenter/joiner. Special interest: photography. Overseas travel inc Ethiopia, France. Photographs in *A Photographic Guide to the Birds of Southern Africa* by Ian Sinclair (1984) and *Rare Birds of the British Isles* by David Saunders (1991); also in *British Birds*. Found first Oriental Pratincole for Western Palearctic (Dunwich, Suffolk, 1981). 36 Pennhouse Avenue, Penn, Wolverhampton WV4 4BE. 01902 334975.

BURNS, Seamus; *b:* 13 March 1969 in Magherafelt, N Ireland; *w:* Jean. Upholsterer. Founder-member Moyola Conservation Group (South Derry), also Group Co-ordinator/Projects Organiser. BTO Regional Representative Co Derry. Voluntary warden Creighton's Wood Nature Reserve (UWT). Barn Owl Recorder for N Ireland Raptor Study Group. Special interests: identification, Barn Owl studies, swan fatalities and overhead powerlines. Fieldwork inc national surveys, wildfowl and wader counts, Goldeneye nestbox scheme, photography. 8 Derramore Gardens, Magherafelt, Co Londonderry BT45 5RW. 01648 34234.

BURTON, John Frederick; *b:* 19 April 1931 in Greenwich, Greater London; *w:* Helga (deceased); *p:* Wega Ingeborg Schmidt-Thomée. The Roan School, Greenwich. BA Zoology (Oxford, 1958). FRES 1949, FZS 1962. Retired. Prev: radio producer and organiser of wildlife sound library, BBC Natural History Unit, Bristol 1960-88. Asst Secretary BTO and Secretary BTO Scientific Advisory Committee 1953-56. Committee and Editorial Committee RSPB Junior Recorders' Club (now YOC) 1948-49. Official Observer in Greenwich Park for the then Ministry of Works Royal Parks Bird Sanctuaries Committee 1946-53, 1958-59. Recorder for the South and member London NHS Ornithological Section's Records Committee 1950-53. Organiser BTO Nest Record Scheme 1953-59 and of

BTO National Heronries Census 1953-56. BTO Regional Representative Bristol and Somerset 1970-72. BBC representative on Executive Committee of Council for Nature 1962-70. Organiser European Broadcasting Union's wildlife sound recording competition 'A Bird Song for Europe' 1970. Lecturer on ornithological and other wildlife topics. Special interests: effects of climatic change on birds (etc); zoogeography; archaeological history of European birds; migration (birds and insects); food and feeding studies; *Acrocephalus* warblers; sound production (esp mimicry); sound recording. Expedition (with D F Owen) in 1953 to study autumn bird and insect migration along SW coast of France (papers published in French and English); repeated solo in 1966 when recordings also made for BBC Sound Archives. Sound recording expeditions to Netherlands 1963, France (Provence and Languedoc) 1973, Spain 1982 and 1983, The Gambia and Senegal 1984, various parts of British Isles 1960-88. Bird-related travel in other European countries and N America. Author *Field and Moor* (1976), *Downland Wildlife* (1992), *Birds and Climate Change* (1995); editor *The Pollution of Our Environment* (Liberal Party, 1971); contributor to *The Birds of the London Area* ed by R C Homes (1957, rev ed 1964), *Wings of Light* comp by Garth Christian (1965), *Birds of the World* ed by John Gooders (1970), *The Living Countryside* (partwork encyclopedia, 1980s), *A Passion for Birds* comp by Tony Soper (1988). Many articles in specialist journals inc *Alauda*, *British Birds*, *Bird Study*, *New Scientist*; national magazines inc *BBC Wildlife*, *Country Life*, *Natural World*; local bird reports inc Avon, Hampshire, London, Oxfordshire, Somerset. Speaker on numerous BBC radio programmes (producer of some) eg *Birds in Britain*, *Birds of the Air*, *A Day at Minsmere*, *A Return to the Camargue*; devised and produced Radio 4 series *Sounds Natural* featuring personalities (eg Joyce Grenfell) interested in birds. TV work on eg *The Private Life of the Heron*, *The Natural World*, *The Living Isles*. Compiler/contributor many LP discs and cassettes for BBC inc *Ludwig Koch: Recollections and Recordings* (1971), *British Wild Birds in Stereo* (1974), *A Sound Guide to Waders in Britain* (1984). Shared in the Italia Prize 1968 for *Signals for Survival* (BBC TV film on behaviour of Lesser Black-backed Gulls at Walney Island). Past Chairman and Past President of Wildlife Sound Recording Society. OIR: watching soccer (Charlton Athletic and Clevedon Town) and rugby (Bristol, Clifton and TV Heidelberg); cartophily and philately (bird and insect themes); operetta and opera. Germany: In der Etzwiese 2, D-69181 St Ilgen, bei Heidelberg. +49 6224 3578. UK (mail will be forwarded): 36 Westacre Close, Westbury-on-Trym, Bristol BS10 7DH. 0117 950 9609.

BURTON, Philip John Kennedy; *b:* 9 January 1936 in London; *w:* Jennifer. Finchley Catholic Grammar School (1947-54). BSc Zoology (London, 1959), PGCE (London, 1959), PhD (London, 1969). Freelance ornithological writer, artist and consultant. Prev: 1967-70 Senior Scientific Officer, British Museum (Natural History), Sub-department of Ornithology, then Principal Scientific Officer until retirement in 1988; biology teacher 1959-67. Committee Essex Birdwatching and Preservation Society late 1960s. Co-ordinator Brent Goose population surveys c1959-65. First organiser, with David Glue, of BTO/IWRB Estuaries Survey 1960s. Brit Mus (Nat Hist) observer on BTO Bird-ringing Committee 1970s to 80s. County Ringing Recorder for Bucks and Herts (latter with D A Lees). Founder Committee member Buckinghamshire Bird Club 1981-83. Vice Chairman Hawk and Owl Trust 1991-93, later Hon Editor. Co-ordinator Farmland Bird of Prey Survey since 1980, latterly in conjunction with H&OT. Member of International Ornithological Committee since 1986. BTO ringer since 1953. Special interests: avian anatomy and taxonomy in relation to feeding adaptations; breeding performance in farmland birds of prey, esp Kestrel; Siskin movements and ecology; bird art and illustration. Expeditions: Blaavandshuk, Denmark 1955 (Cambridge-based migration study); Lapland 1956 (Lesser White-fronted Geese); Spitsbergen 1957 (leader, Univ College London Expedition); Iran 1963 (UCL Expedition to the South Caspian); BM(NH) study trips to Texas 1969; South Africa and Kenya 1969; Panama and Colombia 1972 (attached to British Trans-Americas Expedition); Guyana 1974; Sarawak and Sabah 1976; N Australia, Indonesia and Papua New Guinea 1980; Canada and USA (Pacific NW) 1986; WWF/Univ Kuala Lumpur study trips to Malaysia 1990, Malaysia and Thailand 1991. Doctoral thesis published as *Feeding and the Feeding Apparatus in Waders* (1974); scientific papers in eg *Bull BM(NH), Ibis, J Zool, Ornis Scandinavica*; several entries in *A Dictionary of Birds* ed by Campbell and Lack (1985); section on Kestrel monitoring in *Biology and Conservation of Small Falcons* (1993). Popular writing includes *The Birdlife of Britain* with P Hayman (1976), *Vanishing Eagles* with T Boyer (1970s), *Birds of Prey of the World* with T Boyer *et al* (1989); also numerous other smaller books and articles. Illustrations in eg *Birds of the World* (partwork encyclopedia, 1960s); *A Field Guide to the Nests, Eggs and Nestlings of European Birds* (1975); *BWP* Vols 3, 5, 8; *An Identification Guide to Birds of Prey of the World* by James Ferguson-Lees (in press). Occasional exhibits at Society of Wildlife Artists and elsewhere. Occasional radio and TV. Founder-member SWLA. OIR: music of many kinds (inc playing blues piano), archery, medieval history, computing. High Kelton, Doctors Commons Road, Berkhamsted, Herts HP4 3DW. 01442 865020.

BURTON, Richard Graham (Graham); b: 8 March 1953 in Ripon, Yorkshire. BSc Zoology (Nottingham, 1974). Reserves Manager RSPB North England since 1992. Prev: Information Officer then Reserves Manager RSPB Wales Office 1984-90; Warden Vane Farm Nature Reserve 1979-84; Development Officer RSPB Scottish HQ 1978-79; Warden Slapton Ley Nature Reserve 1975-78. Tutor on birds and birdwatching National Extension College 1983-. Bird Recorder Montgomeryshire 1985-89. Chairman Conservation Committee Montgomery WT 1986-90. Special interest: visitor services on reserves, esp hide design and interpretation. Co-author (with I Mercer) *Birds of Slapton Ley* (1977). OIR: league cricket, science fiction, loud music. RSPB North England, 4 Benton Terrace, Sandiford, Newcastle upon Tyne NE2 1QU. 0191 281 3366.

BUTCHER, Roger John; b: 29 November 1943 in Redmarley, Glos. Farmer. Bird Recorder Exmoor and Committee Exmoor NHS 1978-. Special interests: breeding bird censusing and population monitoring; wildfowl; study of birds of Wimbleball Lake. Co-author with Noel Allen *Birds in Exmoor National Park* (1984). Other interests: butterfly monitoring, Odonata. Rock Cottage, Brompton Regis, Dulverton, Somerset TA22 9NP. 01643 851292 (business).

BUTLER, Andrew Simon (Andy); b: 1 June 1957 in Leeds, Yorkshire; w: Pamela. MRSC 1982. Safety and environmental manager for construction company. Partner in Birdline North East since inception in 1989; proprietor of Nature Vision. Special interests: identification and the use of video and photography for this. Widely travelled for birds in N America, Europe, N Africa, Middle East, India, Nepal, Hong Kong. Articles esp on identification and migration in *Bird Watching, Birding World*. Photographs in all major UK birdwatching magazines. Producer/publisher of video guides for birdwatchers. Member: ABC, NBC, OBC, OSME, Wildlife Sound Recording Society. 162 Austhorpe Road, Cross-Gates, Leeds LS15 8EF. 0113 264 6381.

BUXTON, Ian; b: 29 March 1957 in Jersey. Channel Island ringer since 1974. Channel Islands BTO Representative since 1979, co-ordinator for BBRC records since 1992 and for *British Birds* European News since 1995. Channel Islands Ringing Committee 1984-. Committee La Société Jersiaise Ornithology Section 1984-. Wader count organiser 1986-; breeding Cormorant recorder 1991-; breeding Common Tern recorder 1974-; co-ordinator Great Black-backed Gull Channel Islands Colour Ringing Survey 1996. Special interests: identification, migration, ringing, seabirds. Seabird ringing expeditions to the Shiant Islands 1977 and 1980; BTO ringing expedition to Mallorca 1984. Author *Winter Shorebirds in Jersey* (1986); co-ordinator and contributor *Jersey Bird Report* 1991-. Le Petit Huquet, La Rue du Hucquet, St Martin, Jersey JE3 6HU. 01534 855845.

BYERS, Clive; *b:* 8 May 1957 in Dublin, Ireland; *w:* Audrey. Bird artist and illustrator; ornithologist; naturalist guide. Numerous trips to much of Europe and parts of Middle East, Africa, SE Asia, Indian subcontinent, Australia, N, Central and S America. Specialism illustrating bird books, eg *A Guide to the Warblers of the Western Palearctic* (Parmenter and Byers) (1991); *Buntings and Sparrows: a guide to the buntings and North American sparrows* (Byers, Olsson and Curson) (1995); *Where to Watch Birds in Eastern Europe* by Gerard Gorman (1995); several other titles in prep inc field guides to birds of Argentina and Bolivia. Contributor of articles and illustrations to journals and magazines inc *Birding World*, *Birdwatch*, *British Birds*, *Cotinga*. Member: ABC, NBC, OBC. OIR: all natural history; photography; indigenous people and culture; 'the usual human hedonistic pursuits and indulgences.' 167 Unthank Road, Norwich NR2 2PG. 01603 615231. From April 1997: c/o Manu Expeditions, PO Box 606, Cuzco, Peru. +51 84 226671.

BYLE, Philip Andrew Frank; *b:* 23 July 1963 in Hyde, Cheshire; *w:* Jane. BSc Zoology (Durham, 1984), PhD Behaviour and ecology of the Dunnock (Cambridge, 1987); ACA 1992. Chartered Accountant. RSPB research scientist (Bitterns) 1987-89. Special interests: behaviour and ecology, censusing. Articles and papers on Dunnock and Bittern in *Behaviour*, *Bioacoustics*, *Birding World*, *Ibis*. Item on Bittern calls in *Natural History Programme* (Radio 4, 1991). OIR: water polo, cricket. 20 Greengarth, Holme, Carnforth, Lancs LA6 1RF. 01524 781894.

CADWALLENDER, Thomas Andrew (Tom); *b:* 29 January 1952 in Morpeth, Northumberland; *w:* Muriel. Nat Dip in Land Use and Recreation. Asst Coast Officer for Northumberland Coast, Northumberland CC. Prev: species protection warden RSPB 1986; teacher/naturalist RSPB 1987. BTO Regional Representative Northumberland since 1990. BTO Membership and Development Committee 1994-. Local co-organiser of European Atlas and BTO New Breeding Atlas; organiser of numerous BTO surveys. Council Northumberland WT 1992-. Druridge Bay Management Committee 1992-. Lindisfarne NNR Wildfowl Panel 1996-. BTO 'A' ringer since 1978. Special interests: migration, ringing, Roseate Tern, breeding surveys, coastal birds. Author *Bird-watching Sites in*

Northumbria (1987). Co-author ringing recoveries *Birds of Northumbria* (annual report) 1981-92, also occasional article. Contributor *Northumbrian Breeding Bird Atlas* by Day, Hodgson and Rossiter (1996). Co-organiser of Northumbria Birdwatchers Festival 1991-93. OIR: general natural history, golf, cooking, drinking wine. 22 South View, Lesbury, Alnwick, Northumberland NE66 3PZ. 01665 830884.

CALVERT, Malcolm; *b:* 14 June 1943 in Stockport, Cheshire; *w:* Audrey. FCII 1971; Chartered Insurer 1989; Chartered Insurance Practitioner 1993. Independent financial adviser. BTO 'A' ringer since 1967. Secretary South Manchester Ringing Group 1971-. RSPB Local Representative Stockport 1968-72. Voluntary warden Rostherne Mere 1985-. Occasional tutor in ornithology WEA 1972-. Asst leader then leader High Peak RSPB Group holidays to Mediterranean 1978-85. Special interests: long-term study of breeding Reed Warblers at a Cheshire site since 1973; Cuckoo involvement with Reed Warbler nests in Cheshire. Compiler of ringing reports in *Birds of Greater Manchester* (annual report) 1981-92. Short papers on Reed Warblers in Cheshire in *BTO News, The Naturalist, North Western Newsletter* etc. Occasional guest on GMR (radio) *The Outsiders* programme. OIR: cricket (Lancashire), football (Stockport County), foreign travel, caravanning, railways, National Trust. Hilbre, 12 Hill Drive, Handforth, Wilmslow, Cheshire SK9 3AR. 01625 523696.

CANHAM, Michael (Mick); *b:* 22 September 1950 in Walthamstow, London; *w:* Georgina. Head Conservation Ranger, Forest Enterprise North Scotland Region since 1981. Highland Raptor Study Group species co-ordinator. Member Capercaillie Working Group and Scottish WT's Operation Puffin Team. BTO 'A' ringer 1992 and trainer. Special interest: Kestrel breeding productivity in newly afforested areas. Author of Forestry Commission research note on nestboxes for Kestrels. Radio and TV interviews on Capercaillie. OIR: insect study, bee-keeping. Whinhill Farmhouse, Cawdor, Nairn IV12 5RF. 01667 404314.

CANTELO, John; *b:* 26 September 1950 in Southampton. BA History and Sociology (Keele, 1974), Cert Ed (Alsager and Crewe, 1975). Teacher. Committee Canterbury RSPB Members' Group 1980-82 and 1992, Leader 1982-87; YOC Leader 1991. Special interests: identification, history and literature of ornithology. Co-author *The Birds of Keele* booklet (1975). Articles, notes and letters in *Bird Watching, Birding, Birding World, Birdwatch, British Birds*. Illustrations in *Birding, British Birds, Kent Bird Report*. Recipient of British Birds Rarities Committee Carl Zeiss Award for description and illustrations of Arctic Redpoll (*BB*, 1993). Co-organiser Kent Ornithological Society conferences from 1989. OIR: reading, history, drawing. 17 Clyde Street, Canterbury, Kent CT1 1NA. 01227 762316.

CAREY, Geoffrey John (Geoff); *b:* 15 April 1952 in Birkenhead, Merseyside; *w:* Selina. BSc Economics and Politics (Bristol, 1984). Freelance conservationist/ornithologist, inc work at wetland and forest nature reserves in China and bird surveys in Hong Kong, also bird-strike hazard at airports. Hong Kong Records Committee since 1992. International Waterfowl Census, Hong Kong co-ordinator since winter 1992/93. Special interests: wader migration; Eastern Palearctic birds, esp waterbirds; identification; Saunders' Gull; photography. Cambridge Ornithological Expedition to China 1985 and 1986 (China Cranewatch). Articles (inc migration at Beidaihe) in *Birding World, Forktail, Hong Kong Bird Report* (editor since 1992); co-author *Migration of Cranes at Beidaihe, Hebei Province, China: Procs of the International Crane Workshop, Qiqihar, May 1987*; editor and contributor *Report on the Cambridge Ornithological Expedition to China 1985*. Member: Hong Kong Bird Watching Society. Flat 11D, Block 3, Royal Ascot, Fo Tan, New Territories, Hong Kong. Tel/fax +852 26081281.

CARLSON, Kevin Johan Vernon; *b:* 5 September 1914 in Bristol, Avon; *w:* Christine. Bristol College. MB, ChB (Bristol, 1938), MRCGP 1952. ARPS. Retired medical practitioner and anaesthetist. Special interests: photography, bird-related travel (inc Iceland, Scandinavia, Europe, Africa, Australia, N America). Worked with the Portuguese, advising on a number of conservation projects. Lectures to natural history and photographic societies. Publications with wife: *A Descoberta das Aves de Portugal* (1994), *A Birdwatching Guide to the Algarve* (1995). Illustrations in many natural history books and magazines. Bird Photographer of the Year (*British Birds*) 1987; Best Bird Photograph in *BBC Wildlife* 1983. Council and Past President Zoological Photographic Club; member Nature Photographers Portfolio and Royal Photographic Society. Path Cottage, Hickling, Norwich NR12 0YJ. 01692 598360.

CARR, Geoffrey Malcolm; *b:* 4 February 1947 in Chapeltown, S Yorkshire; *w:* Christine. MA Countryside Management (Sheffield Hallam, 1992). FRGS 1993. BTO Regional Representative SW Yorkshire from 1992. BTO 'A' ringer since 1982. Barnsley Ringing Group Treasurer and Trainer from 1982. Barnsley & Dist Bird Study Group, Secretary and Chairman 1984-93. Special interests: migration, identification, surveys, species projects, education, photography, talks. Heron Colour Ringing Scheme (Barnsley area) 1988-92; Raptor Ringing Scheme (Barnsley area) from 1988. Migration ringing at Ngulia, Kenya 1986. Natural history field leader on expeditions to Morocco, Kenya, Zimbabwe, Botswana; also visits to India and most European countries. OIR: hiking, running, art, gardening, watching motor cycle racing and athletics. 300 Higham Common Road, Higham, Barnsley, S Yorkshire S75 1PF. 01226 384694.

CARRIER, Michael (Mike); *b:* 12 May 1934 in Derby; *w:* Ann. British Rail operating manager, retired. With WWT team studying effects of large power station on Solway estuary 1991-93. BoEE count organiser for S Solway 1980-90; participation in counts since 1969. Carlisle RSPB Committee from foundation in 1974, Chairman since 1986. Vice Chairman Cumbria Bird Club from inception in 1989. County Rarities Panel from formation in 1991. County Recorder Carlisle and Eden Valley 1988-. BTO 'A' ringer since 1979. N Solway Ringing Group 1975-. Special interests: population changes (esp Solway estuary); population dynamics and post breeding dispersal of Cormorant; migration and fortunes of Sand Martin and Pied Flycatcher. Editor and contributor *Birds in Cumbria* (annual report) 1975-. RSPB President's Award 1992. Member: OSME, Wader Study Group. OIR: countryside matters (inc land-use changes), military aircraft, railway operations, travel, gardening. Tiree, 6 Brackenrigg, Armathwaite, Carlisle, Cumbria CA4 9PX. 01697 472218.

CARSWELL, Margaret; *b:* 20 February 1935 in India. MB, BS (Westminster Hospital, London, 1962). Physician. Special interest: all aspects of Ugandan ornithology esp status, distribution and atlas work. Active in the field in Uganda 1968-87. Compiler of computer database of all published, and many unpublished, records of Uganda birds since 1891 (available for reference on request). Senior author *Bird Atlas of Uganda* (in prep); various papers in *Scopus* on Ugandan ornithology, inc Special Supplement No 2: 'Birds of the Kampala Area' (1986). 38 Park Avenue, Orpington, Kent BR6 9EH. 01689 875770.

CARTER, Clifford (Cliff); *b:* 24 July 1931 in Rochdale, Lancashire; *w:* Eleanor. BSc Chemistry (Sheffield, 1955). AIInfSc c1979-80. Medical information scientist, retired. Voluntary warden Tophill Low Nature Reserve (Yorkshire Water) 1992-. Special interests: ringing, esp in population studies; methods of ageing and sexing; tropical birds, esp SE Asia; farmland birds, their censusing and the effects of farming methods. BTO ringing expedition to Santo André, Portugal 1977 and Albufera,

Mallorca 1984; European Migrant Birds in Africa Project expedition to Senegal 1991. Contributor of records to *Birds of Lancashire* by C Oakes (1955) and to *The Birds of Yorkshire* by J R Mather (1986). Member: Haribon Society (Philippines), Malta Ornithological Society, OBC. OIR: marathon running and hang-gliding (retired). Moorholme, 15 Queens Gardens, Hornsea, E Yorks HU18 1AU. 01964 535038.

CARTER, Derek Barry (Barry); *b:* 17 May 1933 in Chatham, Kent; *w:* Margaret. Gillingham Grammar School 1944-52. BA Natural Sciences (Downing College, Cambridge, 1957), MA 1961. Lecturer and head of science, retired. Short residential courses given on the birds of Mid Wales since 1989. Lecturer in natural history, Univ Kent Dept of Continuing Education 1980-87. Adult education lecturer for LEA and WEA (ornithology and other nat hist) 1972-87. Founding Leader Thanet RSPB Group 1976-80. Founder-member of Kent Ornithological Society and of Foreness Group. Group Leader, Machynlleth, Montgomeryshire WT 1992. Wildfowl counter 1949-53. Special interests: the history of Kent ornithology, history of birdwatching, raptors and titmice. Articles on birds and other wildlife in Welsh magazines eg *Country Quest, Window on Wales*; contributions to several magazines of wildlife trusts etc; former editor of the *Rochester Naturalist*. OIR: botany, marine biology, history (inc local), sport, politics. Fron-y-Gog, Machynlleth, Powys SY20 8HZ. 01654 702415.

CARTER, Ian; *b:* 4 October 1967 in Sale, Cheshire; *w:* Selena. BSc Ecology (East Anglia, 1989). Ornithologist, English Nature since 1993. Prev: JNCC Offshore Animals Branch 1990-92; Ecosurveys Ltd, river corridor survey 1990. Special interests: conservation issues affecting birds in Britain; the role of reintroduction projects in species conservation work (involved in Red Kite project); photography. Widely travelled for birds in Europe, N Africa and Asia. Numerous photographs and articles published in eg *Birding World, Birdwatch, British Birds, British Wildlife*; also in JNCC and EN publications. Member: Dutch Seabird Group, OSME, Seabird Group, Wader Study Group. OIR: playing and watching football and other sports, mammals and their conservation. c/o Eastfield, Potkiln Lane, Goring Heath, Reading, Berks RG8 7SR. 01408 477430. Or English Nature, Northminster House, Peterborough PE1 1UA. 01733 340345.

CARTER, Nicholas (Nick); *b:* 3 April 1953 in Solihull, W Midlands; *w:* Diane. BSc Applied Zoology with Agriculture (Reading, 1975), PhD Applied Entomology (East Anglia, 1979). Director of Development, BTO since 1992. Council, Suffolk WT 1995-. Common Birds Census at Castle Marsh, Suffolk since 1993. Special interests: farmland birds, population modelling, birds of prey. Bird-related travel in Morocco, Oman, The Gambia, Spain. Co-author (with D A Hill) 'Population simulation models as an aid to gamebird management' in *Ecology and Management of Gamebirds* ed by P J Hudson et al (1988); paper on simulation model of an Avocet population in *Ornis Scandinavica* (1991). Editorial Board *Annals of Applied Biology*. Member: Association of Applied Biologists, BES, IEEM. OIR: walking, overseas travel. BTO, The Nunnery, Thetford, Norfolk IP24 2PU. 01842 750050.

CASEMENT, Michael Bernard; Commander, RN Retd; OBE 1984; *b:* 23 January 1933 in Oxted, Surrey; *w:* Christina. Winchester College 1946-50; BRNC Dartmouth (1951); RN College Greenwich (1954, 1960, 1973-75). Royal Navy/Crown Servant 1951-93. Royal Naval Birdwatching Society: Chairman 1980-89, Editor *Sea Swallow* (annual journal of RNBWS) 1980-. British Ornithologists' Club: Committee 1990-94, Hon Sec 1996-. Special interests: bird migration, navigation, orientation; landbirds recorded aboard ships at sea; bird photography. Paper on migration across the Mediterranean observed by radar in *Ibis* (1966). Article on history of RNBWS in *Birdwatcher's Yearbook* 1996. OIR: fly fishing, gardening, travel. Dene Cottage, West Harting, Petersfield, Hants GU31 5PA. 01730 825280.

CASTLE, Richard Lucas; *b:* 22 April 1960 in Tanzania; *w:* Frances. BSc Biological Sciences (Birmingham, 1982). Medical sales account manager. BTO 'A' ringer since 1994. Secretary Mercian Ringing Group since 1987. Special interests: colour ringing of an inland Common Tern colony to study interaction between it and other inland and coastal colonies; ringing study of warblers in Tame Valley; co-ordination of group activities, eg for cannon netting Wigeon; photography (slides used for talks on bird ringing and identification). Compiler of ringing group's annual reports and bulletins. OIR: gardening, badminton, voluntary nature reserve management (eg coppicing and pond digging). The Pipits, 91 Maney Hill Road, Sutton Coldfield, West Midlands B72 1JT. 0121 686 7568.

CATLEY, Graham Peter; *b:* 15 September 1953 in Cleethorpes; *w:* Julia. BSc Environmental Sciences (East Anglia, 1975). Treasurer and President Univ East Anglia Bird Club 1973-75. Bird Recorder Lincolnshire and S Humberside 1981-87, 1990-92. Chairman Lincolnshire Records Committee 1981-87, 1990-92. British Birds Rarities Committee 1990-95. Special interests: identification (esp waders, notably the Golden Plover complex); migration; photography; studies of Woodlark, Hobby, Bearded Tit. Bird-related travel to most parts of Britain and several European countries; also to Canada, China, Israel, Sweden, USA (Arizona and Texas). Attended international identification meetings during Euro Bird Week on Texel 1991. Author *Where to Watch Birds in the East Midlands* (1996). Editor and contributor *Lincolnshire Bird Report* 1981-87, 1990-92; identification articles and shorter notes published in *Bird Watching, Birding World, Birdwatch, British Birds*; photographs in these and other publications, inc Delin and Svensson's *Photographic Guide to the Birds of Britain and Europe* (1988). Talks given to groups. OIR: badminton, tennis, cycling. 13 West Acridge, Barton-on-Humber, N Lincs DN18 5AJ. 01652 634752.

CHANCELLOR, Robert Duff (Robin); *b:* 24 October 1921 in London. Eton and Cambridge. Retired from business. Hon Secretary and Treasurer World Working Group on Birds of Prey and Owls. Formerly Secretary British National Section, ICBP. Special interests: conservation of all birds of prey and owls. Frequent visits to Hungary as an Hon Member of the Hungarian Ornithological Society. Member of WWGBP expedition to Java to investigate endangered Java Hawk Eagle (1986). Member: Fonds d'Intervention pour les Rapaces (France). OIR: literature, music, travel, gardening. 15 Bolton Gardens, London SW5 0AL. 0171 370 1896.

CHANDLER, Richard John; *b:* 20 September 1939 in Brighton, Sussex; *w:* Eunice. BSc Civil Engineering (Loughborough, 1961), MSc Foundation Engineering (Birmingham, 1965), PhD Soil Mechanics (Birmingham, 1967). FICE 1989. DSc(Eng) (London, 1990). Professor of Geotechnical Engineering, Imperial College London. Editorial Board *British Birds* 1988-; photographic consultant *BB* 1980-91. Special interests: all aspects of shorebird/wader studies worldwide; bird photography, esp shorebirds. Author *Macmillan Field Guide to North Atlantic Shorebirds* (1989); numerous published papers, particularly in *British Birds*; many published photographs. Member: Nature Photographers' Portfolio, Wader Study Group. OIR: dragonfly and real ale enthusiast - not necessarily in that order. 2 Rusland Avenue, Orpington, Kent BR6 8AU. 01689 853993.

CHAPMAN, Anthony Hugh; *b:* 24 May 1943 in London. MSc Ecology (Durham, 1970). Land Agent (Acquisitions) RSPB since 1990. Prev RSPB: Reserves Officer 1983-90; Asst Reserves Manager 1973-83;

Personal Asst to Director 1972-73. Special interests: the Hobby, bird sounds. Wheelchair user. Seeks to promote opportunities for disabled to enjoy birdwatching and practical access to the countryside. Compiler of two editions of *The Countryside and Wildlife for Disabled People*, a guide formerly published by the Royal Association for Disability and Rehabilitation. Winston Churchill Memorial Fellowship 1979 for travel to Sweden to study nature reserves and opportunities for birdwatching by disabled people (internal report produced). OIR: choral singing. 8 Havelock Close, Gamlingay, Sandy, Beds SG19 3NQ. 01767 650822.

CHEKE, Robert Alexander (Bob); *b*: 14 July 1948 in London. BSc Zoology (St Andrews, 1970), PhD Entomology (Leeds, 1974). Principal Scientific Officer, Natural Resources Institute, Univ Greenwich, specialising in applied ecology esp entomological problems in tropics. Research asst BTO Jan-Jul 1966. Committee BOC 1991-95. Meetings Committee BOU 1993-. Special interests: Afrotropical ornithology esp W African (compiling BOU check-list of the birds of Togo with J F Walsh); sunbirds; bird parasites. Oxford Univ expeditions to Ghana 1968, and Cherangani Mountains Kenya 1969; BOU expedition to the Mascarene Islands 1974. BTO 'A' ringer since 1966. Author of some thirty articles in eg *British Birds, Bull BOC, East African Wildlife J, Ibis, Malimbus* (also Editorial Board); contributor to *Statistics in Ornithology* ed by B J T Morgan and P M North (1985). Photographs of birds in eg *Malimbus* and *Birds of the World* ed by J Gooders (1970). Member: ABC, WAOS. c/o Natural Resources Institute, University of Greenwich, Central Avenue, Chatham Maritime, Chatham, Kent ME4 4TB. 01634 880088.

CHESHIRE, Neil; *b:* 9 January 1942 in Colchester, Essex; *w:* Carol. Colchester Royal Grammar School. Ship's Captain (Master's Certificate 1973). Committee Seabird Group, Royal Australasian Ornithologists' Union, Dec 1994-. Special interests: Procellariiformes (inc bibliography thereof); seabird distribution, feeding and behaviour in relation to oceanography; photography of seabirds. Contributor to *Handbook of Australian, New Zealand and Antarctic Birds* Vol 1 (1990); author of annual seabird report in *Sea Swallow* (journal of RNBWS) 1990-95; author or co-author of seabird papers and notes in *Notornis* and local Australian journals. Member: ABC, African Seabird Group, Orn Soc NZ, RAOU, RNBWS, S Australian Orn Assocn. 'Enjoys showing Australian birds to overseas visitors.' OIR: gardening, property maintenance, occasional twitching, outback camping. 4 Willora Road, Eden Hills, 5050 South Australia. Tel/fax +61 (0)8 3702212.

CHESTER, Mark; *b:* 26 October 1960 in Bromley, Kent. Wildlife artist. Projects Advisory Committee Hawk and Owl Trust since 1994. Special interests: birds of prey photography; lecturing on conservation of birds of prey, esp owls. Sets up Barn Owl conservation projects in Buckinghamshire and W Herts. Many wildlife painting and photographic expeditions to Africa and America. One-man exhibitions annually since 1991; exhibited at Royal Society of Painters in Watercolours, London 1991. Many articles, photographs and paintings published in numerous wildlife magazines; limited edition prints etc for wildlife charities. Occasional TV broadcasts. Winner Kodak International Photographic Salon, Canada 1984. Member: Hawk and Owl Trust, Society of Wildlife Art of the Nations. Fellow of the Wildlife Art Society. Runs photography and painting workshops. OIR: skiing, water skiing, motorsport. 67 London Road, Aston Clinton, Aylesbury, Bucks HP22 5LD. 01296 631857.

CHEVERTON, James Milton (Jim); *b:* 15 May 1921 in Shanklin, Isle of Wight; *w:* Veronica. Engineer Lt Cdr (L) RN retired. Leader of IOW Nat Hist & Archaeol Society's Ornithological Section, member of Ornithological Committee and responsible for rarity reports 1991-. BTO Birds of Estuaries Enquiry count organiser for Brading Harbour 1979-96 and wildfowl counter for same 1965-96. Official Bird Observer, Osborne House Estate (one of five, first appointed by Dept of Environment in 1978). Organiser/counter various other surveys and censuses. Co-author (with Bill Shepard) *Watching Birds in the Isle of Wight* (1987); author *Breeding Birds in the Isle of Wight* (1989); author/co-author of Bird Report and Escaped Birds in *Isle of Wight Birds* (annual report) since 1986, and of various papers in that publication. OIR: ballroom, Latin American and sequence dancing; dragonfly, butterfly and moth recording. 6 Westhill Drive, Shanklin, Isle of Wight PO37 6PX. 01983 863331.

CHITTENDEN, Robin, *b:* 11 February 1960 in Chester. BSc Environmental Sciences (East Anglia), BSc Environmental Health (Aston). Bird and wildlife photographer. Established Rare Bird Photographic Library in 1988, superseded by Harlequin Pictures in 1995, to market own photographs. Initiated Birdline East Anglia in 1989. Photographic researcher for *British Birds* and photographic consultant to *Birding World*. Travel for bird photography inc Spain and Canary Islands, Turkey, Israel, Venezuela, Poland, Egypt, Morocco. Photographs regularly published in leading magazines, many also used in books. 65 Sandringham Road, Norwich NR2 3RZ. 01603 633326.

CHRISTIE, David Andrew; *b:* 23 August 1945 in Bristol; *w:* Carmelia. BA French with Swedish (Hull, 1967). Freelance ornithological editor and translator since 1980. Asst Editor *British Birds* 1973-. Survey co-ordinator for Hampshire Ornithological Society 1988-. Special interests: populations, distribution, migration, taxonomy, woodpeckers, waterbirds, raptors. Co-author *Woodpeckers: a guide to the woodpeckers, piculets and wrynecks of the world* (1995) and *Macmillan Birder's Guide to European and Middle Eastern Birds* (1996). Series editor of Hamlyn Species Guides. Co-editor *The Birds of Israel* by Hadoram Shirihai (1996). Translator of eg *Bird Migration* by Thomas Alerstam (1990), *Birds of Europe* by Lars Jonsson (1992). In-house editor of Helm series of ornithological handbooks. Regular fieldwork on 'local patch' from 1973 (irreg back to 1960), inc BTO/WWT wader and wildfowl counts, breeding surveys and population studies. Member: Colonial Waterbird Society, NBC, OBC. OIR: general natural history, languages, fine art, watching cricket and soccer, socialising. 4 Steventon Road, Harefield, Southampton SO18 5HA. 01703 462955.

CHRISTMAS, Stephen Eric (Steve); *b:* 29 December 1953 in Kingston Surrey; *w:* Kathryn. BA Biochemistry (Oxford 1976), DPhil (Oxford, 1981). University lecturer. Secretary/Chairman Oxford Ornithological Society 1974-79. Co-organiser North West Swan Study since 1988. BTO 'A' ringer since 1974. Special interests: migration, ringing, population dynamics, Mute Swan, Sand Martin, Grey Heron, Coot, Black-headed Gull. Expedition to Yugoslavia 1976. Papers in eg *Bird Study*, *Colonial Waterbirds*, *Gerfaut*, *Ringing & Migration*. Weekly nature column in *Salford City Reporter* 1992-. Member: Swan Study Group. OIR: moths, butterflies, dragonflies, hoverflies, flora. 6 Holly Road, Swinton, Manchester M27 0DY. 0151 706 4356 (work).

CHRISTOPHERS, Stanley Michael; *b:* 14 September 1949 in Newquay, Cornwall; *w:* Anne. Newquay Grammar School. Police officer. County Recorder and Editor of *Ydhyn yn Kernow* (*Birds in Cornwall*) 1982-95, asst 1981. Recorder Cornwall Bird Club 1996-. BTO 'A' ringer since 1979. Special interest: the birds of Cornwall, inc research into historical data. Several short articles on Cornish birds in *Bird Watching* and *Birdwatch*; also ornithological sections for various local brochures, eg the official Cornwall CC book *Cornwall*. 'Anti-twitcher and well known "suppressor"!' OIR: butterflies and dragonflies; athletics and football; natural history books; The Moody Blues. Bramblings, Rachels Way, St Columb Major, Cornwall TR9 6EP. 01637 881279.

CLARK, Jacqueline Anne (Jacquie); *b:* 6 December 1957 in Chesterfield, Derbys; *h:* Nigel. BSc Biology (Nottingham, 1979), PGCE (Nottingham, 1980). Head of Ringing Unit, BTO since 1992. Prev: Ringing Unit Manager, BTO 1987-92; Manager of Bird Bookshop, SOC 1985-87. BTO 'A' ringer since 1983. Joint Membership Secretary Wader Study Group 1980-87. Scientific Committee Wash Wader Ringing Group 1991-94. Ringer in charge of Market Weston RG 1992-. Special interests: ringing (esp waders); effect of severe weather on waders, inc study on this for Dept of Trade and Industry 1991-93. Papers and articles on waders in journals and bird reports. Compiler of national ringing reports in *Ringing & Migration* 1986-. Author of Purple Sandpiper text in BTO Breeding Atlas. Member: Market Weston and Wash Wader Ringing Groups, Wader Study Group. OIR: gardening (esp alpines), dog training, badminton. BTO, The Nunnery, Thetford, Norfolk IP24 2PU. 01842 750050.

CLARK, James Ernest (Jim); *b:* 26 March 1944 in South Shields, Co Durham; *w:* Pat. Head Ranger, Llyn Alaw, Anglesey since 1980. Wildfowl Count organiser for Anglesey and Caernarfonshire since early 1980s. BTO Regional Representative Anglesey 1985- and latterly, with wife, BTO Reg Development Officer. Chairman Bangor University Bird Group 1993-. Special interest: wetland birds. Occasional radio, TV and press. Member: Countryside Management Association, Welsh Ornithological Society. OIR: classical music and modern jazz; visiting art galleries; theatre; being in the country; all aspects of natural history. Glan Dwr, Llyn Traffwll, Caergeiliog, Holyhead LL65 3LR. 01407 730762.

CLARK, John Morrill; *b:* 3 May 1953 in Aldershot, Hants. BSc Zoology (Southampton, 1974), PGCE (Southampton, 1975). Senior teacher. Hampshire Editorial & Records Committee (later Records Panel) 1976-. Surrey Records Committee 1976-. Management Committee Hampshire Orn Soc from foundation in 1979. Bird Recorder Hampshire 1994-. Special interest: recording the birds of Hampshire and Hants/Surrey Border. Organised monitoring of heathland species (inc Dartford Warbler, Woodlark, Nightjar, Stonechat) in Hants/Surrey Border 1994-. Worldwide travel for birds, esp S America and Africa. Author *Birds of the Hants/Surrey Border* (1984). Co-editor (with J A Eyre) *Birds of Hampshire*, wrote most species accounts and edited rest (1993). Started *Hants/Surrey Border Bird Report*, editor from first edition (1971) to 1989 edition. Co-editor/editor/asst editor *Hampshire Bird Report* from 1979 edition. Member: ABC, NBC, OBC, OSME. OIR: supporter of Aldershot Town FC and Hampshire CCC. 4 Cygnet Court, Old Cove Road, Fleet, Hants GU13 8RL. Tel/fax 01252 623397.

CLARK Nigel Anthony; *b:* 19 June 1954 in Taunton, Somerset; *w:* Jacquie. Millfield School 1968-73. BSc Zoology (Nottingham, 1977), PhD Ecology of Dunlin (Edinburgh, 1983). Head of Projects at BTO since 1995. Prev: Head of Habitats Advisory Unit, BTO 1993-95; Contracts Manager and other BTO posts 1989-92; Perth & Kinross DC, Research Leader NCC Loch Leven Nature Reserve 1986-87; earlier posts inc Consultant, European Ornithological Atlas Committee and Research Asst, Edward Grey Institute of Field Ornithology. BTO 'A' ringer since 1977. Chairman Lothian Ringing Group 1984-87; Scientific Committee Wash Wader Ringing Group 1984-; organiser Wader Study Group Severe Weather Project 1981-86; Membership Secretary Wader Study Group 1980-87; Management Committee Attenborough Nature Reserve 1977-78. Special interests: wader population ecology (esp survival in relation to weather conditions and population density, distribution in winter in relation to habitat type, factors affecting the capacity of estuaries to hold wintering birds); wader migration throughout the world (related expeditions in Europe and Australia). Constant Effort Site ringing on a fenland site in Suffolk. Over 70 publications in a wide variety of journals and reports, mainly relating to waders and wildfowl. Member: British Ecological Society, Market Weston Ringing Group, Wader Study Group, Wash Wader RG. OIR: gardening, esp alpines and peat loving plants; fish keeping, koi carp; breeding Rift Valley cichlids; renovation and restoration of 16th century farm house. BTO, The Nunnery, Thetford, Norfolk IP24 2PU. 01842 750050.

CLARKE, Roger Geoffrey; *b:* 8 July 1952 in Bedford; *w:* Janis. ACA 1979, FCA 1990. Chartered Accountant, Registered Auditor. Chairman Cambridge Bird Club 1995-. Vice Chairman The Hawk and Owl Trust 1993-, also Chairman Projects Committee. BTO Regional Representative Cambridgeshire 1989-. Organiser (with Donald Watson) Hen Harrier Winter Roost Survey (BTO/Hawk and Owl Trust supported project) 1983-. Special interests: raptors (esp Harriers, also feeding ecology and pellet analysis), birds of India, writing, lecturing, leading tours. Organiser of Hawk and Owl Trust international conference 'Biology and Conservation of Small Falcons' (Univ Kent, Sept 1991), and Raptor Research Foundation First European Meeting in conjunction with the Hawk and Owl Trust (Univ Kent, Sept 1993). Author *Harriers of the British Isles* (1990), *The Marsh Harrier* (1995), *Montagu's Harrier* (in press). Co-editor (with M K Nicholls) *Biology and Conservation of Small Falcons* (1993). Papers and notes on harriers and other raptors in eg *Bird Study, British Birds, Ibis, Irish Birds, The Raptor*; articles in eg *Bird Watching*. Member: Raptor Research

Foundation, World Working Group on Birds of Prey and Owls. OIR: unplugged electric guitar. New Hythe House, Reach, Cambridge CB5 0JQ. 01638 742447.

CLAY, Philip John; *b:* 2 June 1954 in Castle Bromwich, Birmingham. Architectural surveyor. BTO 'A' ringer since 1972. Formed Steyning Ringing Group in 1976, Secretary 1976-89. Author of Ringing Group Report in *Shoreham District Ornithological Society Annual Report* 1976-90. Articles in *Sussex Ornithological Society Annual Newsletter*. Purchased own 2.5 acre site in 1980 to develop for conservation and as ringing site. OIR: music, pubs, snooker, photography. Byways, Castle Lane, Bramber, Steyning, W Sussex BN44 3FB. 01903 815889.

CLAYDEN, Christopher Norman (Norman); Lt Col Retd; MBE 1984; *b:* 10 July 1921 in Egypt; *w:* Enid. Army Staff College. Army 33 years. Ministry of Defence Conservation Officer 1973-87. Secretary Army Bird Watching Society 1970-91, Vice President since 1991. Organised World Bird Count for ABWS 1971-78, Ministry of Defence Annual Bird Count 1978-94, MOD Nest Box Scheme 1980-90, Banding Birds in SE Asia 1967-69. During nine months in Guyana in 1966 recorded 102 species for the museum at Georgetown. Adviser on conservation generally, and esp for birds, on all MOD property in Great Britain and military training areas in Germany, India and Australia 1980-85. Produced *Conservation*, the charter for the MOD. Initiated *Sanctuary*, the MOD conservation magazine, in 1977. Internal reports for ABWS and MOD on fieldwork and on conservation matters, eg heathland management, individual site management, protection against fire. Article on history of ABWS in *Birdwatcher's Yearbook* 1990. Illustrated talks given to 190 organisations between 1973 and 1991. Received RSPB/ESSO Award for services to birds and their conservation, 1987 (first presentation). Member: Army and Royal Air Force Ornithological Societies. OIR: stamp collecting (esp bird sets), gardening, giving talks. Candlewick Cottage, Avenue Road, Fleet, Hants GU13 8NG. 01252 617553.

CLEERE, Nigel; *b:* 21 September 1955 in Newbury, Berkshire. BTO 'A' ringer since 1974 and member of Sponsors Panel from 1988. Special interest species: Sedge Warbler, Siskin, Reed Bunting, nightjars (all species). Has ringed tens of thousands of birds of over 300 species at sites in Britain and overseas, inc Israel, Kuwait, Mallorca, Portugal (several times a year since 1987), Kenya, Senegal and Malawi. Author *Nightjars of the World* (in prep); articles and notes on nightjars in *ABC Bulletin, Birding World,*

British Birds. Many illustrated talks on the nightjars of the world. Member: ABC, OSME. OIR: moths. 25 Bedford Close, Newbury, Berks RG14 6SU. 01635 38092.

CLEEVES, Timothy Richard (Tim); *b:* 26 January 1951 in Hanham, Gloucestershire. *w:* Ann. Rodway Technical High School. Conservation Officer, RSPB North England since 1987. Prev: Asst Reg Off, RSPB Midlands 1983-86; Ranger, Wirral Country Park 1981-82; Warden, Hilbre Island LNR 1977-81; RSPB species protection warden, Wales 1976-77. Committee Bristol Naturalists' Society (Junior Section) 1966-69. Committee Bristol Ornithological Club 1969-71. Member Chew Valley Ringing Station 1967-71, 1975-76. Voluntary Warden Chew Valley Lake 1970-76. Member Hilbre Island Bird Observatory 1977-83. Wirral Recorder for *Cheshire Bird Report* 1979-82. Tutor, Liverpool Univ Adult Education Programme (Ornithology) 1980-83. BTO 'C' ringer 1979-87. Merseyside Ringing Group 1980-83, Wychavon RG 1984-86. DoE Wildlife Act Inspector (voluntary post) NW England and Midlands 1981-86. Special interests: counting waders and wildfowl, seawatching, conservation and management of Lindisfarne NNR, birds of Fair Isle, Leach's Petrel. Minor contributions to *BWP* Vol 4 (Fish Owl, voice and behaviour), to *Gulls: a guide to identification* by P J Grant (1986), and *Shorebirds* by Peter Hayman *et al* (1986). Member: Friends of Fair Isle Bird Observatory, Friends of Portland BO. OIR: art (sketching and appreciating), listening to music, cooking (esp Indian), films, theatre, dancing, football (Bristol Rovers FC), seeing more species in Blyth Valley District than Maurice Hepple. 19 Holywell Dene Road, Holywell, Northumberland NE25 0LB. 0191 237 1323.

CLEMENT, Peter; *b:* 6 September 1948 in Eastbourne, Sussex; *w:* Angela. Licensing Officer and Species Adviser for English Nature (and formerly NCC) since 1988. British Birds Rarities Committee 1987-. Special interests: identification of difficult groups or families of species (esp thrushes, wheatears, warblers, finches and seabirds); migration and the occurrence pattern of scarce migrants, rarities and vagrants. Author *Finches and Sparrows: an identification guide* (1993); *Thrushes of the World: an identification guide* (in prep); joint editor *Red Data Birds in Britain* (1990); contributed to identification and movement sections on wheatears and warblers in *BWP* Vols 5 and 6. Editor *London Bird Report* 1980-85. Major articles on the origin of species (with S J M Gantlett) *Birding World* 1993, and on the field identification of West Palearctic wheatears *British Birds* 1987. Member: OBC, OSME. Tour leader (esp India, Himalayas, Africa).

OIR: travelling (to new places), eating and drinking, antique English furniture, sailing ships. 69 Harecroft Road, Wisbech, Cambs PE13 1RL. 01733 340345 (business).

CLEMENTS, Frederick Andrew; *b:* 25 October 1954 in Morecambe, Lancs; *w:* Dr Nicola Bradbear. BSc Zoology (Wales, 1976), PhD Motion perception in mink (Wales, 1980). English Nature since 1991. Prev: Chief Wildlife Inspector Dept of the Environment, Bristol 1987-91; Scientific Officer NCC (upland bird surveys, Scotland and England) 1982-85; post-doctoral research fellow, School of Biology, Univ Sussex (functional aspects of evolution of bird song; mate selection in Zebra Finch) 1980-82. Special interest: world travel for birds (inc leading tours for Naturetrek), particularly Himalayas. Articles in journals inc *Behaviour, Forktail, Sandgrouse.* Founder-member OBC. OIR: bee-keeping. The Elms, Troy, Monmouth, Gwent NP5 4AB. 01600 713648; fax 01600 716167.

CLEWS, Brian David; *b:* 28 December 1943 in London; *w:* Hazel. Church administrator. Chairman E Berks RSPB Members' Group 1981-82 and trip leader several years. Special interest: effects of habitat changes on birds in Berkshire. Co-author *Where to Watch Birds in Bedfordshire, Berkshire, Buckinghamshire, Hertfordshire & Oxfordshire* (1987, 2nd ed 1995). Founder and compiler *Berkshire Bird Bulletin*, monthly publication of bird sightings, first issued Oct 1986. Occasional speaker and trip leader. OIR: playing trumpet. 118 Broomhill, Cookham, Berks SL6 9LQ. 01628 525314.

CLOYNE, John Michael; *b:* 11 August 1945 in Blackburn, Lancashire; *w:* Elizabeth. Office for National Statistics. Organiser, Ornithological Survey of the Itchen Valley, Hampshire 1976; former organiser for a number of tetrads in breeding bird surveys. Special interests: avifauna of the Itchen Valley; bird life of sewage farms and sewage works in England and Wales. Holds large manuscript database of records and an extensive library covering these interests. Library also includes natural history and countryside publications covering all Hampshire and adjacent areas. National Wildfowl Counts in Itchen Valley. OIR: general natural history. 2 Fordington Road, Winchester, Hants SO22 5AL. 01962 862980.

COCKBURN, Thomas (Tom); *b:* 11 April 1938 in Bonnyrigg, Midlothian; widower, *p:* Mrs Pamela Thompson. Retired police constable. Honorary warden Drakelow Wildfowl Reserve since 1970. Committee Derbyshire Ornithological Society 1977-; Records Sub-committee and asst compiler of DOS annual report 1980-. Organised Derbyshire element of National Rook

Survey 1975. Special interests: inland migration, waterfowl and waders. OIR: dragonflies, butterflies, botany. 1 Dickens Drive, Swadlincote, Derbys DE11 0DX. 01283 217146.

CODD, David William; *b:* 21 July 1942 in Buxton, Derbyshire; *w:* Linda. Kingston School of Art 1960-64. Instructor/lecturer in art and design. Wetland Bird Survey count organiser for Sussex 1975-. St Leonards Forest Reserve Manager (Sussex WT) 1987-. Conservation Officer Horsham NHS and Committee Warnham LNR Advisory Group from 1987. Past Council Member Sussex Ornithological Society. Special interest: waterfowl. Bird and wildlife illustrations in various publications and commercial work. OIR: Scout Troop Leader, canoeing, cycling, lecturing, natural history subjects. 12 Broome Close, Horsham, W Sussex RH12 5XG. 01403 268547.

COETZEE, Eric Frans Courtenay; *b:* 28 June 1933 in South Africa; *w:* Joan. BA (Open Univ, 1988). FIBMS 1965, CBiol, MIBiol 1990. Head Medical Laboratory Scientific Officer, Public Health Laboratory, Dorchester, now retired. Secretary Dorset Bird Club 1976-87. Member, Natural History and Geological Committee Dorset County Museum and editor of *Newsletter* 1984-96. Founder-member South Dorset RSPB Group. Organiser for Dorset of BTO Natural Habitats Survey 1976. Special interests: distribution of various species in Dorset, esp Kestrel and Buzzard; common garden birds within a 1km urban area. Participant in several national ornithological surveys. Author of report to Dorset Nat Hist & Archaeol Soc, *Lodmoor: a fourteen year field study 1968 to 1982*; reports of various bird surveys in *DNHAS Proceedings*. Member Portland Bird Observatory. Catalogued and card indexed the ornithological collection of the Dorset County Museum. OIR: participant in several national entomological surveys. 53 Weymouth Bay Avenue, Weymouth, Dorset DT3 5AD. 01305 785449.

COGHLAN, Stephanie Mary; *b:* 18 September 1943 in Rugby, Warwickshire; *h:* Jim. Teacher's Cert (Univ Durham Inst of Education, 1965). Managing Director Snail's Pace Natural History Holidays since 1987 and freelance lecturer. Summer Education Officer WWT Martin Mere 1980, 1981. YOC Schools Project Officer 1981-86 and holiday course leader since 1981. Part-time lecturer in ornithology, Schools of Continuing Education, Univs Leeds and Bradford 1986-92. Hon Secretary Huddersfield Birdwatchers' Club 1981-86. Special interest: birds of Crete. Hon Secretary Crete Records Committee 1992-. Author *Easter Birdwatching in Crete* (1985), *Birdwatching in Crete* (1988, 3rd ed 1993), *A Birdwatching*

Guide to Crete (1996); editor and compiler *Annual Crete Report* since 1986. Tours to European countries; also Borneo-Sabah and Sarawak, and Costa Rica. Member Djibouti II Expedition 1985. Member: OSME. OIR: reading, photography, gardening. 25 Thorpe Lane, Almondbury, Huddersfield, W Yorkshire HD5 8TA. 01484 426259.

COLE, Elizabeth Anne (Liza); *b:* 4 November 1966 in Reigate, Surrey. BSc Zoology (Manchester, 1988), MSc Pollution and Environmental Control (Univ Manchester Inst Sci Tech, 1989). Countryside Ranger Elan Valley since 1992. Prev: short-term information warden at South Stack (RSPB) and naturalist field guide at Aigas Field Centre. Voluntary warden Cefn Cennarth (Radnorshire WT). Committee Lundy Field Society. Member of Red Kite Watchers Group. MSc study of effects of organic pollution on populations of Dippers and Grey Wagtails on R Wye, Derbyshire. OIR: listening to music and singing (jazz to early church), hiking, scuba diving, swimming, playing squash. The Agent's House, Elan Village, Rhayader, Powys LD6 5HP. 01597 810889 (home); 810880 (work).

COLEMAN, Albert Edward (Bert); BEM 1991, for work with Mute Swans; *b:* 1 September 1936 in Porth, Mid Glamorgan; *w:* Patricia. BSc Zoology (Wales, Bangor, 1959). Lecturer in biology. Also part-time lecturer in ornithology, School of Continuing Studies, Birmingham Univ since 1992. BTO 'A' ringer since 1974. Ringing Secretary West Midland Bird Club 1983-. Chairman British Swan Study Group 1980-85. Warden Alvecote Pools Nature Reserve 1965-. Swan Warden to Tamworth BC 1974-. Special interest: Mute Swan. Articles on this subject in *Bird Study* and *Wildfowl*. Member: British Swan Study Group. 67 Park Lane, Bonehill, Tamworth, Staffs B78 3HZ. 01827 285517.

COLEMAN, Bruce; *b:* 18 October 1937 in Wembley, Middlesex; *w:* Gillian. Company director. Past member RSPB Publications Committee. Past Chairman Appeals Committee ICBP (British Section). Chairman of Judging Panel, Wildlife Photographer of the Year Competition 1977-93. Council Fauna & Flora Preservation Society 1988-. Trustee World Wide Land Conservation Trust 1989-. Special interest: wildlife photography. Articles and reviews in *BBC Wildlife* and *Oryx*. Editorial Board *Birds of the World Encyclopedia*. OIR: cinema, theatre, music, travel. Watercoombes, West Milton, Dorset DT6 3SJ.

COLES, Royston Keith (Roy); BEM 1983; Imperial Service Medal 1989; *b:* 21 December 1927 in Hastings, Sussex; *w:* Phyllis. Ashford Grammar

School. School of Photography, Regent Street Polytechnic. Professional industrial photographer. Hon Secretary and Warden Bough Beech Nature Reserve 1970-. Founder-member Kent Farming and Wildlife Group 1980. Council and Conservation Committee Kent TNC 1974-94. Special interests: development of man-made habitats, eg reservoirs, clay pits; nesting protection for Little Ringed Plover; Kestrel nestboxes. Worldwide travel for birds and photographing them. OIR: furniture making, Kent history (esp cultivation of hops), devising gadgets for disabled. Member: ABC. 12 Lennard Road, Dunton Green, Sevenoaks, Kent TN13 2UU.

COLLINS, Richard Thomas; *b:* 19 April 1944 in Limerick, Ireland; *w:* Barbara Meade. BEng (Nat Univ Ireland, 1967), BA Philosophy and English (NUI, 1974), PhD The Mute Swan in Dublin and North Wicklow (NUI, 1993). MIEE, CEng 1983. BTO 'A' ringer since 1983. Hon Secretary Irish Wildbird Conservancy 1977-82. Part-time lecturer in ornithology, Adult Education Dept Univ College Dublin since 1983. Environmental consultant, lecturer and broadcaster. Special interests: Mute Swan, wildfowl population dynamics, oiled bird rehabilitation, passerine ringing studies. Articles in eg *Biology and Environment, Irish Birds, Ringing & Migration, Wildfowl.* Member: Swan Study Group. OIR: travel and reading philosophy. 10 Biscayne, Malahide, Co Dublin, Ireland. +353 (0)1 8453474.

COOK, Jill; *b:* in Bickley, Kent; widow of James R Cook. Hon Gen Secretary Surrey Bird Club 1992-. Volunteer fieldworker for BTO Breeding Bird Survey, Organic Farms Project, Setaside Project. Other fieldwork inc BTO Breeding Atlas, Hampshire Breeding Atlas, Surrey Breeding Atlas, BTO Woodlark Survey. Widely travelled for birds in UK, Europe, Middle East and beyond, eg USA (Florida), Caribbean. OIR: snorkelling over coral reefs, breeding horses. Moorings, Vale Wood Drive, Lower Bourne, Farnham, Surrey GU10 3HW. 01252 792876.

COOK, Martin John Howard; *b:* 28 December 1949 in Windsor, Berkshire; *w:* Jennifer. BSc Zoology (Aberdeen, 1972). Teacher. County Recorder Moray and Nairn 1984-. BTO Regional Representative 1977-93. Special interests: bird distribution within Moray and Nairn; Crested Tit (organised survey of Crested Tit breeding distribution 1979-80 and article in *Scottish Birds* 1982). BTO 'A' ringer since 1969, trainer and sponsor. Author *The Birds of Moray and Nairn* (1992); Crested Tit species accounts in BTO Winter Atlas and New Breeding Atlas, also European Atlas; editor *Moray and Nairn Bird Report* 1985-. OIR: botany, gardening, bee-keeping. Rowanbrae, Clochan, Buckie, Banffshire AB56 2EQ. 01542 850296.

COOMBER, Richard Frank; *b:* 17 April 1947 in Crediton, Devon. Tour leader for Ornitholidays. Prev: proprietor Mull Wildlife Safaris. County Recorder, BTO Winter Atlas organiser and BTO Regional Representative Argyll late 1970s and early 1980s. Special interests: identification, photography, raptors, wildfowl and waders. Author *Birds of the World* (1991), *The Living World of Canadian Birds* (1991); several notes in *British Birds*; photographs published in wide range of books and magazines in UK and overseas. Lectures to bird and natural history societies. Member: ABA, ABC. OIR: botany, moths, walking. c/o Ornitholidays, 1 Victoria Drive, Bognor Regis, W Sussex PO21 2PW. 01243 821230.

COOPER, Anthony Ashley (Tony); *b:* 12 August 1934 in Macclesfield, Cheshire. King's School, Macclesfield 1946-53. BSc Botany, Zoology, Geology (Leicester, 1956), PGCE 1957. MIBiol, CBiol. Head of Biology, Clitheroe RGS, retired 1995. Hon Conservation Officer for the Ribble Valley District of Lancs WT and on Trust's Conservation Committee. BTO Regional Representative and organiser of all local BTO surveys since 1981. Chairman East Lancashire Ornithologists' Club 1996-. Wildfowl counter at Stocks Reservoir, Forest of Bowland for very many years. Special interests: population studies, atlas and census work. OIR: DIY enthusiast, garden landscaping. 28 Peel Park Avenue, Clitheroe, Lancs BB7 1ET. 01200 24577.

CORRAN, Robert Dawson (Bob); *b:* 4 March 1943 in Talacre, Flints; *w:* Kathryn. Holywell Grammar School 1954-61. Liverpool Polytechnic 1965-69. FIBMS 1969. Biomedical scientist. Clwyd Rarities Group 1994. BTO Regional Representative W Clwyd 1984-92. Regional organiser for BTO New Breeding Atlas 1988-92. Council Welsh Ornithological Society 1988-92. Welsh Raptor Study Group 1990-92. Clwyd county co-ordinator for 1991 Peregrine Survey. Regular participant in Birds of Estuaries Enquiry counts 1984-91. RSPB voluntary species protection warden: Little Tern 1975-91, Red Kite 1981, 1983, Golden Eagle 1982. Active 'local patch' birder. Special interests: survey work, migration, raptors, gulls and seawatching. Author of Clwyd coast report in *Bird Watching* 1987-. Travel for birds to Greek Islands, Spain (inc islands), Portugal. OIR: swimming, hill walking, natural history, archaeology, local history. Tir Eithin, Maes-y-Bryn, Berthengam, Holywell, Flints CH8 9BA. 01745 560150.

COSGROVE, Peter John; *b:* 19 June 1969 in Coventry, West Midlands. BSc Environmental Studies (Hatfield Polytechnic, 1991), PhD Ornithological value of non-conifer habitats for songbirds of an upland spruce forest (Aberdeen, 1995). Research Fellow Univ Aberdeen (see address) 1995-.

Prev: asst to Forestry Policy Officer, RSPB 1989-90. Upland Breeding Wader Survey (Northumberland WT) 1993-94. Voluntary warden at several RSPB reserves 1987-91. Committee SOC Grampian Branch 1992-94. Recorder North Sea Bird Club 1995-. Special interests: ringing, migration, forest finches (esp Chaffinch, Siskin, Redpoll, crossbills). BTO 'C' ringer. Member Grampian Ringing Group 1991-. Expedition to study the ecology of Lake Baikal and its environs 1990. Paper on Siskin population dynamics and movements in *Birds in Northumbria* 1993; article on owl identification in *North Sea Bird Club Report* 1994. c/o Culterty Field Station, Newburgh, Ellon, Aberdeenshire AB41 0AA. 01358 789631.

COTTON, Donald Charles Francis (Don); *b:* 19 November 1950 in Carlisle, Cumbria; *w:* Elaine. BSc Applied Zoology (Reading, 1973), PhD Insect population dynamics (Reading, 1977). MIBiol Ireland 1977. College lecturer since 1981. Council IWC 1979-82. Founder IWC Sligo Branch 1982, Chairman 1992-. Co-ordinator of BTO Winter Atlas project for Counties Sligo and Leitrim, and of most other ornithological surveys for these counties. Special interests: gathering data on all aspects of birds occurring in Co Sligo and Leitrim (esp Whooper Swan, Barnacle Goose); wetland counts; seabird colonies. Published a coded *Checklist of Irish Birds* for field use (1981); author of IWC booklet *Beginning Birdwatching* (1982, 1984); papers in *Irish Birds* on eg Pied Wagtail roosting and results of gull and tern survey. Wrote and presented series of eight radio programmes *In Nature's Realm* 1986-87. Founded Dublin Young Ornithologists in Nov 1977 (first club for young birdwatchers in Ireland, later extended to become the IWC youth wing). OIR: botanical and invertebrate recording, cetaceans, gardening, raising children. Rathrowan House, Rathaberna, Co Sligo, Ireland. +353 (0)71 43251.

COTTON, Peter Angus; *b:* 23 October 1964 in Dundee. BSc Zoology (Dundee, 1987), DPhil The hummingbird-plant community of a lowland Amazonian rainforest (Oxford, 1993). Research asst Edward Grey Institute 1993-. Special interests: bird behaviour, neotropical birds. Dundee Rainforest Expedition, Trinidad 1987. BOU Colombia Expedition 1987-89. Scientific articles in *Anim Behav, Biol J Linn Soc, Ibis*. BOU David Lack Studentship 1987. OIR: sub-aqua diving, photography. c/o Edward Grey Institute of Field Ornithology, Dept of Zoology, South Parks Road, Oxford OX1 3PS. 01865 271171.

COTTRIDGE, David Michael; *b:* 14 October 1946 in Looe, Cornwall; *w:* Rita. Freelance bird photographer since 1986. Prev: taught photography

1971-86. Co-founder of Take Two which markets slide duplicates and prints of birds. Tour leader for Limosa Holidays. Photographic consultant for *Bird Watching* and *Birding World*. Special interests: photographing birds in Britain and abroad (esp Israel), history of bird photography. Regular contributor of photographs and articles to magazines. Photographic editor *Hamlyn Photographic Guide to the Waders of the World* (Rosair and Cottridge) (1955). Photographs published in numerous other books on ornithology, eg *The Birds of Israel* by Hadoram Shirihai (1996). Photographs exhibited eg at WWT (Slimbridge and Llanelli) and Rutland Water. Winner Bird Photograph of the Year (*British Birds*) 1983; first prize in photographic section of the Society of Wildlife Artists 1992. Lecturer on bird photography and holder of workshops throughout UK. OIR: growing fuschias, classical music (esp Mahler), cooking Indian food. 6 Sutherland Road, Tottenham, London N17 0BN. 0181 808 1341.

COUNSELL, David James Radford; Major Retd; *b:* 7 February 1931 in Birmingham; *w:* Erica. Manchester Grammar School 1943-49. Royal Military Academy Sandhurst 1950-51; Royal Military College of Science Shrivenham 1960-63. Royal Air Force Ornithological Society Expeditions Officer 1977-86, Committee 1977-91. Treasurer OSME 1988-93. Special interests: Common Birds Census since 1977; nest records, inc Red-throated Divers in the Uists 1982, 1983. Leader or member of RAFOS expeditions to Belize, Brunei, Masirah Island (Oman), Berlin, Gibraltar, Unst; member of Army Bird Watching Society expeditions to Belize, Cyprus, Morocco, Bulgaria; bird-related travel to Australia and countries in Africa, Asia and N America. Ringing: European Migrant Birds in Africa Project, Senegal 1991; Kuala Krau Forest Reserve, Pahang, W Malaysia 1992; also on expeditions. Author of reports and articles in eg *ABWS Newsletter, The Adjutant* (journal of the ABWS), *RAFOS Journal, RAFOS Newsletter*. OIR: bats, wildlife conservation, walking, caravanning. Woodside Lodge, 8 Darnley Drive, Southborough, Tunbridge Wells, Kent TN4 0TL. 01892 529110.

COUZENS, Dominic Michael; *b:* 3 January 1963 in London. BSc Biology (Portsmouth Polytechnic). Self-employed ornithologist since 1988. National Sound Archive (Wildlife) tape editor from 1989; RSPB Film Unit Film Librarian 1990-92; Waxwing Associates writer from 1990; adult education classes at Univ Surrey and others 1988. Special interests: bird sounds and their recording. Author (with Mike Langman, illus) *Mitchell Beazley Pocket Guide to Garden Birds* (1996). Translator and adaptor *The Bird Walker* cassettes (1990); joint author and sound recordist *Teach*

Yourself Bird Sounds cassettes (1992-). Regular contributor to *Bird Watching* on a variety of subjects. OIR: moths, plants, sports, Christian activities. 67 Speer Road, Thames Ditton, Surrey KT7 0PJ. 0181 398 0942.

COWDY, Susan; MBE 1990; *b:* 6 August 1914 in The Lee, Great Missenden, Buckinghamshire; *h:* John. Educ: Common Lane House, Letchmore Heath, Herts; Tachbrook Manor, nr Leamington Spa, Warwickshire. Council Berks, Bucks & Oxon NT from inception in 1959; also Vice President for Bucks. Council RSPB in 1970s. Council BTO for eight years, inc four as Hon Sec. Council Bardsey Bird and Field Observatory 1958-; also Vice President from 1970s. President Bardsey Island Trust from 1994. President Buckinghamshire Bird Club from 1981. Various other voluntary posts. Special interests: lighthouse bird attractions on Bardsey Island; Chough ecology; ertswhile egg collector, 1925-30. Chairman of fundraising appeal to purchase and endow Bardsey Island (now a National Nature Reserve) 1976-82; fundraising for the BTO Winter Atlas. Contributor to *The Birds of Buckinghamshire* ed by P Lack and D Ferguson (1993). Articles in *Bardsey Bird Observatory Annual Report* and *Birds*. Bernard Tucker Medallist (BTO) 1968; Jubilee Medallist (BTO) 1986; Christopher Cadbury Medallist (The Wildlife Trusts) 1995. OIR: horse dealer (Ireland) and steeplechase devotee. **Deceased** (9 July 1996).

COWIE, Richard John; *b:* 2 December 1952 in London. BSc Ecology (Ulster, 1974), DPhil (Oxford, 1979). Lecturer in Zoology since 1979. Special interests: behavioural ecology of passerine birds, esp in relation to feeding; bird-strike problems at airfields; nutrition of passerines; ecology of birds in suburban environments. Articles in *Ardea, Anim Behav, Bird Study, Ibis, J Animal Ecol, Nature, Physiological Zoology*. Member: ASAB, BES. OIR: sailing, gardening, watercolour painting. School of Pure & Applied Biology, Cardiff University, PO Box 915, Cardiff CF1 3TL. 01222 874000.

COX, Robin Anthony Frederick; *b:* 29 November 1935 in Leicester; *w:* Maureen. MA, MB, BChir (Cambridge, 1954-57), FRCP, FFOM. Consultant occupational physician. President Cambridge Bird Club, also Past Chairman. Council BTO 1992-95. Founder-member North Sea Bird Club. Member of expeditions to Portugal and Denmark while at Cambridge. Main interest: the fun of birdwatching. Occasional notes in *British Birds*, articles in *Bird Watching* (also editorial consultant) and other journals. OIR: fly fishing, gardening, travel. Linden House, Long Lane, Fowlmere, Royston, Herts SG8 7TG. 01763 208636; fax 01763 208549.

COX, Simon; *b:* 12 August 1942 in Clacton-on-Sea; *w:* Pat. General medical practitioner (qualified King's College Hospital, 1966). MB, BS, MRCS, LRCP, DObstRCOG. BTO 'A' ringer since 1961 and member of Trainers Panel. Vice President and member of Identification Panel, Essex Birdwatching Society. Estuary counter (R Colne) 1971-. Special interests: identification (UK list mid 460s), migration. Travel for birds inc Antarctica, S and Central America, SE Asia, E, W & N Africa, Europe. Senior editor *A New Guide to the Birds of Essex* (1984); contributor to BTO Winter Atlas; sub-editor *Essex Bird Report* 1969-. Contributor to *Bird Watching* (regular), *Birding World, British Birds.* Member: OBC. OIR: singing (has made record and appeared on TV), supporting Derby County FC, food and wine. Burnsall, 754 St John's Road, Clacton-on-Sea, Essex CO16 8BN. 01255 820749.

CRAIK, James Clive Angus (Clive); *b:* 20 November 1942 in India; *w:* Mary. Clifton College Bristol. MA, PhD Chemistry (Cambridge, 1964, 1967), BSc Zoology (Durham, 1969). Research scientist. Argyll Bird Club: founder-member 1983, Committee 1983-, Vice President 1983-88. Special interests: ringing and study of seabirds, factors affecting breeding success of terns and gulls in particular, effects of predation at seabird colonies (esp by mink). Several papers on terns in W Scotland in ornithological journals. Editor *Argyll Bird Report* 1993-. Several radio and TV reports on effects of mink on seabirds. OIR: biogeochemistry, self-organisation, origin and early evolution of life, Gaia hypothesis. Grendon, Barcaldine, Oban, Argyll PA37 1SG. 01631 720327.

CRANBROOK, 5th Earl of; *b:* 20 June 1933; *w:* Caroline. Eton. MA Natural/Moral Sciences (Corpus Christi College, Cambridge, 1953-56), PhD Exteroceptive factors affecting incubation among birds (Birmingham, 1960), Hon DSc (Aberdeen, 1989), Hon DSc (Cranfield, 1996). FLS, FZS, FRGS, FIBiol. Chairman English Nature since 1991. Prev: (Senior) Lecturer in Zoology, Univ of Malaya 1961-70; Fellow, Yayasan Siswa Lokantara (Indonesia) 1960-61; Assistant, Sarawak Museum 1956-58. Made special study of the cave swiflets of SE Asia and SW Pacific. From 1963-70 ran the bird ringing project of the University of Malaya, at that time the principal ringing scheme in Malaysia. Edited 3rd edition of B E Smythies' *Birds of Borneo* (1980); co-author (with D R Wells) *Birds of the Malay Peninsula* Vol 5 (1976); co-author (with D S Edwards) *A Tropical Rainforest* (1994). Editor *Ibis* 1973-80. House of Lords, London SW1A 0PW. Home fax 01728 663339.

CREAN, Aidan Gerard; *b:* 22 November 1961 in Belfast; *w:* Claire. St Mary's Grammar School Belfast 1972-77. Collector of Taxes since 1988. Extra mural tutor in ornithology Queen's Univ Belfast 1993-. BTO 'C' ringer since 1983. Committee N Ireland Raptor Group. Fieldwork for RSPB Breeding Wader Survey and BTO Breeding Atlas (both 1980s), also Breeding Bird Survey 1994-96. Special interest: birds of the Irish islands; local active conservationist. OIR: hill walking, playing football, travel. 48 Riversdale Park North, Belfast BT11 9DL. 01232 625814.

CREWE, Michael David (Mike); *b:* 29 September 1958 in Oxford. Nat Dip Hort 1983. Ecologist. Prev: BTO Membership Development Officer 1993-95; earlier in horticulture. Suffolk Ornithological Records Committee since 1993. Bird Recorder for SE Suffolk from 1996. BTO 'A' ringer since 1995. Ringer at Landguard Bird Observatory since 1986. Council Suffolk Naturalists' Society from 1990. Regular contributor to Wetland Bird Survey counts and local and national surveys (eg Woodlark, Nightjar). Special interests: identification, taxonomy, migration, birds of E Palearctic and Oriental regions. Extensive bird-related travel in W Palearctic as well as India and E Siberia. Editor *The Harrier* (bulletin of Suffolk Ornithologists' Group) 1991-93; editor *Suffolk Bird Report* 1993-95. Member: OBC. OIR: all branches of natural history, esp plant surveying and recording. 29A Quilter Road, Felixstowe, Suffolk IP11 7JJ. 01394 272561.

CRICK, Humphrey Quentin Pitts; *b:* 7 December 1957 in London; *w:* Catherine. Sevenoaks School 1970-75. BA Zoology (St Johns College, Oxford, 1978), PhD Weight changes, foraging and the role of helpers in Red-throated Bee-eaters (Aberdeen, 1984). Head of Nest Records Unit BTO since 1988. Hon Visiting Lecturer, Zoology Dept Univ Aberdeen 1988-91. Chairman Meetings Committee BOU (ex-officio Council) 1991-95. Council West African Ornithological Society 1986-90. JNCC Barn Owl Liaison Group 1988-. DoE Barn Owl Working Group 1991-. Rare Breeding Birds Panel 1995-. BTO 'C' ringer from 1976. Special interests: population monitoring, breeding biology, side-effects of pesticides, co-operative breeding, photography. Field research carried out in Scotland, Nigeria, Egypt, Zimbabwe. Editor *Ibis* supplement 'Ecology and Conservation of Palearctic-African Migrants' (1992); editor *Malimbus* (journal of WAOS) 1986-90. Scientific papers in eg *Bird Study, Ibis, J Animal Ecol, Ostrich*; also in various proceedings and edited volumes. Photography: exhibition 'A Naturalist in Africa',

Sevenoaks, Kent 1989. Radio and TV appearances. Member: ASAB, BES, WAOS. OIR: jazz piano: music composed and played at eg Oxford Reviews, Edinburgh Festival Fringe; watersports; badminton; reading. BTO, The Nunnery, Thetford, Norfolk IP24 2PU. 01842 750050.

CROCKER, Nigel John; *b:* 7 April 1946 in Horrabridge, Devon; *w:* Beryl. Callington County Grammar School 1957-63. Lay Fellow Cheltenham & Gloucester College of HE 1993. ACIB 1971. Manager, Branch Operations, Chief Office, NatWest Investments. Hon Treasurer BOU 1984-. Trustee, BOC Herbert Stevens Trust 1991-. Finance Committee Birdlife International, British Section 1990-93. BOU Representative, UK Dependent Territories Conservation Forum 1996-. Leader RSPB Cheltenham Group 1978-81. Wildfowl Counts organiser for Glos 1979-81. Council and member of Reserve Mangement Committees Glos TNC 1974-82. Executive Committee Glos Naturalists' Trust late 1980s. Special interests: riparian birds, esp wildfowl, waders, warblers; studies of *Acrocephalus* warblers in Severn/Avon valleys. Member: ABC. OIR: foreign travel (esp France), photography, art/antique collecting, computer studies, church activities. Salida, The Street, Ubley, Bristol BS18 6PN. 01761 462678.

CROMACK, David; *b:* 4 June 1950 in Wolvey, Warkwickshire. BA Fine Art (West Australian Inst of Technology, 1977). Editor *Bird Watching* since 1989; prev deputy editor. Journalist since 1966. *Bird Watching*, Bretton Court, Bretton, Peterborough PE3 8DZ. 01733 264666.

CROSBY, Michael John (Mike); *b:* 27 February 1959 in Sale, Cheshire; *w:* Lin-ping. BSc Zoology (Durham, 1980), MSc Biological Computation (York, 1987). Research Officer BirdLife International since 1988. Prev: Computer Programmer/Systems Analyst, World Conservation Monitoring Centre 1987-88; several short-term contracts carrying out ornithological fieldwork for eg RSPB Wales Office, British Waterways Board. OBC: Council 1989-, Secretary 1989, Memb Sec 1990-93; also Bulletin, Check-list and Conservation Committees. BirdLife/World Pheasant Assoc Pheasant Specialist Group Core Committee 1993-. Special interests: birds of Asia (esp China); avian biogeography and its application in conservation. Bird-related travel to China, Japan, S Korea, Thailand, peninsular Malaysia, Indonesia, Mexico, Guatemala, USA. Co-author *Putting Biodiversity on the Map: priority areas for global conservation* (1992); chapter in *Mapping the Diversity of Nature* ed by R Miller (1994); co-author *Birds to Watch 2: the world list of threatened birds* (1994) and *A Global Directory of Endemic*

Bird Areas (in prep). Articles in eg *Birding World, British Birds, Kukila, OBC Bulletin*. Interviews on BBC local radio. Member: OBC. OIR: field botany, travel, photography, reading, music, sport (inc five-a-side football, badminton, squash, tennis). 30 Molewood Close, Cambridge CB4 3SR. 01223 358802.

CROUCHER. Anthony James (Tony); *b:* 12 August 1942 in Reading, Berkshire; *w:* Eileen. Stoneham Grammar School, Reading. Planning Engineer British Telecom, retired 1992. Committee and Conservation Officer, Reading Ornithological Club in early 1980s. Special interests: photography (since late 1950s); study of gulls at winter roosts over many years. Recorded first fully documented *michahellis* race of Herring Gull in Britain and first Ring-billed Gull for Berks. Photographs published in *Berkshire Bird Report* and *British Birds*. OIR: all aspects of natural history esp orchids, dragonflies, butterflies (with wife, found and photographed first blue form of Small Skipper), railways, collecting (inc books, stamps, antique bottles). 11a Burney Bit, Pamber Heath, Tadley, Hants RG26 3TJ. 01734 700804.

CROXALL, John Patrick; *b:* 19 January 1946 in Birmingham. Royal Grammar School, Newcastle upon Tyne 1952-57, King Edward's School, Birmingham 1957-64. BA Zoology (Queen's College, Oxford, 1968), MA (Oxford, 1987), PhD Marine Ecology (Auckland, 1971). Head, Birds and Mammals Section, British Antarctic Survey since 1976. Prev: Senior Research Associate and Director, Oiled Seabird Research Unit, Dept Zoology, Univ Newcastle upon Tyne. BOU: Council 1974-78, 1992-94; Meetings Committee 1976-85 (Chairman 1979-85); Vice-Pres 1987-91; Ornithological Affairs Committee 1989-94 (Chairman 1993-94); President 1995-. Commission for the Conservation of Antarctic Marine Living Resources: Member of UK Delegation 1987-. BirdLife International (prev ICBP): Biodiversity Programme Advisory Committee 1989-92; Seabird Specialist Group Executive Committee 1982-. Falklands Conservation: Trustee 1987-, Chairman 1993-. International Ornithological Congress: Standing Committee for the Co-ordination of Seabird Research, Member 1978-, Secretary 1982-; International Ornithological Committee, Member 1990-. Royal Society Interdisciplinary Committee on Antarctic Research 1990-94. RSPB: Council 1989-; Chairman Conservation Committee 1993-. Seabird Group Council 1975-79, 1982-83, Chairman 1984-87. Scientific Committee for Antarctic Research: various posts inc Bird Biology Subcommittee, Member 1978-; Secretary 1981-82; Chairman 1986-94. Special interests: ecology and conservation of seabirds (esp in polar regions), formerly also of tropical insectivorous birds (esp in Borneo and New Guinea). Numerous expeditions inc Royal Geographical Society Mulu (Sarawak) Expedition. Author *Guide to Identification of Shearwaters and Petrels in New Zealand Waters* (1971); co-author *The Distribution of Penguins on the Antarctic Peninsula and Islands of the Scotia Sea* (1979); co-editor *Status and Conservation of the World's Seabirds* (1984); editor *Seabirds: feeding ecology and role in marine ecosystems* (1987) and *Seabird Status and Conservation: a supplement* (1991). Many scientific papers in journals (*Condor, Ecology, Ibis, J Anim Ecol*), books and conference proceedings; many other published papers and reports; innumerable book reviews and other shorter notes. Editorial Boards of *Bird Cons Internat* (1991-), *J Appl Ecol* (1983-93), *J Zool* (1989-94), *Marine Ornithology* (1984-). Scientific Medal, Zoological Society of London 1984. Polar Medal 1993; President's Medal, British Ecological Society 1995. Member: BES, NBC, OBC, Orn Soc of New Zealand, Seabird Group. OIR: scuba diving. 3 Oakington Road, Girton, Cambridge CB3 0QH. 01223 234287.

CULLEN James Patrick (Pat); *b:* 26 June 1937 in Altrincham, Cheshire; *w:* Nini. King William's College, Isle of Man 1947-56. BA Medicine (Gonville and Caius College, Cambridge, 1959), MB, BChir (1962), DObstRCOG (1964). Principal in general practice, Douglas IoM since 1971 and Associate Specialist in Obstetrics, Noble's Isle of Man Hospital since 1986. Bird Recorder for IoM 1972-. Vice Chairman Manx Ornithological Society 1982-. BTO Regional Representative IoM 1992-. Count organiser, heronries and wildfowl; Manx breeding censuses: terns, Raven, Rook; local co-ordinator of national surveys inc BTO New Breeding Atlas, habitats, single species. Co-author (with P P Jennings) *Birds of the Isle of Man* (1986); contributor for IoM to *Important Bird Areas in Europe* (1989) and (with G Williams) *Important Bird Areas in the United Kingdom including the Channel Islands and the Isle of Man*; author 'The history and present status of the Chough in the Isle of Man' in *Choughs and Land-use in Europe* by the Scottish Chough Study Group (1988) and 'The Hen Harrier in the Isle of Man' in *Birds and Pastoral Agriculture in Europe* ed by D J Curtis *et al* (1991). Article 'Birds of the Isle of Man: the Manx Ornithological Society 1967-1992' in *Birdwatcher's Yearbook* 1993. Editor *Peregrine* 1976-89 and author of many articles on Manx ornithology therein since 1973; compiler of *Manx Bird Report* 1972-82, 1984-87. Troutbeck, Cronkbourne, Braddan, Isle of Man IM4 4QA. 01624 623308.

CUNDALE, Graham Clifford; *b:* 5 December 1948 in Ashton, Lancashire; *w:* Celia. BA (Warwick, 1970), MSc (Aberdeen, 1973), Teaching Cert

(Moray House Coll of Ed, 1974), CertFBiol (London, 1981). MRTPI, MIEEM. Planning Inspector Dept of the Environment. Several posts with Brecon Beacons National Park Authority (inc surveys, conservation policies) 1974-91. Regional organiser National Waterfowl Counts 1984-92. BTO Regional Representative for Breconshire 1990-92 and participant in national surveys and censuses. Organiser for Powys of BTO Peregrine Survey 1991. Voluntary nature reserve warden for Rhos Goch NNR. Bird survey contract work for Countryside Council for Wales. BTO 'A' ringer 1974-88. Special interests: bird surveys and habitat studies. Various articles for county nature trust journals. Editorial Board and contributor *Nature in Wales* in early 1980s. c/o Room 14/16 Tollgate House, Houlton Street, Bristol BS2 9SZ.

CUNDALL, Arthur Winspear; *b:* 12 July 1929 in Birmingham; *w:* Valerie. Qualified mechanical engineer. West Midland Bird Club Research Committee 1950-72 (Secretary 1956-67). Executive Secretary Nature Photographers' Portfolio 1957-. Special interest: bird photography. Occasional published photographs. OIR: horticulture, general natural history. 8 Gig Bridge Lane, Pershore, Worcs WR10 1NH. 01386 552103.

CUNNINGHAM, William Alfred John (Peter); Deputy Lieutenant of the Islands Area of the Western Isles since 1975; *b:* 1 July 1918 in Sheringham, Norfolk; *w:* Anne. Jordanhill College School, Glasgow, and Royal Navy (1939-46). Retired Civil Servant. Local Recorder for SOC since inception of annual report in 1969. Author *A Hebridean Naturalist* (1979) and *Birds of the Outer Hebrides* (1990). Co-author (with Tim Dix) *Birdwatching in the Outer Hebrides* (1995). Contributor to *Outer Hebrides Bird Report* since 1981. Nature column in weekly newspaper *Stornoway Gazette* since 1975. OIR: angling, gardening, music and natural history. 10 Barony Square, Stornoway, Isle of Lewis HS1 2TQ. 01851 702423.

CURRIE, Andrew (Andy); *b:* 26 August 1930 in Edinburgh; *w:* Hazel. Royal High School Edinburgh. CBiol, FIBiol 1988. Retired Senior Scientific Officer, NCC. Prev: Hill Farming Research Organisation and Royal Botanic Garden Edinburgh. Birds of Estuaries Enquiry counter in Moray Firth Basin, jointly with C G Headlam and Maeve Rusk 1969-75. Founder-member Highland Ringing Group (1973). BTO Representative on Skye 1985-94. Special interests: wildfowl, waders, seabirds and birds of prey, distribution (summer and winter) and conservation. Author *Moray Firth: prospectus for conservation* (1972); articles in *Hebridean Naturalist, Proc Royal Soc Edin*. Member: Seabird Group, Wader Study Group. OIR:

botany; mammals; Scottish language, literature, history and culture; gardening. Glaiseilean, Harrapool, Broadford, Isle of Skye IV49 9AQ. 01471 822344.

CURSON, Jon Mark; *b:* 22 April 1962 in London; *p:* Carole Henderson. Self-employed ecologist and author; also social worker. Asst warden Long Point Bird Observatory, Ontario, Canada autumn 1984 and all year 1986-87. Participant in county tetrad surveys in Sussex. Founder-member and Committee Neotropical Bird Club 1993-. Special interests: identification, ageing and sexing techniques, esp relating to N American landbirds (long-term studies of American warblers and sparrows). Author *New World Warblers* (1994). Co-author (with Urban Olsson) *Buntings and Sparrows* (1995). Numerous articles published in *Birders Journal* (Canada), *Birding World*, *Birdwatch*; also trip reports 'Birding Mexico' and 'Birding Southern India and the Andamans' (both 1991). Worldwide travel for birds. OIR: general natural history, dragonflies and butterflies, keen botanist. 324 Queens Park Road, Brighton BN2 2ZL.

CURTIS, William Frederick (Bill); *b:* 4 October 1942 in Grantham, Lincolnshire; *w:* Margery. Senior Communications Officer Min of Defence. Yorkshire Naturalists' Union Records Committee (1977-), Ornithological General Committee (1985-), County Recorder (1985-). *British Birds* Seabirds Advisory Panel since inception. Voluntary warden Tophill Low Nature Reserve. Special interests: local ornithology esp Yorkshire; pelagics esp S Atlantic. Identification, distribution/status articles in *British Birds* and *Sea Swallow*. Joint editor *YNU Ornithological Report* 1985, editor since 1986. Member: Gibraltar Ornithological and NHS, Falklands Conservation, OSME, Seabird Group, Southern African Orn Soc. OIR: bats, equine hybrids, Lepidoptera, walking. Farm Cottage, Church Lane, Atwick, Driffield, E Yorks YO25 8DH. 01964 532477.

DARBY, Adrian Marten George; *b:* 25 September 1937 in London; *w:* Meriel. Eton (Oppidan Scholar) 1950-55. BA Philosophy, Politics & Economics (Christ Church, Oxford, 1961). Tutor in Economics, Keble College, Oxford 1963-85 (also Bursar 1968-82). Council RSPB 1981-93 (Chairman 1986-93); Hon Treasurer 1984-86. Special interest: interaction of birds and farmed habitats in Europe. Radio and TV interviews on conservation work. Worcestershire Farming and Wildlife Award 1986. Member: World Pheasant Association. OIR: botany (Chairman of Plantlife); general nature and landscape conservation. Kemerton Court, Tewkesbury, Glos GL20 7HY. 01386 725254.

DARE, Peter John; *b:* 30 May 1934 in Plymouth, Devon; *w:* Gillian. BSc Zoology (London, 1955), PhD Buzzard breeding ecology and food habits (Exeter, 1961). Principal Scientific Officer (Fisheries Biologist), Min of Agriculture, Fisheries & Food 1967-94. Prev: Fisheries Ornithologist, MAFF 1962-66; Government Ornithologist, Dept of Agriculture, Republic of Sudan 1958-62. BTO Regional Representative Caernarvonshire 1970-78, inc co-organiser first BTO Breeding Atlas, counts organiser for Birds of Estuaries Enquiry, county organiser for various other censuses and surveys. Hon Secretary Cambrian Ornithological Society 1971-72; editor of *Annual Report of the Cambrian Orn Soc* 1973-80. Special interests: raptor ecology (esp Buzzard); Raven population ecology; seabird and shorebird ecology (esp Oystercatcher); Palearctic migrants in Africa. Current projects: bird populations in a Dartmoor study area since 1955; recording of seabird migration in Anglesey and Suffolk. Ornithological visits to E Africa, Spain, Greece, Austria, Faeroes, Norway, Sweden, Canada and USA, Seychelles. Co-author (with P Hope Jones) *Birds of Caernarvonshire* (1976); many papers and articles in eg *Bird Study, British Birds, Ibis, The Naturalist.* Article on the Oystercatcher in BTO New Breeding Atlas and on the Buzzard, Raven and Carrion Crow in *Devon Breeding Bird Atlas* (1988). Member: Seabird Group, Wader Study Group. OIR: meteorology, astronomy, hill walking. Glebe House, Toad Row, Henstead, Beccles, Suffolk NR34 7LG. 01502 740340.

DARLING, Ian Marshall; *b:* 16 April 1945 in Perth, Scotland; *w:* Kate. College of Estate Management, Univ London. FRICS 1978. Chartered Surveyor. Director, Chesterton Scotland. Hon Secretary Isle of May Bird Observatory 1989-. Vice President Scottish Ornithologists' Club 1994-. Council BTO 1995-. Special interest: migration. Editor *Isle of May Annual Report* from 1989. West Acres, 579 Lanark Road West, Balerno, Edinburgh EH14 7BL. 0131 449 4282.

DAVENPORT, David; *b:* 16 October 1946 in Gillingham Kent. Special interests: status of birds in Kent; skua migration around Britain and Ireland, esp spring migration off Hebrides. Joint editor and contributor *Birds of Kent* (1981) and same for *Kent Bird Report* 1970-94. Articles on skua migration in *Birding World, British Birds, Irish Birds, Scottish Birds.* 11 Scotney House, Cypress Court, Rochester, Kent ME2 4PY. 01634 723944.

DAVEY, Philip R (Phil); *b:* 9 February 1950 in Wolverhampton, West Midlands. BA French and German (London, 1971), MPhil French (London,

1974), Cert Ed (Exeter, 1975). Site Manager, Lindisfarne NNR (English Nature) since 1991. Prev: Warden, Gibraltar Point NNR (Lincs Trust) 1988-91; contract warden RSPB 1985-88. Wetland Bird Survey and Goose Count organiser, also Beached Bird Survey co-ordinator, for Lindisfarne. Articles on shorebird protection, effect of wind-generators on breeding birds, spartina control in eg *BTO News*. Editor *Gibraltar Point Report* 1988-90. Occasional national and local radio and TV. Lindisfarne NNR, Beal Station, Berwick-on-Tweed TD15 2SP. 01289 381470.

DAVIES, Nicholas Barry (Nick); *b:* 23 May 1952 in Liverpool; *w:* Jan. BA Natural Sciences (Cambridge, 1973), MA 1977, DPhil Feeding behaviour of insectivorous birds (EGI Oxford, 1976). Professor of Behavioural Ecology, Univ Cambridge since 1995, Fellow of Pembroke College since 1979. Prev: Demonstrator 1979-84, then Lecturer 1984-92 and Reader 1992-95 in Zoology, Univ Cambridge; Demonstrator in Zoology at EGI, Univ Oxford 1976-79. Council BOU 1987-91. Special interests: bird behaviour and ecology, esp territorial behaviour (Pied Wagtail) and breeding systems (Dunnock, Cuckoo and their hosts). Co-editor (with J R Krebs) *Behavioural Ecology: an evolutionary approach* (1978, 3rd ed 1993); author *Dunnock Behaviour and Social Evolution* (1992). Papers on behaviour and ecology of birds in eg *Anim Behav*, *British Birds*, *Ibis*, *J Animal Ecol*, *Nature*, *Scientific American*. FRS 1994. Scientific Medal of the Zoological Society of London 1987. Medal of ASAB 1996. OIR: cricket. Dept of Zoology, Downing Street, Cambridge CB2 3EJ. 01223 336600.

DAVIES, Stanley George Francis; MBE 1993, for services to conservation; *b:* 13 March 1937 in London; *w:* Carole. Raines Foundation Grammar School. RSPB Regional Officer SW England since 1974. Technical Co-ordinator, Wildlife Conservation Society of Tanzania from 1994 (RSPB secondment). Secretary Severn Estuary Conservation Group 1976-93. Special interests: practical measures for conservation of threatened habitats, esp southern heathland, lowland wet grassland (Somerset Levels), estuaries; international conservation work, esp E Africa. Ornithological expeditions in Tanzania; actively involved in the Tanzania Bird Atlas project. Author *Birds of the Westcountry* (1979), *Wildlife of the Exe Estuary* (1980), and (with P Thomas) *The Exe Estuary: wildlife in camera* (1983). Experienced lecturer and broadcaster on conservation, esp in W of England. Leader of ornithological and wildlife tours. OIR: gardening, wildlife photography, opera, bridge. PO Box 2, c/o Rodgers-Gef, Dar es Salaam, Tanzania.

DAVIS, Andrew Henry; *b:* 12 February 1949 in Bristol; *w:* Gillian. Cert Ed (Sussex, 1970). Schoolteacher. Special interests: migration, identification. Articles published in *British Birds* (field identification of Long-eared and Short-eared Owls, with Robin Prytherch) and *Bristol Ornithology*. Senior editor *Avon Bird Report* 1991- and member of Editorial Committee since 1987. Editorial Committee *Somerset Birds* 1972-78. OIR: watching sport. 30 Lulworth Road, Keynsham, Bristol BS18 2PX. 0117 983 0489.

DAVIS, Eric George; *b:* 20 October 1920 in Birmingham; *w:* Emily. Greenmore College, Birmingham. Retired. Chairman East Lancashire Ornithologists' Club 1966-96. Wildfowl Count organiser 25 years to 1990. Organiser for E Lancs of BTO gull surveys and RSPB birds of prey surveys in 1960s. Participant in Club's local surveys, eg 10-year survey of House Martin colonies, 25-year study of rookeries. Special interests: status and distribution of birds in E Lancs, esp gulls and wildfowl. Chairman E Region of Lancs TNC mid 70s to mid 80s. OIR: photography, watercolour painting, walking, swimming. 7 Rock Lane, Trawden, Colne, Lancs BB8 8RR. 01282 867809.

DAVIS, Peter Edward; *b:* 8 October 1928 in Bradford, Yorkshire; *w:* Angela. BA Geography (Leeds, 1951). Wildlife consultant since 1988. Prev: Ornithologist, NCC Wales Field Unit 1981-88; Field Officer, Carrion Feeding Birds in Central Wales (attached to ITE) 1975-80; Asst Regional Officer, Nature Conservancy (NCC from 1973) 1970-75; Warden Naturalist, NC (Tregaron) 1966-70; Migration Research Officer, BTO 1963-66; Warden Fair Isle Bird Observatory 1957-63; Warden Skokholm Bird Obs 1954-57; Warden Lundy Bird Obs & Field Station 1951-54. Bird Recorder Cardigan 1967-. Kite Recorder for Wales 1968-. BTO Regional Representative 1967-78 (later Asst Rep). Numerous committees. Special interests: formerly migration; in past 25 years mainly Red Kite and other predators. Author *Birds of Lundy* (1954); over 150 papers, notes etc in bird journals. Edited bird observatory reports and bulletins 1951-63, *Bird Migration* 1963-66, *Dyfed (later Ceredigion) Bird Report* 1967-88. Occasional radio and TV appearances on bird programmes and RSPB films/videos on Red Kite. OIR: local history and topography, Roman numismatics. Felindre, Aberarth, Aberaeron, Dyfed SA46 0LP. 01545 570870.

DAVIS, Timothy John (Tim); *b:* 24 September 1952 in Bath, Somerset. Bicester Grammar School; Barnstaple GS. Programme Information Manager, WWF International since 1994. Prev: WWT Membership Officer 1988-91, Head of Design & Publications 1991-93; BTO Membership

Officer 1983-88. N Devon Area Conservation Officer, Devon Bird Watching & Preservation Society 1980-83. N Devon Area Committee, Devon TNC 1979-83. Birds of Estuaries Enquiry count organiser, Taw/Torridge Estuary 1979-83. Committee Buckinghamshire Bird Club 1986-88. BTO Regional Representative (joint) for Gloucestershire 1988-90. Participant in BTO Constant Effort Site ringing scheme (Slimbridge Decoy Wood). BTO Heronries Census organiser for Glos 1990-93. Joint editor *Managing Mediterranean Wetlands and their Birds* (1992); editor *Towards the Wise Use of Wetlands* (1993); compiler/editor *The Ramsar Convention Manual* (1994). Contributor to *Bird Watching, Birdwatcher's Yearbook, Devon Birds, Gloucestershire Bird Report*. Editor of *BTO News* 1986-88 and of *Wildfowl and Wetlands* magazine 1988-94. c/o WWF International, Ave du Mont-Blanc, CH-1196 Gland, Switzerland. +41 22 3649111.

DAVISON, Colin Norman; *b:* 30 June 1962 in Larne, Co Antrim; *w:* Margaret. BSc Zoology (Aberdeen, 1985). Registered General Nurse. Spells as asst warden at Calf of Man Bird and Sandwich Bay Bird Observatories in 1980s. BTO 'A' ringer since 1988. Secretary Lothian Ringing Group 1990-94. Special interests: migration, identification, ground-nesting passerines (Nest Record Scheme), waders, 'local patch' work. OIR: all natural history, esp moths. 5 Steel's Place, Edinburgh EH10 4QR. 0131 447 3450.

DAWES, Colin Malcolm; *b:* 12 November 1943 in Kirkcaldy, Scotland; *w:* Tatsuko. St John's College, Southsea. BSc Zoology (Queen Mary College, Univ London, 1966), PhD Avian Physiology (Reading, 1970). Freelance writer, artist and lecturer. Prev: Lecturer in Avian Physiology, Royal Veterinary College, Univ London 1970-87. Visiting lecturer in Avian Physiology, Birkbeck College, Univ London from 1980. Tutor in natural history, Dorset Adult Education Service 1992-. Special interests: the mechanism of hatching; seabirds and waders of the Dorset coast; life history of Purple Sandpiper. Articles in scientific journals on development of the avian embryo and the mechanism of hatching. Author, illustrator and publisher *The Natural History of Lyme Regis* (1992). Artwork (mostly bird themes) exhibited at the Royal Academy, the Royal Society of Painter-Etchers & Engravers, and the Centre International d'Art Contemporain, Paris. First one-man show: 'Avian Fantasies', The Gallery Soleil, Cambridge 1980. Scientific Fellow Zoological Society of London. Member: World's Poultry Science Association. OIR: sailing. Colin Dawes Studios, 47 Broad Street, Lyme Regis, Dorset DT7 3QF. 01297 443758.

DAWSON, Ian Keith; *b:* 13 March 1951 in Stretford, Manchester; *w:* Louise. Warwick School 1962-68. BA French & English (Lancaster, 1973), PGCE 1974, Post Grad Dip Lib 1977. Librarian RSPB since 1978. Prev: Librarian, Dumbarton District Libraries 1975-76; teacher 1974-75. BOU Records Committee 1989-95, Secretary 1996-. Special interests: waders and starlings; ornithological literature; distribution and numbers; historical changes; 'the British list'; optics for birdwatching. Numerous popular articles, book and optics reviews for eg *Bird Watching, Birds, Birdwatcher's Yearbook, British Birds*; 'Monthly reports' (with Keith Allsopp) in *British Birds* 1984-89. OIR: dragonflies, insects (esp spiders). RSPB, The Lodge, Sandy, Beds SG19 2DL. 01767 680551; fax 01767 692365.

DAY, John Charles; *b:* 5 October 1939 in Hoylake, Cheshire; *w:* Prof Joan M Day. MPhil Historial Studies (Strathclyde, 1987). ALA 1964, FLA 1971. Senior Lecturer, Dept of Information Studies, Univ Northumbria. Committee member and Hon Treasurer Northumberland and Tyneside Bird Club (prev Tyneside BC) 1974-89 (Hon Member since 1990). BTO 'C' ringer with Northumbria Ringing Group from 1973, specifically involved with Constant Effort Sites and nestbox schemes. Participant in most major BTO and locally organised breeding and winter surveys in home area since 1970s. Travel for birds includes every country in W Europe, Israel, Tunisia, Morocco, Kenya, Seychelles, Sierra Leone, India, Nepal, Thailand, N & S America. Joint author (with D Britton) *Where to Watch Birds in Northeast England* (1995); joint editor *Atlas of Breeding Birds in Northumbria* (1995). Frequent lecturer on local circuit. Member: OSME. OIR: book collecting, local history. 2 Grange Avenue, Benton, Newcastle upon Tyne NE12 9PN. 0191 266 3071.

DAZLEY, Robin Anthony (Rob); *b:* 7 October 1956 in Luton, Bedfordshire; *w:* Jackie. Telecommunications engineeer. Council Bedfordshire NHS 1992-. Records and Research Committee Bedfordshire Bird Club 1992-. Member of steering group for development of birdwatching interests at Dunstable Sewage Treatment Works. Co-ordinator spring migrant counts on Blows Downs, Beds since 1985. Organiser county tetrad atlas 1990-92. Evening class lecturer on birdwatching. Co-author (with Paul Trodd) *The Breeding Birds of Bedfordshire* (1994); article in *The Bedfordshire Naturalist* on results of spring migration observations. 15 Index Drive, Dunstable, Beds LU6 3TU. 01582 696656.

DEAN, Alan Robert; *b:* 23 June 1947 in Birmingham. BSc Physics (Aston, 1969). Computer Officer, Univ Birmingham. BTO Regional Representative Birmingham area 1973-78. British Birds Rarities Committee 1984-92. Special interests: identification, esp gulls, shrikes, warblers. Travel for birds: widely in Europe; also Turkey, Morocco, Canary Islands, Israel, India, Nepal, Thailand, Siberia, China, Canada, USA. Co-author *The Birds of the West Midlands* (1982). Over 20 papers, notes or letters in *British Birds* since 1975 on identification, behaviour, status and distribution; five in *West Midland Bird Report* 1973-89 (also asst editor 1975-80); note in *Alauda* on the Blue-winged Teal in Morocco. *British Birds* Identification Notes Panel 1986-93. Member: OBC, OSME. 2 Charingworth Road, Solihull, W Midlands B92 8HT.

DEAN, Timothy Peter (Tim); *b:* 1 May 1952 in Birmingham; *w:* Julia Robinson-Dean. Kettering Grammar School. Kettering Tech College. BA History (Polytechnic of N London, 1973), PGCE 1974. RSPB Rousay and Egilsay Warden 1996. Research in Seychelles and Hawaii on island endemics 1994,95,96; RSPB Orkney Mainland Warden 1993-95. Warden and Committee member of South Walney Nature Reserve and of Walney Bird Observatory 1979-93. Committee Belvide Bird Reserve 1978-79. Cumbria County Bird Recorder 1992-. Cumbria Records Panel 1991-. Committee Cumbria Bird Club 1990-. Tutor for WEA in Cumbria since 1979. BTO 'A' ringer since 1983 and trainer. Special interests: migration; Great Black-backed Gull colour-ringing study; the Nuthatch in Cumbria. Author *The Natural History of Walney Island* (1990). *Wings over Walney* BBC film 1985. OIR: non-league football, listening to Joni Mitchell. Echna View, Burray, Orkney KW17 2SX. 01856 731204.

de BUITLÉAR, Éamon; *b:* 22 January 1930 in Dublin, Ireland; *w:* Laillí. Hon DSc (University College Dublin, 1990). Wildlife film-maker; cameraman/director. President Irish Wildbird Conservancy 1983-91. Involved in making TV programmes since 1962, many about birds, also films for eg BBC Natural History Unit, RSPB, Central TV. Author of several books on wildlife and regular broadcaster on radio. Winner of several Jacob Awards for TV series. Univ College Dublin Lifetime Environmental Achievement Award 1992. OIR: watching wildlife and enjoying the countryside; traditional and classical music; still photography; painting and sketching. Hillside House, Delgany, Co Wicklow, Ireland. +353 (0)1 2876094.

DEDICOAT, Peter Kenneth; *b:* 10 March 1946 in Birmingham; *w:* Beverley. Bank manager. Tour leader with Avian Adventures since 1994. BTO Regional Representative South Staffordshire from 1983. West Midland

Bird Club: Belvide Reserve Management Committee 1978-, Chairman 1987-; Research Committee 1979-; Bulletin Editor 1983-88; Annual Report Editorial Committee 1979-82; Main Committee 1982-88, 1993-94; Staffs Branch Committee 1978-84, 1988-; Promotions and Fund Raising Committee 1986-88, 1993-. WEA tutor for evening classes on birdwatching 1978-82. Special interests: cormorants, photography. Wetland Trust expeditions to Senegal 1991,92,93; other bird-related travel to Hungary, Menorca, Africa, USA. Member: ABC, Bardsey Bird Observatory. OIR: following Birmingham City FC. 2 The Elms Paddock, Pattingham, Wolverhampton WV6 7DW. 01902 700514.

DEE, Christopher William Andrew (Chris); *b:* 17 June 1956 in Edmonton, London; *w:* Mandy. BA Zoology (St Catherine's College, Oxford, 1985), MA (Oxford, 1990). Computer consultant. Fieldwork Secretary, Oxfordshire Ornithological Society 1983-84. Ringing Secretary, Rye Meads Ringing Group 1986-. BTO Regional Representative for Herts 1990-. BTO Research and Surveys Committee 1993-96. BTO 'A' ringer since 1985 and trainer. Special interests: population dynamics of migrant warblers; distribution and population survey work organisation; use of computers to customise survey paperwork; use of effective design in publicity and the presentation of results. Faeroe Islands Wren Project, July 1984 (colour-ringing Wrens for study of inter-island movement); Univ Oxford Cameroon Project, July-Sept 1985 (study of montane rainforest bird populations, inc four endemic). Organiser Herts Bird Club Breeding Corn Bunting Survey 1992 and Rookeries Census 1993. Joint editor (with K W Smith *et al*) *The Breeding Birds of Hertfordshire* (1993) (first repeat county tetrad atlas). Various survey-related articles for *Hertfordshire Bird Report* and general analyses on ringing-related data for ringing group report. 26 Broadleaf Avenue, Thorley Park, Bishop's Stortford, Herts CM23 4JY. 01279 755637.

DELANY, Simon Nicholas; *b:* 31 May 1956 in Plymouth, Devon; *w:* Martina Bernhard. Hardye's Grammar School, Dorchester. BA Geography (Southampton, 1977). IWC: National Organiser Irish Wetland Bird Survey since 1994. Prev: Research Officer (Special Surveys) WWT 1989-94; zoological field asst British Antarctic Survey 1985-88; countryside ranger Oldham BC 1984-85; also asst warden Portland Bird Observatory 1978. BTO 'A' ringer 1978-88. Expeditions and travel: for BAS, conducted long-term studies of population dynamics and feeding ecology at albatross breeding colonies (Wandering, Black-browed, Grey-headed) on Bird Island, S Georgia and assisted with studies of Gentoo and Macaroni Penguins 1985-88; on the way home travelled one year in S America;

Southampton Univ Ornithological Project (Ladakh) 1981-82, their Ladakh Expedition 1980 and Himalayan Expedition 1977 (a series of expeditions studying bird migration in the NW Himalaya), also travelled extensively in India, Nepal and Pakistan between and after them; member of ringing expedition to the Ebro delta, Spain 1976. Ladakh and Antarctic expedition reports in *OBC Bulletin* and *BAS Bulletin*; many WWT reports; papers in eg *British Birds, Conservation and Monitoring Review, Hydrobiologia*; popular articles in *BTO News, Birding World, Wildfowl & Wetlands*. OIR: photography, books, music, boats (lived 4 years on narrowboat), cycling. c/o Irish Wildbird Conservancy, Ruttledge House, 8 Longford Place, Monkstown, Co Dublin. +353 (0)1 2804322.

DENNIS, Roy H; MBE 1992, for services to nature conservation in Scotland; *b:* 4 May 1940 in New Forest, Hampshire; *w:* Marina. Wildlife and environmental consultant. Main board member of Scottish National Heritage. Director of the Cairngorms Partnership. Director of the Highland Foundation for Wildlife. Prev RSPB: Regional Officer (N Scotland) 1986-91; Highland Officer 1972-86; Speyside Officer 1971-72. Earlier: Warden/Director of Fair Isle Bird Observatory 1963-70; various contracts with wildlife authorities in Scotland and England. Wildlife Inspector (part-time), Dept of Environment 1983-. Cairngorms Working Party 1991-93. Various SNH Task Forces and Working Groups from 1992. Regional member NCC Scotland 1990-91. Advisory Committee on Birds 1972-80. Rare Breeding Birds Panel 1974-90. British Birds Rarities Committee 1966-87. Chairman Fair Isle Bird Observatory Trust. Founder-member and Chairman Highland Raptor Study Group 1985-. Sea Eagle Project Team. 1974-. Red Kite Project Team 1988-. BBC Scotland Rural Affairs Committee 1988-93. UK Working Party on Birds of Prey 1980-82. Prior to 1988: Council Scottish Ornithologists' Club and Chairman of Highland Group; founder-member and Chairman Highland Ringing Group. Major areas of experience: conservation of rare breeding birds and natural habitats; monitoring, ringing and radio-tracking of birds; restoration of rare species (esp Osprey, Goldeneye and reintroduction of Sea Eagle, Red Kite); threat and impact assessment of North Sea oil, spills, public inquiries; legislation enforcement (esp re illegal killing, egg and chick stealing of protected species, poisoning of birds of prey); effects of large-scale afforestation and skiing; restoration of native pinewoods; wildfowl, waders and seabird studies (esp Moray Firth); public relations for conservation; promotion of large ecosystem concepts and their restoration, inc large mammals. Numerous ornithological/conservation visits to Asia (Indonesia, Mongolia, Siberia), Africa (The Gambia, Kenya, Zimbabwe,

Seychelles), N and S America, Europe and the Arctic (Svalbard and NE Greenland); consultancies for Greek government, Operation Raleigh, DBV Germany; two-man ICPB team to assess damage to birds by Gulf Oil Spill. Author *Peregrine Falcons* (1992), *Puffins* (1991), *Birds of Badenoch & Strathspey* (1984, new ed 1995), *Ospreys and Speyside Wildlife* (1973), *Divers* (1993); *The Loch* (1993); papers in eg *Bird Study*, *British Birds*, *RSPB Conservation Review*, *Scottish Birds*; technical and popular reports in various journals; specialist contributions to conservation books, reports and working party documents. Many lectures at popular and scientific meetings and conferences, and frequent appearances on radio and TV. Inchdryne, Nethybridge, Inverness-shire PH25 3EF. Tel/fax 01479 831384.

DENSLEY, Michael (Mike); *b:* 3 December 1937 in Leeds, W Yorkshire; *w:* Rita, Joan. AMA 1979, FMA 1986. Principal Officer (Museums and Exhibitions) Met Bor Rotherham 1974-92, retired. Recorder and Wildfowl Count co-ordinator Leeds Bird Club 1960-70. W Yorks organiser BTO Breeding Atlas 1968-73. BTO Regional Representative W & S Yorks 1964-84. Hon Sec Ornithological Section of Yorkshire Naturalists' Union 1977-93, 1995-. Founder President Rotherham Bird Club 1975. President YNU 1986-87, Vice Pres since 1988. General interest: ornithology of old county of Yorkshire. Early special interests: ringing and study of visible migration on Yorks coast, inc long association with Spurn Bird Observatory (served on Management Committee). Lifelong specialism: distribution, migration and biology of Ross's Gull, and the life and achievements of its discoverer Sir James Clark Ross. Winston Churchill Memorial Trust Travelling Fellowship in 1975 to carry out the first systematic documentation of the autumn migration of Ross's Gull at Point Barrow, Arctic Alaska. At invitation of Russian co-workers, and jointly funded by the Royal Society and USSR Academy of Sciences, carried out first-ever study by a Westerner of biology of Ross's Gulls on their Russian breeding grounds 1990. Other extensive travel in Europe, Scandinavia, Iceland, Turkey, Cyprus, N Africa, Canary Islands, Madeira, Israel. Member of first party of Western ornithologists to visit Siberia and Mongolia 1980; leader of groups to E Siberia and/or Soviet Central Asia on five occasions. Co-author (with David Hill) *Turner's Birds* (1988); edited part 2 of manuscript of *Birds on the Spurn Peninsula* by Ralph Chislett (publ with facsimile reprint of part 1 in 1996). Papers on Ross's Gull and other subjects in *British Birds*, *Dutch Birding*, *The Naturalist*, *Polar Record*, *Scottish Birds*. Editor *Leeds Bird Club Annual Report* 1960-70. OIR: study and photography of British butterflies and wild orchids; the work of bird artist Eric Ennion; literature on Arctic ornithological exploration; English 20th century piano music. 22 Ridgewood Close, Baildon, Shipley, W Yorks BD17 6HE. 01274 584061.

DENTON, Michael Leslie (Mike); *b:* 26 April 1950 in Huddersfield, W Yorkshire. Museum Ornithologist, Yorkshire Museum since 1993. Founder-member Huddersfield Birdwatchers' Club and various posts, inc President 1988-89. BTO Regional Representative for Bradford area and organiser/participant all surveys from 1985; also BTO Regional Development Officer from 1991. Committee Ornithological Section of Yorkshire Naturalists' Union from 1989. BTO 'A' ringer since 1969. Special interests: migration, identification, populations; main species: gulls and warblers. Djibouti II Expedition 1985 (migrant raptor counting); Senegal Expedition 1992 (ringing at Djoudj National Park). Further ornithological travel to most European countries, Scandinavia, Africa, India, N America, Israel, Australia. Author *Birds in the Yorkshire Museum* (1995); author of annual ringing report in *Birds in Huddersfield* from 1971 and various other contributions. Member: OSME. OIR: Coleoptera. 77 Hawthorne Terrace, Crosland Moor, Huddersfield HD4 5RP. 01484 646990; work 01904 629745.

DES FORGES, Charles Grahame (Grahame); *b:* 30 March 1913 in Rotherham, S Yorkshire; *w:* Beryl. St Edwards School, Oxford. Solicitor. Founder-member Sussex Ornithological Society, also Council member, President 1979-89. First BTO Regional Representative for Sussex. Formerly RSPB Council. Special interest: ethology, esp Woodcock. Co-author (with D D Harber) *A Guide to the Birds of Sussex* (1963); editor *Birds in Sussex 1962-1987* (1987); *Sussex Bird Report* compiler 1946-47, editor and producer 1948, joint editor 1949-55. Bowders Farmhouse, Balcombe, Haywards Heath, W Sussex RH17 6QH. 01444 811270.

DICKINSON, Edward Clive; *b:* 6 March 1938 in Bermuda. Head of Operations, WWT 1989-91. Founder and Hon Secretary, Trust for Oriental Ornithology from 1992. Council (1992-93) and Chairman (1993-) The World Pheasant Association. Research Asst, Chicago Museum of Natural History 1987-92. Special interests: Oriental ornithology; avian evolution in relation to continental drift. Co-author (with B F King) *A Field Guide to the Birds of South-east Asia* (1975), (with K C Parkes and R S Kennedy) *The Birds of the Philippines: an annotated check-list* (1991); articles in eg *Bull BOC, Forktail, Ibis, J Bombay NHS, Nat Hist Bull Siam Soc* (also joint editor 1967-70). Member: OBC, WPA. Norman Chapel, Aston Magna, Glos GL56 9QN. 01608 650403; fax 01608 652000.

DICKSON, Douglas Edward (Dougie/Doug); *b:* 11 August 1956 in East Wemyss, Fife. Fire officer. Bird Recorder Fife 1984-. Founder Fife Bird Club 1985, various posts inc Chairman 1985-90. Editor *Fife Bird Report* 1986-94 and previously co-editor *Fife and Kinross Bird Report* 1984-85. Extensive bird-related travel in Europe, Africa, N & S America, eastern Australia. OIR: listening to rock music and playing guitar. Member: ABC, NBC, OSME. 45 Hawthorn Terrace, Thornton, Fife KY1 4DZ. 01592 774066.

DICKSON, Robert Christie (Bert); *b:* 6 June 1933; *w:* Anne. Retired. RSPB Local Representative 1970-79. Conservation Committee SSSI Torrs Warren 1979-89. Special interests: all-year studies of Hen Hariers since 1963 and Merlins since 1965. Author *The Birds in Wigtownshire* (1992); contributions to journals inc *British Birds*, *Scottish Birds*, *Western Naturalist*. Member: Dumfries and Galloway Raptor Study Group. Lismore, New Luce, Newton Stewart, Wigtownshire DG8 0AJ. 01581 600279.

DICKSON, Wendy Eaton; *b:* Brighton. Micklefield School, Seaford 1952-57. Dip Dom Sci (Eastbourne School of Dom Econ, 1958). Freelance naturalist. Prev: BBC Natural History Unit (inc Film Library, asst on Radio 4's *The Living World*, re-cataloguing the Sound Library) 1970-81; summer on Fetlar, Shetland working for RSPB at Snowy Owl Camp 1970; cook/caterer at Fair Isle Bird Observatory 1965. Special interests: photography, Arctic birds, seabirds (esp Eider). Author *Northumbrian Nature Diary* (1993); articles for national and local birdwatching and specialist magazines; one of species authors for *Atlas of Breeding Birds in Northumberland* ed by J C Day *et al* (1995); co-compiler 'News and Comment' in *British Birds* 1994-. Member: Falklands Conservation, Seabird Group. OIR: all natural history (esp seashore/rockpool life), swimming, cooking, lighthouses, travel, islands, collecting socks. Flat 4 Muckle Flugga Shore Station, Burrafirth, Haroldswick, Unst, Shetland ZE2 9EQ. 01957 711275.

DOBBS, Austen; *b:* 30 May 1919 in Nottingham; *w:* Hilda. Retired teacher. Secretary Trent Valley Bird Watchers (later Nottinghamshire Birdwatchers) 1950-85, editor (and recorder) annual reports 1950-83, editor monthly newsletter 1954-85. Survey co-ordinator for TVBW's own surveys (eg Redshank, rookeries, Kestrel). Local organiser of BTO surveys and continued to assist after BTO began to appoint Regional Representatives. Supplied Notts wildfowl count data to Phyllis Barclay-Smith,

International Wildfowl until formation of the Wildfowl Trust (now WWT) by Peter (later Sir Peter) Scott; thereafter organised WWT wildfowl counts until 1992. Special interests: numbers and distribution of common species; meteorology, esp effect of weather on British migration and English nature in general. Editor *The Birds of Nottinghamshire* (1975); contribution on birds to *Nottingham and its Region* (British Assocn for the Advancement of Science, 1966); paper on Rook numbers in Notts over 35 years in *British Birds* 1964; articles in eg *The Countryman, Countryside*. Fairly frequent broadcasts for a time on Radio Nottingham and occasional TV appearances. Numerous talks locally and to a BTO annual conference. In retirement carried out two-year study of food and feeding of Black-headed Gulls on River Trent, results published by Notts WT (of which a founder-member and served on Committee); also on-going study of local rookeries begun in 1968 and wildfowl counts in two areas. Organiser of the Phenological Survey of the British Naturalists' Association since 1989. OIR: gardening, photography, enjoying music. Cloverleigh, Old Main Road, Bulcote, Nottingham NG14 5GU. 0115 931 2379.

DOHERTY, Paul Anthony; *b:* 1 January 1956 in Leeds; *w:* Kim. Filming and producing bird videos. Prev: surveyor. Special interest: photography (film and video) esp birds of prey and unusual species. Regular contributor of photographs and articles to *Birding World* (also photographic consultant) and *Bird Watching*. Photographic editor for OSME. Producer of the *Bird Images* range of video guides. Finder of first Golden-winged Warbler for Britain and Europe. 28 Carousel Walk, Sherburn-in-Elmet, N Yorks LS25 6LP. Tel/fax 01977 684666.

DONNISON, Andrew; *b:* 5 January 1963 in Shotton Colliery, Co Durham. BSc Geography (Liverpool Coll of HE, 1984). Senior Warden at WWT Washington Centre since 1985. Asst Research Officer for Wetlands Advisory Service 1992-94. Committee Durham Bird Club 1989-93, Surveys and Projects Sub-committee 1991-93. National Waterfowl Counts (later Wetland Bird Survey) local organiser for Durham from 1989, also organiser for single-species surveys. Participant in BTO Nest Record Scheme. Experience as volunteer warden in 1980s on RSPB reserves at Leighton Moss, Snettisham, Dungeness. Special interests Grey Heron marking scheme (yellow Darvic rings) from 1992 at Washington. 63 Rotherfield Road, Hylton Red House, Sunderland, Tyne and Wear SR5 5DH.

DONOVAN, Jack William; MBE 1988; *b:* 3 March 1928 in Cranwell, Lincs; *w:* Jean. Acton Technical College 1940-45. Field Engineer, ADAS (MAFF-

WOAD), also conservation adviser, retired 1988. Bird Recorder Pembrokeshire 1967-. Council RSPB 1967-72. Committee RSPB Wales 15 years. Regional (Wales) Forestry Advisory Committee 1990-94. Dyfed WT: Vice President, Vice Chairman, Chairman County Conservation Committee, Chairman Ornithological Committee, Chairman Pembs Chough Panel, Chairman Skomer and Skokholm Management Committee. Chough Survey organiser for Pembs 1971, 1992. Formerly Wildfowl Counts organiser for Pembs for many years. Special interests: since late 1960s, Chough and Peregrine. Co-author (with G H Rees) *Birds of Pembrokeshire* (1994); contributor and past editor *Pembrokeshire Bird Report*; occasional radio broadcasts. OIR: general natural history and reserve management; angling; founder in 1981 of Pembrokeshire Farming, Forestry and Wildlife Advisory Group. Member: Game Conservancy. The Burren, 5 Dingle Lane, Crundale, Haverfordwest, Pembrokeshire SA62 4DJ. 01437 762673.

DOTT, Harry Edwin Morton; *b:* 5 March 1945 in Edinburgh; *w:* Wilma. BSc Zoology (Aberdeen, 1968), Cert Sec Ed (Moray House College, 1969), Dip Ed (Edinburgh, 1969). Teacher-naturalist for Lothian Regional Council. Co-ordinator Wetland Bird Survey shorebird counts for Forth South since 1991. Committee SOC Lothian Branch from 1991. Special interests: behaviour and distribution. Formerly BTO 'A' ringer. Expeditions to Scottish islands and Turkey. Articles on attendance of seabirds at land (inc Fulmar, Great Skua, Guillemot) in *Bird Study, British Birds, Scottish Birds, Seabird Report,* 1967-75; on birds in Bolivia (inc native species and spread of House Sparrow) in *Bull BOC, Condor, Ibis,* 1984-86; on densities of Magpie, Carrion Crow, Oystercatcher in urban habitat, roof-nesting gulls in Lothian, also various short notes, in *Scottish Bird News* and *Scottish Birds*; compiler of wader section in *Lothian Bird Report* from 1990. Co-editor *Breeding Bird Atlas of South-east Scotland* (in prep). OIR: walking with Wilma, nature, mountaineering, munroist. 70 Findhorn Place, Edinburgh EH9 2NW.

DOUGALL, Robert Neill; MBE 1965; *b:* 27 November 1913 in Croydon, Surrey; *w:* Nan. Whitgift School. BBC presenter and newsreader, retired. President RSPB 1965-74. Author *A Celebration of Birds* (1978) and (with Herbert Axell) *Birdwatch Round Britain* (1982); text for *Basil Ede's Birds* (1980) and *Ladybird Book of British Birds* (1982). Kendal House, 62 New Street, Woodbridge, Suffolk IP12 1DX. 01394 383767.

DOUGALL, Thomas William (Tom); *b:* 4 March 1956 in Hawick, Roxburghshire; *p:* Gillian Arbuthnott. MA Geographical Studies (St Andrews,

1978), PhD Breeding passerine communities (St Andrews, 1986). ARICS 1990. Senior Valuer with Lothian Valuation Joint Board. NCC contracts to census breeding Wigeon in Ettrick Forest, Borders and (with J P Johnston) to investigate distribution of feeding waders on Eden Estuary, Fife. Voluntary warden at RSPB Minsmere reserve July 1975. Committee Isle of May Bird Observatory 1987-93. BTO 'A' ringer since 1982. Ringing Secretary (and founder with the late R J Robertson) Borders Ringing Group 1991-. BTO Ringing Committee 1994-. Special interests: ornithology of the Scottish Borders, the Isle of May, Crete; migration, post-breeding dispersal, ringing studies; breeding Common Sandpiper, wintering Skylark, autumn dispersal of Meadow Pipit and Pied Wagtail. Papers and shorter notes in eg *British Birds*, *BTO News*, *The Ring*, *Ringing & Migration*, *Scottish Birds*, *Scottish Naturalist*, *Wader Study Group Bulletin*; compiler of ringing report in *Borders Bird Report* 1984-. Member: Hellenic Ornithological Society, Wader Study Group. OIR: family, films, wine. 62 Leamington Terrace, Edinburgh EH10 4JL. 0131 229 6358.

DOUGHARTY, Francis William (Frank); *b:* 12 October 1930 in West Chiltington, Sussex; *w:* Madeleine. Farmer. Reserve manager of The Mens reserve (Sussex WT) since 1981. Special interests: breeding surveys, sound recording, photography. Co-author (with S W M Hughes) 'The Recolonisation of Sussex by the Tree Sparrow' and 'The Lesser Spotted Woodpecker in Sussex 1964-88' *Sussex Bird Report* 1977, 1989. OIR: general natural history. Cattlestone Farm, West Chiltington, Pulborough, W Sussex RH20 2LG. 01798 813156.

DOUGLAS, Ian Robert; *b:* 14 August 1958 in Rothbury, Northumberland; *w:* Debora. King Edward VI School, Morpeth. Cert in Environmental Management (Durham, 1990). Habitats Manager Northumberland WT since 1992. Prev: Warden/Asst Warden Druridge Bay Nature Reserve 1986-92. Special interests: birds and wetlands; visible migration; wetland habitat creation; restoration of raised and blanket bog. Lectures given on these and on wildfowl. Expedition to Salinas de Torreueja, Spain 1983; survey of birds of La Gomera, Canary Islands (1988-90) with report on status and distribution. Author *Wetland Habitat Creation following Opencast Coal Mining* (1991). Member: LIPU. OIR: hill walking, photography, motorcycles. 17 Crawhall Crescent, Morpeth, Northumberland NE61 2RH. 01670 511774.

DOWELL, Simon Derek; *b:* 17 August 1965 in Cuckfield, Sussex. BSc Biological Sciences (Exeter, 1986), DPhil The ontogeny of anti-predator behaviour in gamebird chicks (Wolfson College, Oxford, 1990). Lecturer in Conservation Ecology, Liverpool John Moores University since 1992. Prev: Research Scientist, Game Conservancy Trust 1989-92. Organiser, First International Symposium on Partridges, Quails and Francolins (Fordingbridge 1991) and co-editor of proceedings in *Gibier Faune Sauvage* (1992). Chairman Species Survival Commission/BirdLife International/World Pheasant Association Specialist Group on Partridges, Quails and Francolins 1991-96. Scientific Advisory Committee World Pheasant Association 1991-95. Research: taxonomy and conservation breeding programmes of Amazon parrots; ecology of Lapwing on agricultural set-aside land; conservation status and ecology of avian communities in the southern Chinese forests Endemic Bird Area, esp Sichuan Hill Partridge. Earlier: ecology of Grey Partridge on agricultural land in Britain; reintroduction of Cheer Pheasant to Pakistan (involved expeditions to Pakistan and India). Other ornithological interests: farmland birds, birds and their habitats as a teaching resource, birds of NW England. Co-author (with P J K McGowan *et al*) *Partridges, Quails, Francolins, Snowcocks and Guineafowl: status survey and conservation action plan 1995-1999* (1995). Editor *J World Pheasant Assocn* 1992-94. Several articles and papers in journals and conference proceedings. OIR: general natural history. School of Biological & Earth Sciences, Liverpool John Moores University, Byrom Street, Liverpool L3 3AF. 0151 231 2210; fax 0151 298 1014.

DOWNING, Ronald Ernest (Ron); *b:* 30 March 1935 in Alexandria, Egypt; *w:* Pat. BSc Geography (Aberdeen, 1969), Sec Teachers Cert (Aberdeen Coll of Ed, 1970), Cert Field Biol (London, 1993). Adult tutor, community education. Research asst/fieldworker for RSPB on Hen Harrier and Merlin (Tayside, Orkney, Yorks) 1988-93. Species co-ordinator, Merlin, Hen Harrier, Raven for Angus/E Tayside. Dundee & E Tayside RSPB Members' Group Leader 1990-. Member of Bird Working Group for NCC's Tayside Indicative Forestry Strategy 1989. Bird survey for NCC of SSSI in the Sidlaws 1990. YOC Leader Dundee late 1970s to 1994. Participant in BTO Winter Atlas survey 1981-84, Birds of Estuaries Enquiry, Beached Bird Survey. BTO 'C' ringer since 1985. Tay Ringing Group 1984-. Special interests: birds of prey (esp Merlin, Hen Harrier). Articles/broadcasts on these. OIR: history, pre-history, archaeology, natural history. 3 Lynnewood Place, Dundee DD4 7HB. 01382 451987.

DRIESSENS, Gerald Jozef Clara Robert; *b:* 27 May 1966 in Lier, Belgium; *p:* Viki Meeuwis. Art School Kunsthumaniora-Lier 1982-85. Self-employed bird illustrator since 1993. Manager Belgian Birdline (ie *Dutch Birding*

Birdline - Belgium) since 1989. Involved in centralisation of Belgian bird records, publication of records in *Birding World*, *Dutch Birding* and *Oriolus*, and broadcasting of records on EuroBirdNet (Internet); also member of Belgian Rarities Committee (BAHC) 1988-91, 1996-. Special interests: bird identification and topography; field sketching. Projects: swifts 1993-95, Old World flycatchers 1996-. Travel for birds inc UK (Scilly), Spain, Morocco, Kenya. Articles (as author and/or illustrator) published in eg *British Birds*, *Cotinga*, *Dutch Birding*, *Limicola*. Books (as illustrator) inc *Vogels in Vlaanderen* by Vlaamse Avifauna Commissie (1989), *Natuurbeheer* by M Hermy (1989), *Swifts: an identification guide* with P Chantler (1995), *Where to Watch Birds in Holland, Belgium and Northern France* by A van den Berg and D Lafontaine (1996). Illustrations also in local and national magazines and newspapers, and shown in various exhibitions in Belgium. Editorial Board *Dutch Birding* 1985- and *Oriolus* 1988-. Bosstraat 44, 2500 Lier, Belgium. +32 (0)3 4808212.

du FEU, Christopher Robin (Chris); *b:* 1 March 1949 in Paulton, Somerset. BSc Mathematics (Warwick, 1970). Teacher, head of mathematics. BTO Ringing Committee 1986-89. B-RING software for ringers (co-ordinator 1985-90; advisory panel 1984-). Special interest: nestboxes. Author *Nestboxes (BTO Guide)* (1985, latest ed 1993); papers relating to woodland birds in eg *Ibis*, *Ringing & Migration*. Bernard Tucker Medal, BTO 1992. OIR: statistical education. 66 High Street, Beckingham, Doncaster, S Yorks DN10 4PF. 01427 848400.

DUCKWORTH, John William (Will); *b:* 16 June 1964 in Kenley, Surrey. BA Zoology (Cambridge, 1986), MA Natural Sciences (Cambridge, 1991), PhD Zoology (Cambridge, 1990). Freelance researcher/surveyor. Council OBC 1991-94, also Checklist Sub-committee. Special interests: status, distribution, nomenclature and conservation of the world's birds, esp in Oriental region; long-running observations in farmland near Bath; behavioural ecology. Foreign surveys (general wildlife/habitat) in Borneo, Madagascar, Ethiopia, Ecuador, Abu Dhabi, Laos; also bird-related travel to Hungary, Venezuela, Java, Thailand, W Malaysia. Some two dozen papers in eg *Bird Cons Internat*, *Bristol Ornithology*, *Bull BOC*, *Forktail*, *Ibis*, *Ringing & Migration*, *Scopus*; also reports and contributions to books. Member: ABC, Indonesian Orn Soc, NBC, OBC. Major interest in mammals esp small carnivores and prosimians. East Redham Farm, Pilning, Bristol BS12 3JG. 01454 633133.

DUDLEY, Stephen Paul (Steve); *b:* 10 July 1967 in Chorley, Lancs; *w:* Caroline. UK optical product manager since 1995; freelance birdwatching consultant. Prev: Director, Fern Publishing 1994; BTO Membership Development Officer 1991-94, Ringing Recoveries Team 1988-91; RSPB contract warden 1986-87. Residential voluntary warden Fairburn Ings (RSPB) 1985-86. Full-time volunteer BTO Ringing Unit 1987-88. Committee Herts Bird Club 1989-90. Special interests: identification; migration (esp visual); rare birds; participating in surveys (esp atlases and single species); a passion for seabirds and pelagic trips. Editor *BTO Bird Recording Handbook* (promoting record submissions) (1993); co-author *Rare Birds Day by Day* (1996). Popular articles published in eg *Bird Watching, Birdwatcher's Yearbook, BTO News*. Regular contributor to BBC Radio Norfolk on birdwatching subjects and Breckland conservation. Made conservation education film for secondary schools with Granada TV. OIR: butterflies, dragonflies, moths, Breckland, photography. 46 Bracken Road, Thetford, Norfolk IP24 3EB. 01842 755969.

DUFFY, Kevin John; *b:* 25 December 1963 in Edinburgh. St Thomas of Aquins High School, Edinburgh 1976-82. MSc Conservation Biology (Kent, 1994). Sea Eagle Project Officer, Scottish Natural Heritage since 1995 (carrying out reintroduction of Sea Eagle to W Scotland). Prev: fieldworker in Mauritius on conservation programme for Echo Parakeet, employed by Jersey Wildlife Preservation Trust 1990-93; Moorland Bird Survey in Galloway and Central Ayrshire, NCC team contract, 1990; Senior Bird Keeper at Penscynor Wildlife Park, W Glamorgan 1988-90; Bird Keeper Edinburgh Zoo 1982-87, also assisted with studies of the feral colony of Night Heron (inc colour ringing and nest observation). Surveyed tetrads for *West Glamorgan Breeding Atlas* 1988-90. Brief voluntary posts: Forestry Commission study of Tawny Owl involving telemetry 1989; Kakapo Recovery Programme (Little Barrier Island, New Zealand) 1993; RSPB wader survey Shetland; Madagascar Teal Expedition (Lake Bemamba) 1994. Special interests: parrots, owls, waders; island birds and their conservation; captive breeding of endangered species; impact of introduced species on native avifaunas; general conservation. Articles and notes published in *Dodo, Lothian Bird Report, Psittascene* (newsletter of the World Parrot Trust), *Ratel, Royal Zoological Society of Scotland Annual Report*. Member: IUCN/SSC Reintroduction Specialist Group, World Parrot Trust. OIR: mammals (esp carnivores), British vertebrates. OIR: music, travel, playing football. 4 Homebank Cottages, Birgham, Coldstream, Berwickshire TD12 4ND. 01890 830387.

DUNBAR, James John (Jim); *b:* 3 January 1930 in Old Deer, Aberdeenshire; *w:* Anna. Warden (first) RSPB Loch of Strathbeg Reserve 1973-93. Prev: Warden (first) St Cyrus (now National Nature Reserve, SNH) 1970-73. One of founder-members Tay Ringing Group. Special interests: conservation; study of Little Tern colony at St Cyrus reserve. OIR: keen amateur archaeologist, local history. The Lythe, Crimonmogate, Lonmay, Fraserburgh, Aberdeenshire AB43 8SB. 01346 532265.

DUNN, Peter James; *b:* 4 January 1955 in Goole, E Yorkshire; *w:* Kathleen. Police officer. A Wildlife Liaison Officer for the N Yorkshire Police since 1989. Asst Recorder York Ornithological Club in early 1970s. Founder-member Filey Brigg Ornithological Group in 1977, Recorder 1980-90. Yorkshire Naturalists' Union Ornithological Committee 1985-93, also YNU Protection of Birds Committee 1985-87, 1991-93, and Hon Secretary YNU Bird Records Committee (a rarity committee) 1993-96. Survey co-ordinator Seabird Colony Register from Scottish Borders to Humber Estuary 1985-87. BTO 'A' ringer since 1986 and trainer. Founder-member, ringing officer, newsletter and report editor, Filey Ringing Group in 1991 (later amalgamated with Flamborough RG as East Yorkshire RG). Special interests: identification, migration and ringing; occasional twitching, with a passion for E coast migrants; photography and some sketching; giving illustrated talks; computing, esp bird lists. A number of short notes and an article in *British Birds* since 1979; other articles in *Bird Watching, Filey Brigg Bird Report, The Naturalist, Yorkshire Birder* and local newspaper. Occasionally on local radio. OIR: family life. 43 West Garth Gardens, Cayton, Scarborough, N Yorks YO11 3SF. 01723 583149.

DURDIN, Christopher John (Chris); *b:* 26 April 1956 in Hendon, London. BA Economics (East Anglia, 1977). RSPB Conservation Officer East Anglia since 1988 (Asst Cons Officer 1981-88). Prev: Asst Development Officer, RSPB HQ 1978-81. Univ East Anglia expedition to SE Turkey 1976 counting raptors and other birds in Belen Pass, Iskenderun. RSPB sabbatical work on green tourism and wildlife holidays 1990, and on Stone Curlews in SW France and N Spain autumn 1995. Author of East Anglia section in *Ordnance Survey Natural History Atlas* (1989) and wildlife section in *AA Regional Guide: East Anglia* (1989); occasional contributions to *Birds, Birdwatch, Norfolk Bird Report.* Frequent radio broadcaster, esp as regular contributor 1981-95 to Radio Norfolk's 'Dinnertime Show' (c400 broadcasts), and occasional regional TV broadcasts on conservation (c30). Leader of wildlife holidays since 1984 and founder of Honeyguide Wildlife Holidays in 1991. Member: EAWLS, LPO, OSME, SEO. OIR: gardening and dog walking; former Chairman Norwich Barbershop Singers; occasional juggler. 36 Thunder Lane, Thorpe St Andrew, Norwich NR7 0PX. 01603 300552.

DYE, Keith Robert; *b:* 11 December 1941 in Cheltenham, Gloucestershire; *w:* Susan. Electrician. Chairman Great Yarmouth Bird Club 1992-. Committee Gt Yarmouth RSPB Members' Group 1986-. Voluntary RSPB warden for Berney Marshes and Breydon Water reserve 1986-. Editorial asst *Norfolk Bird Report* 1991, 1993-. Joint Wetland Bird Survey counter for Breydon Water. Fieldwork for BTO New Breeding Atlas and other BTO surveys, also RSPB Beached Bird Surveys. Special interests: wildfowl, waders, gulls, terns; recording counts and species on 'local patch'; Norfolk listing. Finder of Norfolk's first Franklin's Gull (30 June 1991 at Breydon Water). OIR: reading, watching sport and films; keen local footballer after leaving Royal Navy in 1968 until ornithology took over at age 38; Chelsea supporter. 104 Wolseley Road, Great Yarmouth, Norfolk NR31 0EJ. 01493 600705.

DYMOND, John Nicholas (Nick); *b:* 29 June 1943 in Bedford. Bedford School 1950-61. Freelance birdwatching/wildlife tour leader since 1986. Prev: Warden, Eyre Bird Observatory, Western Australia 1984-86; RSPB Reserve Warden at HQ and various reserves inc Fetlar 1974-83; Warden Lundy Bird Observatory 1972-73; Ringing Office asst BTO 1967-71; asst warden Fair Isle Bird Obs 1966. County Bird Recorder Bedfordshire late 1960s and early 70s. BTO Breeding Atlas organiser for Beds 1968-71, also organiser Beds tetrad survey. Bird Recorder Shetland 1987-89. Hon Sec British Birds Rarities Committee 1974-76. BTO 'A' ringer, active in Shetland Ringing Group from 1977. Special interests: identification, migration and distribution, esp Orient, Middle East, Africa. OSME expedition to Yemen and Socotra 1993; Senegal ringing expeditions 1991-92, 1992-93; numerous private trips in Oriental and S Asia regions, inc grant-aided survey work for the OBC in Sumatra. Author *Birds of Lundy* (1980) and *The Birds of Fair Isle* (priv print, 1991); co-author (with P Fraser and S J M Gantlett) *Rare Birds of Britain and Ireland* (1989). Member: ABC, OBC, OSME. OIR: all mobile wildlife (esp mammals, reptiles), travel to wild places, TV sport. Burgadies, South Punds, Levenwick, Shetland ZE2 9HX. 01950 422365.

EARL, Timothy David Cadman (Tim); *b:* 10 September 1949 in Guernsey; *w:* Marilyn. High Storrs Grammar School, Sheffield. HNC Applied Biology (Llandaff College of Technology, Cardiff, 1972). Freelance journalist and

author. Birdwatching tutor Guernsey College of Further Education since
1976. Secretary La Société Guernesiaise Ornithological Section 1974-78,
President 1986-88. Guernsey Rare Birds Committee 1974-78. Channel
Islands Ringing Scheme ringer since 1974. Special interests: ringing,
migration, leading tours. Author *A Field Guide to the Birds of Guernsey*
(1977, 1981); numerous ornithological travel guides. Member: Falklands
Conservation. Founder of Silbe, Colin McCathie Vale Pond and La Claire
Mare nature reserves. Successful campaigner for bird protection legislation
in Guernsey. Les Landes Cottage, Rue des Landes, St Peter's, Guernsey
GY7 9SH. 01481 64504; fax 01481 66562; work 01481 45866.

EDWARDS, George Ernest; *b:* 9 April 1950 in Chalfont St Giles,
Buckinghamshire. Chiropodist. BTO Regional Representative Essex 1978-
1993. Leader RSPB Members' Group Southend from 1993 and YOC Group
Leader Southend 1994-. Voluntary warden Essex WT 1981-85. Special
interests: identification, photography, waders. Talks on subjects inc
reserves, local habitats, work of BTO and RSPB. OIR: walking, keep fit,
woodwork, conservation projects. 3 Dalmatia Road, Southend-on-Sea,
Essex SS1 2QG. 01702 619233.

EDWARDS, Thomas William (Bill); *b:* 21 July 1934 in Oswestry,
Shropshire. Oswestry Technical Institute. Motor vehicle mechanic.
Committee Shropshire Orn Soc 1964-68. Leader RSPB Members' Group
Oswestry 1972-81 and RSPB Local Representative 1968-84. Committee
Oswestry Branch Shrops WT 1988-94. Voluntary warden various reserves
1960s to 1980s. Course director for ornithology courses Field Studies
Council, Preston Montford 1975-94. Part-time ornithology tutor Oswestry
College 1982-91, WEA (N Wales) 1987-90, N Shrops College 1991-94.
Leader YOC and other holiday courses. Special interests: various BTO
species surveys since 1961; Common Birds Census plot 1964-94; observer
and fieldworker for both BTO Breeding Atlases and Winter Atlas, and for
Atlas of the Breeding Birds of Shropshire by P Deans *et al* (1992). Occasional
short articles in *Shropshire Bird Report* and *Bulletin of the Shropshire
Wildlife Trust*. Talks on birds to local societies. Conservation work inc
hedge-laying on reserves. OIR: walking, gardening, all natural history.
Hopton Villa, Maesbury Marsh, Oswestry, Shrops SY10 8JA. 01691 656679.

EKINS, Graham Ronald; *b:* 13 April 1950 in Tottenham, London; *w:* Evie.
BEd Ecology and Microbiology (Nottingham, 1974). MIBiol 1978, CBiol
1985. Teacher. Committee Teesmouth Bird Club 1967-69. Gen Sec Essex
Birdwatching Society 1975-77. Sub-editor *Essex Bird Report* 1978-,

compiler of ringing section and member Rarities Committee. BTO 'A' ringer since age 18, Trainers Panel 1989-, Sponsors Panel 1991-. Member of Basildon, Abberton and Tay Ringing Groups. Dept of Environment Wildlife Inspector 1993-. Special interests: breeding biology of the tree-nesting Cormorant population at Abberton Reservoir (articles and conference papers); wing-tagging Ruddy Duck at Abberton (part of international research programme); five-year study of site fidelity and dispersal patterns of a village Greenfinch population (paper on results). Bird-related travel throughout Europe, also The Gambia, N America, Israel, Turkey, Egypt; ringing expeditions to Thailand (organiser) and Portugal. Published paper on Long-eared Owl predator/prey relationships, articles in *Essex Bird Report*, also description and photograph of first Bateleur for Western Palearctic in *Dutch Birding* and *Birds of Israel*. OIR: butterflies, moths, plants (all European), mammals. 35 Church Road, Boreham, Essex CM3 3BN. 01245 460656.

ELLIOTT, Graham David; *b:* 1955 in Leicester. Head of Investigations Section RSPB since 1966. Prev RSPB: Head of Conservation Management Advisory Section 1991-95; Species Management Officer 1986-91; Investigations Officer 1980-86. Earlier asst warden Rutland Water 1979; asst warden Calf of Man Bird Observatory 1978. Bird Recorder for old county of Huntingdon and Peterborough 1992-. Organiser Wetland Bird Survey counts for Hunts 1985-. BTO 'A' ringer since 1978. Special interests: populations and distribution, migration, birds of prey, Palearctic migrants in Africa. Bird tours led to S Europe and N Africa. Joint editor *Red Data Birds in Britain* (1990); several papers and articles on the management of Red Data Birds in the UK; assistance with writing of *Cambridge Bird Report* and *Huntingdon Fauna and Flora Society Annual Report*. Member: ABC, OSME. RSPB, The Lodge, Sandy, Beds SG19 2DL. 01767 680551.

ELLIOTT, Simon Timothy; *b:* 13 May 1955 in Sheffield, Yorkshire. MB, ChB (Sheffield, 1978), FRCR 1985. Consultant radiologist. Special interest: sound recording. Editor *Wildlife Sound* 1987-89. Author/editor *Sounds of Britain's Endangered Wildlife* (audio cassette, 1986); author/producer *Border Forest Ballad: wildlife sounds from Kielder* (audio cassette, 1990). Various articles on wildlife sound and technical aspects of sound recording; supplier of recordings to film, TV, radio, theatre and publishing companies. Winner 'Tape of the Year' (British Amateur Tape Recording Contest) 1984, also class winner in this and Wildlife Sound Recording Society Competition several years. Member: WSRS. 103 Kenton Road, Gosforth, Newcastle upon Tyne NE3 4NL. 0191 285 7520.

ENNIS, Thomas (Tom); *b:* 8 August 1938 in Holywood, Co Down; *w:* Evie. Admin Principal, Dept of Environment (NI) 1956-94. Part-time tutor (specialising in ornithology), Inst of Continuing Education, Queen's Univ Belfast 1968-. Voluntary part-time post in the Ulster Museum (specialising in ornithology) 1961-65. NI Regional Committee RSPB during 1970s. Founder-member Northern Ireland Ornithologists' Club in 1965, Chairman c1973-92, Vice President 1993-. Wildfowl Counts organiser (NIOC) for Lough Neagh Basin 1965-70, also Lough Foyle in mid 1970s and again in early 80s. Organised Ireland's first telephone bird information service (on behalf of NIOC). Special interests: identification, taxonomy, photography. First editor of *Northern Ireland Bird Report* 1980 and 1981. Member ABA. OIR: botany (esp orchids, cyclamen, alpines), all natural history, travel, reading, music, painting, TV, films, gardening. 51 Rannoch Road, Holywood, Co Down BT18 0NB. 01232 424745.

EVANS, Andrew David (Andy); *b:* 31 May 1961 in Maidenhead, Berks; *w:* Julianne. BSc Biological Sciences (Zoology) (Edinburgh, 1983), PhD Individual differences in foraging behaviour, habitat selection and bill morphology of wintering Curlew (Edinburgh, 1988). RSPB Research Biologist since 1992. Prev: BTO Scientific Officer 1991-92; RSPB Research Biologist 1988-91. Research has included nocturnal foraging in Dunlin; ecology of Cirl Bunting; lowland farmland, esp set-aside. UK representative on International Shrike Working Group. BTO 'A' ringer since 1986. Member of Wash Wader Ringing Group 1988-. Special interest: ecology and conservation of Red-backed Shrike. Papers and articles in eg *Bird Study*, *Birds*, *Devon Birds*, *RSPB Conservation Review*, *Wader Study Group Bulletin*. Contributions to *Britain's Birds 1990-91* and BTO New Breeding Atlas. Chapter on importance of mixed farming for seed-eating birds in the UK in *Farming and Birds in Europe: the Common Agricultural Policy and its implications for bird conservation* ed by D J Pain and M W Pienkowski (in press). RSPB, The Lodge, Sandy, Beds SG19 2DL. 01767 680551.

EVANS, Ceri Elizabeth; *b:* 8 October 1958 in Caerphilly, Mid Glamorgan; *h:* Russell Cryer. BSc Botany (Cardiff, 1980), PhD Seed germination ecology (Cardiff, 1986), Dip Management Studies (Anglia Poly Univ, 1993). Reserves Ecologist RSPB since 1986. Prev: RSPB contract botanical surveyor 1984, 1986. Special interests: habitat management for birds; reserves management plans; vegetation surveys on reserves. Papers and articles in eg *Biol Cons*, *J Environmental Management*, *RSPB Conservation Review*; chapters in books eg *A Guide to Field Techniques for the Study of Game-birds* ed by P J Garson (1991); contributions to RSPB Management

Case Studies series, eg co-author *The Management of Reedbeds for Birds* (1989). OIR: swimming, skiing, gardening. 11 Cranleigh Close, Cambridge CB2 2NP. 01223 842683; work 01767 680551.

EVANS, Hugh William; *b:* 8 May 1942 in Ferryhill, Co Durham; *w:* Caroline. Marlborough College. Duty Manager, British Airways Flight Operations. BTO Regional Representative Surrey 1991-. Committee Surrey Bird Club 1991-. Special interests: survey and census work (organiser of all BTO surveys in Surrey since 1991 and author of related papers in *Surrey Bird Report*). Member: BirdLife Malta. OIR: walking, cycling, music. 31 Crescent Road, Shepperton, Middx TW17 8BL. 01932 227781.

EVANS, Ifan Brazell (Ifor); *b:* 19 October 1925 in Caerbryn, Carmarthenshire; *w:* Elaine. Llandilo Grammar School; Trinity College, Carmarthen. Schoolmaster, retired. RSPB Local Representative since 1974. Committee Herefordshire Ornithological Club 1974-88, Hon Secretary 1988-95, Hon Editor 1995-. Special interest: bird photography. Articles on Rooks, wintering Blackcaps, Bullfinches and Cormorants in *Herefordshire Ornithological Club Annual Report* and *The Flycatcher* (magazine of the Herefordshire Nature Trust). OIR: philately (bird stamps), travel, relief carving, landscape painting, gardening, collecting bird books. 12 Brockington Drive, Tupsley, Hereford HR1 1TA. 01432 265509.

EVANS, Julianne; *b:* 1 December 1966 in Haslemere, Surrey; *h:* Andy. Royal Naval School, Haslemere 1979-83; Lancing College, Shoreham-by-Sea 1983-86; Guildford Coll of Tech 1986-87. BSc Biological Sciences (Zoology) (Edinburgh, 1989). Research Biologist, RSPB since 1996. Prev: Wetland Bird Survey Low Tide Count Organiser, BTO 1992-96. Earlier: contract research biologist for RSPB and BTO 1989-92. BTO 'A' ringer since 1994. Member of Wash Wader Ringing Group 1988-. Executive Committee Wader Study Group 1996-. Special interests: waders, ringing. Articles in *Birdwatch, British Wildlife, BTO News*. Asst editor *WSG Bulletin* 1995-. Member: Wader Study Group. OIR: horse riding, sailing, swimming, badminton, squash, running. RSPB, The Lodge, Sandy, Beds SG19 2DL. 01767 680551.

EVANS, Lee Geoffrey Richard; *b:* 4 October 1960 in Luton, Bedfordshire. BSc Mechanical Engineering (Hatfield Polytechnic, 1980). Ornithological consultant. 'Most obsessive twitcher/birder, concentrating on British life and year listing and Western Palearctic exploits...Has achieved over 300 species in Britain annually since 1977 and has covered 1.45 million miles in this pursuit...After maintaining the "grapevine network of information" from 1979 to 1986, set up "Birdline" in 1987 after leaving GM Motors, where worked as design stylist since 1979...Has lost at least one marriage due to twitching exploits.' A founding partner in *Birding World* and Birdline. Publishes *Rare Birds in Britain* an annual report aiming to list all vagrants and scarce migrants occurring in the UK. Author *The Ultimate Site Guide to Scarcer British Birds* (priv print, 1996). Runs the UK400 Club and magazine *Rare Birds*, serving to monitor the nation's top twitchers and their life lists, and to keep under review contentious species occurrences. 8 Sandycroft Road, Little Chalfont, Amersham, Bucks HP6 6QL. 01494 763010.

EVANS, Matthew Richard; *b:* 12 January 1966 in Leicester; *w:* Dr Thais Martins. Brecon Comprehensive School. BSc Zoology (Bristol, 1987), PhD The role of plumage signals in mate choice and aggressive interactions in the Scarlet-tufted Malachite Sunbird (Cambridge, 1991). Lecturer in Animal Ecology, Univ Stirling. Prev: Lecturer in Ornithology, Univ Oxford 1991-94. Special interests: the communication of information between birds; photography, birding and travel in various parts of the world (eg Kenya, Jamaica, Chile, Antarctica, Brazil). BTO 'A' ringer since 1992. Scientific papers in eg *Anim Behav*, *Behavioural Ecol and Sociobiol*, *Bioacoustics*, *Biol J Linn Soc*, *Proc Roy Soc Lond (B)*, *Ringing & Migration*. OIR: mountaineering, fell running. Dept of Biological and Molecular Sciences, University of Stirling, Stirling FK9 4LA. 01786 467761.

EWINS, Peter John (Pete); *b:* 5 March 1956 in Worksop, Nottinghamshire. BSc Zoology (Edinburgh, 1977), DPhil Zoology (Oxford, 1986). Wildlife biologist with Canadian Wildlife Service since 1990. Prev: NCC Asst Regional Officer Herts 1987-90, Shetland 1985-87; NCC Warden, Isle of May NNR 1985; RSPB species protection and survey officer in Speyside 1981; asst warden Fair Isle Bird Observatory 1978, 1980; biologist, Station Biologique de la Tour du Valat, Camargue, France 1979. BirdLife International Canada Executive Committee 1990-. Committee Ontario Bird Banding Assocn 1990-. Secretary Seabird Group 1987-90. Voluntary wardening at many bird observatories and RSPB reserves throughout UK and volunteer on marine bird surveys off Vancouver Island, Canada 1989. Participation in many BTO national surveys and enquiries 1970s-80s. Ornithological survey work in Nepal, Morocco, Thailand, Turkey, Egypt, Venezuela; also tour guide in UK and Nepal. Special interests: applied avian ecology, esp effects of contaminants on marine and freshwater bird species; development and application of accurate census methods; indicator species. Over 30 scientific papers published in eg *Bird Study, Colonial Waterbirds, Condor, Ibis, J Wildlife Management, New Scientist, Ontario Birds, Ringing & Migration, Scottish Birds*; many short notes and comments in journals in Asia, Canada and UK; some 40 articles in regional bird reports in Canada and UK; also contributions to books. Member (inter alia): AOU, Federation of Canadian Naturalists, International Osprey Foundation, Pacific Seabird Group, Raptor Research Foundation, Seabird Group. OIR: global environmental conservation issues, travel, music (classical and traditional folk, both playing and listening), cross-country skiing, swimming and snorkelling on coral reefs, woodwork, gardening, camping, canoeing, back-packing. Canadian Wildlife Service, Environment Canada, 4905 rue Dufferin, Downsview, Ontario M3H 5T4, Canada. +1 416 7395846; fax +1 416 7395845.

EYRE, John Alton; *b:* 28 September 1945 in Ripley, Derbyshire; *w:* Sue. BSc Chemistry (Leeds, 1966), PhD Chemistry (Leeds, 1969). Post-doctoral Fellowship, Ohio State Univ 1969-71. FInstEnergy 1991. Research manager in oil industry. Chairman Hampshire Ornithological Society 1991-, and Chairman Field Studies Committee 1986-91. Past Chairman Chester and District Ornithological Society. BTO Research and Surveys Committee 1993-. Organiser of several surveys inc Hampshire tetrad atlas. Special interests: identification, breeding birds on lowland heaths. Widely travelled for birds in Australia, Asia, Europe, Africa, N and S America. Co-editor (with J M Clark) *Birds of Hampshire* (1993); asst editor *Hampshire Bird Report* 1988-90. Member: ABC, NBC. OIR: travel, photography, reading, science and technology. 3 Dunmow Hill, Fleet, Hants GU13 9AN. 01252 620141.

FAIRBANK, Richard John; *b:* 5 June 1954 in Bath, Somerset; *w:* Megan. BSc Statistics (Wales, 1976); MSc, MPhil Operational Research (Sussex, 1979, 1982). Planning Asst, University of Sussex. Sussex Ornithological Society: Council 1982-86, Asst Recorder 1982-86, Records Committee 1982-93, 1995-. Records Committee Isles of Scilly 1982-84. Special interests: migration; identification; tropical, sub-tropical and montane forests (esp S America, SE Asia). Further travel outside Western Palearctic inc Africa, Australia. Contributions on scarce migrants to *Birds in Sussex 1962-87* ed by G des Forges (1987); author of scarce/rare species accounts in *Sussex Bird Report* 1980 and 1982-, and in *Birds of Sussex* ed by Paul

James (1996); several identification-related notes in *British Birds* 1978-82. Member: ABC, NBC, OBC. Seen approx half the world's bird species. 19 Crown Road, Shoreham-by-Sea, W Sussex BN43 6GB. 01273 452969.

FAIRCLOUGH, Keith; *b:* 16 May 1952 in Liverpool; *w:* Shirley. BA Biological Sciences (Lancaster, 1972), Dip Ed (St Martins College, Lancaster, 1973). RSPB Senior Site Manager since 1992. Prev RSPB: Warden North Hoy 1984-91; asst warden Minsmere 1983-84, Balranald 1980-82; contract warden 1978-81. Ran school bird club, Motherwell 1970s. BTO 'C' ringer. Member of Orkney Ringing Group 1984-. Committee Orkney Field Club 1992-. Co-ordinator of several ornithological surveys during time with RSPB. Special interests: seabird and raptor ecology. Month in China (1989) based at Beidaihe, Hebei Province with aims of collecting data on migration (inc several Red Data Book species) and seeking to persuade the Chinese authorities to prevent further habitat loss and create an educational reserve and visitor centre; month in Tanzania (1995) as part of African Waterfowl Census based in Southern Highlands. Widely travelled for birds in Western Palearctic; also USA (Florida), Thailand, Sri Lanka, The Gambia. Regular broadcasts on radio and occasional TV news items. Articles in journals inc *Birding World, Ecos*. OIR: Orkney recorder for Odonata, Orthoptera, Coleoptera; passion for growing trees from native Orkney stock. 'Fortyish but still sportyish. Still keen hill walker but knees not too keen.' Viewforth, Swannay by Evie, Orkney KW17 2NR. 01856 721210.

FARRAR, André Robert; *b:* 9 January 1957 in Ashford, Kent; *w:* Helen Corbet. BSc Animal Physiology and Nutrition (Leeds, 1978), PhD Studies on magnesium metabolism (Leeds, 1982). RSPB Public Affairs Officer (NW England) since 1994. Prev RSPB: Conservation Officer 1988-94; Asst Regional Officer 1982-88; species protection warden 1982. Special interests: waders, wetland conservation. Articles on lowland raised mire conservation and the Mersey Barrage proposal in *RSPB Conservation Review*. Member: Liverpool Bay Wader Study Group (Chairman 1995-), Wader Study Group. OIR: searching for the perfect curry. Tara Court, 22 Sharp Lane, Almondbury, Huddersfield HD4 6SW. 01484 518840.

FEARNSIDE, John David (Jack); *b:* 1 March 1947 in Watford, Herts; *w:* Paula. BA Graphic Design (Ravensbourne College of Art and Design, 1968). Partner in LTD Design Consultancy. Committee Herts Bird Club 1992-, editor of its *Bulletin* 1992-, Rare Birds Panel 1994-. Co-editor (with K W Smith *et al*) *The Breeding Birds of Hertfordshire* (1993). Co-author (with R A Young and D H Russell) *Birds at Tring Reservoirs* (1996). Special interest: application of design to ornithological interests. 18 Wilcot Avenue, Oxhey, Watford WD1 4AT. 01923 237984.

FENTER, Dennis William; *b:* 25 January 1930 in Whalley Range, Manchester. Ashville College, Harrogate. Professional photographer 1954-77. Prev: medical technician 1948-54. Began caring for injured wild birds in 1971; formed Brent Lodge Bird and Wildlife Trust in 1978; completed construction of purpose-built wildlife hospital in Sidlesham with full surgical unit and washing unit for oiled birds. Steering Committee British Wildlife Rehabilitation Council 1990-95. OIR: listening to music; computers. Brent Lodge Bird and Wildlife Trust, Cow Lane, Sidlesham, Chichester, W Sussex PO20 7LN. 01243 641672.

FERGUSON-LEES, Ian James (James); *b:* 8 January 1929 in Italy; *w:* Karen. Executive Editor *British Birds* 1954-73; RSPB Deputy Director (Conservation) 1973-75; Director West Palaearctic Birds Ltd 1970-75. President and Chairman BTO 1969-73; earlier two terms on Council and one as Vice President; at various times 1950s-80s member of all BTO committees inc Populations and Surveys, Ringing; also Chairman 1967-85 of the working groups that planned the BTO Breeding Atlas and Winter Atlas, and member 1986-92 of the working group for the New Breeding Atlas; also member of working group set up in 1972 to plan BTO's Register of Ornithological Sites which led to R J Fuller's *Bird Habitats in Britain* (1982). BOU Council 1973-77; Records Committee 1960-86 (Chairman 1970-86). RSPB Council 1963-73, variously also Chairman of Conservation and Education Committees. Editorial Board *British Birds* 1952-79; in 1958 devised and (with P A D Hollom) founded the Rarities Committee, remained member until 1963; in 1973 (with David Lea) devised Rare Breeding Birds Panel, remained member until 1979. Member 1962-66 of British Executive Committee for XIV International Ornithological Congress, held in Oxford in July 1966. Planned and chaired international conference at Green Park, near Tring, in December 1971, held under joint auspices of BTO and Vogelwarte Radolfzell, Germany, to develop ornithological co-operation in Europe and standardise recording of nest records, habitat codings, biometrical and moult data, and other matters. At various times founding member and later Vice Chairman and Chairman Bedfordshire & Huntingdonshire NT; committee Bedfordshire NHS. Chairman Seychelles Bird Records Committee 1992-94. Committee Wiltshire Ornithological Society 1993-; Chairman Wiltshire Tetrad Atlas Group, started 1994. Special interests: identification, population, breeding biology, migration. Studies: raptors since 1946 (inc first Peregrine census in Britain and Ireland 1947-50); breeding biology and behaviour of the Dunnock 1950-55; Common Birds Census; and other census work, currently on Longleat Estate. Expeditions: Edinburgh University to St Kilda 1949; Mountfort to Coto Doñana 1956/57, Bulgaria 1960 and Jordan 1963/65; Anglo-Spanish to Cazorla 1959; International Jordan 1966; BOU to Lake Chad 1967/68. Other travel: widely in Europe, Africa, southern Asia, S America, eastern USA; led over 50 tours to Ukraine, Russia, Morocco, The Gambia, Ethiopia, Kenya, Seychelles, Jordan, Sri Lanka, Thailand, USA, 1970-87; private expeditions to S America (mainly Argentina) 1982-95. Collaborated in revised 2nd and 3rd editions of *A Field Guide to the Birds of Britain and Europe* by Peterson, Mountfort and Hollom (1965, 1974); with J L F Parslow, part-compiled *The Status of Birds in Britain and Ireland* ed by D W Snow (1971). Co-author of *A Field Guide to Birds' Nests* with Bruce Campbell (1972); *A Guide to Bird-watching in Europe* with Quentin Hockliffe and Ko Zweeres (1975, also Dutch ed); *BWP* Vol 1 with Stanley Cramp *et al* (1977); *The Shell Guide to the Birds of Britain and Ireland* with Ian Willis and J T R Sharrock (1983), also adapted as *Tirions Vogelgids* (1986) and *Vögel Mitteleuropas* (1987); *Endangered Birds* with Emma Faull (1992); *Raptors: a guide to the birds of prey of the world* with Kim Franklin *et al* (in press). Co-editor (with Bruce Campbell) and part-author *The Natural History of Britain and Northern Europe* (5 vols, 1978-79, also Dutch ed). Numerous notes, papers and articles in *British Birds* and other journals, magazines and newspapers, inc 'The Hastings Rarities' (1962, with E M Nicholson and J A Nelder). Regular broadcaster on birds in 1950s and 1960s, from which developed first concept of 'Recent reports' in *British Birds* (1958). BTO's Tucker Medal for work during 1967-76 on first Breeding Atlas. Began using tripod-mounted Mirador telescope in the field in 1972 and may thus have been the first in UK to carry a full-sized tripod for birding (short-draw Nickel telescopes had been tried earlier on monopods). Member: ABC, Cooper OS, Seychelles Bird Group. OIR: crosswords, occasional bridge or chess, gardening, very amateur photography, bird stamps, watching rubbish on TV. 4 Walnut Close, Rode, Bath BA3 6QA.

FERNS, Peter Norman; *b:* 3 May 1945 in Birmingham. BSc Zoology (Manchester, 1966), PhD Biology (Exeter, 1970). MIBiol 1969, CBiol 1984, MIEEM 1992. Senior Lecturer in Ecology University of Wales, College of Cardiff since 1988. Prev: Lecturer in Zoology, Univ Coll Cardiff 1971-88; Lecturer in Vertebrate Zoology, Univ Leicester 1970-71. Regional Co-ordinator of Welsh section of the Severn Estuary for the Birds of Estuaries

Enquiry 1972-90. Co-ordinator of the Wader Study Group Spring Passage Project on the migration of Dunlin, Sanderling, Ringed Plover and Turnstone through Britain, 1979. WWT Scientific Advisory Committee 1978-80, 1992-96. RSPB (Wales) Committee 1981-85. BTO Ringing and Migration Committee 1983-85. RSPB Council 1985-90. BTO 'A' ringer since 1974. Special interests: all aspects of avian ecology and behaviour; breeding biology and foraging behaviour of waterbirds; conservation and habitat management for birds. Member of Joint Biological Expedition to NE Greenland 1974 (breeding waders). Organiser 6th International Workshop on the Ecology of Shorebirds under the auspices of the IWRB 1983. Studied breeding sandgrouse in Spain in 1986, and at the Ben Gurion Univ of the Negev in Israel 1987. Author *Wading Birds of the Severn Estuary* (1977) and *Bird Life of Coasts and Estuaries* (1992); joint author *The Birds of Gwent* (1977). Over 60 papers on ecology of wading birds, wildfowl, gulls and sandgrouse published in British and overseas scientific journals inc *The Auk, Bird Study, Environmental Pollution, Wildfowl*. Member: Seabird Group, Severn Estuary Conservation Group (Chairman), Wader Study Group. OIR: archaeology, squash, opera, poetry. PABIO, University of Wales, College of Cardiff, PO Box 915, Cardiff CF1 3TL. 01222 874302.

FFRENCH (ffrench), Richard Patrick; MBE 1984, Trinidad Chaconia Medal 1984; *b:* 15 September 1929 in Aldershot, Hampshire; *w:* Margaret. MA Lit Hum (Balliol College, Oxford, 1954), Dip Ed (Oxford, 1955). Secondary school teacher (Deputy Principal 1976-84), retired. Trinidad and Tobago Field Naturalists' Club: President 1965, journal editor 1965-84. Trinidad and Tobago Wildlife Conservation Committee: ornithologist 1963-85. Bird bander (US Fish & Wildlife Service) 1959-85. Editor *Gloucestershire County Bird Report* 1991-95. Special interests: ornithology of Trinidad and Tobago, neotropical ornithology. Leader of tours to Trinidad and Tobago, Venezuela, Brazil, Ecuador, Belize, Costa Rica, Yucatan, Scottish Highlands and islands. Author *A Guide to the Birds of Trinidad and Tobago* (1973, 2nd ed 1991), *Birds of Trinidad and Tobago* (1986); joint author (with Peter Bacon) *Nature Trails of Trinidad* (1982). Articles in journals inc *Ibis, Living Bird, Wilson Bulletin*. Member: AOU, NBC. OIR: choral music. Buscombe Noake, Stump Lane, Chosen Hill, Hucclecote, Gloucester GL3 2LT. 01452 610005.

FIELD, Geoffrey Dingley; *b:* 24 August 1930 in Ceylon (Sri Lanka). Marlborough College 1944-48. BA Classics (Trinity Hall, Cambridge, 1953), MA 1958. University Lecturer/Senior Lecturer, Fourah Bay

College, Sierra Leone, retired. Many years W African fieldwork, esp Sierra Leone. Author *Birds of the Freetown Peninsula* (1974), *BOU Check-list of Birds of Sierra Leone* (in prep). Papers and notes on birds in Sierra Leone in eg *Bull BOC, Ibis, Malimbus, Ostrich*. Member: WAOS. 37 Milton Grove, New Milton, Hants BH25 6HB. 01425 614518.

FINDLEY, Peter William John; *b:* 28 October 1950 in Fareham, Hampshire; *w:* Jane. Taunton's Grammar School, Southampton. Christ Church College, Canterbury. Special educational needs teacher. Sandwich Bay Bird Observatory: Council since 1973, Trustee since 1990; other posts held inc Chairman, Secretary, Ringing Officer, Report Editor. Chairman Bird Observatories Council 1981-84. BTO Ringing and Migration Committee 1981-84. Hon Warden Sandwich Bay Nature Reserve 1980-85. Conservation Committee Kent TNC 1984-85. Special interests: migration, ringing, waders. BTO 'A' ringer since 1971. Christchurch Harbour Ringing Group 1967-68, Farlington RG 1967-70, Gull Study Group 1980-83. Member of SBBO expeditions to Morocco 1972 and 1979. Co-author *Seasonal Movements of Summer Migrants* (1981). Many papers since early 1970s in *Sandwich Bay Bird Observatory Trust Reports*; articles and notes in eg *Bird Watching, East Kent Mercury, Kent Bird Report, Ringers Bulletin*. Report to Thanet DC on shorebird migration and site fidelity 1979-89; reports to NCC for Stodmarsh surveys 1981-82, 1983-85, 1986-87. Illustrations for *Sandwich Bay Bird Observatory Report* and *Kent Bird Report*. Member: Wader Study Group, Wash Wader Ringing Group. OIR: driving daughters to parties; local and global 'green' issues. 75 Gladstone Road, Walmer, Deal, Kent CT14 7ET. 01304 379074.

FINNIS, Robert Gerald (Gerald); TD; *b:* 3 July 1921 in Margate, Kent; *w:* Olga (deceased 1974). King Alfred's College, Winchester. Teaching Cert 1949. Retired teacher (head of rural science). Founder-member Kent Ornithological Society, Secretary 1953-60, Hon Life Vice President. Special interests: migration, song, morphology of skull. In Egypt, Cyrenaica, S Italy 1941-45. Papers on migration in those countries for Egyptian Zoological Society (member 1941-43) also in *Ibis* and *Rivista Italiana di Ornithologia*; on other subjects in *Bird Study* and *Bull BOC*; skulls prepared for J G Harrison's various papers on pneumatisation in bird skulls. Forced to give up active ornithology by severe disablement due to multiple sclerosis. OIR: painting, mainly landscapes (several exhibitions locally). 90 Surrenden Road, Folkestone, Kent CT19 4AQ. 01303 275834.

FIRMIN, Joseph (Joe); *b:* 2 July 1926 in Fordham, Essex; *w:* Linda. Colchester Royal Grammar School. Agricultural and environmental journalist and author. Regular columnist for Essex newspapers, *Essex Countryside* and *Essex Wildlife*. Founder, Vice-President, Past President Colchester NHS; founder and past committee member Essex Birdwatching Society. Co-ordinator of field surveys and censuses in NE Essex since 1954. Special interests: habitat management and ecological changes affecting birds, their distribution and migration in Britain and Europe; protection of endangered species worldwide and creation of public awareness of and support for conservation; leader of birdwatching and wildlife study groups in E Anglia, southern France and Denmark. Author of *Your Bird Table Book* (1978), *Birds of Prey* (Factfinders series, 1979), *Sea Birds* (Factfinders series, 1980), *Popular Garden Birds* (1988, repr 1992); author and editor of National Trust Nature Notebooks series (10 titles), also of Dinosaur Publications' *Birds*, Nos 1 and 2; editor and main contributor *Nature in Essex* (transactions of Colchester NHS) 1953-75. Member: Association Régionale pour la Protection des Oiseaux et de la Nature (Provence, Alpes, Côte d'Azur et Corse), Conservatoire et Etude des Ecosystèmes de Provence (CEEP). 55 Chapel Road, West Bergholt, Colchester CO6 3HZ. 01206 241389.

FISHER, David John; *b:* 13 December 1954 in Cardiff. Cert Ed Environmental Science etc (Weymouth College of Education, 1976). Managing Director, Sunbird since 1982. Prev: RSPB Activities Organiser for YOC 1977-81. Glamorgan Records Committee several years in late 1970s. East African Rarities Committee and Seychelles Records Committee. Special interests: identification and distribution of the world's birds; recording bird song in many countries (all recordings donated to National Sound Archive, Wildlife Section, British Library). Editor of 'Birdwatchers' Guide to' series; articles in eg *Birding World, British Birds*. Member: ABC, NBC, OBC, OSME (Council 1978-88). 56 Western Way, Sandy, Beds SG19 1DU. 01767 682377.

FISHER, John Bower; *b:* 14 January 1926 in Hazel Grove, Cheshire; *w:* Lucy Ann. BSc (Eng) (London, 1947). MIEE 1954. Retired Chartered Electrical Engineer. Hon Sec Wildlife Sound Recording Society 1969-77; editor of *WSRS Journal* 1970-78. Special interest: wildlife sound recording involving travel in Europe, Australasia, E Africa, USA. Author *Wildlife Sound Recording* (1978); contributions to *Song Birds* by Edward Percy (1974). Articles in *J Brit Institute of Recorded Sound* and *J Wildlife Sound Recording Soc.* Recordist and publisher of audio cassettes: *Australian Birds*

(1984), *More Australian Birds* (1984), *Beginners' British Birds* (1986), *More British Birds* (1986), *My Favourite Birds* (1986), *East African Safari* (1988). Winner of Class I (Individual Bird Species) European Broadcasting Union Wildlife Tape Recording Competition 1970. Founder-member Wildlife Sound Recording Society. Inventor and manufacturer of Fisher Collapsible Microphone Reflector. OIR: golf and gardening. Chadswell, Sandy Lane, Tilford, Farnham, Surrey GU10 2ET. 01252 792673.

FITTER, Richard Sidney Richmond; *b:* 1 March 1913 in Streatham, London; *w:* Alice Mary (Maisie) (deceased). Eastbourne College. BSc (Econ) (London School of Economics, 1933). Director, Intelligence Unit, Council for Nature 1959-63. Prev: Asst Editor, *The Countryman* 1946-59; Secretary to Wildlife Conservation Special Committee of the Hobhouse National Parks Committee 1945-46 (whose report led to the creation of the Nature Conservancy). IUNC (now World Conservation Union): Steering Committee, Chairman, Member of Honour since 1963. BTO: Hon Secretary, Hon Treasurer, Council c1941-1950s. RSPB: Council, Chairman of Finance & General Purposes Committee c1948-c1968. Fauna & Flora Preservation Society: Vice President, Chairman, Vice-Chairman, Hon Secretary, Council since 1952. Royal Society for Nature Conservation (now The Wildlife Trusts): Council 1960s-1992. ICBP (now BirdLife International): representative successively of RSPB, FFPS and RSNC on British Section from 1950s until Section wound up. Berks, Bucks & Oxon Naturalists' Trust: President, Vice President, Chairman, Hon Secretary since 1959. London NHS: Chairman, Hon Secretary of Ornithological Section, also Editor of *London Naturalist/Bird Report*, 1935-46. Special interests: identification, introduced birds, Black Redstart (for which once ran an inquiry for BTO), Black Woodpecker. Author of *London's Natural History* (1945; pbk c1985), *The Starling* (1946), *London's Birds* (1949), *Pocket Guide to British Birds* illus by R A Richardson (1952; rev ed 1966), *The Natural History of the City* with J E Lousley (1953), *Birds of Town and Village* (1953), *Pocket Guide to Nests and Eggs* illus by R A Richardson (1954, rev ed 1968), *Fontana Bird Guide* illus by R A Richardson (1956), *Your Book of Bird Watching* (1958), *The Ark in Our Midst* (introduced birds and other wildlife in Britain) (1959), *Guide to Bird Watching* (1963, 2nd ed 1970), *Britain's Wildlife: rarities* (1966), *Birds of Britain & Europe with North Africa & the Middle East* with J Parslow, illus by H Heinzel (1972, 4th ed 1979, comp new ed 1995), plus other natural history books which include birds. Editor of *British Birds in Colour* (1951), *Book of British Birds* (1969), *John Clare's Birds* with Eric Robinson (1982). Numerous articles in eg *Birding World, British Birds, Bull BOC, Country Life, The Countryman*.

Editor of *London Bird Report* 1939-44 (latterly with E R Parrinder) and 'Birds in Surrey' in *South-eastern Bird Report* 1940. Member of Honour, Species Survival Commission, IUCN. Member: OSME. OIR: other aspects of natural history, esp other vertebrates and wild flowers; cataloguing bird and other wildlife inn signs. Drifts, Chinnor Hill, Chinnor, Oxon OX9 4BS. 01844 351223.

FITZPATRICK, John; *b:* 17 November 1930 in Tottenham, London; *w:* Margaret. Retired engineer. Bird Recorder Metropolitan Essex 1974-90. Essex Birdwatching Society: Recording Committee and member of editorial team. London NHS: Recording Committee, Research Committee. Wildfowl and wader counter Dengie peninsula 1959-72 and Lea valley reservoirs 1972-96. Heronry counter at Walthamstow reservoirs 1961-66. Local organiser of BTO Breeding Atlas and Winter Atlas. Field meeting leader and report writer for Lea valley in *Essex Birds* twice yearly. Special interests: bird population surveys, bird song studies, identification and distribution. Bird-related travel to four continents. Contributions to various county bird reports and other publications, inc *British Birds* and *Birds of Essex* by Simon Cox (1984). Member: OBC. OIR: many other natural history subjects. 18 Edwick Court, High Street, Cheshunt, Herts EN8 0AB. 01992 639956.

FLATTERS, Edward (Ted); *b:* 21 November 1937; *w:* Julie. Retired Civil Servant. City & Guilds Photography Final, 1965. Ornithological adviser to Lewell Conservation Project 1990-. General Purposes Committee Portland Bird Observatory & Field Study Centre 1990-95. Management Committee South Dorset Group of Dorset WT 1995. Formerly Committee RSPB South Dorset Group, Lulworth Ranges MOD Conservation Group, Bovington Camp Conservation Group, all for ten years. BTO 'A' ringer since 1982 and two years as trainer. Special interest: project to enhance farmland habitat, with particular emphasis on passerines. Annual project reports. Past appearances on local radio and regional TV. OIR: bowls. 7 Britannia Way, Castle Park, Dorchester, Dorset DT1 2QR. 01305 265564.

FLEMING, Jack; *b:* 16 March 1958 in Edinburgh. Berwickshire High School 1970-76, Oatridge College 1980-82. Founder-member of Institute of Agricultural Management. MIAgrM 1992. Farm Manager RSPB Loch Gruinart Reserve 1986-94; Area Reserves Manager Dumfries & Galloway since 1994 with nationwide advisory role. Special interest: the integration of practical land management with conservation/ornithological requirements. Articles in *Luing Cattle Society Journal*, *Scottish Farmer*. Interviews on local, national radio and World Service, also TV. OIR: rugby (qualified Scottish Rugby Union Club coach), tennis, keep fit, music, reading, travel, film, theatre. Mersehead, Southwick, Dumfries DG2 8AH. 01387 780298.

FLETCHER, Mark Richard; *b:* 8 August 1948 in London; *w:* Susan. BSc Applied Biology (Hatfield Polytechnic, 1971). MIBiol 1975, CBiol. Head, Wildlife Incident Unit, Central Science Laboratory since December 1990. Prev: MAFF 1972-79. Work concerned with effects of pesticides on wildlife. BTO Ringing and Migration Committee 1982-85. Compiler of Surrey Ringing Report 1981-85. Co-ordinator of London Gull Study Group from c1974. Chairman and initiator Gull Study Group from 1979 until merger with Seabird Group in 1984. Cannon Netting Advisory Panel 1984-89. Special interests: pesticide effects on birds; diseases of birds; movements, migrations and identification of gulls; waders; Mandarin Duck. BTO 'A' ringer since 1975, trainer and cannon net licence holder. Member of Dutch-Mauritanian Project, Banc d'Arguin 1985. Author of several papers, book chapters and articles. Member: London Gull Study Group, Wader Study Group, Wash Wader Ringing Group. OIR: skiing. Wildlife Incident Unit, Central Science Laboratory, Sandhutton, York YO4 1LW.

FLUMM, David Steven; *b:* 13 October 1952 in Brighton, E Sussex; *w:* Gerda. OND Science (Brighton Tech Coll, 1980), BSc Zoology with Marine Zoology (Univ Wales, Bangor, 1983). RSPB Warden Marazion Marsh and Hayle Estuary since 1990. Previous occupations (1970-90) include first warden at Rye Harbour LNR, catalogued Bentley Wildfowl Collection, ornithological survey of the Hayle Estuary, work for Peter Harrison on his book *Seabirds of the World*, RSPB Information Warden in W Cornwall, WWT 'Shooting Disturbance' project, investigation of seabird deaths in W Cornwall. Records and Scientific Committee Sussex Ornithological Society 1969-72. County organiser: BTO Winter Shorebird Count 1984/85, WWT National Wildfowl Counts 1984-91, BTO National Cormorant Survey 1986/87, BTO Birds of Estuaries Enquiry 1989-91. Conservation Officer for Cornwall Birdwatching & Preservation Society 1988-89 and YOC Leader for RSPB in Cornwall. Special interest: identification. Expeditions of 2-4 months in 1970s in Europe and Scandinavia, Turkey, N Africa and the Canary Islands. In 1973 discovered (with N A G Lord) the now famous autumn raptor passage route through the Pontine Mountains. Later travels to Florida and India, esp as tour leader. Articles and notes in *Birding World* and *British Birds*, and author of *A Guide to the Wildlife of the Hayle Estuary* (1988). Regular contributor to BBC's Wildlife News Service on Ceefax in late 1980s. OIR: all aspects of natural history. 6 Beacon Crescent, Sancreed, Penzance, Cornwall TR20 8QR. 01736 810783.

FORMAGGIA, Robert (Bob); *b:* 14 April 1938 in Greenford, Middx; *w:* Hazel. Sales manager (engineering). Special interest: Barn Owl conservation. Local adviser with Barn Owl Conservation Network for Montomeryshire and Radnorshire since 1991, inc recording of breeding sites and monitoring breeding success. Active in habitat improvement through local farmers, Forest Enterprise, National Rivers Authority/ Environment Agency and others; also extensive nestbox programme throughout the two counties. OIR: photography. Dolfallen Newydd, Llawr-y-Glyn, Caersws, Powys SY17 5RJ. 01686 430674.

FORRESTER, Bruce Campbell; *w:* Eleanor. Teacher of Art. Member of Scottish Birds Records Committee and Ayrshire Bird Records Committee. Special interests: Brazilian birds and twitching in UK. Author and illustrator of *Birding Brazil: a check-list and site guide* (1993). Co-compiler of *Birds of Ayrshire* (1983). Articles in *Stonechat* (pub by SOC Ayrshire Branch, of which formerly Secretary and Chairman) and *Scottish Bird News*. Artwork shown in several exhibitions. Member: NBC. Knockshinnoch Bungalow, Rankinston, Ayrshire KA6 7HL. 01292 590274.

FORRESTER, Ronald William (Ron); *b:* 15 March 1948 in Liverpool; *w:* Edith. Eastwood High School, Renfrewshire. MCIBS 1970. Bank manager. Secretary Scottish Birds Records Committee since 1987. SOC Council 1985-91. Bird Recorder for Ayrshire, Renfrewshire, Bute, Dunbartonshire, Lanarkshire and W Stirlingshire 1972-74. Special interests: identification, distribution, photography. Bird-related travel in five continents (inc Kenya, Senegal, Morocco, Turkey, Trinidad, Venezuela). Edited *Clyde Bird Report* 1973 and 1974. Member: ABA, NBC, OBC. OIR: sport and hill walking. 31 Argyle Terrace, Rothesay, Isle of Bute PA20 0BD. 01700 505352.

FORSHAW, Wilfred Derek (Derek); *b:* 28 November 1946 in Southport; *w:* Rosalind. Public Health Inspectors Diploma, Liverpool, 1971. MCIEH 1971. Senior Environmental Health Officer. RSPB Group Leader Wigan 1978-82. Special interest: geese (esp Pink-footed), swans and gulls. Introduced and leader of Pink-footed Goose counts in Lancashire and N Merseyside 1977-; also independent studies of the species in Lancashire since 1971. Studied geographical origins of gulls wintering on N Merseyside coast by sighting of ring numbers 1982-89. Report on geese and swans in

Lancashire published annually since 1978. Various articles on geese and swans in *British Birds, Brit Ecol Soc Bull, Cheshire Bird Report, Lancashire Bird Report, Lapwing, WAGBI Magazine, Wildfowl World*. Major paper: 'Numbers, distribution and behaviour of Pink-footed Geese in Lancashire', *Wildfowl*, No 34. OIR: music, reading, model making. 46 Bakers Lane, Southport, Merseyside PR9 9RN. 01704 26462.

FORSMAN, Dick Kenneth Vindician; *b:* 26 February 1953 in Helsinki, Finland; *w:* Inki. Studies in Zoology and Genetics at Univ Helsinki 1974-84. Co-founder and Manager, Earlybird Birding Tours in Finland since 1990; freelance writer, bird photographer and artist since 1985. Prev: presenter of wildlife programmes at Finnish Broadcasting Corporation 1981-90; Research Asst Finnish Game and Fisheries Research Institute 1975-81. Ringers' Council 1978-89. Finnish Rarities Committee 1984-95 (Chairman 1994-95). Identification consultant *Birding World* 1988- and consulting editor *Dutch Birding* and *Limicola*. One of the founders and an editor of Finnish birding magazine *Alula*. Special interests: identification (esp birds of prey), moult studies, raptor ecology, bird photography, drawing and painting birds. Population studies on Goshawk, Buzzard and Eagle Owl in S Finland 1976-84. Travelled extensively in W Palearctic, with over 20 trips to Israel and numerous tours each to Greece, Spain and Turkey; also wide experience of the Nordic countries with many trips to Arctic regions since 1975. Author of several bird books in Finnish, and editor or photographic editor of others; also author of *Handbook to the Identification of the Raptors of Europe and the Middle East* (in press) and co-author (with P Burton and I Lewington) *Birds of Prey of Britain and Europe* (in press). Tens of articles on bird identification in Finnish, Swedish, English, Dutch, German and Italian birdwatching magazines, and articles on birds in several books. Bird photographs published in magazines and books in over ten countries, eg in *The Hamlyn Photographic Guide to the Birds of Britain and Europe* (1988), *The Hamlyn Photographic Guide to the Waders of the World* (1995), *Birds of Prey of Japan* by Teruaki Morioka (1995), *The Birds of Israel* by Hadoram Shirihai (1996). Bird paintings exhibited in Finland in 1988, 1989, 1995. Member: ABA, BirdLife Finland, Finnish Wildlife Photographers' Union, OSME, Swedish Ornithological Society. OIR: sea trout fishing. Box 25, Fin-02421 Jorvas, Finland. +358 (0)9 2963353 or 2961280; mobile +358 (0)400 441704; fax +358 (0)9 2963464.

FORSYTH, Ian; *b:* 27 November 1949 in Malta. HM Inspector of Taxes. Recorder for Tophill Low Nature Reserve 1981-93. Chairman Tophill Low Wildlife Group 1994-. Recorder for Vice-County 61, E Yorkshire since

1993. Special interests: migration and identification, waders and seabirds. Travel for birds to N America, Middle East, Far East and much of Europe. Editor of Tophill Low Nature Reserve annual reports 1981-93. OIR: watching sport (esp test cricket, rugby, football); listening to music from classical to pop. 65 Priory Road, Cottingham, E Yorkshire HU16 4RR. 01482 875583.

FORSYTH, John (Ian); *b:* 4 August 1929 in Perth, Scotland; *w:* Pamela. Perth Academy. BSc Zoology (Aberdeen, 1952). MIBiol 1952, CBiol. Senior Lecturer in Natural History, Inst Continuing Education, Queen's Univ of Belfast, retired 1994. Chairman North Down Ringing Group since 1975. Committee Copeland Bird Observatory 1974-77. BTO Ringing Committee 1982-86. Organiser for Northern Ireland of BTO Rookery Survey 1975, BTO/IWC Corncrake Survey 1976, BTO Winter Atlas Survey 1981-84. Common Birds Census plot since 1970. Special interest: study of the movement of Irish breeding and wintering birds from a programme of ringing. Active member of Copeland Bird Observatory and North Down Ringing Group, helping to run a Constant Effort Site. Editor of Irish Ringing Report since 1977, published annually in *Irish Birds*. From 1970-75, with BTO Ringing Office, organised a series of annual 10-day ringing courses at QUB Field Centre. Founder-member of Ulster TNC (now Ulster WT) and deeply involved in purchase by UWT of Isle of Muck, Co Antrim, an important seabird colony. OIR: bats, gardening, DIY. 24 Malone Park, Belfast BT9 6NJ. 01232 665534.

FOWLER, James Allan (Jim); *b:* 13 December 1943 in Cardiff; *w:* Eurgain. BSc Biochemistry (Wales, Cardiff, 1965), PhD Biochemistry (Wales, Cardiff, 1969). MIBiol 1969, CBiol 1980, FRES 1986. Principal Lecturer in Environmental Science, De Montfort University, Leicester; post involves research and supervision of undergraduate, MPhil and PhD programmes in ornithology (subjects inc use of disused gravel workings by birds, urban Starling roosts, swan parasites, and analysis of records at Dungeness Bird Observatory). Prev: Leader, Vanda Station, Antarctica (New Zealand Antarctic Research Programme) 1972-73. Secretary Ornithological Society of New Zealand 1973-75. BTO Council 1980-83. BTO 'A' ringer since 1975 and trainer. Special interests: seabirds, esp Storm Petrel, Fulmar; ectoparasites, esp feather lice. Leader of 20 consecutive annual expeditions to Shetland to undertake environmental (inc ornithological) monitoring near the Shetland Oil Terminal. Co-author (with L Cohen) of BTO Guide *Statistics for Ornithologists* (1986, 2nd ed 1995). About 80 ornithological papers in eg *Bird Study, Ecological Entomology, Ringing & Migration*,

Scottish Birds, Seabird. Editor of *Ringing & Migration* 1989-95. Numerous conference presentations. OIR: sea fishing; classical music and ballet; learning Welsh and French languages. Hafod Heli, High Street, Borth, Dyfed SY24 5JE. 01970 871347.

FRANCIS, Christopher John (Chris); *b:* 30 September 1962 in Birmingham; *w:* Michele. BSc Zoology & Plant Science (Univ Coll Cardiff, 1984), PGCE 1986. Centre Manager, The Wildfowl & Wetlands Trust, Washington Centre since 1991; prev Deputy Manager/Education Officer 1989-91. Bulletin editor, West Midland Bird Club 1988-89. Special interests: captive breeding, environmental education. OIR; cricket, genealogy. Middle Barmston Farm, District 15, Washington, Tyne & Wear NE38 8LE. 0191 4162836.

FRANCIS, Ian; *b:* 31 August 1959 in Sheffield. BA Geography (Sheffield, 1980), PhD Blanket peat bog erosion and afforestation (Univ Wales, Aberystwyth, 1987). Conservation Officer, Grampian, RSPB since 1992. Prev: Project Leader, Biological Survey of Common Land, NCC/UCW Aberystwyth, 1987-90; Conservation Officer, Berks, Bucks & Oxon Naturalists' Trust 1985-87. Joint co-ordinator Greenland White-fronted Goose Study 1985-. Surveys of rainforest birds, Uganda/Ivory Coast 1990-92. Special interests: Greenland White-fronted Goose (Winston Churchill Travelling Fellowship 1986, Iceland); Lapland Bunting; African forest birds. Papers in eg *Bird Cons Internat, Bird Study, Ibis, Ringing & Migration, Wildfowl*; various articles in magazines inc *BBC Wildlife, Birds, Geographical Magazine.* RSPB East Scotland Regional Office, 10 Albyn Terrace, Aberdeen AB1 1YP. 01224 624824.

FRAY, Robert Michael (Rob); *b:* 20 February 1970 in Leicester. Manor High School, Oadby 1975-81. Beauchamp College, Oadby 1984-88. Insurance broker. County Recorder Leicestershire since 1995. Committee Leics and Rutland Orn Soc 1990-, co-editor annual report 1992-, editor monthly newsletter 1991-95, Referees' Sub-committee 1994-. County Wetland Bird Survey organiser 1992-95. Many 'local patch' studies, inc database of own records and others from annual reports for three sites going back to 1941. Others include the effect of Cormorants on angling and other recreational activities at Rutland Water, and a study of an area in NW Leics which was to have been developed by British Coal. Articles in county's annual reports and regular contributor to *Bird Watching* on local sightings. Young Ornithologist of the Year in 1984 and 1985. OIR: watching Leicester City FC. 5 New Park Road, Leicester LE2 8AW. 0116 223 8491.

FROST, Roy Anthony; *b:* 3 October 1943 in Chesterfield, Derbys. BEd (Nottingham, 1987). Formerly teacher. Joint County Recorder for Derbyshire, with special responsibility for rare breeding birds, since 1981; former annual report editor. Rarities Committee of Derbyshire Ornithological Committee since 1965 and of Sheffield Bird Study Group since 1973. Special interests: breeding biology and performance of local breeding birds; visible migration, esp over S Pennines. BTO 'C' ringer since 1983. Ringer with Sorby-Breck Ringing Group 1980-. Widely travelled for birds in four continents. Author *Birds of Derbyshire* (1978). Co-author (with D Herringshaw) *Birdwatching in the Dukeries & North Nottinghamshire* (1979) and *Birdwatching in the Sheffield Area* (1981); also (with Steve and Andrew Shaw) *A Derbyshire Wildlife Guide* (1990). OIR: Butterfly Recorder for Derbyshire and editor of annual butterfly report embracing N & E Midlands; Orthoptera Recorder for Derbyshire; other natural history; folk music; home brewing; watching cricket. 66 St Lawrence Road, North Wingfield, Chesterfield, Derbys S42 5LL. 01246 850037.

FRY, Charles Hilary (Hilary); *b:* 13 February 1937 in Skegness; *w:* Kathleen. BA Zoology (Cambridge, 1960), MA 1963, PhD Bee-eater sociobiology (Ahmadu Bello, Nigeria, 1966), DSc for publications in African ornithology (Aberdeen, 1985). Professor of Biology, Sultan Qaboos University 1986-95. Retired 1995 with Hon Professorship in Zoology, Aberdeen Univ. Prev: Lecturer/Senior Lecturer in Zoology, Aberdeen Univ 1967-86; Lecturer in Zoology, Ahmadu Bello Univ 1962-67. Originator of Nigerian Ornithologists' Society (later West African OS) and editor of its journal *Malimbus* 1964-85. BOU Council in late 1970s. Special interests: bee-eaters and kingfishers, also rollers and songbirds; all aspects of ornithology in Africa and in tropics generally; systematics, relationships at high and low taxonomic levels, geographical differentiation and speciation; migration. Bird expeditions: Annobon Island, Gulf of Guinea, three months in 1958. Three ringing expeditions to Lake Chad and one to Lake Turkana. Two months of exploratory ornithological travel in Mato Grosso State, Brazil, 1969. Central section of African Great Rivers Hovercraft Expedition, 1969, counting waterbirds. Two-week study of Eleonora's Falcon on Dragonada Island, Crete, 1976. Attendee at most International Ornithological Congresses and Pan-African OCs since 1960, and contributor to all of latter. Fieldwork on bee-eaters and kingfishers in 16 countries in 5 continents. Over 150 papers and articles in European and African periodicals. Author *The Bee-eaters* (1984). Joint author (with K Fry and A Harris) *Kingfishers, Bee-eaters and Rollers* (1992). Advisory Editor for *The Birds of Africa* Vol 1 (1982) and co-editor (with S Keith and

E Urban) of Vols 2-5 (1986-95), also author of 207 species accounts and co-author of 122. Invited by Southern African Ornithological Society to give Inaugural Cecily Niven Memorial Lecture, delivered in Port Elizabeth 1994. Member: AOU, Cooper OS, EANHS, OA Zimbabwe, OSME, Soc d'Etudes Ornithologiques, Southern African OS, WAOS, Wilson OS, Zambian OS. OIR: watercolour sketching, seashells. Bridge End House, Kentmere, Kendal, Cumbria LA8 9JP. 01539 821506.

FULLER, Robert John (Rob); *b:* 29 November 1950 in Aylesbury, Bucks; *w:* Angela. Cavendish Technical Grammar School, Hemel Hempstead. BSc Zoology (Imperial College, London, 1973), PhD Bird community ecology (London, 1987). Director of Habitats Research BTO since 1988. Prev BTO: Head of Populations Section 1983-87, Research Officer 1979-82, National Organiser of Register of Ornithological Sites 1973-78. Founder Chairman Buckinghamshire Bird Club 1981-84. Secretary International Bird Census Committee 1983-87. Bucks, Berks & Oxon NT Conservation Committee 1986-89. BOU Council 1995-. Special interests: habitat selection in birds; effects of habitat management on birds; responses of birds to land-use change; woodland birds; breeding waders of the Hebridean machair; wintering Lapwing and Golden Plover. Research mainly in British woodlands but also in Bialowieza National Park, a primeval forest in E Poland. Books: *Bird Habitats in Britain* (1982) and *Bird Life of Woodland and Forest* (1995). Booklets (with M S Warren): *Coppiced Woodlands: their management for wildlife* (1990, 2nd ed 1993) and *Woodland Rides and Glades: their management for wildlife* (1990, 2nd ed 1993). Approximately 50 scientific papers in journals or as chapters in books. OIR: angling, music and the visual arts, riding motorcycles, enjoying the British countryside. BTO, The Nunnery, Thetford, Norfolk IP24 2PU. 01842 750050.

FURPHY, Joseph Sands (Joe); *b:* 11 July 1937 in Banbridge, N Ireland; *w:* Margaret. BA Geography (Queen's Univ Belfast, 1960). Chief Conservation Officer, Environment Service, Dept of the Environment for Northern Ireland since 1990. Former BTO Regional Representative for N Ireland. Organiser of BTO Breeding Atlas 1968-72 for N Ireland. IWC Council 1970s-early '80s. Member of former Northern Ireland Bird Records Committee. Special interest: distribution studies. Material published in *Irish Naturalists' Journal* from 1961, and *Irish Birds* from 1974. Regular broadcaster 1970-mid 1980s on wide range of conservation issues/wildlife magazine programmes. OIR: church organist; railway history; hill and coast walking. 119 Greystown Avenue, Upper Malone, Belfast BT9 6UH. 01232 612311.

FURSE, John Richard Chris (Chris); OBE 1987, Polar Medal 1988; Commander RN Retd; *b:* 10 June 1935 in Chippenham, Wilts; *w:* Victoria. RN Engineering College Manadon 1955-59. RN College Greenwich 1961-63. Dagger Marine Engineer 1963. FRGS. Author; illustrator/artist; youth expedition leader. Special interests: drawing birds in action; penguins and other polar seabirds (populations and ecology). Polar expeditions: Joint Services to Elephant Island 1970-71 (ornithologist); Joint Services to Elephant Island Group 1976-77 (leader and ornithologist); Joint Services to Brabant Island 1983-85 (leader and ornithologist); British Schools Exploring Society to Svalbard 1987 (leader), 1993 (logistics) and 1996 (leader). Author *Elephant Island* (1979), *Antarctic Year* (1986); contributor to *Distribution of Penguins, Antarctic Peninsula* by Croxall and Kirkwood (1979). Articles in eg *BAS Bulletin, Geographical Journal, Ibis, Sea Swallow.* Illustrations in Patterson's *The Shelduck* (1982), *Ardea, The Countryman, Kent Bird Report, Sea Swallow* and own books. Photographs in *British Birds,* own books and articles. Two TV documentaries on polar expeditions, including wildlife. Awarded Busk Medal of Royal Geographical Society in 1986. Member: Antarctic Club, RN Birdwatching Society, Seabird Group. OIR: writing, drawing, rebuilding ruins, mountaineering, skiing, kayaking. Hegg Hill Oast, Smarden, Kent TN27 8NX. 01233 770360. Also C'an Boley, 12 Barri Sa Creu, S'Arraco, Andratx, Mallorca.

GALE, John; *b:* 28 May 1964 in Reading, Berks. Leighton Park School, Reading 1977-83. BVSc (Liverpool, 1989), MRCVS. Bird illustrator/artist. Veterinary surgeon (part-time). Travel in SE Asia, E Africa. Illustrated *Birds of Mount Kinabalu* by W H Davison (1992), *Field Guide to the Birds of the Middle East* by R F Porter *et al* (1996), *The Avifauna of the Malay Peninsula* by D R Wells (in prep). Pictures also in various bird reports and journals. Bird Illustrator of the Year (*British Birds*) 1992. OIR: general natural history (esp mammals). Bryn Hebok, Castell Fflemish, Tregaron, Ceredigion SY25 6LL.

GALE, John Ashton Bradley; *b:* 16 January 1917 in Bridport, Dorset. Sir William Turner's School, Coatham. MA Modern History (New College, Oxford, 1935-38). Retired social work administrator. Voluntary warden of Pett Pools Wildlife Reserve (Sussex Orn Soc) since 1989. Secretary Hastings and East Sussex NHS. Special interest: birds of Pett Level, esp migratory waders. Editor of *The Hastings and East Sussex Naturalist* since 1979, and of the annual report of the Pett Pools Project (for Sussex OS) since 1987. OIR: natural history in general, Swedish literature. Argosy, 11 Rockmead Road, Fairlight, Hastings, E Sussex TN35 4DJ. 01424 812240.

GALLAGHER, Michael; Major Retd; MBE 1994, for services to conservation; *b:* 3 September 1921 in Beddington, Surrey. Public school (ISC) and Army. FRGS 1975, FLS 1994. Curator Oman Natural History Museum since 1982. Prev: Asst Adviser (Field Studies), Office of the Adviser for Conservation of the Environment, The Palace, Muscat, 1977-81. Hon Sec Christmas Island (Pacific) Nat Hist Soc and Editor *Bull CINHS* 1958-59. Co-founder member and Hon Sec Rheindahlen Birdwatching Society (BAOR) 1967-68. Co-ordinator Arabian Gulf Birdwatchers and Editor *The Gulf Birdwatchers' Newsletter* 1969-71. Hon Sec Oman Bird Group and Oman Bird Records Committee, and Editor *Oman Bird News* Nos 1-19, 1977-96. Field studies: two ornithological expeditions within UAE, 1970, 1971 (leader); expedition to Oman's mountains 1973 (leader); Zaïre River Expedition 1974-75 (member for ornithology etc); Oman Flora & Fauna Survey No 1 Jabal Akhdar April 1975 (member for admin, birds etc); reconnaissance for Oman FFS No 2 (1976); Oman FFS No 2 Dhofar Sept-Oct 1977 (leader); RGS Oman Wahiba Sands Project 1985-87 (member for ornithology etc); fieldwork for nat hist exhibitions, environmental studies and ornithology of Oman since 1977. Author *The Birds of Oman* (1980, Arabic ed 1985). Many papers and articles in eg *Bull BOC, Ibis, J Oman Stud, J RAF Orn Soc, Sandgrouse, Sea Swallow, Vulture News.* Stamford Raffles Award, Zoological Society of London 1983 for 'contributions to zoology, in particular to Arabian ornithology.' OIR: botany, entomology, reptiles, cetaceans, skiing. Oman Natural History Museum, PO Box 668, Muscat 113, Sultanate of Oman. +968 605400; fax +968 602735.

GALLOWAY, Bryan; *b:* 28 February 1943 in Newcastle upon Tyne; *w:* Margaret. Heaton Grammar School 1954-61. BSc Chemical Engineering (Newcastle, 1964). Pharmaceuticals production manager. Founder-member Tyneside Bird Club (now Northumberland and Tyneside BC); also committee member 1958-88 holding several posts including Chairman. Northumberland County Recorder 1970-78. BTO 'A' ringer since 1962. Founder of Low Hauxley Ringing Station in 1962 (with Brian Little). Founder-member Northumbria Ringing Group in 1963 and Secretary since 1981. WEA ornithology tutor since 1974. Member Northumberland Breeding Atlas Committee 1987-95. Northumberland Red Data Book Committee 1995-96. Organised Peregrine nest-site wardening 1984-85. Special interests: monitoring breeding populations of raptors (esp Merlin, Peregrine) in Northumberland, commenced 1962; monitoring Pied Flycatchers nesting in boxes in Northumberland, commenced 1977; monitoring breeding species on MOD training area at Otterburn and developing nestbox scheme there to attract a range of species; set up a Constant Effort Ringing Site at Seaton Burn, Tyne and Wear. Co-author *Birds in Northumbria* (annual report) 1970-78, and co-author (with E R Meek) *Northumberland's Birds* (in parts, 1978-86). Ornithology guide for holiday company during summer holidays at various sites in France 1983-90. OIR: fell walking, gardening. 34 West Meadows, Westerhope, Newcastle upon Tyne NE5 1LS. 0191 286 4850.

GALSWORTHY, Anthony Charles (Tony); CMG 1985; *b:* 20 December 1944 in London; *w:* Jan. St Paul's School. BA Classics (Corpus Christi College, Cambridge, 1966), MA 1973. Diplomatic Service. BTO 'A' ringer since 1989. Special interest: ringing and migration studies. Secretary Hong Kong Ringing Group 1990-93. Ringing reports in *Hong Kong Bird Report* 1990-93 and article on *Locustella* warblers in *HKBR* 1990. OIR: Lepidoptera. c/o FCO, King Charles Street, London SW1A 2AH. 0171 270 0370.

GAMBLE, David James S (Dave); *b:* 31 December 1949 in Hereford; *w:* Janet. Electrician. Wildfowl Count organiser for Leicestershire 1986-91. Committee Leics and Rutland Ornithological Society since 1983; various posts inc Referees' Committee 1986-91. Editor *Birds of Leicestershire & Rutland* (annual report) 1985-91. Fieldnotes and articles in *LROS Newsletter*; also occasional articles in annual report and notes in *British Birds*. 2 Shanklin Gardens, Leicester Forest East, Leicester LE3 3JR. 0166 239 5294.

GAMMELL, Alistair Byres; *b:* 28 July 1949 in Kensington, London; *w:* Elizabeth. Clifton College, Bristol. Director, International Operations, RSPB since 1994. Various publications on the EC Birds Directive and Habitat Directive. Recipient of De Gouden Lepelaar 1989 (award given by Nederlandse Vereniging tot Bescherming van Vogels for conservation achievement). OIR: politics, opera, skiing, photography, fishing, travel, District Councillor (Mid-Beds DC). 23 The Avenue, Sandy, Beds SG19 1ER. 01767 681883.

GANTLETT, Stephen John Michael (Steve); *b:* 29 August 1953 in Epsom, Surrey. Editor *Birding World* since its inception and Partner in Birdline. Isles of Scilly Records Committee 1984-. British Birds Rarities Committee 1987-94. Norfolk Records Committee 1987-. Special interests: migration and rarities. Author *The Birds of Cley* (1984 and 1995), *The Birds of Scilly* (1991). Co-author (with J N Dymond and P A Fraser) *Rare Birds in Britain* *and Ireland* (1989). Sea Lawn, Coast Road, Cley next the Sea, Holt, Norfolk NR25 7RZ. 01263 740913; fax 01263 741014.

GARCIA, Ernest Francis John; *b:* 16 September 1951 in Gibraltar. BSc Zoology and Botany (London, 1974), Teacher's Cert (St Mary's College, 1973), DPhil Interspecific territoriality in *Sylvia* warblers (Edward Grey Institute, Oxford, 1981). CBiol, MIBiol 1990. Teacher, Deputy Head of Science, George Abbot School, Guildford. Founder-member Gibraltar Ornithological Society, also General Secretary 1975-77. Chairman Surrey Bird Club 1987-90. BTO Surrey Representative 1986-91. Iberian Peninsula Rarities Committee (CIR) 1989-95. Special interests: birds of Iberia; migration of raptors; warblers; ringing. Author *The Blackcap and the Garden Warbler* (1989). Co-author (with J E Cortes *et al*) *Birds of Gibraltar* (1980), and (with Andrew Paterson) *Where to Watch Birds in Southern Spain* (1994). Numerous articles in popular press and several papers. Assistant editor *Surrey Bird Report* 1983-93. Presented 'World of Birds' programme on Gibraltar Television for 32 weeks in 1976-77. Member: Gibraltar Ornithological and Nat Hist Society, Seabird Group, Grupo Ibérico de Aves Marinas, Sociedad Española de Ornitología. Woodpecker House, 2 Pine View Close, Chilworth, Guildford, Surrey GU4 8RS. 01483 539053.

GARR, John James; GSM(Malaya) 1957; *b:* 22 December 1936 in Lewisham, London. BSc Geography/Geology (London, 1974), MSc, DIC Environmental Technology (London, 1979). Geology technician. Special interests: Hawfinch, bird geography, conservation. Articles in environmental journals; also contributor to *London Bird Report* c1950-60, *Kent Bird Report* 1952-c1963, *Hampshire Bird Report*, *British Birds*, *The Hawfinch* by Guy Mountfort (1957), *Birds of Malaya* by Medway *et al* (1976), *Birds of Japan* by Mark Brazil (1991). OIR: geology, sea fishing, travel photography, wilderness survival. 1 Widbury Road, Pennington, Lymington, Hants SO41 8EF. 01590 671095.

GARROD, Jean Doris; *b:* 15 January 1928 in Dovercourt, Essex; *h:* Ken. Northgate School for Girls. Retired from Zürich Insurance in 1991. Various positions in Suffolk Ornithologists' Group, inc Management Council (first female member) and Vice Chairman. Woodlark surveys for Forest Enterprise. Special interest: birds of Suffolk and their habitats. Articles published in *The Harrier* (SOG) and *Suffolk Bird Report*; also contributions to *British Birds*. Bird-related travel in Europe and North America. OIR: other wildlife (esp butterflies), gardening, walking, cooking, ballet and opera. 769 Foxhall Road, Ipswich IP4 5TJ. 01473 723264.

GEORGE, Brian Charles; *b:* 12 May 1933 in Birmingham; *w:* Dorothy. Operations director. Wardening at RSPB Coombs Valley Reserve in 1950s. Committee Drakelow Wildfowl Reserve since 1989. Adviser to Combined, Handicapped and Disabled Society on their two nature reserves since 1992. Committee West Midland Bird Club 1969-71. Tutor for adult education bird and wildlife courses at Univ Birmingham since 1974, and at Keele Univ since 1994. Special interests: sound recording, photography, leading wildlife tours (esp Switzerland, Camargue), local conservation issues. During military service studied the birds of the Middle East and carried out ringing on behalf of Museum of Cairo. Joint editor of *The Birdwatcher's Day List* (1988). Extensive writing on wildlife and country matters for magazines and newspapers; broadcasts for BBC local and national radio inc live dawn chorus and Nightingale. Lectures on birds and other wildlife to clubs and societies. OIR: walking, old churches, cricket. 22 Bond End, Yoxall, Burton-on-Trent, Staffs DE13 8NH. 01543 472456.

GERRARD, Edward Charles (Ted); *b:* 5 August 1933 in Finchley, London. Voluntary fieldwork with Museu Municipal do Funchal. Special interests: migration, navigation, orientatation. Author *Instinctive Navigation of Birds* (1972, 1981) and journal articles on this subject. BTO 'A' ringer. PO Box 143, 9000 Funchal, Madeira, Portugal. +351 91 792591.

GIBBONS, David Wingfield; *b:* 19 November 1958 in Luton, Beds; *w:* Alexandra Hanford. BA Natural Sciences (Queens' College, Cambridge, 1981), MA 1983, PhD Behavioural Ecology (Queens' College and Dept Zoology, Cambridge, 1985). Head of Monitoring and Survey Section, RSPB since 1994. Prev: Organiser of BTO New Breeding Atlas and latterly Head of Land Use Unit BTO 1987-94; Academic Visitor to Edward Grey Institute, Dept Zoology, Univ Oxford 1985-86; Post-doctoral Research Fellow at Station Biologique de la Tour du Valat, Camargue 1985-86. Special interests: brood parasitism, co-operative breeding, reproductive strategies, parental care, bird distributions, comparative life history strategies, biodiversity, birds and environmental change, bird population monitoring. Co-author (with J B Reid and R A Chapman) *The New Atlas of Breeding Birds in Britain and Ireland: 1988-1991* (1993). Scientific papers in eg *Ibis, J Animal Ecol, Nature*; numerous more popular articles. Member of Board of Co-ordinating Commission for Biological Recording 1991-93. Editorial Panel *Bird Study* 1993-. OIR: natural history (esp behavioural ecology of damselflies), hill walking, gardening, DIY, contemporary cinema. Research Department, RSPB, The Lodge, Sandy, Beds SG19 2DL. 01767 680551.

GILLAM; Beatrice; MBE 1983; *b:* 25 January 1920 in Carlisle, Cumbria. Cert Ed (Bedford Froebel Training College, 1941), first year of BSc course in Zoology and Botany (Univ Bristol 1963-64), Cert of Proficiency in Natural History (London Univ Extra-mural, 1966). Occupational therapist, retired. BTO Asst Regional Representative then Reg Rep for Wiltshire mid 1970s-mid 1980s approx. Wildfowl Count organiser and Rookery Survey organiser for Wilts 1975. Joint organiser of fieldwork in Wilts for BTO Breeding Atlas 1968-72. Founder-member and Committee Wilts Ornithological Society. Committee Wilts WT and Wilts Farming and Wildlife Advisory Group from their formation in 1978 to 1989. Special interests: inland breeding birds; farmland Common Birds Census 1962-83 and woodland CBC since 1981; participant in most BTO surveys since 1960; construction and monitoring use of nestboxes. Editor of *Hobby* (annual publication of Wilts OS) 1975-80 and author 'Breeding birds of Sunnyhill Farm, Pewsey 1962-83' in that publication; also joint author of article on breeding birds of Tiree 1969 in *Scottish Birds*. OIR: practical conservation management on nature reserves and MOD land; all aspects of wildlife; edited *The Wiltshire Flora* (1993) following participation in fieldwork over eight-year period, and edited *The Butterflies of Wiltshire* by Michael Fuller (1995). 19 Roundway Gardens, Devizes, Wilts SN10 2EF. 01380 722636.

GILLMOR, Robert Allen Fitzwilliam; *b:* 6 July 1936 in Reading, Berks; *w:* Susan Norman. Leighton Park School 1949-54. Fine Art Dept, Reading Univ 1954-59, Nat Dip in Design 1958, Art Teaching Dip 1959. Freelance artist and illustrator. Prev: Director of Art and Craft, Leighton Park School 1959-65. Reading Ornithological Club: Secretary 1958-64, Chairman 1964-67, Vice President 1967-71, President 1971-. President Reading Guild of Artists 1969-84. Cape Clear Bird Observatory: Chairman 1961-70, President 1971-79. BTO Council 1971-76, also Vice President c1973-76. RSPB Council 1965-70 and member of Education Committee. BOU Council 1967-70, Vice President 1981-84. Society of Wildlife Artists: Secretary 1964-74, Chairman 1974-84, President 1984-94. Council Berks, Bucks & Oxon NT 1975-78. Special interest: bird behaviour. Two-man expeditions to Iceland studying geese 1954, 1956; Reading Univ expedition to Spitsbergen 1957. Edited C F Tunnicliffe's *Sketches of Bird Life* (1981), *Shorelands Winter Diary* (1992) and *The Peregrine Sketchbook* (1996). Artwork appears in over one hundred books, including jackets (eg designer of jackets for 'New Naturalist' series since No 71, 1985); art editor of *BWP* (1966-96). Occasional TV broadcasts. BTO Jubilee Medal 1984; winner of *Natural World* Art Award 1990. 58 Northcourt Avenue, Reading RG2 7HQ. 01734 871516.

GLADWIN, Rev Thomas William (Tom); *b:* 13 June 1935 in Hertford, Herts; *w:* Janet. St Albans Ministerial Training Scheme Certificate. Ordained Priest 1982. Priest in charge of Digswell Village (part-time). Wildlife consultant since 1981. BTO 'A' ringer 1957-79. Founder-member Rye Meads Ringing Group 1960. BTO Regional Representative Herts 1968-79. Council Herts and Middlesex WT 1966-78 and Scientific and Conservation Committee 1988-90. Chairman Herts Bird Club 1971-76. Hon Warden Lemsford Springs Nature Reserve 1968-78. Committee BOC 1990-93 and Vice Chairman since 1993. Special interest: population changes. Principal co-author of *The Birds of Hertfordshire* (1986). Author of various papers in eg *Bird Migration, Bird Study, British Birds, London Bird Report*. Occasional broadcaster. Designer of plans for restoration to nature conservation of gravel pits in Herts and Kent which have won national and European awards. Holder of Amateur Radio Licence G3UFA (participant in radio net with ornithologists in S Europe and N America). OIR: recorder of dragonflies (Odonata) and lacewings (Neuroptera) for Herts; author of books on railway history. 99 Warren Way, Digswell, Welwyn, Herts AL6 0DL. Tel/fax 01438 714700.

GLUE, David Edward; *b:* 7 April 1947 in Testwood, Totton, Hants. BSc Zoology (Royal Holloway College, Univ London, 1965). Scientific Research Officer BTO since 1968. Prev: joined late Kenneth Williamson to help develop BTO Common Birds Census (1968); co-organised (with Philip Burton) BTO Birds of Estuaries Enquiry (1969-70); initiated and developed BTO Garden Bird Feeding Survey (1970-); edited *BTO News* (1970-82); initiated and expanded BTO Raptor Research Register (1974-); helped develop BTO Nest Record Scheme (1983-). Special interests: feeding ecology (esp owls and diurnal raptors); nesting habits (esp owls, woodpeckers, heathland birds); the bird communities of special habitats (eg gravel pits, sewage works, heathland, churchyards); nestbox design and development; management of garden habitat for birds and their food preferences. Editor *The Garden Bird Book* (1982); co-editor (with David Stroud) *Britain's Birds 1989-90: the conservation and monitoring review* (1991), the inaugural issue of this annual publication. Author of over sixty scientific papers in eg in *Bird Study, British Birds, Mammal Review*; many articles in such magazines as *Birds* (RSPB) and *Country Life*. Script for David Cobban's film *Private Life of the Barn Owl*. OIR: photography, radio, supporting Southampton FC and Hampshire CCC, adult education lecturing and giving talks to bird clubs. Wheelchair-bound. Broke neck and paralysed (c.6 tetraplegic) in road crash Weston Turville, Bucks in 1971. Processed by National Spinals Unit, Stoke Mandeville Hospital and now a firm advocate of birdwatching and bird study from the wheelchair. Zoological Museum, Akeman Street, Tring, Herts HP23 6AP. 01442 891552; home 01442 822341.

GOLLEY, Mark Arthur; *b:* 15 December 1967 in Exeter, Devon. Freelance writer and ornithologist since 1994; from Sept 1995 working as researcher for 'Survival Anglia' in Norwich. Prev: Park Ranger, Hartsholme Country Park, Lincoln 1993-94; asst warden, Cley Marshes 1990-93; shorebird protection warden, Gibraltar Point Bird Observatory 1989. Reserve volunteer Devon WT 1986-88. Voluntary work in RSPB SW Regional Office 1988-90 and E Anglia Office winter 1991 (co-ordinator of Beached Bird Survey), also in Conservation Dept of Norfolk NT winters of 1991-92. Devon Birds Record Committee 1988-89; editorial asst *Norfolk Bird and Mammal Report* 1990-93; press officer Neotropical Bird Club 1992-93. Regular participant in national censuses and surveys. Special interests: identification and migration, esp seabirds and shorebirds. Widely travelled in Europe; also visits to North, Central and South America, and to North Africa. Co-author (with S Moss and D Daly) *The Complete Garden Bird Book* (1996). Many articles and shorter items, esp on identification, in *Birdwatch, Birding World* and *British Birds*; numerous features in *Norfolk Bird and Mammal Report* 1990-93 and *Norfolk Bird Club Bulletin* since 1993. OIR: other aspects of natural history (esp whales and dolphins); rock music. Little Knoll, Church Lane, Cley next the Sea, Holt, Norfolk NR25 7UD. 01263 740254.

GOMERSALL, Christopher Hugh (Chris); *b:* 4 February 1954 in Grimsby, Lincs; *w:* Pat. Photographic Manager RSPB since 1993. Prev: Photographer RSPB 1984-93; contract research biologist RSPB 1980-83; contract warden RSPB 1976-78. Special interests: bird and wildlife photography, divers and terns. Participant in Roseate Tern breeding survey expedition to Azores 1984. Photographs published widely, esp in RSPB publications. Studies on breeding populations of terns in Orkney (1980) and Red-throated Divers in Shetland (1983) in *Bird Study, Holarctic Ecology* and elsewhere. Member: Nature Photographers' Portfolio. OIR: music (playing 'cello). 18 Manor Way, Potton, Sandy, Beds SG19 2RH. 01767 260769.

GOODALL, Anne Lesley; *b:* Wakefield, West Yorks. MIBiol (Trent Polytechnic, 1977); MSc Use of the Humber Estuary by Dunlin (Hull, 1993). Managing Director, Ecological Services (ESL) Ltd since 1995. Prev: Senior Ornithologist, Ecosurveys Ltd from 1989 and Managing Director 1993-95. Earlier: medical researcher. Lincolnshire Bird Club: Hon

Sec/Editor *Lincs Bird Report* 1980-86, Hon Chairman 1993-. South Humber BoEE organiser 1976-83. Lincs Wildfowl Counts regional organiser 1980-86. BTO 'A' ringer since 1970. Ringing Secretary, Mid-Lincs Ringing Group 1973-77. BTO: Ringing and Migration Committee 1975-79; Research and Surveys Committee 1985-88; New Breeding Atlas Working Group 1986-92; Regional Representative South Humberside 1981-87 and West Lincs 1987-96. Special interests: all aspects of waders, esp Dunlin. Publications include papers on various species in bird reports and articles on many aspects of ornithology and general natural history for a range of publications. Occasional local radio interviews. Many, mainly unpublished, reports eg for environmental assessments, including defence at public inquiry. Member: Wader Study Group. OIR: Venture Scout Leader, walking and climbing, local history. 8 Townley Close, Holmes Way, Horncastle, Lincs LN9 6AT. 01507 523881; fax 01507 523882.

GOODERS, John Martin; *b:* 10 January 1937 in London; *w:* Robbie. BSc Philosophy and Politics (Southampton, 1958), PGCE (London, 1959), Dip Phil Ed (London, 1967). Freelance writer. Director (and founder) Birding Tours since 1980. Prev: Lecturer in Education, Avery Hill College 1967-69; teacher in London comprehensive schools 1959-66. Director (and founder) Ardea London Ltd 1971-80. Council London NHS 1962-63; editor LNHS *Ornithological Bulletin* 1961-63. Author: *Where to Watch Birds* (1966-86), *Where to Watch Birds in Britain and Europe* (1969-89, transl into Danish), *The How and Why of Birds* (1971), *Wildlife Photography* (co-author with Eric Hosking, 1973-76; also USA ed), *How to Watch Birds* (1975), *Wildlife Paradises* (1975; transl into French), *Birds: a survey of the bird families of the world* (1975; publ in USA as *The Great Book of Birds*); *A Day in the Country* (1979); *Collins Bird Guide* (co-author with Stuart Keith, 1982); *Birds that Came Back* (1983); *Kingfisher Guide to the Birds of Britain and Ireland* (1986); *Ducks of the Northern Hemisphere* (1986); *Kingfisher Complete Birdwatcher's Guide* (1988); *Pocket Guide to Ducks of the Northern Hemisphere* (1989); *The Outdoor Guide to Britain* (1989); *Kingfisher Guide to the Birds of Britain and Europe* (1990); *The Complete Ornithologist* (1990; also USA ed); *The Survival World of Birds* (1992; also German and USA eds); the *Birdwatcher's Site Guide to Britain* (1993); *Larousse Field Guide to the Birds of Britain and Ireland* (1995); *Larousse Field Guide to the Birds of Britain and Europe* (1995); *Larousse Pocket Guide to the Birds of Britain and Ireland* (1995). Editor *Birds of the World Encyclopedia* (1969-71); *The Birdwatcher's Book* (1976); *The Second Birdwatcher's Book* (1977);

The Third Birdwatcher's Book (1978); *The Encyclopedia of Birds* (7 vols, 1979-80; Editor in Chief). Founder and Editor *World of Birds Magazine* 1971-72. Many articles in eg *Animals, Daily Mail, Observer* and various bird magazines. TV scripts for eg *World About Us* (BBC); *World of Survival* (Survival-Anglia); *Wild, Wild World of Animals* (Time-Life). Presenter of *Taste of the Country* (TVS) 1990-92. Churchill Fellow 1970. Finches House, Hiham Green, Winchelsea, E Sussex TN36 4HB. 01797 223223; fax 01797 222911.

GOODFELLOW, Peter Frank; *b:* 18 October 1935 in Rochester, Kent; *w:* June. Devonport High School for Boys 1947-54. BA English Language & Literature (London, 1957); Guildhall School of Music & Drama, Cert for Teachers, 1962. Retired schoolteacher. Chairman Devon Birdwatching and Preservation Society 1996-. Former Slapton Bird Observatory secretary and Editor *Devon Birds*. Co-ordinator of various county surveys inc Wetland Bird Survey; regular atlas surveyor. BTO 'C' ringer since 1972. Special interests: Pied Flycatcher nestbox scheme; 'local patch' surveys; woodland birds, esp Wood Warbler; song, particularly subsong; historical birdwatching (ie which birds our ancestors knew). Author *Birds of Saltram* (1971), *Projects with Birds* (1973, 1992), *Birds as Builders* (1977, also USA and Dutch eds); *Shakespeare's Birds* (1983, also USA ed). Co-author *AA Multi-media Guide to Birds of Britain and Europe* (CD-ROM, in prep). Illustrated talks to local societies. OIR: Methodist local preacher; travelling with camper-van. 6 Dunraven Drive, Derriford, Plymouth PL6 6AR. 01752 775909.

GOODWIN, Richard Patrick (Derek); *b:* 26 February 1920 in Woking, Surrey. Strodes School, Egham, Surrey. Army Service April 1940 to June 1946 spent largely overseas in Egypt, Libya and Malta. Commenced in the Bird Room of the British Museum (Natural History) as a temporary attendant and progressed to Principal Scientific Officer, retiring in Feb 1982 (the bird section of BM(NH) moved in early 1970s from London to Tring and re-named The Sub-department of Ornithology). Professional work largely taxonomic. Special personal interests: behaviour and ecology, pigeons, corvids, estrildid finches. Author *Bird Behaviour* (1961), *Domestic Birds* (1965), *Pigeons and Doves of the World* (1967, 2nd ed 1970, 3rd enlarged ed 1983), *Crows of the World* (1976, 2nd ed 1986), *Birds of Man's World* (1978), *Estrildid Finches of the World* (1982). Many articles on taxonomy, behaviour and ecology of birds in eg *The Auk, British Birds, Emu, Ibis*. Member of Behaviour Notes Panel of *British Birds* in approx early 1970s. Awards: Avicultural Society Award 1954 (for breeding the

Lanceolated Jay *Garrulus lanceolatus* for the first time in captivity in UK); Union Medal, BOU 1972; William F Hollander Merit Award Medal (presented by *The Pigeon Genetics Newsletter* (USA) on 7 April 1976 for published work on pigeons, Columbidae); elected corresponding fellow of AOU in 1960s and of Deutsche Ornithologen-Gesellschaft in 1970s.

Self-portrait at 76

There was an old man who said: "My!
What a beautiful bird I espy."
When they asked: "Is it rare?"
He replied: "I don't care,
So long as it pleases my eye."

6 Crest View Drive, Petts Wood, Orpington, Kent BR5 1BY.

GORIUP, Paul David; *b:* 8 July 1955 in Reading, Berks. Stoneham Grammar School, Reading 1966-73. BSc Botany and Zoology (Reading, 1976), MSc Conservation Science and Diploma of Conservation (Univ College, London, 1977). MIEEM, MInstD. Managing Director, The Nature Conservation Bureau Ltd since 1989. Prev: Project Officer then Programme Director ICBP 1982-86. Leader/Principal Investigator of bustard projects for WWF, IUCN and ICBP in Morocco, Pakistan, Portugal and Turkey; also Avicultural Research Officer Great Bustard Trust 1980. Chairman Steppe and Grassland Birds Specialist Group of Birdlife International/IUCN since 1994. Chairman International Advisory Committee of National Avian Research Centre, Abu Dhabi, UAE 1993-96. Founder-member and Council, OBC 1985-88. ICBP Specialist Group on Bustards: Secretary 1979, Co-chairman 1982, 1987-89 (also Editor of *Bustard Studies*). Special interests: conservation of steppe and grassland birds, esp bustards; development of satellite and radar telemetry techniques for tracking migration; application of international wildlife conventions for bird conservation. Scientific papers (esp on above subjects) in eg *Avicultural Magazine, British Birds* (on behaviour of Black-winged Stilt), *Bustard Studies, Oryx, RSPB Conservation Review, Swara*; also reports and conference proceedings. Duke of Edinburgh Award, Gold (1973). Visiting Research Fellow, Rutherford College, Univ Kent. Scientific Fellow, Zoological Society of London. Member: ABC, Bombay NHS, OSME. OIR: table tennis, swimming. The Nature Conservation Bureau Ltd, 36 Kingfisher Court, Hambridge Road, Newbury, Berks RG14 5SJ. 01635 550380.

GORMAN, Gerard; *b:* 12 November 1960 in Haydock, Merseyside; *w:* Ivett. International Affairs Officer, Hungarian Ornithological and Nature Conservation Society 1989-93. Project Leader of Zemplén Hills Owl Project in 1991/92. Special interests: Eastern European habitats and species, esp how political change is affecting habitats. Awarded The Eric Hosking Trust conservation bursary in 1995 for project entitled 'Birds and Political Change in E Europe'. Travels throughout E Europe have included visits to eastern Romania in April 1989 to search for Slender-billed Curlew, and in January 1991 and February 1994 to count Red-breasted Geese. Author *A Guide to Birdwatching in Hungary* (Budapest 1991), *Where to Watch Birds in Eastern Europe* (1994), *The Birds of Hungary* (1996). Articles on birdwatching, travel in search of birds and conservation in E Europe in eg *Aquila, Bird Watching, Birding World, Birdwatch, Birdwatcher's Digest, Buteo, L'Homme et l'Oiseau, Linnut, Living Bird, Mens en Vogel, Wildfowl & Wetlands*. Member: Hungarian Ornithological and Nature Conservation Society (MME), Romanian Orn Soc (SOR) and Czech Orn Soc (COS). OIR: translation of poetry and folktales from Hungarian into English. Pf.701-1047, Budapest 1399, Hungary. Tel/fax +36 1 3199689.

GOSLER, Andrew Graham (Andy); *b:* 28 February 1958 in Ealing, London; *w:* Caroline Jackson-Houlston. BSc Environmental Biology (Wales, Aberystwyth, 1979), MSc Pure and Applied Plant Taxonomy (Reading, 1981), DPhil Some aspects of bill morphology in relation to ecology in the Great Tit (Edward Grey Institute, Oxford, 1987). University Research Officer, EGI since 1987. Prev: Research Asst, EGI 1981-87. BTO: British Ringing Committee 1988- (Vice Chairman 1991, Chairman 1995-); Council 1993-; Biometrics Working Group 1988-; Ringing Standards Select Committee 1990-92. Natural History Museum Bird Exploration Fund Committee 1988-. Berks, Bucks & Oxon TNC: Conservation Committee 1990-91, Conservation Advisory Group 1991-93, Conservation Support Group 1993-95. Oxford Orn Soc: President 1987- (prev Vice Pres, Chairman). Shotover SSSI Consultative Committee 1988-. Oxfordshire Rare Birds Committee 1990-. Oxfordshire Bird Conservation Co-ordinating Committee (Chairman 1992). Lower Windrush Conservation Group. BTO 'A' ringer since 1984, also member of Trainer and Sponsor Panels. Ornithological tour leader for various organisations. Special interests: ecology and behaviour, esp ecomorphology of tits; ecology of Common Tern on inland waters; ringing: use of biometrics (to determine body size and condition) in network ringing programmes; travel. Author *The Great Tit* (1993); editor *The Hamlyn Photographic Guide to Birds of the World* (1991); co-editor (with J Blondel *et al*) *Population Biology of*

Passerine Birds, an integrated approach (1990), and (with J W Brucker and A R Heryet) *The Birds of Oxfordshire* (1992). Editor *Bird Study* from 1993 (Editorial Board 1990-92); Editorial Board *Ornis Hungarica* from 1989. Scientific papers in eg *Ardea, The Auk, Bird Study, Bot J Linn Soc, Ibis, J Animal Ecol, J Avian Biol, Nature, Ringing & Migration, Watsonia.* Ornithological consultant. Edward Grey Institute of Field Ornithology, Dept of Zoology, South Parks Road, Oxford OX1 3PS. 01865 271158, fax 01865 271168; home tel/fax 01865 61110.

GOVETT, John Reginald; *b:* 26 March 1931 in Hayes, Middlesex; *w:* Maureen. BA English (Leeds, 1953), Grad Cert in Education 1954. Freelance artist. Founder-member Leeds Birdwatchers' Club, Recorder and editor of reports 1951-64. Yorkshire Naturalists' Union: member 1950-67, served on Executive Council for several years and on Ornithological Committee; Secretary of the Protection of Birds Committee 1961-63. Wiltshire Orn Soc: joint founder (with Miss B Gillam MBE) in 1974; Secretary until 1978; editor of bulletin *WOS News* 1975-79; Chairman 1985-88. Produced all line drawings and contributed text for *Birds of Wiltshire* (1981). Bird drawings in various reports and other publications inc covers of *British Birds*. Joint author (with Ken Hall) and illustrator of *Where to Watch Birds in Somerset, Avon, Gloucestershire and Wiltshire* (1988, 2nd ed 1995). Exhibitions of paintings in Yorkshire, Wiltshire and at Society of Wildlife Artists in Mall Galleries, London. One-man shows at WWT centres at Slimbridge 1992, 1994 and Llanelli 1993; also National Birds of Prey Centre, Newent 1993 and Wilts County Branch Library, Bradford-on-Avon 1992. Work exhibited and sold abroad. Lecturer on natural history and ornithology since 1957 to a variety of audiences inc WEA and local societies. OIR: listening to classical music; gardening and pond keeping; exploring countryside; reading non-fiction; naval history and twentieth-century warships. 15 Chepston Place, Trowbridge, Wilts BA14 9TA 01225 754746.

GRANT, Douglas; TD; *b:* 6 January 1918 in Edinburgh. Hon DLitt (St Andrews, 1986). FRSE 1949. Consultant editor. Responsible for the editing and publication of many major ornithological works, eg *The Birds of the British Isles* by Bannerman and Lodge (12 vols, 1953-63); *The Birds of Scotland* by Baxter and Rintoul (1953); *The Birds of Burma* by Smythies (1953); *Birds of Cyprus* by Bannerman (1958); *A Birdwatcher in Kenya* by Van Someren (1958); *Pirates and Predators* by Meinertzhagen (1959); *Birds of British Somaliland and the Gulf of Aden* by Archer and Godman (1961); *Birds of the Atlantic Islands* by Bannerman (4 vols, 1963); *Birds of Natal and*

Zululand by Clancey (1964); *Fair Isle and its Birds* by Williamson (1965); *Birds of Moor and Mountain* by Watson (1972); *A Field Guide to Australian Birds* by Slater (1975); and others. Flat G, The Lodge, 2 East Road, North Berwick, East Lothian EH39 4HN.

GRANT, Murray Craig; *b:* 3 April 1962 in Edinburgh; *w:* Catherine Todd. Linlithgow Academy 1974-80. BSc Ecological Science (Edinburgh, 1984), PhD The breeding ecology of Whimbrel in Shetland (Durham, 1989). Research Biologist, RSPB since 1993. Prev: Senior Research Assistant, Durham University 1989-92. Special interests: avian breeding biology; conservation studies; effects of habitat changes on bird populations; ecology of wading birds. General ecological expeditions to island of Yioùra, Sporades, Greece 1982 and 1983. Study on status, feeding behaviour and food supply of Black Vultures in Evros, Greece Apr-Sep 1985. Three-year study on habitat use and breeding ecology of Curlew in Orkney 1990-92. Study of causes of decline of breeding Curlew population in Northern Ireland commenced in 1993, and of habitat use by breeding Curlew in the Pennines in 1995. Publications from doctoral research in *Bird Study*, *Ibis*, *J Appl Ecol*. Text for Curlew in BTO New Breeding Atlas. Member: Wader Study Group. RSPB, The Lodge, Sandy, Beds SG19 2DL. 01767 680551.

GREEN, Andrew John (Andy); *b:* 24 March 1964 in Worsley, Manchester; *w:* Caroline Smith. Walkden High School, Salford 1975-80; Eccles Sixth Form College, Salford 1980-82. BA Zoology (Magdalen College, Oxford, 1985), DPhil Zoology (Wolfson College, Oxford, 1989). Post-doctoral scientist at Doñana Biological Station, Spain since 1993 (focusing on ecology of the Marbled Teal). Prev: Senior Research Officer (Threatened Species), WWT 1989-93; also Co-ordinator of the Threatened Waterfowl Specialist Group of the IUCN (World Conservation Union). Prev: Tutor in Biological Sciences, Univ Oxford 1985-89. Experience in wetland and waterfowl conservation outside Europe during 1991-93 inc Turkey, Pakistan, Thailand, Indonesia, Kenya, Madagascar and Florida. Special interest: conservation and ecology of globally threatened Anatidae. Many papers on this subject in journals eg *Forktail, Kukila, Wildfowl*, the IWRB 'Special Publications' series and elsewhere. Numerous popular articles in eg *BBC Wildlife Magazine, Oryx, Wildfowl and Wetlands*. Member: Survival International and Friends of the Earth. OIR: classical guitar, cycling, learning languages, photography, reading, travel, walking. Doñana Biological Station, Apartado 1056, 41080 Sevilla, Spain. +34 5 4232340; fax +34 5 4621125.

GREEN, Graeme Edwin; *b:* 15 September 1954 in Irvine, Ayrshire; *w:* Carole. Gillingham Grammar School for Boys. BSc Biological Sciences (Westfield College, London, 1976), PGCE 1984. Environmental consultant (part-time). Tutor on bird study courses for WEA. Special interests: taxonomy, identification, ecology and conservation of tropical birds. Worldwide bird-related travel. Contracted to co-author book *Cotingas and Manakins.* Member: ABC, NBC (Council), OBC. OIR: collecting bird books, socialising, real ale, playing cricket, watching sports. 33 Long Plough, Aston Clinton, Aylesbury, Bucks HP22 5HD. 01296 631089.

GREEN, Michael (Mick); *b:* 7 October 1959 in St Albans, Herts. BSc Environmental Science (Wales, Aberystwyth, 1981). Founder-member and Associate, Institute of Ecology and Environmental Management (AIEEM) 1991. Conservation Liaison Officer, Welsh Wildlife Trusts (co-ordinating the work of the seven WTs in Wales) since 1995. Prev: freelance environmental scientist 1984-95; reserve management work at RSPB Ynys Hir 1982-83. Freelance work included ornithological surveys (eg impact of agricultural grants on Isles of Coll and Tiree); single-species studies of breeding biology and distribution of several upland birds for RSPB and CCW (also Wales organiser for 1992 Chough Survey); management plans for National Nature Reserves in North Wales and other reserves covering upland, coastal, wetland and woodland sites. Friends of the Earth board member and representative on Wales Wildlife and Countryside Link. Special interests: upland birds and effects of upland management; wader migration. Joint leader Dubai Shorebird Project; two expeditions to United Arab Emirates to assess migrant shorebird populations and wetland habitats 1986 and 1987. Organiser (for BTO, IWC, WWF) of project to assess the numbers of wintering waders on west coast of Ireland, winter 1987/88. Member 1989 Greenland White-fronted Goose Study Expedition to W Greenland. Joint leader of expedition to Sultanate of Oman (Dec 1989) to assess wintering shorebird populations at large wetland site and advise on importance of the area with view to it becoming a national park. Member of ICBP Tai Forest Avifaunal Project Dec 1990. National Commission for Wildlife Conservation & Development Demoiselle Crane Survey, Saudi Arabia 1993. Ongoing project with Groupe Ornithologique du Maroc Central to investigate habitat loss in Atlas Mountains, with particular reference to Ring Ouzel. Papers on wader migration and surveys published in *Irish Birds, Sandgrouse, Wader Study Group Bulletin, Welsh Bird Report*; many contract reports. OIR: drinking. Bronhaul, Pentrebach, Talybont, Ceredigion SY24 5EH. 01970 832625.

GREEN, Paul Trevor; *b:* 3 February 1954 in Cambridge; *w:* Eng-Li. BA Psychology and Biology (Keele, 1977), PhD Behaviour and ecology of Rooks (Edinburgh, 1981). Director of Conservation and Education, American Birding Association since 1996. Prev: Head of Membership Unit BTO 1990-96; Research Officer BTO (effects of sewage inputs to estuaries on bird populations) 1989-90; Biological Recording in Scotland Campaign Co-ordinator, Scottish WT 1988-89; Lecturer in Ecology and Terrestrial Vertebrate Zoology, Univ of Malaya, Kuala Lumpur, Malaysia 1985-88; NERC Post Doctoral Research Fellow, Univ Edinburgh 1981-85. Editorial Board and Launch Committee, African Bird Club 1993-. Publicity Committee, Norfolk Bird Club 1993-96. Special interests: biology of crows of the genus Corvus; comparative social organisation of birds. Editor *BTO News* 1990-96. Variety of papers on the behaviour and ecology of Rook and Jackdaw, also on behaviour of Blue-throated Bee-eater (following three-year study of species in Malaysia); papers on ringing various species. Member Malaysian Nature Society. OIR: the birds of SE Asia, promotion of bird clubs, computer-aided publishing, long distance running. c/o American Birding Association, PO Box 6599, Colorado Springs, CO 80934, USA.

GREENHALF, Robert Ralph (Bob); *b:* 28 June 1950 in Haywards Heath, Sussex; *w:* Sally. Scrase Bridge Sec Mod School, Haywards Heath 1961-66. Eastbourne School of Art 1966-68. Diploma in Art and Design in Graphics (Maidstone College of Art, 1971). Member Society of Wildlife Artists (SWLA) 1981; Member Royal Society of British Artists (RBA) 1982. Artist. Council Sussex TNC 1972-73. Committee Friends of Rye Harbour Nature Reserve 1980-. Voluntary warden Rye Harbour NR at various times. Special interest: drawing and painting birds from life. Member of Artists for Nature Foundation visits to NE Poland 1992 and Extremadura 1994. Artist's Residency Parc des Ecrins, French Alps, May annually 1993-96. Illustrations in various publications inc *Birds*, *British Birds*, *Sussex Bird Report*. Chapter on work in *Twentieth Century Wildlife Artists* by Nicholas Hammond (1986); examples of work in *Drawing Birds* by John Busby (1986) and in *Portrait of a Living Marsh* by Robin d'Arcy Shillcock (1993). First solo book *Towards the Sea* (in prep). Paintings, etchings and drypoints exhibited in mixed and one-man shows throughout England and Wales, Ireland, Germany, Spain, France, Holland, Switzerland and USA. Romney House, Saltbarn Lane, Playden, Rye, E Sussex TN31 7PH. 01797 222381.

GREENSMITH, Alan; *b:* 2 September 1949 in London; *w:* Elizabeth. Bird tour leader abroad since 1993. Prev: ornithological consultant to publishing companies. Special interest: birds of the world. Extensive travel since 1969 in over sixty countries; spent two-and-a-half years birding in South America, 'pioneering' many countries eg Colombia, Ecuador. Attained largest personal 'world list' of those Britons entering the listings of the American Birding Association in 1994. Experienced bird photographer and sound recordist. Active in local conservation and environmental issues, including environmental education. Member: ABC, NBC, OBC. 14 Woodfield Avenue, Carshalton Beeches, Surrey SM5 3JB. 0181 773 2150.

GREENWOOD, Jeremy John Denis; *b:* 7 September 1942 in Horsforth, Yorks; *w:* Cynthia. Royal Grammar School, Worcester. BA Zoology (St Catherine's College, Oxford, 1964), PhD Ecological Genetics (Manchester, 1972). CBiol 1990, MIBiol 1990, MIEEM 1992, FLS 1980, FZS 1965. Director BTO since 1988. Prev: Lecturer in Biological Sciences, Dundee Univ 1967-87 (also Visiting Professor in Animal Ecology, University of Khartoum 1976). Scottish WT Tayside Branch Committee 1969-71. SOC Council 1976-80, 1983-87, Vice President 1983-87; President 1987. RSPB Scottish Committee 1977-82, Council 1983-88. Montrose Basin LNR Committee 1981-86. ICBP British Section Grants Committee 1988-92. NERC Terrestrial Life Sciences Committee 1988-91. NCC Advisory Committee on Birds 1988-91. British Agrochemicals Association Environmental Research Committee 1988-93. BOU Council 1989-93. WWT Scientific Advisory Committee 1989-92. European Ornithological Atlas Committee 1992-. European Bird Census Council Executive Committee Chairman 1992-. Special interests: statistical analysis and survey design; population biology. Studies have included fledging of auks, year-round colony attendance by auks, population biology of Blue Tit. Birds of NE Greenland expeditions 1972, 1974, 1977. Birds of Trinidad expedition 1985. Joint organiser, national Mute Swan Survey 1990. Co-editor of 1972 and 1974 Greenland expedition reports, and of *Birds as Monitors of Environmental Change* (with R W Furness) (1993). Editor *Bird Study* 1984-87. Editorial Board *Heredity* 1987-92. Large number of scientific papers in eg *British Birds*, *Ibis*, *J Animal Ecol*, *J Zool*, *Nature*, *Ornis Scandinavica*. Numerous popular articles in eg *Birds*, *BTO News*, *Scottish Birds*, *Wader Study Group Bulletin*. Contributions to books, conference proceedings and other publications. Examiner for Certificate in Ornithology, Birmingham Univ 1992-. Hon Lecturer in Biological Sciences, Dundee Univ 1988-. Director, West Palaearctic Birds Limited 1990-. OIR: walking and gardening. BTO, The Nunnery, Thetford, Norfolk IP24 2PU. 01842 750050.

GREENWOOD, Julian Garth; *b:* 10 September 1949 in Sale, Cheshire; *w:* Mary. BSc Applied Biology (Liverpool Polytechnic, 1973), PhD Geographical variation in the Dunlin (Liverpool Polytechnic, 1980). CBiol 1986. Senior Lecturer in Teacher Education since 1979. Prev: research asst Merseyside County Museums (bird egg collections) 1976-77; research asst Liverpool Polytechnic 1973-76. RSPB N Ireland Committee 1984-95. RSPB Council 1990-95. National Trust Strangford Lough Committee 1983-93. N Ireland organiser for BTO/SOC Cormorant Survey 1984-86. NI organiser for Black Guillemot counts as part of NCC/Seabird Group's Seabird Colony Register 1987. Special interests: Black Guillemot, tits. Over twenty papers in eg *Bird Study, British Birds, Ibis, Irish Birds, Ringing & Migration.* Contributor to *BWP* Vol 3. Lectures to RSPB members' groups throughout N Ireland and to a range of conferences throughout Britain and Ireland. Member: Seabird Group, Wader Study Group. OIR: walking (esp in the Irish uplands), French holidays, listening to Van Morrison and Mary Black. Science Dept, Stranmillis College, Belfast BT20 3DJ. 01232 381271.

GREGORY, Brian John; *b:* 19 May 1950 in Glasgow. BSc Mathematics (Exeter, 1972). Schoolmaster. YOC holiday course leader 1973-85. Gwent County Recorder 1985-91. Welsh Ornithological Society Council 1988-. Bird-related travel in Europe, Morocco, Kenya, New Zealand. Editor *Gwent Bird Report* 1985-95. OIR: natural history of the Wye Valley, chess. 18 Blake Street, Monmouth, Gwent NP5 3TH. 01600 714953.

GREGORY, Christopher (Chris); *b:* 17 February 1953 in Cambridge. BA Fine Art and Sculpture (Kingston Polytechnic, 1975), City and Guilds Award for Biological Surveying (Otley College of Horticulture and Agriculture, 1988). Site Manager for BTO Nunnery Lakes Reserve and Conservation and Wildlife Ranger for West Stow Country Park 1993-. Prev: asst conservation officer English Nature 1992-93; ornithological surveyor/team leader Ecosurveys Ltd 1990-93; ecological surveyor Suffolk WT 1987-88. Asst voluntary warden and member of Management Committee, Lackford Wildfowl Reserve 1987-94. Rare breeding bird warden, Forestry Commission 1988. Co-ordinator for annual FC/RSPB Woodlark Survey in Thetford Forest 1991-94. Special interests: Breckland birds, birds of prey, habitat creation and restoration. Produced environmental impact report (including bird survey) for a proposed ecological housing park in N Spain 1990. Travel inc Seychelles. Author of *Wildlife Watchers Guide* (1990). Co-author of report commissioned by the British Orienteering Federation on 'The Effect of the May 1st 1991

Orienteering Event on the Breeding Bird Community of Brandon Park' (1991). Various articles and illustrations for the annual *Lackford Bird Report*. OIR: illustration, walking, badminton. 3 Wideham Cottages, West Stow, Bury St Edmunds, Suffolk IP28 6HE. 01284 728212.

GREGORY, John; *b:* 26 August 1959 in Stockport. BSc Geography and Geology (Manchester, 1983). ACA 1991. Financial accountant. Partner, Birdline North West since 1990. Participant in various censuses. Special interest: Oriental birds. Extensive travel in Thailand, Malaysia, India, Nepal, Sabah, Vietnam. Member: OBC. OIR: watching cricket, playing squash, consuming wine. 8 Holly Bank Cottages, The Avenue, Comberbach, Northwich, Cheshire CW9 6HT. 01606 892371.

GREGORY, Philip Andrew; *b:* 30 January 1951 in Southampton; *w:* Sue. BA Geography (Southampton, 1973). Principal, Tabubil International School, Papua New Guinea; also writer and radio announcer. Occasional freelance tour guide. Organiser of school wildlife clubs in UK, Zambia, Falkland Islands, Papua New Guinea. Special interests: field identification (currently endeavouring to see all the birds-of-paradise), vocalisations, geographical distribution, taxonomy. Bird-related travel in some fifty countries. Relief editor and regular writer for *Chembe News* (Zambian Orn Soc) 1981-88. Author *Birds of Chembe* (sanctuary near Kitwe, Zambia) (1986, rev ed 1988) and *The Birds of the Ok Tedi Area* (1995). Wildlife columnist for *Penguin News* (Stanley, Falkland Islands) 1989-90 and unofficial recorder for Falkland Islands 1988-90. Editor since 1993 of *Muruk*, journal of the Papua New Guinea Birdwatching Society. Articles in *Birding World* and *Bull BOC*, and various notes in eg *British Birds* and *Ostrich*. Tape of local Ok Tedi species deposited with National Sound Archive, with first recordings of Sooty Whistler. A species likely to be an undescribed form, a small *Melanocharis* Berrypecker, documented in *Muruk*. Member: ABA, ABC, PNG Bird Soc, RAOU, SAOS. OIR: music (esp African), had weekly World Music spot on *FIBS* in the Falklands; science fiction, ornithological and travel books. PO Box 69, Tabubil, Western Province, Papua New Guinea. Tel/fax: +675 589310.

GREGORY, Richard David; *b:* 3 September 1963 in Stockport, Cheshire. BSc Ecology (York, 1985), DPhil Population and community ecology (Oxford, 1990). Head of Census Unit BTO since 1992. Previous voluntary work with RSPB, NCC and RSNC; former asst recorder York Ornithological Club. Special interests: bird conservation, community ecology, population monitoring, survey design and analysis, bird identification. Several papers related to ornithology, ecology and epidemiology in scientific journals eg *Bird Study, J Animal Ecol, Oikos, Phil Trans Roy Soc Lond (B)*. Regular contributions to *BTO News* and a number of popular journals; also radio broadcasts. European Bird Census Council delegate for the UK. BTO, The Nunnery, Thetford, Norfolk IP24 2PU. 01842 750050.

GRENFELL, Harold Edwin; *b:* 6 August 1936 in Swansea. Swansea Grammar School. Member, Incorporated Assocn of Surveyors 1959. Director of building firm. Council and Executive Committee, Welsh Ornithological Society since its formation in 1988 (Chairman 1996). Records Secretary and/or Chairman of Gower Ornithological Society since 1965. Hon Bird Recorder Gower/West Glamorgan since 1966. Special interest: bird photography (away from nests, mainly from hides), esp coastal species. Co-author (with D K Thomas) *Guide to Gower Birds* (1982); author and illustrator (inc bird photos) *Gower Images* (1985). Editor or member of Editorial Committee *Gower Birds* (annual report) from first publication in mid 1960s. Articles and bird photos over many years in *The Gower Journal*. Photos published many times in 'Best Recent Work' feature of *British Birds*; photos in books inc *Dictionary of Birds* by Bruce Campbell and Elizabeth Lack (1985) and *Birdlife of Coasts and Estuaries* by Peter Ferns (1992). Member: Nature Photographic Society (Hon Sec) and Zoological Photographic Club. OIR: general nature and landscape photography, watching rugby. The Woods, 14 Bryn Terrace, Mumbles, Swansea SA3 4HD. 01792 360487.

GRIBBLE, Frank Colin; *b:* 3 October 1929 in Bedford; *w:* Hilary. Bedford School 1941-46. ACII 1952. BTO: Council 1963-67, 1978-81, Hon Sec 1967-71, Populations and Surveys Committee 1971-75 (1967-70 ex officio), Finance and General Purposes Committee 1967-71, 1978-81, Regional Representative for Beds 1955-58, Shrops 1960-63, Staffs (all or part) 1965-. Organiser of BTO Black-headed Gull Survey (England and Wales) 1958 and 1973, Nightjar Survey (GB and Ireland) 1981. Shropshire Orn Soc: Hon Sec 1958-63, Vice President 1965-94, President 1994-. West Midland Bird Club: Vice President 1990-, Chairman Staffs Branch 1993-. Council Staffs WT and Chairman Conservation Committee 1986-93. MAFF Advisory Panel for North Mercia Region 1993-. Lectures given to clubs and societies locally in W Midlands. Special interests: Black-headed Gull, Nightjar, wildfowl and waders, breeding distribution, migration, conservation. Bird-related travel to Norway, Sweden, France (Camargue), Mallorca, Crete, Canada, USA, Australia, New Zealand. Articles on censuses in *Bird Study*. Co-author (with E M Rutter and T W Pemberton) *Handlist of Shropshire Birds* (1964). Awarded BTO's Bernard Tucker Medal 1973. Member: Miranda Naturalists Trust (NZ). OIR: mountain flowers, butterflies and dragonflies, hill walking, natural history photography, TV sport. 22 Rickerscote Avenue, Stafford ST17 4EZ. 01785 254166.

GRICE, Philip Victor (Phil); *b:* 19 April 1966 in Edmonton, London. BSc Geography (North London, 1988), MSc (Univ College, London, 1990). Ornithologist, English Nature since 1992. Prev: Ornithologist, JNCC 1991-92 and NCC 1991. Member of Lowlands Research Sub-committee of Game Conservancy Trust 1995-. Special interests: bird conservation; habitat management for birds; ecology of lowland farmland and wetland birds (esp on man-made waterbodies); the effects of recreation, developments and other potentially damaging activities on bird populations. Editorial Committee *Wader Study Group Bulletin* 1991-93. Author of a number of EN, JNCC and NCC reports on bird conservation, eg *Birds in England: context and priorities* (with A F Brown, 1993) and *Birds in England: a Natural Areas approach* (with A F Brown *et al*, 1994); also many entries in English Nature's *Species Conservation Handbook*. Several articles in popular magazines. OIR: coarse angling, photography, playing guitar and racket sports. English Nature, Northminster House, Peterborough PE1 1UA. 01733 340345.

GRIFFIN, David; *b:* 16 February 1930 in Cardiff; *w:* Sian. MA Modern Languages (Oxford, 1952). Retired from British Coal. Cardiff Naturalists' Society (Ornithological Section): Hon Sec 1959-67, President 1967-68. London NHS (Ornithological Section): Chairman 1971-74. Surrey Bird Club: Hon Sec 1969-77, Chairman 1978-80, President 1988-92. British Ornithologists' Club: Committee since 1983, Vice Chairman 1986-89, 1990-93, Chairman 1993-. Co-editor (with A Heathcote and H Morrey Salmon) *Birds of Glamorgan* (1967). Joint editor *Glamorgan Bird Report* 1962-66. Series of papers on Common Birds Census and Waterways Bird Surveys in Surrey published in *Surrey Bird Report*. 51a Palace Road, East Molesey, Surrey KT8 9DN. 0181 979 0748.

GRIFFIN, Mervyn; *b:* 17 December 1949 in Bolton, Greater Manchester; *w:* Brenda. Bolton County Grammar School 1961-68. Bolton Institute of Technology 1968-70. BSc Chemistry (Leeds, 1973), PhD Chemistry (Leeds, 1976), Grad Cert of Education (Huddersfield Polytechnic, 1977). College lecturer. Member of local rarities committee 1993-. Secretary Lothian Records Committee 1994-. Special interests: autumn migration of skuas through the Firth of Forth; Dotterel on the Scottish hills. Joint compiler of systematic list in *Lothian Bird Report* 1989-91 and author of articles. Contributor to site descriptions in *Birdwatching Sites in Lothian* comp by I J Andrews (1989). Talks on birds to local clubs. OIR: hill walking, skiing, sampling malt whiskies. 9 Baberton Mains Lea, Edinburgh EH14 3HB. 0131 442 1872.

GRIFFIN, Peter Robert (Pete); *b:* 3 September 1949 in Leeds; *w:* Jane. Optical equipment consultant. Secretary New Swillington Ings Bird Group since its formation in 1989. Adult education tutor in field ornithology 1990-91. Special interest: the development of Swillington Ings in the Lower Aire Valley: a long-term project, started in 1986, to regenerate former mining area into a major country park. Editor *Birds of the Lower Aire Valley* (annual report) 1981-88. Monthly articles on this subject in the *Rothwell Advertiser* (now defunct) 1980-89. OIR: moths, mammals. 4 Fleet Lane, Oulton, Leeds LS26 8HX. 0113 282 1133.

GRIFFITHS, Gerald Ivan (Gerry); *b:* 28 February 1942 in Hednesford, Staffs; *p:* Judith Bloor. Qualifications in business studies and accountancy. Founder and Senior Partner, Avian Adventures 1992-. Lecturer in natural history (mainly ornithology) field study courses for Univ Birmingham School of Continuing Studies since 1978. Special interests: identification, migration, breeding biology. Contributor to both the national and West Midlands breeding atlases 1968-72. Widely travelled leading tours. Much data published in *West Midland Bird Report* during 1970s. OIR: butterflies, dragonflies, orchids, cricket, soccer, golf. 49 Sandy Road, Norton, Stourbridge DY8 3AJ. 01384 372013.

GRIFFITHS, Richard; *b:* 25 March 1965 in Newcastle upon Tyne. BSc Applied Biology (Bath, 1987), DPhil The isolation and application of W chromosome related DNA sequences in the Lesser Black-backed Gull (Oxford, 1991). Post-doctoral research scientist, Zoology Dept, Univ Oxford since 1991. Special interest: the identification of sex in birds and its use as a tool to investigate if and how birds change the sex ratio of their offspring in response to various environmental and other factors. Papers on this subject in eg *Ibis, Molecular Ecology, Proc Roy Soc Lond*. OIR: cycling. Dept of Zoology, South Parks Road, Oxford OX1 3PS. 01865 271282.

GRIMMETT, Richard; *b:* 6 June 1960 in London; *w:* Helen Taylor. BA Social Sciences (East Anglia, 1983). Head of Asia Division, ICBP/BirdLife International since June 1993. Prev: Senior Programme Officer responsible for the European and Asia Programme, 1989-93; compiler of Important Bird Areas in Europe Inventory from 1986 to 1989; Programme Officer 1984-86. OBC: founder-member and chairman of launch committee 1984-85, Chairman 1985-89, Committee 1989-93. OSME Council 1983. Special interests: bird conservation; conservation and threatened species research in Asian region; identification of birds in the Palearctic and Orient. Author of *A Review of the Problems Affecting Palearctic Migratory Birds in Africa* (1987); joint compiler (with T A Jones) *Important Bird Areas in Europe* (1989) and junior author (with G M Tucker *et al*) *Birds in Europe: their conservation status* (1994). Contributed colour plates and black-and-white illustrations for *Birds of Nepal* by C and T P Inskipp (1985). OIR: football, art, walking. 3 Madras Road, Cambridge CB1 3PX. 01223 242884.

GRISS, Donal Ivan (Don); *b:* 27 April 1939 in West Hartlepool, Co Durham; *w:* Mary. Queen Elizabeth Grammar School Darlington. Retired research chemist. Industry-based bird censuses undertaken as consultant since 1991. Ornithological leader for Darlington and Teesdale Naturalists' Field Club since c1980. Special interests: bird behaviour, wagtails. Travel for birds in N America, India, Kenya, Tanzania and Europe. Organiser of survey of Dippers on River Tees in 1989, results published in *Natural History in and around Darlington* by DTNFC (1991). OIR: angling, walking, badminton. 95 Salutation Road, Darlington, Co Durham DL3 8JP. 01325 350402.

GUEST, Andrew John; *b:* 1 April 1944 in Maidstone, Kent. Sevenoaks School 1955-62. BA Natural Sciences (St Catharine's College, Cambridge, 1965), MA 1968. MInstP 1972. Principal Scientist, Philips Research Laboratories. Leader of Reigate Birdwatchers since 1979; leader of over 500 birdwatching trips for them or other local groups (eg RSPB, Sussex WT). Tutor for evening classes on watching birds, Reigate 1979-90 and WEA Crawley 1980. Sussex Orn Soc 10km square steward (TQ33) for national and county surveys since 1981. Special interests: identification (esp by songs and calls), behaviour, local surveys. Widely travelled in Europe; also Norway, Iceland, USA and Canada, Costa Rica, Belize, Australia. Compiler of divers to ducks section in *Surrey Bird Report* 1977-81; occasional short articles in local newsletters. OIR: natural history, walking, gardening, classical music, reading. 40 Ash Road, Three Bridges, Crawley, W Sussex RH10 1SH. 01293 523009.

GULLICK, Thomas Mirfield (Tom); *b:* 7 March 1931 in Westgate-on-Sea, Kent; *w:* Katharine. Royal Naval College, Dartmouth 1944-48. Retired.

Organiser of bird tours in Spain and Morocco since 1977. Instigator of saving Spanish population of White-headed Duck in late 1970s; census work on Spanish Imperial Eagle, Great Bustard and Lammergeier. Special interests: identification; sound recording of rare and supposedly extinct African bird species: four 'extinct' species refound to date in Ethiopia, Cameroon and São Tomé. Published work in *British Birds*, *Bull BOC*, *Scopus*. Member: ABC, Bombay Nat Hist Club, EANHS, NBC, OBC, OSME, SEO, WAOS. India Alta, Infantes, Ciudad Real, Spain. +34 (9) 26 694017.

GUNTON, Trevor Guy; *b:* 5 November 1936 in Leeds; *w:* Veronica. NGO consultant in fields of training volunteers etc. Prev: Development Adviser European Programmes, RSPB 1989-96; Organiser then Head of Development RSPB 1968-89. Earlier: commercial artist. Committee Leeds and District Birdwatchers Club (Protection of Birds Officer) 1965-68. Chairman WWF Leeds Branch in mid 1960s. Volunteer warden, Paxton Pits Nature Reserve. Special interests: lecturing, volunteer training and motivation, recruitment to RSPB, bird tour consultant/organiser. Special interests: gravel-pit birds, herons, cormorants, geese. Mission: to make more people care about birds. Consultant to BTO and numerous overseas conservation organisations. Articles published in *Birdwatcher's Yearbook*. 15 St James Road, Little Paxton, Cambs PE19 4QW. 01480 473562.

GUSH, Geoffrey Howard; *b:* 9 October 1913 in London; *w:* Peggy (deceased). Dip in Agriculture (Berkshire & Wye College, Kent, 1936). Retired, formerly with British-American Tobacco Co in Thailand and Java (1937-58) and London (1958-70). Warden of Venn Ottery Nature Reserve (Devon WT) 1975-89. BTO 'A' ringer since 1961; trained 25 to 'C' permit status, inc 20 to 'A' permit 1964-75. Participant in BTO Garden Bird Feeding Survey since 1970; also Common Birds Census in Surrey and Devon, Constant Effort Site in Devon, and Nest Record Cards since 1950s. Inland wildfowl censusing in 1950s. Fieldwork for first breeding bird atlases in London, Surrey and Devon. Contributor to BTO's *Garden Bird Book* ed by David Glue (1982). BTO Tucker Medallist 1989. OIR: mammals, reptiles, butterflies, flowering plants (with contributions to atlases). Heather Cottage, Higher Metcombe, Ottery St Mary, Devon EX11 1SR. 01404 812811.

GYNN, Elizabeth Grace (Liz); *b:* 28 September 1955 in Isleworth, Middlesex; *h:* Graham. BSc Zoology and Botany (Newcastle, 1976), PhD Botany (Newcastle, 1982). Organiser, leader and tutor birdwatching holidays based at Boswednack Manor, of which joint proprietor. Asst warden Skokholm Island 1981-85. Fieldwork inc BTO Common Birds Census on Skokholm, Nest Record Scheme, BTO Winter Atlas, Hen Harrier Roost Survey. Special interests: identification, migration. Contributor to *Birds in Cornwall* (annual report) since 1970. OIR: organic gardening, walking. Boswednack Manor, Zennor, St Ives, Cornwall TR26 3DD. 01736 794183.

GYNN, Graham Gordon; *b:* 5 August 1952 in Woking, Surrey; *w:* Elizabeth (Liz). BSc Agricultural Zoology (Newcastle, 1975). Joint proprietor Boswednack Manor; tutor for birdwatching holidays based there. Prev: raptor protection warden for RSPB in Lake District and Yorkshire 1980-81; Hancock Museum, Newcastle (researcher for reorganisation of bird gallery) 1978-80; Newcastle Univ, research on blood parasites of Red Grouse 1977-78. Fieldwork for BTO Winter Atlas and Hen Harrier Roost Survey. BTO 'A' ringer since 1987. Special interests: ringing; making music and bird sound tapes (eg 'Macaws & the Rain Leaves' featuring birds of the Peruvian rainforest). Author of environmentally based musical plays for children (eg 'Rainforest Holiday'). Contributor to *Birds in Cornwall* (annual report) since 1985. OIR: music. Boswednack Manor, Zennor, St Ives, Cornwall TR26 3DD. 01736 794183.

HALE, William Gregson (Bill); *b:* 17 February 1935 in Blackburn, Lancs; *w:* Marie. Royal Grammar School, Clitheroe 1945-53. BSc Zoology (Durham, 1959), PhD Zoology (Durham, 1962), DSc (Durham, 1985). FIBiol 1972. Professor of Animal Biology, Liverpool John Moores Univ. Scientific Advisory Committee WWT 1975-78. Founder-member East Lancashire Ornithologists' Club 1955. Special interests: waders (inc long-term population study of Redshank), geographical variation, breeding biology. Author *Waders* (1980), *Eric Hosking's Waders* (1982), *The Redshank* (1989); co-editor (with P R Evans and J D Goss-Custard) *Wildfowl and Waders in Winter* (1984). Contributions to *Handbuch der Vögel Mitteleuropas* by Glutz et al (1977), *BWP* (1982), *Guide to the Identification and Ageing of Waders* by Prater *et al* (1977), *Dictionary of Birds* by Campbell and Lack (1985). Papers in journals inc *Bird Study*, *British Birds*, *Ibis*, *Ornis Scandinavica*, *Ringing & Migration*; numerous articles in popular magazines. OIR: archaeology, books, travel, cricket. 5 Ryder Close, Aughton, Ormskirk, Lancs L39 5HJ. 01695 422472; work 0151 231 2050.

HALES, Stephen (Steve); *b:* 23 June 1952 in Dorchester, Dorset; *p:* Maureen Spencer. Hardyes School, Dorchester; Glamorgan Polytechnic.

British Rail (traincrew). Committee Dorset Farming and Wildlife Advisory Group 1980-. Ornithological representative of MOD Lulworth (Conservation) Group. Participant in BTO Nest Record Scheme incorporating nestbox schemes at two sites since 1986. BTO 'A' ringer since 1994. Special interests: seabird identification and movements (several pelagic trips); local studies on three farms in W Dorset involving ringing; migration trends and breeding; passerine movements along Chesil Beach. Groups led in UK, Europe, Tunisia, USA, Iceland, Canary Islands, India, W Africa. Notes published in *Sea Swallow*; regular articles for *Dorset FWAG Newsletter* and *Dorset WT Newsletter*; contributed chapter on birds for *Endangered Wildlife in Dorset* ed by D Pearman and A Mahon (1993). OIR: French cooking, Macrolepidoptera. 14 Treves Road, Dorchester, Dorset DT1 2HD. 01305 263600.

HALL, Beryl Patricia (Pat); *b:* 13 June 1917 in Epsom, Surrey. Voluntary asst on 'A' List, Bird Room, British Museum (Natural History) 1947-71. BOC: Committee inc Hon Sec early 1950s, Vice Chairman c1968. BOU: Council and Vice President c1967. Secretary Duck Adoption Scheme 1948-c1952. Chairman 4th Pan-African Ornithological Congress, Seychelles 1976. Special interests: systematics and speciation. Collecting trips for the Museum to SW Africa (1949), Bechuanaland (1950, 1957, 1962), Angola (1957), Australia (1965). Co-author (with R E Moreau) *An Atlas of Speciation in African Passerine Birds* (1970); sundry papers in *Bull BOC, Bull Brit Mus (NH), Ibis* between 1950 and 1970. Gill Memorial Medal 1970; Stamford Raffles Award 1971; BOU Medal 1973; Corresponding Fellow AOU 1963; Hon Fellow AOU 1977; Hon Assoc BM(NH) c1971. OIR: horse racing (National Hunt). Woodside Cottage, Woodgreen, Fordingbridge, Hants SP6 2QU. 01725 512459.

HALL, Kenneth John (Ken); *b:* 25 October 1946 in Pembroke Dock, Dyfed; *w:* Lys. BSc Physics (Bristol, 1968). Production Director, Multilingual Matters Ltd. Committee Bristol Ornithological Club since 1972 and Chairman 1977-79. Special interests: birds of Spain and France (many visits since mid 1960s); birds of N Somerset, esp Mendip Hills where bird surveys carried out for Somerset WT at various of their reserves. Lectures to interested bodies on all these topics. Co-author (with John Govett) *Where to Watch Birds in Somerset, Avon, Gloucestershire and Wiltshire* (1988, 2nd ed 1995). Co-editor *Bristol Ornithology* 1975-96, also papers therein on local studies. UK representative for Ligue Française pour la Protection des Oiseaux. Member: SEO. OIR: wine tasting; exploring sites of architectural and historical interest in ornithologically rich areas of the world. The Anchorage, The Chalks, Chew Magna, Bristol BS18 8SN. 01275 332980; fax 01275 332559.

HALL, Michael Allen (Mike); *b:* 22 March 1936 in Ipswich, Suffolk; *w:* Sandra (Sandy). Northgate Grammar School, Ipswich 1947-54. BSc Science (Reading, 1958), BA Behavioural Psychology (Reading, 1959). Retired teacher. From mid 1970s, lecturer on adult education courses (inc ornithology) for Univs Cambridge and Essex, and tutor for bird and wildlife adult education courses in Suffolk; tutor to local YOC group 1974-83. Founder-member Suffolk Ornithologists' Group and Chairman from formation in 1973 to 1976. Organiser of counts on Suffolk estuaries for BTO Birds of Estuaries Enquiry in 1973-74. Active 1970-84 in bird and wildlife conservation in the county, including membership of Council and various committees of Suffolk TNC, and participation in public inquiry for Sizewell-B nuclear power station. Warden of Gromford Meadow, ancient wetland reserve in Suffolk, 1975-82. Special interests: long distance migration, bird vocalisations, imprinting and conditioning behaviour, photography and sound recording. Bird-related travel in Europe inc Germany and Poland. Occasional local magazine articles and radio broadcasts. OIR: landscape and waterscape photography, sailing, rambling and fell walking. Pinetoft, 42 Churchill Crescent, Wickham Market, Woodbridge, Suffolk IP13 0RW. 01728 746775.

HALLCHURCH, Timothy Thomas (Tim); Major; MBE 1971; *b:* 17 January 1941 in Codsall, Staffs; *w:* Heather. RMA Sandhurst (Engineering) 1959-61. MIMgt 1980. Computer consultant. Lecturer on bird recognition for WEA Lisburn, N Ireland 1976-77. Oxford Ornithological Society, Ringing Member 1986-88. Army Ornithological Society, Ringing Member 1978-, Expeditions Organiser 1977-. Organised and led ornithological expeditions to Belize (2), Cyprus (4), Spain (2), Morocco, Kenya, Bulgaria, Israel, W Africa. Special interests: ringing (holds or has held ringing and trainer licences in USA, Belize, Morocco, France, Spain, Cyprus, Bulgaria and UK); bird photography inc 8mm film and video in above countries plus Djibouti, S Arabia (Yemen), Mauritius, Singapore, Yugoslavia, Germany; sound recording (many bird species worldwide); conservation (contributions to many campaigns to conserve ornithological sites inc Cyprus and Belize). Participant in many atlas projects. Compiler of annual report of birds ringed on MOD Lands 1978-; author of many articles for Army Orn Soc and other societies; author of computer programs for ringing data and a database of all Palearctic species; broadcast about birds on British Forces Radio. OIR: classical music (inc playing classical guitar), antique collecting, tennis, gardening, travel, shooting. Millfield, 5 Mill Lane, Horton cum Studley, Oxford OX33 1DH. 01865 358815.

HALTON, Wesley James (Wes); *b:* 9 May 1952 in Farnworth, Lancs. Farnworth Grammar School. Countryside Warden, Croal Irwell Valley, Greater Manchester since 1978. Special interests: Mute Swan, ringing. BTO 'A' ringer for swan species since 1994, 'C' ringer for other species since 1983. Co-ordinator North West Swan Study Group 1988-. Author of general and specialised natural history recording computer programs, eg Bird Recorders, Nest Record Scheme, Common Birds Census, Ringing Records. 5 Westland Avenue, Farnworth, Bolton BL4 9SR. 01204 709302.

HAMBLIN, Anthony Raymond (Tony); *b:* 5 September 1938 in Holcombe, Somerset; *w:* Valerie. Midsomer Norton Grammar School; Bristol Technical College. FRPS 1989. Engineering draughtsman. Special interest: bird photography. Numerous photographic trips to Europe, The Gambia, Kenya, Florida. Photographs used to illustrate over sixty books; also in many magazines eg *BBC Wildlife, Birds, Bird Watching, British Birds*. First winner BTO/Leitz Competition 1992; *BBC Wildlife* Urban Wildlife winner 1984; over twenty international salons. Lecturer on subjects ranging from photographing wildlife to birds of Warwickshire and of other countries. 8 Howard Close, Bidford-on-Avon, Warwickshire B50 4EL. 01789 772795.

HAMLEY, Darrell Bruce Dege, Wing Commander Retd; *b:* 9 April 1927 in Kingston-on-Thames, Surrey; *w:* Josephine (Jo). Kings School Bruton, Somerset. RAF College, Cranwell; Staff College, Camberley; Central Flying School; College of Air Warfare. Retired from RAF (1945-78) and Civil Aviation Authority (1978-87). Chairman RAF Ornithological Society 1976-78. Founder-member and Chairman Buckinghamshire Bird Club 1983-86, Secretary 1989-91. From 1972-78 took an active part in research into and action to reduce bird strikes on aircraft; served on joint civil/RAF Bird Strike Committee. Member of RAFOS expeditions to Unst (Shetlands) and Masirah (Arabian Sea). Contributor to *Birds of Buckinghamshire* (1993). Joint editor *Buckinghamshire Bird Club Newsletter* 1989-93 and author of articles. Articles also for *RAFOS Newsletter*. Talks on birdwatching to local societies and clubs in Buckinghamshire and adjacent counties. Within the University of the Third Age (U3A) started a successful ornithological group for local branch. Lectures for other U3A branches, 'in the firm belief that an active interest in birds is very beneficial in giving the older generation a hobby which is not only healthy but keeps their powers of observation well tuned.' Article on this subject in

Birdwatcher's Yearbook 1997. OIR: music (mainly baroque and operatic), fine arts, travel, aviation. 65 Friars Gardens, Hughenden Valley, High Wycombe, Bucks HP14 4LU. 01494 563438.

HAMPSHIRE, John Stephen; *b:* 23 June 1957 in Birmingham; *w:* Deborah. Window cleaner. Voluntary wardening on fourteen reserves in UK, inc Horsey Mere, Norfolk 1988-90. Voluntary wardening of Golden Eagles in England, Red Kites in Wales and Bonelli's Eagles in France. Participation in study of migrants near Bordeaux, France in spring 1987. Regular counter of Hen Harriers in the Hickling/Horsey area of Norfolk for the national Hen Harrier Winter Roost Survey, and of waterfowl at Hickling for the National Waterfowl Count. Rose Cottage, Beach Road, Lessingham, Norfolk NR12 0SU. 01692 580524.

HANCOCK, James A; OBE 1991, for services to ornithology; *b:* July 1921 in Sheffield; *w:* Sylvia. Solihull School. FRPS 1982. President, Cooper Division, Ethyl Corporation, Richmond, Virginia, USA, retired 1979. Elected Corresponding Fellow AOU 1995. President BTO 1984-89 and Hampshire Ornithological Society 1986-. Past Treasurer, ICBP British Section. Past Chairman, 1937 Bird Club. Past Council Member of RSPB, FFPS and Hants and Isle of Wight NT. Member of Mountfort Expedition to Pakistan (1967). Leader of Research Expeditions to Argentina (1980), China (1981), Australia (1986). Field studies conducted in India, Peru, Chile, Indonesia, Kenya, S Africa, Seychelles, Singapore, Japan, Canada, Zimbabwe, USA (Florida, Texas, Hawaii, California). Author *The Birds of the Wetlands* (1984). Co-author with H Elliott *The Herons of the World* (1978); with J A Kushlan *The Heron Handbook* (1984); with J A Kushlan and M P Kahl *The Storks, Ibises and Spoonbills of the World* (1992). Papers in *British Birds, Condor, Ibis.* Articles in popular magazines. Past Director *Animals Magazine* (now *BBC Wildlife*). Editorial Adviser *Natural World.* BTO Jubilee Medal 1992. Many lectures to leading ornithological and conservation organisations in UK, also in Kenya, China, India, W Europe and USA. Guest lecturer/adviser and organiser for wildlife tours to India and Africa. OIR: dry-fly fishing. Jollers, Sparsholt, Winchester, Hants SO21 2NS.

HANNIGAN, Ronan Denis; *b:* 26 September 1962 in Dublin, Ireland; *w:* Maria. BCL (Univ College Dublin, 1983), Post Graduate Diploma in European Law (Univ College Dublin, 1985). Qualified Solicitor and Commissioner for Oaths (1986) and Chartered Arbitrator (1987). Solicitor and Environmental Lawyer. Chairman, Capercaillie Trust (voluntary conservation organisation) and Wildlife Conservation Society 1980-84. Special interests: research, conservation and establishment of stable populations of certain sub-species endemic to the island of Ireland, eg Irish Red Grouse, Irish Dipper and Irish Jay; protection and conservation of birds of prey in Ireland, inc Barn, Long-eared and Short-eared Owls, Hen Harrier, Buzzard and Merlin; reintroduction of species previously extinct in Ireland, inc White-tailed and Golden Eagles and Capercaillie. Author of journal articles and various papers prepared for lobbying Government Ministers, the European Commission and other vested interest groups. Participant in establishing private reserves specifically to protect species that have drastically declined in the Republic of Ireland, such as Corncrake, Grey Partridge, Quail. OIR: art, history, politics, natural sciences, wines; involved in a number of outdoor recreations and field sports. Lausanne, 13 Airfield Park, Donnybrook, Dublin 4, Ireland. +353 (0)1 6615525.

HARDING, Andrew Vaughan (Andy); *b:* 5 August 1950 in Chepstow, Gwent; *p:* Mairi Grieve. LLB (Manchester, 1971), Dip Ind Relations and Trade Union Studies (Middlesex Polytechnic, 1972). University administrator/manager. Organiser of North Bucks Birders 1983-. Founding committee member Buckinghamshire Bird Club 1980-83. Buckinghamshire Bird Recorder 1989-. Member Buckinghamshire Wildlife Liaison Committee and its Species Sub-committee 1990-92. Wildfowl counter and participant in BTO surveys. Special interest: identification. Editor of revised editions of *Birds Around Milton Keynes*. Editor *North Bucks Bird Report* (monthly) since 1980 and of systematic list in *Buckinghamshire Bird Report* since 1988. Articles on a variety of topics for newsletters, journals and books, largely orientated towards Buckinghamshire and its birds and bird sites, with some on identification. OIR: National Hunt racing, playing golf, watching virtually all other sport, cooking, theatre and opera. 15 Jubilee Terrace, Stony Stratford, Milton Keynes MK11 1DU. 01908 565896; work 01908 653328.

HARDING, Barrie Douglas (Baz); *b:* West Challow, Berks; *w:* Janet. Ashton Grammar School, Dunstable 1956-62. Dip in Management Studies (Norwich City College, 1982). School caretaker. Wardening for varying periods during 1963-72, inc Cairngorms; Calf of Man; Station Biologique de la Tour du Valat, Camargue, France; Point Pelee National Park, Ontario, Canada. Bedfordshire Bird Recorder 1974-78; during this period participated in BTO breeding surveys, acted as wildfowl count organiser and produced a number of reports to RSPB and others on eg inland waters of ornithological importance. Instigator and organiser of Norfolk Breeding Bird Survey 1980-82 (published 1986). Lecturer to many organisations on ornithology and general natural history. Author *Bedfordshire Bird Atlas* (1979). Contributor of notes to *British Birds*. Bird-related travel to several W European countries, Russia (inc Siberia), Canada. Duke of Edinburgh's Gold Award. Finder of Scarlet Tanager on Isles of Scilly, first for Britain. Member: Golden Oriole Group. OIR: dragonflies and butterflies, sport, reading, gardening. 6 Braydeston Avenue, Brundall, Norwich NR13 5JX. 01603 715474.

HARDMAN, Joseph Arthur (Joe); *b:* 5 August 1930 in Cheadle Hulme, Cheshire; *w:* Ann. Bury Grammar School 1941-48. BSc Horticulture (Nottingham, 1954). Agricultural entomologist in Public Service, retired. BTO Council 1989-94. BTO Ringing Committee 1969-73, Chairman 1991-94. BTO Regional Representative Warwickshire 1961-. Co-organiser (with wife, Ann) BTO Ringers' Conference 1971-. Convenor Arden Ringing Group 1975-. Part-time tutor in ornithology, Univ Birmingham Dept of Continuing Education 1966-. Leader of Mediterranean natural history tours for Univ Birmingham and Field Studies Council 1991-. Special interests: ringing and survey work. Member of British Ringing Scheme since 1949; co-originator of Maltese Ringing Scheme (1965); promotion of ringing in Ireland (1970-79). Participant in Common Birds Census (1962-87) and Nest Record Scheme since 1945. Long-term involvement in Mute Swan and Cormorant studies. Occasional articles in county wildlife trust magazines, *Birdwatcher's Yearbook*, *BTO News* etc. Occasional broadcaster on local radio and contributor to Central TV 'Heart of the Country' programme. BTO Bernard Tucker Medallist (jointly with wife) 1975; each a BTO Jubilee Medallist 1995. OIR: active member of Warwickshire WT through professional interest in botany and entomology. Red Hill House, Red Hill, Alcester, Warks B49 6NQ. 01789 763159.

HARDWICK, Mark Andrew; *b:* 15 October 1962 in Trowbridge, Wilts. Investment manager. Member London Ornithological Records Committee 1990-. Bird Recorder for Greater London. Special interests: 'local patch' study (Hampstead Heath), migration, identification, particularly interested in W Palearctic birds (though not necessarily *in* the region). Widely travelled around the world in search of birds, eg Australia, Japan, Malaysia, USA, Israel, several Arabian countries. Leader of numerous field trips, both residential and day. Editor *London Bird Report* 1990-, and *Hampstead Heath Ornithological Report* 1991-. Co-author of paper on rare birds in the London area for *London Bird Report* 1991; also other articles in *LBR*,

Bird Watching and *Birding World*. Member: OSME. The Garden Flat, 13 Southcote Road, Tufnell Park, London N19 5BJ. 0171 700 2745.

HARDY, Eric; *b:* 'USA' (upstairs in the attic, Liverpool). 'Now in my mid-80s' (19.3.96). Freelance naturalist. Weekly 'Countryside' feature etc *Liverpool Daily Post* since 1929. WEA annual lecturer on ornithology and natural history, West Lancs and Cheshire since 1935. Extra-mural lectures on ornithology, Liverpool Univ 1971-75. Oxford Univ Extra-mural lectures, North Staffs 1952-61. BBC broadcaster since 1936; weekly 'Countryside' programme BBC Radio Merseyside since 1969. Director, Bird Studies, Burton Manor Adult College, Cheshire 1958-70. Founder and Hon Sec since 1938 Merseyside Naturalists' Assocn. Ornithological referee and librarian Liverpool Naturalists' Field Club 1932-38. Represented naturalists on Committee of Associated Learned Societies of Liverpool and District 1932-38. Founder and Hon Sec Jerusalem Naturalists' Club 1945-46. Regional organiser National Duck Counts in Liverpool area since 1947. Lancashire and Cheshie Fauna Committee 1931-39. North West representative on Council for Nature 1966-79. Wartime commission (Captain), Army Pigeon Service, Royal Corps of Signals, Middle East etc. Special interest: migration (orientation). Author *Birds of the Liverpool Area* (1941), *Handlist of the Birds of Palestine* (Cairo, 1946), *A-Z Pigeon Guide* (1951), *Bird Lover's Week-end Book* (1952), *The Naturalist in Lakeland* (1973), *Birdwatching in Lancashire* (1979), *Guide to Birds of Scotland* (1978), *Birdwatching in Cheshire* (1988) etc. Editor *Wild Birds* magazine 1946-47, *Nature Lover* monthly magazine 1948-50, *Bulletin Jerusalem Naturalists' Club* 1946-47, *Northwestern Bird Report* (MNA) since 1931. Declined to accept nomination (by Dr W Bourne) for BOU, 1967. Member: Zoological Soc of London since 1935. Hon Member Liverpool Univ Biological Soc 1940. Membership Certificate RSPB 1931 (and local voluntary lecturer). Lancs executive of CPRE 1958-88. OIR: gardening; aquaria (President Merseyside Aquarist Soc 1958-80; 'Naturalist's Notebook' in *Aquarist & Pondkeeper* since 1930); fish (Ministry-appointed representative, Lancs & Western Sea Fisheries Committee 1955-76); botany; entomology; Life Governor, Imperial Cancer Research Fund since 1974. 47 Woodsorrel Road, Liverpool L15 6UB. 0151 722 2819.

HARPER, Rex Arthur; *b:* 12 April 1935 in Bath; *w:* Julie. RSPCA Warden (Home Manager) since 1987. Special interests: bird ailments, rehabilitation, special diets. Wide range of work with many species of bird inc exotics in zoos and bird gardens; breeder of numerous species in captivity. Author *Keeping a Parrot in the Family* (1970). Papers published on several species, inc Fulmar. Restricted licence to ring auks and special licence for swans (to include 'Darvic' rings). Ferndale, Blowing House Road, Perranporth, Cornwall TR6 0BA. 01872 572953.

HARRAP, Simon Charles Benjamin; *b:* 6 October 1959 in Oxford. BA Sociology (Birmingham Polytechnic, 1983). Ornithologist. Staff leader with Birdquest since 1987. Co-author (with Nigel Redman) *Bird Watching in Britain: a site by site guide* (1987) and (with David Quinn) *Tits, Nuthatches & Treecreepers* (1995). Editorial Board *Birding World* 1991-, also many articles and notes; regular contributor to *Bird Watching*; further items in *Birding, British Birds, Bull BOC, Bull OBC, Forktail, Limicola*. Special interests: systematics; cuckoos; robins and chats; song, distribution and taxonomy of babblers; identification and taxonomy of *Cettia, Bradypterus, Acrocephalus* and *Phylloscopus* warblers; bird vocalisations (and recording techniques); bird photography. Member: ABA, ABC, OBC (Council for three years), OSME, WAOS. OIR: mammals, dog walking, Indian food. 1 Norwich Road, Edgefield, Melton Constable, Norfolk NR24 2RP.

HARRIS, Alan John; *b:* 10 April 1957 in Epping, Essex; *w:* Sally. BA Graphic Design (Middlesex Polytechnic, 1980). Freelance bird illustrator since 1980. Committee Rye Meads Ringing Group 1978-. Art consultant *British Birds* 1988-. Judge, Bird Illustrator of the Year 1989-. Special interests: ringing, local survey work, identification (esp Old World warblers and gulls). Many bird-related trips abroad, mainly to Mediterranean and Near East. Illustrations published in books eg *Swallows* by Peter Tate (1981), *A Field Guide to the Birds of Britain and Europe* by John Gooders (1986, extended to cover Europe 1990), *The Macmillan Guide to Bird Identification* by Keith Vinicombe and Laurel Tucker (1989), *Storks, Ibises and Spoonbills of the World* by James Hancock *et al* (1992), *Kingfishers, Bee-eaters and Rollers* by Kathie and C Hilary Fry (1992), *Finches and Sparrows, an identification guide* by Pete Clement and John Davis (1993), *The Macmillan Birders' Guide to European and Middle Eastern Birds* by Hadoram Shirihai and David Christie (1996); also contributor of illustrations to *BWP* Vols 5-7 (1988-93). Many illustrations in magazines and a number of identification papers in *British Birds*. Bird Illustrator of the Year (*British Birds*) 1982. 60 East Park, Harlow, Essex CM17 0SE. 01279 424307.

HARRIS, Michael Anthony (Mike); *b:* 5 February 1954 in Ilford, Essex; w: Anita. Construction manager. Special interests: ringing and migration. BTO 'A' ringer since 1974, trainer 1974-77, sponsor 1978-. Committee Rye Meads Ringing Group since 1973, Ringing Secretary and Trainer 1973-77,

Hon Secretary 1978-91, Chairman 1991-. Also Sawbridgeworth Marsh SSSI 1986-90; Bradwell Bird Observatory 1975-76,87,88,91; Calf of Man Bird Obs 1977,78,79; Herts Barn Owl Release Scheme 1987 and 92. Assisting at many other sites and schemes, inc Sandwich Bay Bird Obs (cannon-net waders, clap-net Snow Buntings, tape-lure Lapland Buntings); Dungeness Bird Obs (mist-net and trap migrants); Rainham Marsh/Pitsea (cannon-net gulls); Long Point Bird Obs, Canada (mist-net New World warblers). Fieldwork for BTO Breeding Atlas and New Breeding Atlas; *Atlas of Breeding Birds of the London Area* 1968-72; *Hertfordshire Breeding Bird Atlas* 1972-73; *Breeding Birds of Hertfordshire* 1988-92. Also all local and county surveys eg Mute Swan, Golden Plover, Corn Bunting. Overseas trips for birds include Canary Islands, France, Switzerland, Germany, Spain (inc Mallorca, Ibiza), Crete, Canada. Co-writer of *Rye Meads Ringing Group Report* Nos 8-11, 1974-88 (co-author of 'Measurements of Rye Meads Skylarks' in No 8). OIR: sea fishing, dragonflies, general natural history, watching sport. 80 White Post Field, Sawbridgeworth, Herts CM21 0BY. 01279 724874.

HARRIS, Michael Philip (Mike); *b:* 28 April 1939 in Swansea, W Glamorgan; *p:* Dr Sarah Wanless. Swansea Grammar School. BSc Zoology (Wales, Swansea, 1960), PhD Aspects of the ecology of *Larus* gulls (Wales, Swansea, 1963), DSc for research on the ecology of breeding seabirds (Wales, Swansea, 1985). Hon Professor, Univ Glasgow 1996. Principal Scientific Officer, NERC, Institute of Terrestrial Ecology (in charge of seabird projects) since 1972. Prev: fellowships and appointments at Edward Grey Institute of Field Ornithology, Univ Oxford 1963-72; period included five years at the Charles Darwin Research Station developing studies on tropical seabirds, control of breeding under constant day length, and the effects of increasing tourism on seabird populations. Current or past member of BTO Council and Bird Ringing Committee, and BOU Council. Special interests: seabirds (esp auks, shags, gulls, petrels) and oystercatchers; population processes and factors influencing numbers; population monitoring; food and feeding. Spent four years in Galapagos Islands, single field seasons in Australia, Bird Island (S Georgia) and the high Andes of Peru. Author *A Field Guide to the Birds of Galapagos* (1974) and *The Puffin* (1984). Current or past member of editorial boards of *Bird Study, Scottish Birds, Seabird*. Many publications in ornithological and ecological journals, mainly on seabirds. BOU Medal 1992. Member: Seabird Group, Pacific Seabird Group. OIR: islands. NERC, Institute of Terrestrial Ecology, Hill of Brathens, Banchory, Kincardineshire AB31 4BY. 01330 823434; fax 01330 823303.

HARRIS, Peter Malcolm; Revd; *b:* 20 May 1952 in Birmingham; *w:* Miranda. King's School Worcester 1965-70. MA Religious Studies (Emmanuel College, Cambridge, 1974), PGCE 1975, Dip HE (Trinity College Bristol, 1980). Warden, A Rocha Christian Field Study Centre and Bird Observatory since 1983. Special interests: ringing, migration, education. Travel in Malawi, Kenya, Turkey, Morocco, Senegal, Iberia. Author *Under the Bright Wings* (1993). Papers in *Ringing & Migration*; several articles in Portuguese conservation magazines; contributor to *A Rocha Observatory Report*; two programmes on TV in Portugal about the work of A Rocha; photographs published in *Gulls: a guide to identification* by P J Grant (1982). OIR: time with family and friends; sport, esp watching rugby; work with Portuguese student movement GBU. Cruzinha, Mexilhoeira Grande, 8500 Portimão, Portugal. +351 (0)82 96380; fax +351 (0)82 96860. Or c/o A Rocha Trust, 3 Hooper Street, Cambridge CB1 2NZ.

HARRIS, Robin Gifford; *b:* 25 February 1941 in Mountfield, E Sussex; *w:* Diane. Bexhill County Grammar School. Former manager in Local Government. Council Sussex Ornithological Society 1983-87. Council Hastings and East Sussex NHS 1988-91, 1993-. Sussex OS representative, Rye Harbour Nature Reserve Management Committee 1986- and Castle Water NRMC 1993-. Sussex OS 10km square steward for TQ72 from start of scheme in 1981. Special interests: survey work and population studies. Participant in BTO, RSPB, Sussex OS and other surveys; Wetland Bird Survey counter at Darwell Reservoir since 1976. Editor of Pett Pools Project Report, 1981-83. Articles in *Sussex Ornithological Society Newsletter* and *Annual Report of the Hastings and East Sussex NHS*. OIR: the countryside in general, walking with the family, photography, the national parks of England and Wales. 16 Fearon Road, Hastings, E Sussex TN34 2DL. 01424 442423.

HARRISON, Graham Roland; *b:* 2 January 1938 in Birmingham; *w:* Janet. Dip Town Planning 1964 and Dip Landscape Architecture 1967 (Birmingham School of Planning). Fellow Royal Town Planning Institute 1984. Head of Policy Development, Dept Planning, Transport and Economic Strategy, Warks CC since 1995. Committee West Midland Bird Club 1969-, Deputy Chairman 1988-. Special interests: habitat photography, local distribution studies. Editor and principal author *Birds of the West Midlands* (1982); co-author (with Jack Sankey) *Where to Watch Birds in the West Midlands* (1987). Editor *West Midland Bird Report* 1975-85. Articles in various country and wildlife magazines. Influence with the creation of nature reserves through job. OIR: photography, esp landscapes and habitats. Bryher, Hatton Green, Hatton, Warwick CV35 7LA. 01926 484412.

HARROP, Andrew Harold John; *b:* 21 October 1959 in Sierra Leone; *w:* Josephine. Manchester Grammar School. BA Lit Hum (Queen's College, Oxford, 1982), MA 1985, PGCE (Newcastle, 1983). Head of Classics at Leicester Grammar School. YOC Leader (Southport RSPB Group) 1970s. Rutland Water Nature Reserve Management Committee 1990-. Leicestershire & Rutland Ornithological Society Referees' Sub-committee 1991-. Wetland Bird Survey organiser for Leics 1995-. Special interests: identification and status; ducks and gulls. Participant in wildfowl counts and breeding bird surveys. Widely travelled in W Palearctic, W and Central Africa, India and Nepal, Canada, New England. Contributor to *Best Days with British Birds* (1989). Author of articles on Red-crested Pochard, Baikal Teal and American Wigeon in *Birding World* and on divers and Herring Gull in *Devon Birds*. Editor of *Caradon Bird Report* 1986 and 1987. Member: ABC, OBC, OSME. OIR: classical and folk music, reading, whisky, theatre, cricket. 30 Dean Street, Oakham, Rutland, Leics LE15 6AF. 01572 757134.

HARROP, Hugh Richard; *b:* 25 February 1969 in Bridgwater, Somerset. Proprietor, Shetland Wildlife Tours. Ornithological consultant and wildlife photographer. Prev: Administrator Fair Isle Bird Observatory 1991; research asst RSPB 1992; research asst Shetland Oil Terminal Environmental Advisory Group 1993. Committee Cardiff Naturalists' Society 1986. National Wildfowl Count organiser for Glamorgan 1986-89. Special interests: identification, migration. Author *Where to Watch Birds in Shetland* and *A Checklist of the Birds of Shetland*. Identification articles in *Birding World* and *Birdwatch*; mystery photograph texts in *British Birds*. Compiler *Shetland Bird Report* 1991,92,95, *Glamorgan Bird Report* 1986,88; joint ornithological compiler *Fair Isle Bird Observatory Report* 1991. Environmental journalist for national press; wildlife correspondent for *The Shetland Times* and BBC. Member: ABA, ABC, Seabird Group. 2 Colonial Place, Scatness, Virkie, Shetland ZE3 9JT. Tel/fax 01950 460254.

HARRUP, Brian Stanley; *b:* 14 October 1928 in Melbourn, Cambs; *w:* Sheila. Retired Master Printer. Town Secretary Cambridge Bird Club 1975-79. Special interests: records for winter Blackcaps and garden Siskins from 1970 (information on these supplied to authors of published work); birds of Whittlesford Gravel Pits from 1982. Participant in Wetland Bird

Survey and in BTO surveys inc Garden Bird Feeding Survey and Nest Records Scheme. OIR: stamp collecting, gardening, trad jazz. 49 Priam's Way, Stapleford, Cambridge CB2 5DT. 01223 842084.

HARVEY, Michael Stephen (Mike); *b:* 27 September 1941 in St Albans, Herts; *w:* Myrth. BSc Eng (Thames Polytechnic, 1970). CEng, MIEE 1976. Technical Director, Lattelkom, Latvia. Survey respondent, migrating shorebirds, Grenada, West Indies for Manomet Bird Observatory, USA 1975-76. Correspondent with James Bond/Academy of Natural Sciences, Philadelphia USA on West Indian migrant records 1962-66. Explored interior of Grand Cayman and Cayman Brac for Grand Cayman Thrush and/or West Indian Red-legged Thrush (again corresponded with Acad of Nat Sci in Philadelphia, ICBP and Univ Florida, Gainesville) 1965-66. Searched mountains of St Lucia for St Lucia Parrot, Sempers Warbler, Whitebreasted Thrasher and St Lucian Black Finch with the late Stanley John of St Lucia, also 1965-66. Joint recorder for Antigua with Carroll Holland of Audubon Society (Florida) 1973-80, and acknowledged in his observations on the birds of Antigua 1978. During this period visited interior of Basseterre, Guadeloupe to ascertain if Guadeloupe Woodpecker present and/or common; also searched for Forest Thrush. Visited Dominica, Saba and Monserrat to look for Forest Thrush and other endemics, and visited Kenscoff in Haiti. Spent 1981-84 in Nigeria, able to photograph Fourbanded Sandgrouse in Borgu Game Reserve. 1987-91 kept records in Bahrain for Bahrain NHS (though not the society's official recorder). Many interesting notes on migrants, esp Grey Hypocolius (passed to BNHS). 1991-92 kept notes on Saudi Arabian migrants through Riyadh, esp Stone Curlew and Caspian Plover (passed to Arthur Stagg). Special interests: West Indian endemics, migration. Member WAOS. OIR: gardening, music, cars. 32 High Street, Milton Malsor, Northants NN7 3AS. 01604 858601.

HATCH, Christopher Michael (Chris); *b:* 28 June 1957 in Ebbw Vale, Gwent. West Monmouth Grammar School, Pontypool. BSc Zoology and Botany (Univ College Cardiff, 1978). CBiol, MIBiol 1984. Area Manager, Hamdden/Welsh Water since 1992 (duties to manage wildlife conservation and recreation on Welsh Water reservoirs in S Wales). Work includes special projects in relation to breeding, passage and overwintering birds; management of bird protection, bird surveys and birdwatching activities; education and woodland management. Committee Gwent Ornithological Society 1992-95. Scientific Sub-committee of Gwent WT 1978. Evening class tutor on birds and wildlife 1994. Voluntary wardening of Peregrine nests. Regular participation in surveys. Co-ordinator of BTO Zeneca Bird

Challenge for business at reservoir sites. Special interests: identification, bird ecology and conservation, photography, organising and leading birdwatching holidays. Countries visited for birds include Turkey, Spain (inc Mallorca), former Yugoslavia, Morocco, Poland, Greece, India, Romania, Bulgaria, Portugal, Tunisia, Israel, The Gambia. OIR: mammals, insect and flower photography, botanical survey work, walking and cycling. 10 Severn View, Pentwyn, Abersychan, Pontypool, Gwent NP4 7TE. 01495 772603.

HAVERS, James Roger; *b:* 21 July 1965 in Crawley, W Sussex. Airline finance clerk. Sussex Orn Soc 10km square steward for TQ23 (Crawley) since 1994; also responsible for part of TQ24 (Gatwick) in Sussex since 1987. Committee Crawley and Horsham RSPB Members' Group since c1988 with position as Recorder. Special interests: collecting data in immediate 10km square, counting and monitoring birds in typical farmland and woodland habitats; mainly interested in common passerines, with an enthusiasm for buntings, finches and thrushes. Compiled study report of wildlife in the Crawley area which includes systematic summaries of birds. OIR: dragonflies and butterflies, new age music, aviation. 9 Hurst Close, Gossops Green, Crawley, W Sussex RH11 8LQ. 01293 534214.

HAWKER, David Martin; *b:* 11 November 1942 in Birmingham; *w:* Hilary. BSc Agricultural Botany (Nottingham, 1964), PGCE (Birmingham, 1965), Cert in Computer Education (Birmingham, 1981). Founder-member IEEM (1992). Ecological and environmental consultant since 1990. Prev: work for NCC (1983-89) with studies ranging from the effect of commercial cockling on winter wader numbers on part of the Solway to breeding bird populations of ancient semi-natural woodland and uplands. WWT Wildfowl Count organiser for three reservoirs in W Midlands 1972-75. Research Committee West Midland Bird Club 1975-80 and Membership Sec 1976-80. Founder-member RSPB Galloway Branch 1986-89. Tutor in ornithology for Glasgow Univ Extra-mural Dept in Dumfries and Galloway 1986-88, and for Community Education classes in D & G 1975-88. Birdwatching guide and organiser of weekend and week-long courses in D & G 1984-92. Special interests: photography, birding in British Columbia, population studies. Carried out a CBC-style survey of two W Midlands reservoirs (1957-80) after the work of H G Alexander (1923-37); annual rookery census in Galloway 1983-; winter roosting Starling numbers in Birmingham, the Midlands and Galloway 1965-90. Count organiser for Auchencairn Bay 1986-90 and Fleet Bay 1984-. Organiser BTO Buzzard Survey, Galloway 1985 and Rook Survey 1996. Participant in large number of other BTO surveys from the 1962 Road Deaths Inquiry onwards, including the Breeding and Winter Atlases. Organiser of the Moseley Bog (Birmingham) Management Committee 1978-82 (site now an LNR after threat to develop for housing). Small number of short articles/letters in *British Birds*; two articles in *West Midland Bird Report* and one in *Bird Walks in Dumfries & Galloway* by Galloway RSPB Members' Group (1989). Lectures on birds to a variety of societies. Windywalls, Upper Drumwall, Gatehouse of Fleet, Castle Douglas, Kirkcudbrightshire DG7 2DE. 01557 814249.

HAWKINS, Andrew Francis Alexander (Frank); *b:* 23 February 1962 in Bristol; *p:* Dr Joanna Durbin. BSc Zoology (Exeter, 1984), MSc Conservation (Univ College London, 1987), PhD Forest degradation and the West Malagasy bird community (London, 1994). Survey contractor, Asian Wetlands Bureau, Kuala Lumpur, Malaysia 1986. Consultant ornithologist, Cordama Foundation survey of Ankarana Special Reserve, Madagascar 1987. Team member, Cambridge Madagascar Rainforest Expedition 1988. ICBP Arabian Gulf Shorebird Survey 1992. Principal Co-ordinator ICBP Angola Scarp Project 1992. Many bird and primate surveys and inventories in Madagascar 1992-96. Special interests: effects of forest exploitation on birds, birds of Madagascar (esp conservation, biogeography and phylogeny), photography, sound recording, relationship between people and birds. Papers published in *Biol Cons* and *Bird Cons Internat*; also conference proceedings and reports to sponsors on eg Malagasy and Angolan bird distribution. Member: ABC, Working Group on Birds in the Madagascar Region. OIR: mammals and reptiles of Madagascar. 10 Lodway Gardens, Pill, Bristol BS20 0DL. 01275 372125. Or BP 8511 Antananarivo, Madagascar. +261 2 31622.

HAYHOW, Simon James; *b:* 18 June 1957 in Wendover, Bucks; *w:* Mary Jane. Oakwood Secondary School, Rotherham; Thomas Rotherham Sixth Form College. BSc Environmental Sciences (East Anglia, 1978), MSc Museum Studies (Leicester, 1990). AMA 1993. Curator (Natural History) Lancashire County Museums Service since 1991. Prev: Keeper (Nat Hist) Oldham Museum 1989-91. Various ornithological research posts 1979-88, eg Univ Hull Dept Zoology (Humber Bird Survey) 1981-82; NCC Upland Bird Survey (Durham/N Yorks) 1983; RSPB Moorland Bird Study (Wester Ross in 1987 and Sutherland/Caithness in 1985 and 1988). Served on Survey Committees of Sheffield Bird Study Group and Rotherham and District Orn Soc. WEA tutor on birds of the Fylde coast 1991/92. Special interests: migration, waders, Corn Bunting, birds of the Philippines.

Regular participant in BTO surveys since 1970. Detailed bird survey of Thrybergh Reservoir, Rotherham 1969-89. Overseas travel for birds to Philippines, France, Spain, Greece, Andorra. Co-editor *Thrybergh Reservoir Bird Report* 1983-89; co-compiler *Fylde Bird Report* 1993. Articles in *Bird Study*, *British Birds*, *The Lapwing* (Doncaster and Dist Orn Soc), *The Magpie* (SBSG), *Lancashire Wildlife Journal*, *Sorby Record*. Member: OBC. Son of Kenneth James Hayhow, ornithologist. OIR: entomology (esp Diptera), photography, Sheffield Wednesday. 15 Brookfield Road, Thornton, Thornton Cleveleys, Lancs FY5 4DR. 01253 876621 (work).

HAYWARD-HARRIS, Martin John; *b:* 28 October 1959 in Reading, Berks. Dip MSIAD. Freelance natural history model maker and dioramist. Prev: Model Maker, Natural History Museum 1984-88; Model Maker, Zoologisk Museum Copenhagen 1988. Cover illustrations for *Birding World*; features in *Bird Watching*. Many exhibitions, eg BTO, RSPB, Wildlife Art Gallery (Suffolk), WWT Arundel, East African Wildlife Society, Society of Wildlife Artists. One-man shows in Britain and Luxembourg. Auctioned by Sotheby's and Christies. Sculptor in bronze. OIR: film, theatre, music (esp saxophone). 47 Clarendon Road, Earley, Reading RG6 1PB. 01734 268977.

HAYWOOD, Sacha; *b:* 13 April 1962 in France; *w:* Agnès. Licence, Biology (Paris, 1983); Maîtrise, Genetics and Development (Paris, 1985); DEA Evolutionary Sciences (Montpellier, 1986); DPhil Ornithology (Oxford, 1991). Post-doctoral Research Fellow, Oxford Univ since 1991. Special interests: evolutionary theory, clutch size. Papers in *The Auk*, *Ibis*, *Quarterly Review of Biology*. Edward Grey Institute of Field Ornithology, Dept of Zoology, Univ Oxford, South Parks Road, Oxford OX1 3PS. 01865 271143.

HAZARD, David Roy; *b:* 18 September 1959 in Doncaster, S Yorks; *w:* Ann. BEng (Bradford, 1983). Doncaster and District Ornithological Society: various posts since 1986, President 1996-. Voluntary warden Thorpe Marsh NR 1991-. Founder-member and Secretary, Doncaster Ringing Group 1992-. BTO 'A' ringer since 1985, also trainer and sponsor. Special interests: ringing, population monitoring, BTO Constant Effort Sites scheme. Compiler of ringing sections of *Doncaster Bird Report* 1987-. OIR: playing squash, badminton, golf; founder-member and captain, Doncaster Mets Rounders Club. 41 Jossey Lane, Scawthorpe, Doncaster, S Yorks DN5 9DB. 01302 788044.

HEALY, Susan Denise (Sue); *b:* 4 December 1962 in New Zealand. BSc Zoology and Physiology (Univ Otago, NZ, 1984), DPhil Zoology (St Hilda's College, Oxford, 1990). Lecturer in psychology. Special interests: behaviour, esp learning and memory in birds; avian neurobiology; food storing in passerines; foraging in hummingbirds. Papers in eg *Anim Behav*, *Behavioural Brain Research*, *Quarterly J Experimental Psychol*. Dept of Psychology, Univ of Newcastle upon Tyne NE1 7RU. 0191 222 5056.

HELM, Christopher; *b:* 1 February 1937 in Dundee; *w:* Amanda. BA Classics and Law (Cambridge, 1960), Postgraduate Diploma in Management (Harvard Business School, 1982). Book publisher (ornithology). BOU Council 1991-99 (Vice President to 1999). Special interests: bird censuses, identification, ornithological literature. Member: ABC, OBC, OSME. OIR: Cricket, bridge, tennis, theatre, opera. The Banks, Mountfield, Robertsbridge, E Sussex TN32 5JY. 01580 880561.

HEMMINGS, Jo; *b:* 25 December 1955 in London. BA Psychology and Education (Warwick, 1979). Publishing Manager, Natural History and Travel, New Holland (Publishers) Ltd since 1994. Prev: Executive Editor, Reed Illustrated Books (Hamlyn) 1991-94; Editorial Director, Christopher Helm Publishers Ltd 1986-90; Natural History Editor, Croom Helm 1980-86. Responsible for numerous ornithological publications inc most Helm identification guides; many avifaunas (eg *The Birds of Nepal* and *The Birds of Japan*); 'Where to Watch' guides; Hamlyn species guides. Member: ABC, NBC, OBC. OSME. Particular interest in bird art. OIR: music, cinema, theatre. 59 Eltham Gardens, Eltham, London SE9 1AP. 0181 859 8696. Or New Holland (Publishers) Ltd, 24 Nutford Place, London W1 6DQ. 0171 724 7773.

HENSHALL, Kenneth William (Ken); *b:* 15 October 1916 in Oldham, Lancs; *w:* Marjorie. Oundle School. BSc Tech in Building (Manchester, 1937). Assoc Inst of Building by exam 1961. Civil engineer, retired. Wales Committee RSPB 1968-70. Council RSPB 1969-74. Secretary, Vice President, President Cardiff Naturalists' Society Ornithological Section 1967-73. Council, Vice President, President Cardiff Nat Soc 1970-77. Fieldwork for county bird report 1967-94, BTO Breeding Atlas 1968-72 and New Breeding Atlas 1988-91; also for many single-species enquiries, pilot census project, Breeding Bird Survey, Waterways Bird Survey 1980-88. OIR: hill walking (prev mountaineering), member of literary society and local Probus Club. Crofthead, Penmark, Barry, S Glamorgan CF62 3BP. 01446 710520.

HERBERT, Clive; *b:* 29 November 1960 in Barnet, Herts. Warden Oak Hill Woods NR, East Barnet 1985-94. Records Co-ordinator Barnet Biological Recording Programme 1993-. Special interests: urban birds, esp status and distribution. Joint author (with John Colmans) *Checklist of the Birds of Barnet* (1989). Contributions to *Naturalist in Barnet* (priv print, 1990), ie history of Red-backed Shrike, status of Tawny Owl and breeding distribution of House Martin in Barnet; also to *Hertfordshire Bird Report* on past and present bird life of Monken Hadley Common. Regular lecturer on wide range of ornithological topics and leader of field trips in Britain. OIR: mammals (esp bats) and herpetofauna, environmental education, youth work, cricket. 67a Ridgeway Avenue, East Barnet, Herts EN4 8TL. 0181 440 6314.

HERBERT, Ian Jeffrey; *b:* 21 October 1948 in Gravesend, Kent; *w:* Victoria. Gravesend Technical High School. PG Dip Environmental Management; completing MSc on Lapwing at Univ Ulster Coleraine, 1996. Head Warden Crom NNR, Upper Lough Erne, since 1989. Prev: Reserves Officer IWC 1986-88. Led first ornithological survey of River Shannon Callows (floodplain) 1987. National Organiser for Republic of Ireland for BTO New Breeding Atlas and member of Atlas working group 1989. Committee IWC Tipperary Branch 1984-89. Organised Little Tern protection on E coast of Ireland and Common Tern conservation project on Lough Derg 1984. Participated in gull, tern, Common Scoter, Corncrake, wildfowl and breeding wader surveys. Special interests: (since age 9) breeding biology and habitats of British birds, esp waders; bird photography. Bird-related visits to Taman Negara, W Malaysia and Taratao Island, Thailand. Co-author of two papers on breeding waders of the Shannon Callows and author of paper on Garden Warbler in Ireland, both in *Irish Birds*. Occasional radio and TV appearances. Several photographs published. OIR: painting in watercolours; trout, salmon and sea angling; soccer (Gillingham). Stableyard, Crom, Newtownbutler, Co Fermanagh BT92 8AP. 01365 738883.

HERLIHY, Dorothy Jean; *b:* 13 December 1921 in Northwich, Cheshire. Executive director of natural history photographic agency, retired. RSPB Local Representative for NE Hampshire since 1967. Committee RSPB Members' Group NE Hampshire since inauguration in 1976. Committee Reading Ornithological Club 1971-77, 1981-84, Chairman 1977-80. Committee Hampshire Farming and Wildlife Advisory Group since inception in 1979. Special interests: birds of Fleet Pond, Shetland and the Surrey Heaths; ornithological bibliophile. Numerous expeditions to

Shetland; visits to Texas and Kenya. OIR: botany, entomology, (esp butterflies, dragonflies, damselflies), natural history books, gardening, the grandchildren. 2 Court Lodge Cottages, Church Road, Mersham, Kent TN25 6NS.

HERRINGSHAW, David (Dave); *b:* 17 August 1948 in Sheffield. Sheffield City Grammar School 1959-66. Cert Ed (Sheffield City Coll of Ed, 1969), BEd Biological Science/Geography (Sheffield, 1970). CBiol, MIBiol 1975. Director of Lower School/Science Teacher, Myers Grove School Sheffield. Part-time lecturer, Sheffield Univ Division of Adult Continuing Education, teaching ornithology, natural history and ecology 1978-. Founder-member Sheffield Bird Study Group 1972, Committee 1973-87, Ornithological Recorder 1972-81, Chairman 1983-85. Sheffield Records Sub-Committee 1973-95 and Derbyshire County Records Committee 1977-81. Yorkshire Naturalists' Union (Ornithological Section): member Yorkshire Records Committee 1980-81 and Protection of Birds Committee 1975-81, Vice-county Recorder (S & W Yorks) 1981. Regional co-ordinator BTO Breeding Atlas 1971-72. Co-ordinator Peak District Goshawk Study Group 1986-94. BTO 'C' ringer 1981-. Special interests: long-term monitoring of Peak District/Sheffield area raptors, and of Black Redstart population in Sheffield; long-term monitoring of breeding birds within the Peak District and Sheffield area; ringing pulli, esp birds of prey; habitat studies in Sheffield region. Co-author (with Roy Frost) *Birdwatching in the Dukeries and North Notts* (1979) and *Birdwatching in the Sheffield Area and the Peak District* (1984); (with Jon Hornbuckle) *Birds of the Sheffield Area including the North-east Peak District* (1985). Co-editor and contributor *Sheffield Bird Report/Birds in the Sheffield Area* 1973-82, 1984-89, and *The Magpie, Journal of Ornithology for the Sheffield Region* 1977-; editor *Sheffield Bird Study Group Bulletin* 1992-95. Articles/short notes in *The Naturalist* and *Sorby Record*. Lectures on above subjects to local societies. OIR: photography, botany, entomology (esp butterflies and dragonflies), mammals, molluscs (esp slugs), music, reading, collecting modern and antiquarian bird books, cooking, motor sport. 269 Shiregreen Lane, Sheffield S5 6AE. 0114 249 2313.

HEUBECK, Martin; *b:* 14 June 1955 in Crickhowell, Breconshire; *w:* Nancy. BSc Zoology (Aberdeen, 1977). Member of Ornithological Monitoring Programme for Shetland Oil Terminal Environmental Advisory Group since 1978. Aberdeen Univ Bird Club, Secretary and President 1974-77. Shetland Bird Club, Secretary and Chairman 1979-93. Seabird Group, Secretary 1991-95. Special interests: seabird population monitoring, seabird migration, beached bird surveys, oil pollution. Field co-ordinator for Esso Bernicia (1978) and Braer (1993) oil spills in Shetland. Expeditions: raptor migration in NE Turkey, autumn 1976; impact of hunting on Brünnich's Guillemot populations NW Greenland, 1987. Editor *Aberdeen University Bird Club Newsletter* 1974-77 and *Shetland Bird Club Newsletter* 1979-93, 1996-. Papers, articles and short notes in *BBC Wildlife*, *Bird Study*, *Environmental Conservation*, *Scottish Birds*, *Seabird*, *Sula*. Member: Dutch Seabird Group, OSME, Pacific Seabird Group, Seabird Group. OIR: beachcombing and cooking. Mansefield, Dunross-ness, Shetland ZE2 9JH. 01950 460304.

HEWETT, David Godfrey; *b:* 25 June 1933 in St Leonards-on-Sea, E Sussex; *w:* Judith. Consultant biologist. Committee Cambrian Ornithological Society 1991-. Council Welsh Orn Soc 1994-. Special interests: distribution and status of British birds (esp Chough, Yellowhammer, House Sparrow, Feral Pigeon), surveys of local areas (inc all-Wales Chough survey and various for BTO). Editor *Cambrian Bird Report* 1993-. OIR: botany, gardening, walking, handcrafts (inc DIY), reading. Bernina, Mount Road, Llanfairfechan, Conwy LL33 0HA. 01248 680660.

HEWITT, John; *b:* 30 March 1956 in Hythe, Kent; *p:* Mandy Higgs. Electrician. Partner in *Yorkshire Birding* magazine since 1992, partner in Budget Bird Tours since 1994. Founder-member Barnsley Bird Study Group (1970) and member of Records Panel since 1980. BTO 'C' ringer since 1978. Formerly Wath Ings Management Committee member and voluntary warden for approx twenty years. Special interests: study of birds in Wath Ings area (visits made most days for twenty-five years), watching migration on E coast, photography (over 6,000 slides from Britain and some thirty other countries visited). Numerous photographs published in *Birding World*, *Birdwatch*, *British Birds* as well as Spurn and Barnsley reports. Editor *Yorkshire Birding* from inception and of several Broomhill Ings reports. Appearance in Yorkshire TV programme on twitching. Many illustrated talks. OIR: playing and watching (Sheffield United) football. 14 Hoober View, Wombwell, Barnsley, S Yorks S73 0SH. 01226 751214.

HEYES, Clifford Peter; *b:* 29 April 1938 in Bolton, Lancs; *w:* Sheila. ARPS 1977. Sales consultant, British Gas. Bird recorder for Bolton Field Naturalists' Society 1988-. Special interest: bird photography. Extensive travel through Iberia and Scandinavia, and to a lesser extent France, Holland and Cyprus. Photographs published in books eg *The First Eden* by David Attenborough (1987) and *Waders* by Desmond and Maimie

Nethersole Thompson (1986); also in magazines eg *Bird Watching, Birds, British Birds*. Member: Royal Photographic Society Nature Group, Nature Photographers' Portfolio. Lectures on wildlife to natural history societies throughout the North West. OIR: playing violin. 275 Bolton Road, Edgworth, Turton, Bolton BL7 0AW. 01204 852510.

HIGGINS, Rupert Johnstone; *b:* 18 September 1962 in Potters Bar, Middlesex; *p:* Dawn Lawrence. BSc Botany and Zoology (Bristol, 1984). MIEEM 1992. Partner and Ecologist, Wessex Ecological Consultancy since 1988. Prev: Conservation Support Officer Avon WT 1985-87. Scientific Officer, Severn Estuary Project, NCC 1987-88. Voluntary warden RSPB, summers 1980-82. Chairman Avon WT Conservation Committee 1988-. Chew Valley Lake Conservation Committee 1988-. Special interests: habitat management and creation. Author of management plans for eg Chew Valley Lake SSSI and Blagdon Lake SSSI; also environmental impact assessments. Co-author (with R Gaines) *A Guide to the Wildlife Sites of Bristol* (1987); contributor to *Nature in the City* by B Smythe (1988). Occasional radio and TV interviews, eg to discuss Ruddy Duck 'problem'. OIR: botany, entomology, history, Stoke City FC. 28 Egerton Road, Bishopston, Bristol BS7 8HL. 0117 944 1034.

HILL, David; *b:* 18 April 1958 in Derby; *w:* Dr Kathleen Raw. BSc Animal and Plant Ecology (Loughborough, 1979), DPhil Population dynamics of wildfowl and the restoration of gravel pits for birds (Edward Grey Institute, Oxford, 1982). MIEEM 1992. CBiol, MIBiol 1984. Chief Executive, Ecoscope Applied Ecologists since 1992. Prev: Director of Development BTO 1989-92; Senior Ecologist RSPB 1987-89; Game Conservancy (head of research on ecology of pheasants) 1982-87. British Ecological Society Council 1990-93. Scientific Advisory Committee WWT 1988-91. Research and Surveys Committee BTO 1984-87. IEEM Council 1993-, Vice President 1995-. Special interests: survey design and methodology, wildfowl ecology, bird community ecology, analysing large datasets, photography. Travel for birds inc China, Australia, USA, Thailand, SE Asia, Japan. Expeditions in Canary Islands to study Fuerteventura Stonechat and Houbara Bustard. Author *The Avocet* (1989). Co-author (with Peter Robertson) *The Pheasant: ecology, management and conservation* (1988); (with C J Bibby and N D Burgess) *Bird Census Techniques* (1992); (with W J Sutherland) *Managing Habitats for Conservation* (1995). Co-editor (with P J Garson and D Jenkins) *Pheasants in China* (conf procs) (1989). OIR: squash, walking, horse riding. Crake Holme, Muker, Richmond, N Yorks DL11 6QH. 01748 886421.

HIND, Christopher Melville (Chris); *b:* 13 April 1950 in Middlesbrough, N Yorks; *p:* Liz Stones. Acklam Hall Grammar School, Middlesbrough. BDS (Newcastle, 1973). General dental practitioner. BTO Regional Representative Yorkshire (North) 1984-92 and survey organiser for the area during that period. BTO Waterways Bird Survey on R Swale (N Yorks) 1985-92. Frequent visitor to Crete since 1988; regular contributor to *Crete Bird Report* (adding two new species to Crete list). Particular interest in E Europe and Central Asia, visiting Poland, Russia, Turkmenia, Uzbekistan, Kirgizia, Kazakstan. Delivered lecture at BTO Ann Conf 1991 on Waterways Bird Survey. OIR: fell walking, gardening, cooking, dilettantism in the arts. Croft House, Skirwith, Penrith, Cumbria CA10 1RL. 01768 88282.

HINDLE, David John; *b:* 10 June 1944 in Preston, Lancs; *w:* Dorothy. Police officer, retired. During 1977-81 instructed police officers on rural beats on duties relating to wildlife, inc Protection of Birds Act 1952 and Wildlife and Countryside Act 1981. Appointed first Liaison Officer (between Constabulary and RSPB) alongside main duty as Training Officer, 1974-81. Assisted RSPB in wardening Golden Eagles and Peregrines in Lake District in early 1970s; also Osprey warden at Loch Garten, spring 1994 and 1995. Lancashire WT Committee for Local Nature Reserves 1984-. Tutor for boys undertaking Duke of Edinburgh Award Scheme in ornithology at Blackburn YMCA 1965-69. Bird surveys of local areas, eg Ribble Valley Woodlands, Gisburn Forest, Inner Ribble Marshes. Overseas travel for birds in Europe, N Africa, The Gambia, Kenya, N and S America, India, Spitsbergen, Antarctica. Co-author (with M Jones *et al*) *The Birds of Lancashire* (in prep). Contributor to *Lancashire Bird Report* over many years. Lectures to local societies. Regular representations to MPs, media, local authorities and natural history societies on conservation matters. OIR: listening to classical music, participating in amateur operatics, sailing, motoring, photography, some voluntary vocational work. Meadowside, 15 Swallowfold, Grimsargh, Preston, Lancs PR2 5JN.

HIRONS, Montague John David (Mont); *b:* 12 May 1916 in Bloxham, Oxon; *w:* Doris. Cert Ed (inc Advanced Biology) (Saltley College of St Peter, 1939), MSc Advanced Ecology (Durham, 1971). CBiol, MIBiol 1985. Senior Lecturer in Biology, Easthampstead Coll of Ed and Bulmershe Coll of Ed. Founder-member Banbury Ornithological Society 1952-. Founder-member Malta Bird Reserves Overseas Committee; ringed first bird on Malta and initiated training of first Maltese ringers, 1965. BTO 'A' ringer since 1964. Ornithologist Joint Forces Expeditions to Chagos Archipelago

1972-73 and Danger Island (Chagos Arch) 1975. Special interest: studies on the Farne Islands (since 1971), esp effect of seabirds on vegetation; findings published by Nat Hist Soc of Northumbria. OIR: photography and microscopy. Betula House, Barford Road, Bloxham, Banbury, Oxon OX15 4EZ. 01295 720573.

HIRST, Paul Timothy; *b:* 13 December 1954 in Lydney, Glos; *w:* Sue. Founder-member (1995) and Secretary Moray Bird Club. Member of Moray and Nairn Rarities Committee. Regular participant in UK and overseas expeditions of RAF Ornithological Society, acting as recorder and photographer. Special interest: artist and illustrator. Papers published in *Birding World, Birdwatch.* Many illustrations in *Moray & Nairn Bird Report* and RAFOS publications; illustrator of *The Birds of Moray and Nairn* by Martin Cook (1992); series of illustrations commissioned for forthcoming *Atlas of Breeding Birds of Europe.* 4 New Street, Hopeman, Elgin, Moray IV30 2SG. 01343 835060.

HOBLYN, Ronald Arthur (Ron); MBE 1992; *b:* 21 March 1933 in London; *w:* Maureen. Ealing County Grammar School for Boys; Joint Services School for Linguists (Cert for Russian), qualified translator 1953; Forester Cert (Forestry Commission) 1957. Forest Officer (Conservation and Environment), retired 1993. Summer contract on Woodlark research with Forestry Commission in Norfolk and Suffolk 1993-95. National Woodlark Survey co-ordinator for Breckland 1986; Nightjar Survey co-ordinator for Thetford Forest 1992. Species protection Red-backed Shrike Breckland, in conjunction with RSPB, 1974-88. Articles on Woodlark and Red-backed Shrike in *Birds, Norfolk Bird and Mammal Report* and *RSPB Conservation Review.* RSPB/Esso Birds and Countryside Awards, Individual Award Winner 1988. OIR: general natural history, travel, sport. Heron Lodge, Santon Downham, Brandon, Suffolk IP27 0TW. 01842 813405.

HOBSON, John Anthony; *b:* 31 October 1932 in Barnet, Herts; *w:* Kate. MSc Eng (Imperial College, London, 1951-58). CEng, MIMechE. British Rail (Financial Services), retired. Hon Treas Reading Ornithological Club 1975-93. Asst Recorder, Sussex Ornithological Society 1995-. National Wildfowl Counts 1972-92; participant in BTO surveys and Berkshire avifauna surveys. Special interests: birds of Nearctic and Palearctic Regions. Travel for birds to Fennoscandia, Greece, Spain, Israel, Iceland, Spitsbergen, Canada, Alaska, Florida, Siberia. OIR: classical music, ballet, opera, Arun Choral Soc, bridge, DIY. 23 Hillside Road, Storrington, Pulborough, W Sussex RH20 3LZ. 01903 740155.

HODGE, Timothy Neil (Tim); *b:* 10 June 1955 in London; *w:* Jane. Wilson's Grammar School, Camberwell 1966-73. BA Economics and Philosophy (Univ College, London, 1980). Fellow Chartered Inst of Housing 1993. Director, Central Services, Kent Community Housing Trust. Chairman of Finance Committee, Thanet Community Housing Assocn. Kent Ornithological Society: Editorial and Records Committee 1985-, Executive Committee 1986-. Special interests: breeding and migration studies. Assisted in organisation of various surveys of birds of Kent, esp of breeding birds 1988-94. Commenced a BTO Common Birds Census plot in 1993. Instrumental in developing use of computers within Kent OS. Senior editor *Birds of Kent* (in prep). Co-editor (with Ian Hodgson) *Kent Bird Report* 1985-88, sole editor 1989-. OIR: running, cooking, growing vegetables, chauffeur and father to four children, trying to avoid DIY. 38 Ethelbert Road, Birchington, Kent CT7 9PY. 01843 845263.

HODGES, Jane Elizabeth; *b:* 27 May 1955 in London. BSc Zoology and Genetics (Univ College, Swansea, 1976). Ecologist. Secretary Pembrokeshire Ornithological Research Committee (Dyfed WT). Special interests: monitoring of populations, relationship between species conservation and land management practices, Chough and Shelduck, general avian ecology. Short notes in county bird report; several unpublished survey reports on particular species. OIR: natural history, travel, music. Pembrokeshire Coast National Park, Winch Lane, Haverfordwest, Pembs SA61 1PY. 01437 764636.

HODGSON, Ian Philip; *b:* 17 August 1951 in Dover, Kent; *p:* Christine Allison. Dover Grammar School for Boys 1962-69. Partner in British Birding Tours (UK-based service for American birders) since 1994. Kent Ornithological Society Editorial and Records Committee 1978-. East Kent Recorder 1978-83. County Recorder 1982-. Joint editor *Kent Bird Report* 1985-88. Editor *Kent OS Newsletter* 1995-. Special interest: migration, esp in St Margaret's area near Dover, with regular observations since 1977. Compiler of annual report on birds and butterflies in the area since 1982 and author of booklet *The Birds of St Margaret's* (priv print, 1991). Extensive travel in Europe and Middle East; also Thailand, Malaysia, China, eastern USA and Costa Rica. Member: OBC. OIR: butterflies (transect at St Margaret's since 1984), cricket (keen player until hand injury). Whitgift House, Hardy Close, Canterbury, Kent CT2 8JJ. 01227 784303.

HODGSON, Michael S (Mike); *b:* 12 January 1949 in North Shields, Northumberland; *w:* Ann. Systems analyst. Northumberland & Tyneside

Bird Club: Committee 1974-90, Chairman 1982-90. County Recorder for Northumberland 1983-90. Northumberland County Records Committee 1983-90, 1994-, Chairman 1983-90. Northumberland Breeding Atlas Committee 1986-95. County organiser: Birds of Estuaries Enquiry 1983-90, BTO Shorebirds Enquiry 1984/85, WWT Breeding Shelduck Survey 1992. Voluntary wardening on local reserve since 1992. Tutor for adult education evening classes in ornithology 1977-79. BTO 'A' ringer since 1966. Secretary Tynesiders Ringing Group 1977-82, and Bamburgh Ringing Station 1977-. Special interests: migration (long-term manning of coastal site); population studies; active ringer since 1966 (inc two large nestbox schemes). Leader of ornithological tours for various companies to countries in Europe, N Africa and Middle East since 1976. Talks/lectures to local clubs and societies. Co-author *Birds in Northumbria* (annual report) 1973-90; editor *Northumberland & Tyneside Bird Club Monthly Bulletin* 1983-90; author of several short papers (eg breeding studies, rare bird records) in annual reports; co-compiler and co-editor *Atlas of Breeding Birds in Northumbria* (in prep). OIR: listening to rock music. 31 Uplands, Monkseaton, Whitley Bay, Tyne & Wear NE25 9AG. 0191 252 0511.

HOGG, Raymond Henry (Angus); *b:* 19 July 1947 in Rutherglen, Lanarkshire; *w:* Mary. BSc (Soc Sci) Geography (Edinburgh, 1968), Scottish Secondary Teaching Cert in Geog (1969) and Modern Studies (1974). Principal Teacher of Geography and Modern Studies at Ayr Academy. Univ Glasgow extra-mural class tutor in ornithology, annually since 1977 (involves running indoor meetings and field outings Oct-May). Course tutor Scottish Field Studies Assocn (Spring Birds Weekends) since 1985. Council SOC 1980-89, 1993-. Committee SOC Ayr Branch 1970-82, Chairman 1979-82. SOC local recorder for Ayrshire since 1975. Scottish Bird Records Committee 1983-95. Scottish Council RSPB 1980-83. Ayrshire YOC Leader 1971-74. Committee Ayrshire Branch Scottish WT 1972-74. Special interests: status of birds within Ayrshire (and Scotland), co-ordinating five-year tetrad atlas project on Ayrshire's breeding birds; autumn migration patterns and numbers of seabirds off Ayrshire coast; numbers of wintering divers on S Ayrshire coast; identification and patterns of occurrence of gulls; distribution of particular species of raptor within Ayrshire, eg Buzzard. Widely travelled within W Palearctic, eg Spain (inc Mallorca), France, Austria, Israel, Morocco, Egypt, Turkey, and N America, with emphasis on identification, migration and photography. Author *Birds of Ayrshire, a county checklist* (1983). Asst compiler *Scottish Bird Report* 1976-82; editor 1982-88. Contributor of information for a wide range of books, eg P J Grant's *Gulls*, A D Watson's *Hen Harrier*, and BTO

Winter Atlas. Editor *Ayrshire Bird Report* 1976-95; notes published in eg *British Birds, Dutch Birding, Scottish Birds*. Occasional radio programmes for BBC World Service and Radio Scotland. Regular 'Nature Diary' in local press. Involved in production of several audio cassettes of birds in Ayrshire. Member: Egyptian OS, OSME; supporter of World Centre for Birds of Prey. OIR: most other aspects of wildlife (esp within Ayrshire and particularly mammals), military aircraft, steam locomotives, music and football ('though I don't know why, since I still keep up an interest in the fortunes of Airdrieonians FC!'). Kirklea, Crosshill, Maybole, Ayrshire KA19 7RJ. 01655 740317.

HOLDEN, Peter N; *b:* 10 December 1948 in Teddington, Middlesex; *w:* Susan. Head of Youth and Volunteer Dept RSPB since 1992. Prev RSPB: National Organiser of Young Ornithologists' Club 1974-92; Asst to Education Officer 1969-74. Earlier, freelance genealogist 1968-69. Special interests: environmental education, writing, broadcasting. Chairman Youth Committee, Council of Environmental Education 1988-93. Author *Spotters' Guide to Birds* (1978), *Collins Wildguide to Birds of Britain and Europe* (1996). Joint author (with R Porter) *Spotters' Guide to Birds of Prey* (1981); *RSPB Book of British Birds* (1982, 3rd ed 1994); (with Bill Oddie) *Bird in the Nest* (1995). Many articles for the YOC magazine *Bird Life*. Consultant for BBC 'Bird Spy' software and for Advisory Unit 'The Migration Pack' software. Contributor to BBC1 TV programme 'Blue Peter'; co-presenter 'Bird in the Nest' (BBC, 1994, 1995). OIR: history, vernacular and church architecture, photography, classical music (esp twentieth-century British). RSPB, The Lodge, Sandy, Beds SG19 2DL. 01767 680551.

HOLLING, Mark; *b:* 15 August 1958 in Scarborough, N Yorks. BSc Zoology (Nottingham, 1979). Project Manager, Bank of Scotland. Chairman, SOC Monthly Discussion Group (forum for Scottish ornithology) 1991-. Active fieldworker involved in most local and national surveys. Co-organiser (with Ray Murray) of SE Scotland Breeding Bird Atlas 1990-. Co-ordinator of Buzzard monitoring in the Borders. Prev: Committee SOC Lothian Branch 1990-93; Committee Leicestershire and Rutland Orn Soc 1984-88. Special interests: bird distributions and status, bird recording, Buzzard. Author of various papers (inc surveys and censuses) in *Borders Bird Report, Lothian Bird Report, Birds of Leics and Rutland* 1985-88. OIR: cycling (usually combined with birding). Burnfoot Cottage, Symington Mains, Stow, Galashiels, Selkirkshire TD1 2SU. 01578 760239.

HOLLOM, Philip Arthur Dominic (Phil); *b:* 9 June 1912 in Bickley, Kent; *w:* Jenefer. Heddon Court, Cockfosters, Herts; Kings School, Bruton, Somerset. Certified Accountant (ACCA). RAF pilot 1942-46. Retired. Memberships and posts: BTO Council, Ringing Committee; BOU Council, Records Committee; Ornithological Society of Turkey Council; Ornithological Society of the Middle East Council; London Natural History Society Records Committee; British Birds Rarities Committee; Surrey Bird Club Records Committee; Director on Board of West Palaearctic Birds Ltd. Co-organiser of Great Crested Grebe Enquiry of 1931. Organiser of Survey of Black-headed Gull colonies in 1938, and of Great Crested Grebe Sample Censuses 1946-55. Special interests: identification, distribution, ringing etc; sound recording in more recent years. Ongoing long-term project: periodic counts of Swallow and House Martin nests near Bruton, Somerset (started in 1929). Participant in expeditions: Oxford Ornithological Society to Holland 1935; Mountfort to Spain 1957, Bulgaria 1960, Jordan 1963; OSME to N Yemen 1985. Less formal trips to Morocco, Egypt, Iran, Turkey, Romania, Finland, Iceland. Also birdwatching ('no guided tours!') in many other countries in Europe, SW Asia, N Africa (inc three months in Tunisia), N America (inc six months in Florida, three months in Quebec), Central and S America. Author *The Popular Handbook of Rarer British Birds* (1960). Editor *Trapping Methods for Bird Ringers*, also contributor to this BTO booklet (1940); *The Popular Handbook of British Birds* (1952, 5th ed 1988). Co-author (with Roger Peterson and Guy Mountfort) *A Field Guide to the Birds of Britain and Europe* (1954, 5th ed 1993); (with Richard Porter *et al*) *Birds of the Middle East and North Africa* (1988). Translator (from French) *The Birds of North Africa* (1967). Member of the editorial team of *BWP* and contributor of some hundreds of sound recordings. Author or co-author of papers in eg *Bird Study, British Birds, Ibis*. An editor of *British Birds* 1951-71, Senior Editor 1960-62. Bernard Tucker Medal, BTO 1954; Union Medal, BOU 1967; Silver Medal, RSPB 1980. Inwood Cottage, Hydestile, Godalming, Surrey GU8 4AY. 01483 424264.

HOLLOWAY, John Francis; *b:* 4 June 1944 in Leeds, Yorks; *w:* Sue. Proprietor of Stronsay Bird Reserve since 1989. First warden of Gillingham's Riverside Country Park and was responsible for the creation of much of the habitat there. Special interests: 'local patch' and 'find-your-own' birding, migration, habitat creation. Author and illustrator of *Fair Isle's Garden Birds* (1984), *The Birds of Gillingham* (1984), *The Birds of Stronsay* (1991), *To Fair Isle and Back* (1995). Many illustrations and articles in eg *Birding World, Birds Illustrated, British Birds*, and several exhibitions of watercolour paintings of birds. OIR: swimming (captained

Gillingham Swimming Club for many years), soccer (represented Medway Towns in English Schools Trophy), athletics. Castle, Stronsay Bird Reserve, Stronsay, Orkney KW17 2AG. 01857 616363.

HOLLYER, John Noel; *b:* 25 December 1935 in Canterbury, Kent; *w:* Joyce. Dover Grammar School. Art Teacher's Diploma 1958, Univ Leicester Cert in Education 1958, Further Education Teacher's Cert 1985. Teacher of Art and Design, retired. Part-time adult education tutor in ornithology since 1974. Associated with Sandwich Bay Bird Observatory since 1950, past Secretary and Chairman, Vice President since 1988. Special interests: migration, eruptive species. Papers on Red-backed Shrike and Cetti's Warbler in *Kent Bird Report* and the invasion of Nutcrackers in autumn 1968 in *British Birds*. Some illustrations for BTO Breeding Atlas and *Birds of Berkshire* by Berkshire Atlas Group (1996). Exhibited oil paintings on five occasions at The Mall Galleries as guest of Society of Wildlife Artists. OIR: swimming, collecting Sudan (camel postman) stamps. 21 Temple Way, Worth, Deal, Kent CT14 0DA. 01304 612565.

HOLMAN, David John; *b:* 25 October 1946 in Bermondsey, London; *w:* Joyce. Bacon School (FE) Bermondsey. Freelance tour leader for ornithological tour companies since 1981; partner in Birdline East Anglia since its inception in August 1989. Bird recorder for that part of Kent covered by the London NHS and on their Rarities Committee 1969-71. Member of British Birds Rarities Committee 1976-85 and of Norfolk Rarities Committee from its formation in 1976 to 1985 and again 1991-. Special interest: identification. Co-author (with Steve Madge) of 'Identifying Serins' in *British Birds*; also contributions to other magazines. Member: ABA, ABC, NBC, OBC, OSME. OIR: playing competitive table tennis in Norwich League; all aspects of wildlife and natural history. 9 Salisbury Road, Norwich NR1 1TU. 01603 437644.

HOLMES, Derek Anthony; *b:* 28 May 1938 in Kettering, Northants; *w:* Patricia. BSc Geology (Bristol, 1960); Dip of ITC, Soil Surveyor (International Training Centre for Aerial Survey, Delft, Netherlands, 1966). Environmental land-use planner as consultant (generally to Indonesian Government). Founder, principal editor and business manager of *Kukila* (bulletin of the Indonesian Orn Soc) 1986-. Formerly joint representative for Indonesia in OBC. Scientific adviser to World Pheasant Assocn 1989-. Special interests: all aspects of avifauna of Indonesia (resident there almost continuously since 1974); sound recording and voice identification of forest birds. Co-author (with S V Nash) *The Birds of Java* *and Bali* (1989) and *The Birds of Sumatra and Kalimantan* (1990); (with K Phillipps) *The Birds of Sulawesi* (1996); (with Sitari bin Supari) *The Birds of Western Malaysia* (in prep). Papers published in eg *Bull BOC, J Bombay NHS, Kukila, Wildfowl*. Member: Indonesian OS, Malay Nature Soc, OBC, Siam Soc. OIR: music (classical to jazz), amateur weather observer, geomorphology, history, etymology. Kukila, PO Box 4087, Jakarta 12040, Indonesia.

HOLMES, John Stuart; *b:* 17 May 1967 in Plymouth, Devon; *w:* Jane. BSc Applied Resources Science (Kingston Polytechnic, 1988), MSc Environmental Technology and Ecological Management (Imperial College, London, 1991); DIC 1991. Ornithologist, Vertebrate Ecol and Cons Branch, JNCC since Dec 1991. Special interest: policy and practice of nature conservation. Secretary UK Ruddy Duck Working Group 1993-95. Secretary UK Lead Poisoning in Waterfowl Working Group 1992-96. Joint editor (with J R Simons) *The Introduction and Naturalisation of Birds* (1996). Co-author of papers in *Biol Cons, Ibis, Oxyura* and other publications. Popular articles in magazines inc *New Scientist*, newsletters and journals of wildlife trusts, bird clubs, and eg IWRB. Various illustrations for newsletters. OIR: dragonflies. JNCC, Monkstone House, City Road, Peterborough PE1 1JY. 01733 62626; fax 01733 555948.

HOLMES, Stephan William (Steve); *b:* 1 May 1953 in Germany; *p:* Marion Barlow. Chester City Grammar School. Chester College of Further Education. Project leader in geographical information systems. Chester area co-ordinator of fieldwork for Cheshire Breeding Bird Survey 1978-83. 10km square co-ordinator for BTO atlas work in Cheshire 1988-90. Recorder for Chester and district 1980-82; co-ordinator between British Birds Rarities Committee and Cheshire rare bird recording 1981-85. Chester & District Ornithological Society: various Committee posts 1972-86, organiser/co-ordinator of two-year studies of buntings and woodpeckers 1974-78. Special interests: identification and migration, 'local patch' work (over 10,000 visits), larks, pipits and buntings. Widely travelled for birds in Europe, Africa, Israel, Turkey, former USSR (Central Asia and Siberia, northern forests), Thailand, USA, Brazil, Argentina, Chile, Antarctica, Canada, Australia, Nepal. Co-editor *Cheshire Bird Report* 1981-83; co-author *Breeding Birds of the Chester Area* (1984); monthly contributor of Cheshire records to *Bird Watching*, occasional articles in magazines inc *Birding World, Birds Illustrated*. Member: ABC. OIR: chess, dragonflies, butterflies and moths. 64 Western Avenue, Blacon, Chester CH1 5PP. 01244 372313.

HOLT, Brayton; *b:* 9 June 1932 in Wallasey, Cheshire; *w:* Wanda. Retired company director. County Recorder Montgomeryshire 1990-. Editor *Montgomeryshire Bird Report.* BTO Regional Representative 1992-. Executive Committee Welsh Orn Soc 1991-. Committee Shropshire OS 1991-95. Conservation Committee Montomeryshire WT 1990-. Participant in surveys for BTO, RSPB and Montgomershire WT. Special interests: photography and travel for birds (widely travelled in Europe, Scandinavia, Africa, N and S America, Falklands and Antarctica, Australia, Russian Arctic, India). OIR: cricket, jazz, watercolour painting. Scops Cottage, Pentre Beirdd, Welshpool, Powys SY21 9DL. 01938 500266.

HOLT, Peter; *b:* 16 October 1941 in Wakefield, W Yorks; *w:* Lydia. George Heriot's School Edinburgh 1951-58. BA Modern History (Stirling, 1971), MA European Politics (Sussex, 1972), DPhil Austrian and Swiss neutrality (Sussex, 1979). Journalist. European Editor of US *Bird Watcher's Digest* since 1983, contributor since 1981. Special interests: publicising bird protection in the Middle East (eg bustards); birds in art and illustration. Articles on bird artists (eg Thomas Bewick, Donald Watson) and bird species (eg storks, bustards) in US, British, Swiss and Middle East magazines. OIR: modern history (esp Irish, Scottish, industrial revolution), Irish poetry and short stories, Beatrix Potter. Egghölzliweg 5, CH-3074 Muri, Switzerland. +41 31 9517103.

HOPKIN, Peter Jeffery; *b:* 13 August 1960 in Bristol; *w:* Elizabeth Wear. BA Geography (Exeter, 1981). Freelance Chartered Land Surveyor. Voluntary warden RSPB Operation Osprey 1979, 1980. President Exeter Univ Naturalists' Society 1980. Special interests: migration and overseas conservation issues, esp Asia. Bird-related travel to France, Greece, Holland, Spain, Portugal, Morocco, India, Thailand, Turkey, Malaysia, Hong Kong, China, Antigua, Nepal, Uganda, Taiwan, Philippines. Assistant with radio tracking of Malaysian Peacock Pheasants at Kuala Lumpur National Park, Malaysia 1989. Articles published in eg *Bristol Ornithology, British Birds, Hong Kong Bird Report*; several itineraries for *Birdwatch*, also travel-style essays. Member: OBC, OSME. OIR: travel, general natural history. c/o W Hopkin, 31 Kewstoke Road, Bristol BS9 1HA. (Note: resident Hong Kong 1994-1997; editor of quarterly *Bulletin of Hong Kong Birdwatching Society* 1994-97.)

HOPKINS, Paul; *b:* 18 February 1961 in Leicester; *w:* Alison. Beauchamp College, Oadby, Leicester. Registered Nurse in Mental Handicap (Charles Frears School of Nursing, Leicester, 1983). Clinical co-ordinator. Special interest: photography, esp birds of The Gambia and rare birds in the South West. Wide range of avian photographic material also from trips including Australia, Costa Rica, Cyprus. Photographs published regularly in eg *Bird Watching, Birdwatch, British Birds*. 9 New Street, Penryn, Cornwall TR10 8EB. 01326 372118.

HORNBUCKLE, Jonathan (Jon); *b:* 23 April 1943 in Bedford; *w:* Evelyn. MA Metallurgy (St Catherine's College, Oxford, 1966). Consultant on quality assurance and metallurgy of stainless steel. Participant in tropical ornithological projects, eg 'Forest Islands in Bolivia' (1994-96, Nottingham Univ); lowland rainforest bird survey in Papua New Guinea (1995, Conservation International); 'Species Conservation as an Integral Part of Forest Maintenance in the Philippines' (1996, Bochum Univ). Committee Sheffield Bird Study Group 1973-95, inc periods as Chairman and Secretary. Peak Park Wildlife Advisory Group 1989-. Former organiser of Peregrine protection scheme in Derbyshire. Co-ordinator of and participant in BTO Waterways Bird Survey since 1973 and various other local surveys, eg rookeries. BTO 'C' ringer since 1989. Special interests: ringing, raptor population monitoring, birding in the tropics. Worldwide travel for birds. Author of *Bird Ringing in the Sheffield Area, 1980-1990* (1992). Co-editor and part-author of *Birds in the Sheffield Area* (annual report) since 1983, annual ringing report of Sorby Beck Ringing Group since 1991, and (with D Herringshaw) *Birds of the Sheffield Area* (1985) and the journal *Magpie*. Various articles on local and tropical ornithology and a considerable number of foreign trip reports. Member: ABA, ABC, Bombay NHS, NBC, OBC. 30 Hartington Road, Sheffield S7 2LF. 0114 236 3481.

HOSKING, David Alan; *b:* 7 May 1955 in London; *w:* Jean. BIPP Diploma 1975, Plymouth College Diploma 1976. FRPS 1992. Freelance bird photographer. Director, Hosking Tours Ltd. Director, Frank Lane Picture Agency. Vice President British Naturalists' Assocn 1985. Photographic visits to N Yemen, Falklands, E and S Africa, Seychelles, India, N America, Australia. Books include *Just a Lark* (1984), *Which Bird?* (1986), *Eric Hosking's Birds of Prey* (1987), *Field Guide to Birds of Britain & Europe* (1990), *Poles Apart* (1990), *Eric Hosking's Classic Birds* (1993), *Common Birds of East Africa* (1996). Son of late Eric Hosking OBE. OIR: music, reading, walking. Pages Green House, Wetheringsett, Stowmarket, Suffolk IP14 5QA. 01728 861113; fax 01728 860222.

HOUGH, Julian Richard; *b:* 11 July 1968 in Bolton, Lancs; *w:* Dawn Lafferty. HND in Printing (Manchester Polytechnic, 1989). Freelance artist

WHO'S WHO IN ORNITHOLOGY

and writer, also slide presentations. Prev: editorial team on *Bird Watching* and *Birds Illustrated* 1992-93; research asst, Long Point Provincial Park, Ontario, Canada Mar-Jun 1991 (ringing programme); Cape May, New Jersey, USA 1987-88 (study of diurnal migration of passerines). Occasional tour leading. Member of Connecticut Rare Records Committee. Special interests: identification and photography, esp Nearctic species. Widely travelled for birds in Europe, N America, Israel, Thailand, India, Nepal, China, Australia. Cape May study report published in *The Auk*; many articles relating to bird identification in *Bird Watching*, *Birding* (USA), *Birding World*, *Birdwatch*, *British Birds*. Artwork and photographs published in wide variety of magazines and books, eg *The Breeding Atlas of Cheshire and Wirral* (1992), *Rare Birds in Britain* by Lee Evans (1991 and 1992 eds), *The Birds of Cape May* by David Sibley (1993), *BWP* Vol 8. Work shown at SWLA annual exhibition, London 1986. OIR: music; reading; playing snooker, football, squash; art (not limited to birds). 51 Brook Street, 6-C, Naugatuck, Connecticut 06770, USA.

HOUNSOME, Michael Vincent (Mike); *b:* 13 February 1943 in Woking Surrey; *w:* Beryl. BSc Zoology (Belfast, 1970), PGCE Biology (Manchester, 1974), PhD Zoology (Manchester, 1975). MIBiol, CBiol 1971. Keeper of Zoology and Lecturer in Zoology, Manchester University since 1975. Custodian of the Henry Dresser Collection of Birds at Manchester Museum, one of the major bird collections in the UK and available for consultation by any ornithologist. President Manchester University Bird Club in 1970s. BTO 'A' ringer since 1966. Special interests: biometry; population dynamics; population estimation; census techniques; ringing; island birds, their evolution, taxonomy and conservation. Expeditions to Atlantic, Caribbean, Indonesian and Mediterranean islands. Contributions to books inc 'Bird life in the city' in *Nature in Cities* ed by I C Laurie (1979), 'Bird population studies' in *Case Studies in Population Biology* ed by L M Cook (1986). Editor *Ringing & Migration* 1995-. Many papers in eg *Irish Naturalists' Journal, Ringing & Migration, Seabird Bulletin*. OIR: freshwater biology, bee-keeping, walking, camping, travelling, computer programming, motor cycling. Manchester University Museum, Oxford Road, Manchester M13 9PL. 0161 275 2673; fax: 0161 275 2676.

HOUSDEN, Stuart David; *b:* 24 June 1953 in Croydon, Surrey; *p:* Catherine Wilkin. Selhurst Grammar School. BSc Zoology (Royal Holloway College, London, 1975). RSPB, Director, Scotland since 1993. Prev RSPB: Head of Conservation Planning 1990-93; Head of Cons Planning Dept 1985-90; Manager, Government Unit 1982-85; Parliamentary Officer 1979-82; Species Protection Officer 1977-79. Special interests: migration studies, recreational birdwatching. Co-editor *Important Bird Areas in the UK* (1992). Numerous articles in popular magazines and journals eg *Country Life, Ecos, Natural World, RSPB Conservation Review*. Churchill Fellow 1992, for marine conservation. Professional interests: conservation of species and habitats, campaigns for better protection of key sites, advocacy of policy measures to secure conservation in the wider countryside. OIR: travel, rugby. RSPB, 17 Regent Terrace, Edinburgh EH7 5BN. 0131 557 3136; fax 0131 557 6275.

HOUSTON, David Charles; *b:* 2 August 1946 in London. BSc Zoology (Bristol, 1968), DPhil Zoology (Oxford, 1972). Senior Lecturer, Applied Ornithology Unit, Zoology Dept, Univ Glasgow since 1974. Prev: Research Fellow, Edinburgh Univ 1972-74. NCC Advisory Committee on Science 1982-90. WWT Science Advisory Committee 1984-88. BOU Council 1978-91, also Hon Sec 1981-91. SOC Council 1984-88. RSPB Council 1985-93. RSPB Scottish Committee 1982-93. Special interest: scavenging birds. Scientific papers in *Ibis, J Zool* and other ornithological journals. Karian, Dumgoyne, Killearn, Glasgow G63 9LA. 01360 550662.

HOWARD, Richard Percival; *b:* 18 May 1936 in Shepperton, Middlesex. Private education. Retired company director. Joint founder of Child-Beale Wildlife Park in 1956. Co-founder and Senior Trustee, The Child-Beale Wildlife Trust 1966-. President BTO 1989-93. Founder Trustee, International Trust for Nature Conservation. Chairman British Section ICBP 1990-93. Committee FFPS 1989-92. Chairman Trust for Oriental Ornithology 1994-. Vice President World Pheasant Assocn. Special interest: photography. Expeditions to Nepal, Thailand, Kashmir, India, China, Maldive Islands, Sub-Antarctic islands. Co-author (with Alick Moore) *A Complete Checklist of the Birds of the World* (1980, rev 1984, 2nd ed 1991). Occasional broadcasts on Radio Berkshire and BBC World Service. Member: Cornell Laboratory of Ornithology, International Crane Foundation, OBC, RAOU. Campaigner for habitat conservation worldwide; fundraising for many conservation bodies. OIR: cricket (member of MCC); radio controlled model boats; classic cars; aeroplanes. Hogg House, Church Farm, Lower Basildon, Reading RG8 9NH. 01491 671388.

HOWE, Antony; *b:* 14 May 1954 in Ipswich, Suffolk; *w:* Jan. Country Park Ranger, St Edmundsbury Borough Council since 1991. Prev: horse physiotherapist. Voluntary warden for Suffolk WT at Lackford Wildfowl Reserve 1980-. Committee Suffolk Ornithologists' Group 1989. Special interests: migration and breeding population studies at local sites. Member of Lackford Ringing Group (BTO 'A' ringer), involved in Constant Effort Site. Articles, species sections and artwork published in *Lackford Reserve Annual Report*. Bird paintings in local wildlife exhibitions. OIR: gardening, sport, local history, horses. Rangers House, Hardwick Heath, Hardwick Lane, Bury St Edmunds, Suffolk IP33 2RA. 01284 704700.

HOWELLS, Robert James (Bob); *b:* 31 December 1928 in Swansea, Glamorgan; *w:* Jean. Swansea Grammar School 1940-46. BA Latin (Univ College of Swansea, 1949), Dip Ed (UC Swansea, 1951), Dip in Russian (Holborn College of Law, Languages and Commerce, 1965). Retired schoolmaster. Joint organiser of schools' summer birdwatching courses on Steepholm 1956-60. Gower Ornithological Society: various posts from 1959 inc Secretary, Chairman, President; now Hon Life Member and member of Records Committee 1960-. BTO Regional Representative for Glamorgan, then W Glam 1974. Organiser of BTO surveys in W Glam, inc Birds of Estuaries Enquiry 1968-93, Wetland Bird Survey 1993- (and prev WWT Wildfowl Counts 1990-93), Winter Birds Survey 1981-84. Voluntary warden for NCC/CCW at Whiteford NNR since 1974 and NCC representative on Whiteford Advisory Committee 1980-86. Special interests: status of wildfowl, waders and gulls in Burry Inlet (S side), Upper Loughor and Blackpill (Swansea Bay), since 1958. Group visit to Great Saltee Island, Eire, for migration and ringing studies, 1962; also Dingle Peninsula 1969-71. Travel for birds in France, Spain, Italy. Joint author of BTO Research Reports on wildfowl and waders in W Glam. Co-author of accounts for wildfowl, waders and gulls in *Birds of Glamorgan* by Hurford and Lansdown (1995). Member Joint Editorial Committee *Glamorgan Bird Report* 1962-67. Many articles, esp on identification, in *Gower Birds*. Occasional broadcasts on Radio Wales. Frequent lectures to Gower OS and adult education groups on birds of Burry Inlet and Blackpill. Member: SEO. OIR: travel, art, architecture, archaeology, photography, literature and language, hill walking, cooking, music (classical, modern jazz, popular). Ynys Enlli, 14 Dolgoy Close, West Cross, Swansea SA3 5LT. 01792 405363.

HUDSON, Peter John; *b:* 22 May 1953 in Bolton, Lancs; *w:* Mary Hudson. Rickmansworth Grammar School. BSc Zoology (Leeds, 1974), DPhil Survival rates and behaviour of British auks (Edward Grey Inst, Oxford, 1979). FLS 1985. Reader in Wildlife Epidemiology, Univ Stirling. Prev: Game Conservancy Trust: Manager of Upland Research 1990-95, Head of Upland Research 1985-90, Project Biologist 1979-85. Research on hummingbirds in Panama 1979. Marsh Warden WWT 1975-76. Research asst/ornithologist Zaire River Expedition. Special interests: population biology of birds, esp impact between birds and their natural enemies including predators and parasites; biology of British species of grouse and other upland birds. Author *The Red Grouse, the biology and management of a wild gamebird* (1986), *Grouse in Space and Time* (1992). Joint author (with D Newborn) *The Handbook of Grouse and Moorland Management* (1994). Editor *The Red Grouse, King of Gamebirds* (1987). Joint editor *Proc Third International Grouse Symposium* (1986), *Ecology and Management of Gamebirds* (1988), *Proc Fourth International Grouse Symposium* (1989). Scientific papers in eg *British Birds, Ibis, J Animal Ecol, Scottish Birds*. Popular articles in a number of magazines. First winner of The Laurent Perrier Award for Game Conservation, 1985. Member: AOU. OIR: long distance running, skiing, training and working dogs. Unit of Wildlife Epidemiology, Dept of Biological and Molecular Sciences, University of Stirling, Stirling FK9 4LA. 01786 467778; fax 01786 464994.

HUGGETT, Duncan James; *b:* 13 November 1964 in Rochdale, Lancs. BSc Ecology (Leeds, 1986), PhD Pied Flycatcher population ecology (Leeds, 1989). RSPB Coastal Policy Officer since 1994 (prev RSPB posts 1990-93 inc Fisheries Officer, Coastal Officer). Special interests: conservation policy, flyway conservation, estuarine and shorebird ecology. Contributions to publications on coastal zone planning, inc conference procs. Author of unpublished RSPB reports inc Bar-tailed Godwit species action plan. Member: Estuarine and Coastal Sciences Assocn, European Union for Coastal Conservation. OIR: keen motorcyclist and motorcycle mechanic; active member of English Civil War Soc; playing squash and hockey; reading science fantasy novels. RSPB, The Lodge, Sandy, Beds SG19 2DL. 01767 680551.

HULBERT, Beryl Maitland; *b:* 19 November 1935 in Woodford Green, Essex; *h:* Jack. Secretary at Nature Conservancy, then Natural Environment Research Council, at London HQ 1958-66. Indoor Meetings Secretary Surrey Bird Club 1958-66. Berks, Bucks & Oxon NT: Council and various committee posts 1973-. Chief voluntary warden Bernwood Forest Reserve 1968-. Special interests: bird identification and habits, bird photography. Extensive travel worldwide. Lived in Aden 1966-67 and studied spring and autumn migrations there. WWT Wildfowl Counts in Bucks since 1968. Monthly bird records since 1968 to Middle Thames NHS then Buckinghamshire Bird Club. Lectures on birds, natural history and travel both at home and abroad. OIR: travel, tennis, walking, reading, gardening, studying all natural history. Lapwings, 67 Worminghall Road, Oakley, Aylesbury, Bucks HP18 9QX. 01844 237574.

HULL, Richard Paul; *b:* 20 October 1946 in Chelmsford, Essex; *w:* Patricia. Mid-Essex School of Art. Freelance bird artist. Committee Essex Birdwatching Society 1964-91 and Essex WT 1972-84. BTO Birds of Estuaries Enquiry count co-ordinator for Essex in 1980s. Bird Recorder for Essex in 1970s. Special interests: wildfowl, waders, seabirds, birds of prey; leading field trips to Denmark, Norway, Sweden, Iceland, Greenland, USA. Illustrator of many books on birds and general natural history eg *Mitchell Beazley Guide to Birds of Prey of the World* by M Walters (1991). Paintings in private collections in many parts of the world; one-man exhibitions throughout UK and Denmark. OIR: classical and romantic music (esp Sibelius), Scandinavian history. 68 Fairhaven Avenue, West Mersea, Colchester CO5 8BT. 01206 384041.

HUME, Robert Arthur (Rob); *b:* 15 June 1950 in Burntwood, Lichfield, Staffs; *w:* Marcella. BA Geography (Wales, Swansea, 1971). Editor *Birds* (RSPB) since 1989. Prev: Editor *Bird Life* (YOC/RSPB) 1983-89; Asst Development Officer RSPB 1978-83. Records Committee Gower Ornithological Society c1974-75. Records Committee and Asst Editor, West Midland Bird Club 1970s. British Birds Rarities Committee since 1987, Chairman since 1993 Special interests: identification, gulls, terns, writing, editing, art. Author: *Usborne Guide to Birds of Britain and Europe* (1981), *Observers Birds* (1987), *Birds by Character* (1990), *Tracker's Guide to Birds* (1991), *Discovering Birds* (1992), *Focus on Birdwatching* (1992), *The Common Tern* (1993), *Seabirds* (1993), *Bird Watching* (Collins Photo Gem, 1995). Co-author (with Trevor Boyer) *Owls of the World* (1991), (with Terance James Bond) *An Artist's View* (1993). Editor *A Birdwatcher's Miscellany* (1984), *A Year of Bird Life* (1985), *The Complete Book of British Birds* (1988). Numerous features, notes, mystery photograph texts *British Birds* on various gulls and terns; many features in *Birds*; occasional items in other magazines, several partworks and encyclopedias. Script for RSPB film 'Early One Morning'. 15 Cedar Gardens, Sandy, Beds SG19 1EY. 01767 682003. RSPB: 01767 680551.

HUNTER, Stephen (Steve); *b:* 1 September 1955 in Birmingham; *w:* Verity. BSc Zoology (Manchester, 1977), PGCE Secondary Science Education (Manchester Polytechnic, 1978), PhD Comparative biology and ecology of the Giant Petrels *Macronectes halli* and *M. giganteus* at South Georgia (British Antarctic Survey and Oxford University, CNAA, 1983). Head, Conservation and Environment Protection Group of the Central Science Laboratory, MAFF since 1993 Prev: Chief Scientific Officer, Percy FitzPatrick Institute of African Ornithology, Univ Cape Town, 1984-87.

Scientific Officer, BAS 1978-83. BTO 'A' ringer since 1973. Special interests: esp giant petrels (above) and skuas. Author/co-author of scientific papers in eg *Colonial Waterbirds*, *Emu*, *Ibis*, *Ringing & Migration*; papers also in *Antarctic Nutrient Cycles and Food Webs* ed by Siegfried *et al* (1985) and *Antarctic Ecosystems: ecological change and conservation* ed by Kerry and Hempel (1990). Member African Seabird Group, Seabird Group. OIR: reading, riding, American Civil War history. Central Science Laboratory, MAFF, Sandhutton, York YO4 1LZ. 01904 822000.

HURFORD, Clive; *b:* 1 June 1956 in Cardiff; *p:* Christine Millican. BSc Botany (Univ College of Swansea, 1991). Monitoring Surveyor, Countryside Council for Wales since 1992. Prev: various RSPB posts 1978-84 inc Red Kite research in mid Wales and Warden of Handa Island reserve NW Scotland. Committee Cardiff Naturalists' Society 1985-88. Mid and S Glamorgan Records Committee 1985-95. Council Welsh Ornithological Society 1988-92. Secretary Welsh Records Panel 1993-. Special interest: Welsh ornithology. Co-author (with Peter Lansdown) *Birds of Glamorgan* (1995). Editor *Welsh Bird Report* 1978-89. Played leading role with Peter Hope Jones in founding the Welsh Ornithological Society in 1988. OIR: botanical and invertebrate recording (inc Fen Orchid Working Group and Butterfly Conservation South Wales Branch Committee), photography, a general enjoyment of sport and music. 3 Litchard Terrace, Litchard, Bridgend CF31 1PL. 01656 663137.

HURRELL, Sir Anthony (Tony); KCVO 1986, CMG 1984; *b:* 18 February 1927 in Norwich, Norfolk; *w:* Jean. MA History (Cambridge, 1948). Retired Diplomat and Civil Servant. BTO 'A' ringer since 1950; over 100,000 birds ringed since 1949. Articles on garden ringing in *Essex Bird Report* and various notes in *British Birds*, *Ibis*, *Ringers Bulletin*. Lapwings, Dunwich, Saxmundham, Suffolk IP17 3DR. 01728 648359.

HURRELL, Leonard Henry; *b:* 24 August 1929 in Yelverton, Devon; *w:* Anne. The Leys School Cambridge. BChir (Cambridge, 1954), MA, MB (Cambridge, 1955), MRCS, LRCP (The London Hospital, 1954). Retired general practitioner. Vice President British Falconers' Club since 1978. Advisory Panel Hawk and Owl Trust since 1975. Special interests: birds of prey, esp ecology and conservation, behaviour, migration and population dynamics (in addition to UK, notably in Scandinavia, E Africa, Malaysia); treatment and rehabilitation of raptor casualties since 1945; initiated Bird of Prey Rescue Scheme of Devon WT in 1965; study of breeding behaviour of raptors in captivity; development of design of enclosure specifically for diurnal raptors, resulting in the 'Skylight and Seclusion' formula; photography. Records in *Devon Bird Report* since 1950. Article on migration and movements of birds of prey over Singapore in *Bull Raffles Museum* 1961; articles in *The Falconer*; chapters in *A Hawk for the Bush* by J Mavrogordato (2nd ed 1973) and in *First Aid and Care of Wild Birds* by J E Cooper and J T Eley (1979). Member: Malaysian Nature Society. OIR: mammals, dragonflies. Peverell Park Villa, 201 Outland Road, Peverell, Plymouth PL2 3PF. 01752 771838.

HUTCHINGS, Stuart Charles; *b:* 26 January 1943 in Penryn, Cornwall; *w:* Kate. Countryside Ranger, Cornwall WT since 1982. Committee, Cornwall Birdwatching and Preservation Society from 1970 and Conservation Officer 1977-83. Staff member Cornwall WT Scientific and Reserves Committee 1980-. Voluntary warden CBWPS bird reserve at Stithians Dam. Special interest: bird photography. Travel for birds to the Arctic, Canada, E Africa, USA, Europe. Photographs published in various magazines and books. Occasional local radio broadcasts on ornithological matters. OIR: rugby, drinking strong ale. 24 Kernick Road, Penryn, Cornwall TR10 8NT. 01872 73939.

HUTCHINSON, Clive Desmond; *b:* 24 April 1949 in Cork, Ireland; *w:* Rachel. Midleton College, Cork. BA (Mod) History and Political Science (Trinity College, Dublin, 1971). Chartered Accountant 1974 and in practice in Cork. Council Irish Wildbird Conservancy 1969-76, 1979-84, 1988-91; Treasurer 1981-84; former Chairman of Cork Branch. Council Cape Clear Bird Observatory since 1967 and Chairman since 1986. Organiser of IWC's Wetlands Enquiry 1971-75. Special interests: distribution and populations; Black-tailed Godwit (esp feeding behaviour in winter) and Little Gull; editing and writing. Author: *Ireland's Wetlands and their Birds* (1979), *Watching Birds in Ireland* (1986), *Birds in Ireland* (1989), *Where to Watch Birds in Ireland* (1994). Editor *The Birds of Dublin and Wicklow* (1975). Joint founder *Dublin and Wicklow Bird Report* and joint editor 1968-72. Founder of *Irish Birds* and Editor 1977-84. Paper (with B Neath) on Little Gulls in Britain and Ireland in *British Birds*; author of several other papers and notes, and of several species texts in BTO Winter Atlas. OIR: windsurfing, hill walking, reading. 11 Knockrea Park, Douglas Road, Cork, Ireland. +353 (0)21 291469.

IMBODEN, Christoph Niklaus; *b:* 26 April 1946 in Zurich, Switzerland; *w:* Eve. PhD Zoology and Ecology (Basel, Switzerland, 1972). Consultant in conservation, sustainable development and ecological orientation of business. Prev: Director-General, BirdLife International (formerly ICBP) 1980-96; Asst Director (Research) New Zealand Wildlife Service 1978-80; Senior Scientist, Leader of Fauna Survey Unit, NZWS 1977-78; Conservation Officer WWF International 1976; Ecologist Swiss League for Nature Conservation 1975. Research Officer Swiss Ornithological Institute 1969-72. Wide range of voluntary posts, inc Chairman Swiss Committee for Bird Conservation and Steering Committee of IUCN Species Survival Commission. Special interests: global bird conservation, threatened species, migration. Many articles in Swiss and NZ journals on a variety of topics inc comprehensive analysis of migration of Lapwing (first European-wide, computer-based analysis of ringing data). Popular book on wetlands of Switzerland. Leading involvement in concept and content of popular book *Save the Birds*, published in nine languages between 1987 and 1989. RSPB Conservation Medal 1993; Primo Gaia, Sicily, 1993. OIR: music, visual arts, travelling. 8 Church Lane, Girton, Cambridge CB3 0JP. 01223 276230.

INNES, Michael Murray Lipp (Mike); *b:* 18 October 1949 in Dumfries; *w:* Frances. MA General (Aberdeen, 1974), Teaching Dip 1975. Teacher. Bird Recorder Grampian (except Moray) 1986-87. Committee NE Scotland Rarities Committee 1986-87. Special interest: seabird migration. Ten-year daily seawatch 1 July 1978 to 30 June 1988. Reports on movement of seabirds off Peterhead in *North-East Scotland Bird Report* 1989-95; also joint author of systematic list 1986-87. Illustrations in the bird report and in *The Birds of North-East Scotland* by S T Buckland *et al* (1990). Local art exhibitions. OIR: studying and recording all forms of local natural history, walking, camping, listening and dancing to rock music, eating and drinking. 106A Queen Street, Peterhead, Aberdeenshire AB42 6TY. 01779 476409.

IRVINE, June; born in Sandgate, Kate. Godolphin School Salisbury. Cert in Environmental Science (Univ Southampton, 1973). Retired secretary. Management Committee Hampshire Ornithological Society 1979-89. BTO 10km square steward 1968-. Fieldwork for BTO Breeding Atlas, Winter Atlas and New Breeding Atlas. Also Common Birds Census and Birds of Estuaries Enquiry counts 1972-. Editor *Hampshire OS Newsletter* 1979-89; article 'Breeding birds of New Forest broad-leaved woodland' in *Bird Study* 1977. OIR: walking, riding, swimming, cycling, music. 4 Clarence Road, Lyndhurst, Hants SO43 7AL.

JACKSON, Christine Elisabeth; *b:* 6 March 1936 in Huddersfield, W Yorks; *h:* Andrew. ALA 1959. Author and researcher in animal art and illustration. Author *British Names of Birds* (1968); *Bird Illustrators: some* *artists in early lithography* (1975); *Collecting Bird Stamps* (1977) (for which awarded Bronze Medal of British Philatelic Society); *Wood Engravings of Birds* (1978); *Bird Etchings: the illustrators and their books 1655-1855* (1985); *Prideaux John Selby: a gentleman naturalist* (1992); *Great Bird Paintings*, Vol 1: *The Old Masters* (1993), Vol 2: *Bird Paintings: the eighteenth century* (1994); *Dictionary of Bird Artists of the World* (in prep). Chapter in *George Lodge: artist naturalist* ed by John Savory (1986). Introductions to Sotheby's NY sale catalogue (1989) for 'The Library of H Bradley Martin. The Original Watercolours for Selby's Illustrations of British Ornithology', and for *Macaws* by Elizabeth Butterworth (1993). Articles on bird artists in eg *Archives of Natural History*, *J Soc Bibliog Nat Hist*, *The Bird Observer* (Australia). Member: Society for the History of Natural History (Council 1992-95), awarded Founder's Medal 1996. OIR: art, music, walking, local history, genealogy. Amberley, Hare Street, Buntingford, Herts SG9 0EQ. 01763 289421.

JACKSON, Colin Harold Walter; *b:* 6 January 1967 in Kenya. Tonbridge School, Kent 1980-85. BSc Environmental Science (Southampton, 1989). All Nations Christian College 1992-93. Training and Records Officer, Ornithology Dept of the National Museums of Kenya 1994-97. Prev: asst warden at the A Rocha Bird Observatory, Portugal 1989-92 and Aug-Dec 1993. Special interests: migration patterns, photography, application of ringing and survey data. Two-year project on the breeding ecology and population movements of Kentish Plovers on the Alvor Estuary, Portugal 1990-92. Note on ageing of Firecrests in *Ringing & Migration*. One of main contributors to the *A Rocha Observatory Report* 1989-93; also several illustrations. Member ABC, EANHS (Orn Sub-Committee), Wader Study Group. OIR: windsurfing, rugby, walking, camping, DIY, singing, playing guitar. Dept of Ornithology, National Museums of Kenya, PO Box 40658, Nairobi, Kenya. +254 2 742131.

JACKSON, George; *b:* 14 April 1930 in Kilmacolm, Renfrewshire; *w:* Megan. Bootham School, York 1944-47; West of Scotland Agricultural College 1950. Farmer twenty-three years in Cornwall, then on Islay (Argyll) since 1983. First NCC Warden on Islay, 1986-90 (post created to try to resolve conflict between farmers and conservationists over the grazing of Barnacle and Greenland White-fronted Geese there). Committee Cornwall Birdwatching and Preservation Society 1970-83, Hon Life Member since 1983. Committee Cornwall TNC 1970-83, Hon Life Member since 1983. Member of Cornwall Farming and Wildlife Advisory Group from inception in c1970 to 1983. Committee Islay FWAG since inception, Chairman since 1992. Chairman Islay Nat Hist Trust Management Committee since 1985. OIR: sailing and boating, travel, drawing and painting birds, photography, creating pond and wetland habitats. Coultorsay, Bruichladdich, Isle of Islay PA49 7UN. 01496 850444.

JAMIESON, Martyn Robert; *b:* 6 June 1957 in Liverpool, Merseyside; *p:* Marion Pope. BSc Zoology (Bristol, 1978). Senior Countryside Ranger, Wirral Country Park 1990-. Other posts in Wirral CP since 1984, inc Interpretative Officer 1986-90. Prev: Warden Cumbria TNC, Peregrine Protection Scheme 1983-84; research asst RSPB Wales, Waterways Bird Survey 1982-83; research asst, Dept of Biology, Liverpool Polytechnic (Shorebirds) 1978-81. External tutor Field Studies Council (inc ranger training). Runs company organising wildlife boat trips in Dee Estuary, also birdwatching weekends. YOC Leader for Wirral 1990-. Committee Wirral RSPB Members' Group (YOC rep) 1990-93. Wetland Bird Survey counter for Ribble Estuary 1978-81 and Dee Estuary 1985-. Participant in BTO surveys inc Waterways Bird Survey, Winter Atlas, Breeding Atlas, Low Water Estuary Counts. Volunteer on Peregrine protection schemes in Cheshire (1993) and N Wales (1988, 1989). Special interests: estuary birds and seabirds (several research projects for Liverpool Poly and Liverpool Univ); sound recording. Bird-related travel to Hebrides, Iceland, Norway, Ireland, Mallorca, Portugal. Several programmes on local wildlife (esp Dee Estuary) on BBC North West, Granada TV, Radio Merseyside. Regular monthly article in *Wirral and Cheshire Insider* (now defunct). Features weekly in local press. Photographs published in several magazines and books. Illustrated wildlife talks. OIR: walking, mountaineering, caving, cycling, photography, malt whisky, Sherlock Holmes. 9 Banks Road, Lower Heswall, Wirral, Merseyside L60 9JS. 0151 342 7813; work 0151 648 4371.

JANES, Ernest (Ernie); *b:* 3 April 1946 in Ringshall, Herts; *w:* Heather. FRPS 1981. Freelance photographer, specialising in wildlife. Hon Sec Nature Photographers' Portfolio 1975-84. President Zoological Photographic Club 1993-94. Photographic trips inc Kenya, The Gambia, USA (Florida), India, Turkey, Iran. Illustrations for numerous books and regular photographic contributor to all leading wildlife and country magazines. OIR: painting in watercolours, cycling, watching football (Watford FC). Parkhouse, Northchurch Common, Berkhamsted, Herts HP4 1LR. 01442 871342.

JARDINE, David Chisholm; *b:* 1 March 1959 in Aberdeen; *w:* Janet. BSc Forestry (Aberdeen, 1982). Member of Institute of Chartered Foresters

(MICF) 1990. Forest District Manager, North York Moors since 1995. Council SOC 1989-92. Council BTO 1990-94. BTO Research and Surveys Committee 1990-94. SOC Surveys and Research Committee since 1990 and Chairman 1993-95. Council RSPB 1994-. BTO 'A' ringer since 1990. Special interests: birds of British forests; forest finches (esp crossbills and Siskin); birds of Argyllshire. Author *Birds of Colonsay and Oronsay* location guide (1986) and *Guide to the Birds of Kielder Forest* (1993). OIR: munro-bagging (slowly!). Lynton, Beacon Park First Avenue, Pickering, N Yorks YO18 8AQ. 01751 477789.

JAYNE, Andrew; *b:* 4 September 1964 in Minsterworth, Gloucester. Royal Forest of Dean Grammar School 1976-83. Computer operator, Barclays Bank Computer Operations. County Recorder Gloucestershire since 1992, and hence Chairman County Records Committee and member of Glos Ornithological Co-ordinating Committee. Special interest: birds of the Forest of Dean. Contributor of ornithological notes for bi-monthly journal of Glos Naturalists' Soc. OIR: playing football (twice player of the year for local team, Westbury-on-Severn). 9 Hayes Court, Longford, Gloucester GL2 9AW. 01452 300035.

JENKINS, David; *b:* 1 March 1926 in Birmingham; *w:* Margaret Wellwood Johnston. West House School, Edgbaston, Birmingham 1933-39; Marlborough College 1939-43. MRCVS (Royal Veterinary College, 1948), MA Natural Sciences/Zoology (Emmanuel College, Cambridge, 1952), DPhil Factors governing population density in the Partridge (Bureau of Animal Population, Oxford, 1956), DSc (Oxford, 1984). FRSE 1986. Hon Professor of Zoology, Univ Aberdeen since 1986; Senior Research Fellow, Univ Aberdeen 1956-86. Prev: Senior Principal Scientific Officer and officer-in-charge, Brathens Research Station, ITE 1972-86; Asst Director (Research), Scotland, Nature Conservancy (Senior Research Fellow, Univ Edinburgh) 1966-72; Chief Scientist/Senior Officer, Univ Aberdeen/ Nature Conservancy Red Grouse Research Team 1956-66. Hon Sec Reading Ornithological Soc 1943-46. Hon Sec Cambridge Bird Club 1950-52. Council BOU in early 1960s. Council British Ecological Soc in late 1960s. Joint Founder Lista Bird Observatory, Norway 1952. Founder Blavandshuk Bird Observatory, Denmark 1953. Member NE Regional Board Scottish Natural Heritage (prev NCCS) 1990-95. Chairman Scientific Advisory Committee, World Pheasant Assocn 1975-95. Special interests: migration, behaviour, population dynamics, local distribution, effects of changes in land use, conservation. Specialist in ecology of gamebirds, but widely experienced in supervising studies in most groups of

British birds. Books edited include *Agriculture and the Environment* (1984), *The Biology and Management of the River Dee* (1985), *Trees and Wildlife in the Scottish Uplands* (1986), *Land Use in the River Spey Catchment* (1988), Symposium on Woodland Grouse in *Ornis Scandinavica* (1991) and 6th International Goose Symposium, Udine, Italy (1994), *Pheasants in Asia* (1989, 1994), *Ann Rev WPA* 1993-94 and 1994-95. Papers in eg *Bird Study*, *British Birds*, *Ibis*, *J Animal Ecol*, *J Appl Ecol*, *Scottish Birds*; also many articles in annual reports and short notes on occurrence of unusual species, distribution, plumage and behaviour in professional journals. Joint editor *Scottish Birds* 1991-; asst editor *Ibis* 1996-. OIR: gardening, walking, photography, editing. Whitewalls, 1 Barclay Park, Aboyne, Aberdeenshire AB34 5JB. 01339 886526.

JENNINGS, Michael Charles (Mike); *b:* 28 April 1947 in Whittlesford, Cambs; *p:* Carol Qirreh. Civil Servant. Co-ordinator *Atlas of the Breeding Birds of Arabia* since 1984. Former Council member Army Ornithological Society. Special interests: Middle Eastern (esp Arabian) birds. Leader or member of numerous ornithological surveys in Middle East, inc Turkey, Egypt, Cyprus, Oman, UAE, Yemen, Saudi Arabia. Author *Birds of the Arabian Gulf* (1981), *The Birds of Saudi Arabia: a checklist* (1981), *Interim Atlas of the Breeding Birds of Arabia* (1995). Editor *Phoenix* (newsletter of atlas project) 1984-96. About fifty papers, reports, notes and articles on Arabian birds, esp relating to breeding species and distribution. Member: OSME (posts held at different times), various Arabian ornithological and natural history groups. 1 Warners Farm, Warners Drove, Somersham, Cambs PE17 3HW. Tel/fax 01487 841733.

JENNINGS, Peter Philip (Pete); *b:* 5 December 1952 in Allbrook, Hants; *p:* Ruth Lowther. Head Ranger Elan Estate, Powys since 1987. Prev: Warden Calf of Man Bird Observatory 1978-81; asst warden Portland Bird Obs 1977. Recorder Radnorshire 1986-. BTO Regional Representative and Development Officer 1989-. Founder Radnorshire Bird Group 1985. Welsh Records Panel 1990-. Chairman Conservation and Scientific Committee, Radnorshire WT 1995-. Organiser of many surveys and censuses since aged 8 (school grounds). Special interests: Pied Flycatcher, behaviour, sexual selection, breeding strategies of summer migrants to Britain, ornitho-geography, habitat use, interpretation, teaching, training and writing. Author *The Good Birdwatchers Guide* (1991); co-author (with Pat Cullen) *Birds of the Isle of Man* (1986). Numerous short pieces on birds published in various local and national journals and newspapers. Garnfawr, Hundred House, Llandrindod Wells, Powys LD1 5RP. 01982 570334.

JOHN, Anthony William Geoffrey (Tony); *b:* 29 September 1941 in Guildford, Surrey; *w:* Jane. Ampleforth College York 1955-60. BSc Zoology and Botany (London, 1967). Marine biologist (long-term research on plankton). Council Devon Birdwatching and Preservation Society 1977-. BTO 'A' ringer and trainer. Special interests: migration, riparian birds (esp Dipper in W Devon since 1976), ringing, wildfowl counting. Editor *Devon Birds* 1979-. Paper on Jay invasion of 1983 in *British Birds.* Author of Jay account in BTO Winter Atlas. On editorial panel of *Tetrad Atlas of the Breeding Birds of Devon* ed by H P Sitters (1988). OIR: mountain walking, visiting islands, music lover, secondhand bookshop browser. Brook Cottage, Sampford Spiney, Yelverton, Devon PL20 7QX. 01822 852172.

JOHNS, Andrew David Grieser; *b:* 9 December 1956 in Taunton, Somerset; *w:* Bettina. BSc Zoology (Southampton, 1978), PhD Natural Sciences (Cambridge, 1983). Co-director, Makerere University Biological Field Station 1988-93. Prev: Project Leader, Wildlife Conservation International 1991-93; Research Fellow WCI 1988-91; Research Fellow in Zoology, Univ Aberdeen and Research Assoc, NERC/Royal Society 1987-88; Research Assoc, WWF-US 1984-86; research asst in tropical forest ecology, Univ Cambridge 1978-83. Bird illustration. Scientific papers in various ornithological and ecological journals and IUCN publications. Member: Assocn for Tropical Biology, OBC, Species Survival Commission Hornbill Specialist Group. OIR: classical music. 48 Doniford Road, Watchet, Somerset TA23 0TG. 01984 631740.

JOHNSON, Ernest David Hope (Johnnie); *b:* 16 June 1919 in London; *w:* Gwen. ARPS 1954. Retired commercial photographer and photographic dealer. Bird Recorder for Jersey 1949-74. Committee Ornithology Section of Société Jersiaise 1951-75 and Hon Life Member. Founder Council Member of Jersey Wildlife Preservation Trust 1963-72 and Hon Life Member. Founder Chairman of Institut ECHO, whose officers founded the International Bioacoustics Council (IBAC) in 1969. Correspondent for population, distribution and status of the birds of Algeria for *BWP.* Special interests: migration (esp trans-Saharan), distribution and status (esp Algeria), the Stonechat, sound recording (pioneered use of parabolic reflector in Britain in early 1950s). Participant in Wildfowl Trust rocket-netting expeditions in Scotland in late 1950s and early 1960s, inc sound recording. 1959: filming and recording with Eric Hosking/BOU expedition to Sierra de Cazorla, N Andalucia; returned with wife, spring and autumn 1960 to complete filming for BBC TV film on Ibex and Lammergeier. 1960: filming and recording with Eric Hosking on Guy Mountfort/BOU

Expedition to Bulgaria. 1961-65: with wife, organised series of spring expeditions to SE Morocco to set up temporary bird observatories. 1964: filming and recording with Royal Military Academy, Sandhurst, Expedition to Ethiopia. 1966-83 almost annual expeditions with wife and colleagues in the Algerian Sahara and Atlas Mountains, collecting data on distribution and status, also sound recordings, for *BWP*. 1968: filming, recording and collecting ornithological data on British Army Great Abbai (Blue Nile) Expedition; and same in 1969-70 on British Army Dahlek Quest Expedition to Red Sea. More recent visits (all inc sound recording) to eg Pakistan, Nepal, Sri Lanka, The Gambia, South Africa, Turkey, Corsica. Summaries of principal observations in Ornithology Section Reports of *Bull Soc Jersiaise* 1949-72. Papers on breeding biology of Stonechat in *British Birds*, and on its wintering in the Sahara in *Bull BOC;* articles on bird sound recording in *The Tape Recorder*; papers (some as co-author) on eg birds of Ethiopia, Algeria, and trans-Saharan migration in *Ardeola, Bull BOC, Dutch Birding.* In mid 1950s, broadcasts, mainly with a Jersey interest, in such BBC series as 'Birds in Britain', sometimes with recordings. BBC TV films in Peter Scott's 'Look' series. Director of photography for ITV film 'The Last Great First', from 1968 Blue Nile Expedition. Continuous contribution to British Library of Wildlife Sounds (now National Sound Archive Wildlife Section) since its foundation in 1969. Member: OSME, SEOF. OIR: gardening, listening to music, philately, food. Crabière Cottage, Grande Route des Mielles, St Ouen, Jersey JE3 2FN. 01534 481224.

JOHNSON, Hazel Monica; *b:* in Pinner, Middx; *h:* Tony. BSc Geology (London, 1952), MSc (Manchester, 1955) and PhD (Wales, 1959) on Silurian calcareous algae. Fellow Geol Soc Lond. Lecturer in Geology (retired) and tutor Univ Durham. Founder-member and Treasurer Durham RSPB Members' Group 1974, Leader 1977-94. Special interests: environment and conservation, migration (esp inland and hirundines), Nuthatch. Participant in BTO Common Birds Census (1975-) and Nest Record Scheme (1972-). Part author *Ornith Rept Trans NHS Northumbria and Newcastle upon Tyne* 1972. Editor/contributor *Durham RSPB Members' Group Newsletter* 1977-; articles in *Dalesman* and *Birdwatch*. Swift Medal, Junior Bird Recorders' Club c1946; RSPB President's Award 1995. OIR: general field studies, drawing, photography, gardening, classical music. Glenside, 11 Quarry Heads Lane, Durham DH1 3DY. 0191 386 5609.

JOHNSON, Paul Nicholas; *b:* 12 June 1958 in Doncaster, S Yorks. BA Ecology and Computers (Bedford College, 1988). Freelance ecologist. Prev: Director of Conservation and Education, Pensthorpe Waterfowl

Trust 1994; Conservation Officer Hawk and Owl Trust 1989-94; Warden and Cons Officer Yorkshire WT 1986-88. JNCC Barn Owl Advisory Group 1989-94. Barn Owl Conservation Network Advisor 1989-94. BTO 'C' ringer for raptors and owls since 1987. Special interests: Tawny Owls in urban environments, long-term monitoring of owl populations and winter habitat requirements of Barn Owls, photography and sound recording. Articles in eg *Bird Watching, BTO News, Country Life, Natural World, Ringing & Migration*. Member: Hawk and Owl Trust. OIR: walking, photography, cinematography, fossil hunting, natural history. Whiterose Cottage, Docking Road, Stanhoe, King's Lynn, Norfolk PE31 8QF. 01485 518180.

JOHNSTONE, Leslie (Les); *b:* 31 January 1941 in Glasgow; *w:* Christine. Civil Servant. Special interests: bird photography, portable hides, calls and decoys for photography purposes. Photographic visits to most of the Western Isles, Orkney and Shetland; also to France and Portugal. Photographs published in books and magazines. Lectures to RSPB and other groups. 14 Castleton Park, Auchterarder, Perthshire PH3 1QA. 01764 663565.

JONES, Gareth; *b:* 2 January 1960 in Tredegar, Gwent; *w:* Anna. BSc Ecology (London, 1981), PhD Parental investment in birds (Stirling, 1985). Royal Society Research Fellow, School of Biological Sciences, Univ Bristol since 1989. Council Bristol Naturalists' Society 1990-. Special interests: behavioural ecology of hirundines, parental investment and mating behaviour, predation on bats by birds, population changes and natural selection on body size in Sand Martins. Fifteen papers on birds in scientific journals on research interests 1986-. OIR: bat biology. School of Biological Sciences, University of Bristol, Woodland Road, Bristol BS8 1UG. 0117 928 7575.

JONES, Martin John; *b:* 15 May 1956 in Newport, Gwent; *w:* Dr Lesley Lace. BSc Zoology (Manchester, 1977); MSc, PhD Gull ecology (Manchester, 1980, 1985). Senior Lecturer in Ecology since 1988. Special interests: conservation, factors affecting island avifaunas. Two main projects: ecology and conservation of the birds of Madeira (thirteen visits/expeditions since 1981); ecological studies of rainforest birds on the islands of Sumba and Buru, Indonesia (expeditions in 1989 and 1992). Papers in *Biol J Linn Soc* and reports to BirdLife International. Winner of BP Conservation Expedition Award 1993. OIR: travel. Department of Biological Sciences, Manchester Metropolitan University, Chester Street, Manchester M1 5GD. 0161 247 1223.

JONES, Maurice; *b:* 12 July 1937 in Oldham, Lancs; *w:* Patricia Ann. Self-employed hardware retailer to 1994. Warden, Lytham St Annes LNR since 1982. Recorder for Lancashire since 1978. Served on committees of Lancashire WT 1960s/70s. Committee Fylde Naturalists' Society 1950s/60s, then Hon Member. Committee Fylde Bird Club c1987-95. Special interests: waders, seawatching, migration, survey work. Participant in many BTO surveys inc Breeding Atlas, Birds of Estuaries Enquiry, Heronries Census; also WWT surveys and, in 1979, a survey of the breeding birds of Warton Marsh, Ribble Estuary, for NCC. Compiler of 'Check List of Birds of the Fylde' published in *The Fylde Naturalist* (1978). Compiling (with others) new Lancs county avifauna. Salzman Prize of Junior Bird Recorders' Club 1953. OIR: botany, conservation, butterflies. 31 Laverton Road, St Annes-on-Sea, Lancs FY8 1EW. 01253 721076.

JONES, Peter Hope; *b:* 21 May 1935 in Llanrhaiadr-ym-Mochnant, Clwyd; *w:* Joan Lewis. MPhil Auk taxonomy/biometrics (Open Univ, 1985), MSc Wildlife data management (Wales, 1990). MIBiol 1976, ALA 1990. Asst Librarian, Countryside Council for Wales, retired 1995. Prev: Researcher, RSPB Black Grouse Wales Project c1985-86; Seabirds at Sea Team c1979-83. Founder/Chairman Welsh Ornithological Society 1988-c1992. Special interests: migration, conservation management, Bardsey. Author *Rhestr o Enwau Adar* [list of Welsh bird names] (1973), *The Natural History of Bardsey* (1988), and numerous booklets. Editor *Bardsey Bird Observatory Report* 1973-. Various broadcasts in Welsh and English on all aspects of ornithology and other wildlife. Winston Churchill Fellow 1968 (included visits to bird sites in eastern USA). OIR: football, cloud watching, Welsh and English poetry, photography, Dark Age Celtic history. The Hide, 49 High Street, Menai Bridge, Gwynedd LL59 5EF.

JONES, Peter Taylor; *b:* 29 June 1932 in Macclesfield, Cheshire; *w:* Anna. Retired college administrative officer. Committee Gloucestershire Naturalists' Society 1981-88, Chairman 1983-88. Committee RSPB Gloucester Members' Group since 1980, Leader 1985-. RSPB County Representative (Glos) 1992-. RSPB Council 1994-. Articles in *Gloucestershire Bird Report*; broadcasts for local radio. RSPB President's Award 1990. OIR: wildlife photography. 2 Beech Close, Highnam, Gloucester GL2 8EG. 01452 413561.

JONSSON, Lars Ossian; *b:* 22 October 1952 in Stockholm, Sweden; *w:* Ragnhild. Autodidact. Artist. Broad interest in birds and habitats; special interest in identification and moult. Author and illustrator of five volumes on European birds published in Sweden with title *Fåglar i Naturen* (1976-80, English ed 1978-82), *Bird Island* (1984), *Birds of Europe with North Africa and the Middle East* (1992, publ in 10 countries), and other books in Swedish. Member of some 20 ornithological societies, also of Society of Wildlife Artists (UK) and Society of Animal Artists (USA). Featured in *Wildlife Painting: technique of modern masters* by Susan Rayfield (USA, 1985), *Twentieth Century Wildlife Artists* by Nicholas Hammond (1986), *Drawing Birds* by John Busby (1986), *Birds in Art, the Masters* by Inga Brynildson and Woody Hagge (USA, 1990), *Masterpieces of Bird Art* by Roger F Pasquier and John Ferrand Jr (USA, 1991). Master Wildlife Artist (Leigh Yawkey Woodson Art Museum, Wisconsin) 1987. Norrgårde, Hamra, S-620 10 Burgsvik, Sweden. Studio: +46 498 499092; fax +46 498 499155.

JORDAN, William James (Bill); *b:* 21 May 1948 in Cambridge; *w:* Elizabeth. MA Agricultural Botany (Cambridge, 1970), PhD Soil Chemistry (Imperial College, London, 1975). Agricultural botanist. Council Cambridge Bird Club 1984-91. Special interests: conservation of Stone Curlew in England (since 1978), surveys, liaison with farmers on conservation action, birds and conservation of Iberian steppes. Joint author (with P M M Bircham and J C A Rathmell) *A Breeding Atlas of the Birds of Cambridgeshire* (1994). Editor *Cambridgeshire Bird Report* 1984-90. 61 Lone Tree Avenue, Impington, Cambs CB4 4PG. 01223 232043.

JOY, Roger Thomas; *b:* 9 March 1934 in USA; *w:* Sylvia. BSc Biology (MIT, 1955), MSc Biophysics (MIT, 1956), PhD Biophysics (Birmingham, 1961). Lecturer, Zoology Dept, Univ Nottingham 1967-84. WEA tutor for courses on bird studies 1963-. Adult education lecturer on various ornithological topics 1990-. Supervisor of ornithological research by students registered with distance learning organisations eg Somerset Univ (UK) and Fairfax Univ (USA). Chairman, Nottingham RSPB Members' Group 1974-78. Representative of Nottinghamshire TNC on Attenborough NR Management Committee 1975-84. Participant in BTO surveys 1988-. Special interests: population and behavioural studies of Ruddy Duck in UK; methods of encouraging Black Tern to recolonise British locations. Member: Cornell Univ Laboratory of Ornithology, Massachusetts Audubon Soc. OIR: wild orchid photography, medieval historical research. 21 Sherborne Drive, Newcastle, Staffs ST5 3JA. Mobile 0589 718790.

JOYNT, Graeme Neil; *b:* 16 August 1966 in Middlesbrough. BSc Chemistry (Nottingham, 1987). Senior Technical Officer, Public Protection Dept, Hartlepool BC. Cleveland Area Records Sub-Committee 1988-, Bird

Recorder 1994-. Special interest: birds of the Western Palearctic. Joint compiler *County of Cleveland Bird Report* 1989-, also articles on birds new to Cleveland (Pied Wheatear, Pacific Golden Plover). OIR: golf, football, playing guitar. 293 Stockton Road, Hartlepool TS25 5DA. 01429 262507.

JULIAN, Derek Ivor; *b:* 1 September 1968 in Truro, Cornwall; *w:* Samantha. Forecourt and security operative. Bird Recorder North Cornwall NHS 1993-95. Field Meetings Officer RSPB Cornwall Members' Group 1991-95. Asst Conservation Officer, Cornwall Birdwatching and Preservation Society 1994-. Warden Walmsley Sanctuary Bird Reserve 1994-. Wetland Bird Survey organiser for the Camel estuary 1990-. Special interests: migration (esp on WeBS site), ringing (trainee ringer). Author of 'Birds of the River Camel and North Cornwall Coasts' (reports 1990, 1991, 1992 published by CBWPS); also three reports for Farming and Wildlife Advisory Group: 'Breeding Birds of the Ruthern Valley' (1992), 'Breeding Birds of the Camel Valley' (1993), 'Breeding Birds of Tremore/Mulberry/ Ruthernbridge Area of Mid Cornwall' (1994). 9 Kernow Close, Wadebridge, Cornwall PL27 7XB. 01208 815799.

KANE, Kyran William Supple; *b:* 23 May 1942 in Dublin, Ireland; *w:* Helen. MVB (Veterinary College, Dublin, 1964), MRCVS 1964. Government Veterinary Inspector. Special interests: raptors, waterfowl, long-term monitoring of a number of breeding and wintering sites. Papers published in *Irish Birds* (historical) and *Ibis* (migration); records in Irish Bird Report since 1958. Member: Avicultural Society. OIR: reading, grand opera, cinema, wild places, deserts, Havana cigars, indolence. Castlebellingham, Co Louth, Ireland.

KEAR, Janet; OBE 1993; *b:* 13 January 1933 in London; *h:* John Turner. Walthamstow Hall, Sevenoaks; Caspar Junior College, Wyoming. BSc Zoology (King's College, London, 1956), PhD Feeding of finches (Girton College, Cambridge, 1959). Hon Fellowship, Manchester Metropolitan Univ, 1983; Hon Doctorate (and title Professor), Liverpool John Moores Univ, 1990. WWT: 1959-93 Research Scientist, finally as Principal Scientific Officer; 1974-77 Avicultural Co-ordinator; 1977-90 Curator of Martin Mere; 1978-90 Asst Director; 1988-93 Member of Management Committee; 1991-93 Director of Centres. Fellow, Zoology Dept, Liverpool Univ 1978-92. Council NCC/English Nature 1990-. Dept of the Environment Wildlife Inspector. DoE's Scientific Authority for Animals 1977-81. Assocn for the Study of Animal Behaviour: Council 1965-76, Secretary 1966-73. Council Avicultural Society 1975-77. Council BTO

1983-86. Zoo Federation's Breeding & Conservation Sub-committee 1974, Chairman 1975-83. RSPB Research Advisory Committee 1977-83, Council 1995-. IUCN: Chairman Endangered Waterfowl Group 1976-87, Captive Breeding Specialist Group 1979-92. Jersey Wildlife Preservation Trust: Scientific Advisory Committee 1979-, Director of Summer School 1993, Council 1994-. BOU: Council 1980-88, Vice President 1989-91, President 1991-95. American Ornithologists' Union: Corresponding Fellow 1983-. International Union of Directors of Zoological Gardens: WWT representative 1982-90. International Ornithological Committee 1982-, Vice President of 1998 Congress. President of Devon Birdwatching & Preservation Society 1995-. Special interests: wildfowl, flamingos, feeding behaviour of birds, conservation, captive breeding. Author *Eric Hosking's Wildfowl* (1985), *The Mute Swan* (1989), *Man and Wildfowl* (1990), *Swans* (1990), *Ducks of the World* (1991). Co-author (with A J Berger) *The Hawaiian Goose* (1980). Joint editor (with N Duplaix-Hall) *Flamingos* (1975). Editor *Ibis* 1980-88, *Wildfowl* 1989-. Editorial Board *International Zoo Yearbook* 1974- and Chairman 1980-88. Approx ninety scientific papers. Some radio and TV work. OIR: gardening, walking, reading. Jewells Lodge Cottage, Umberleigh, Devon EX37 9EY. 01769 580059.

KELSEY, Francis Derek (Derek); *b:* 3 March 1923 in Southsea, Hants; *w:* Magda. MA (Oxford, 1945), BM, BCh (Oxford, 1948), Diploma of Psychological Medicine (Conjoint Board, 1955). Consultant psychiatrist, retired. Gwent Ornithological Society Committee 1973-79, Vice Chairman 1977-79. Special interests: bird censuses and surveys. County organiser (Gwent) BTO Rookery Survey 1975, and Mute Swan Survey 1978. Wildfowl Count organiser, Llandegfedd Reservoir, Gwent 1975-81. Birds of Estuaries Enquiry count organiser, Cley Marsh 1985-. Bird counts on Wattenmeer, N German coast since 1970. Visits to Amazon rainforest, Colombia in 1989 and 1992. Member: NBC. OIR: mammals, botany, gardening. White Cottage, Church Lane, Cley, Holt, Norfolk NR25 7UD. 01263 740693.

KERR, Ian; *b:* 25 April 1940 in Newcastle upon Tyne; *w:* Hazel. Journalist. Committee Northumberland & Tyneside Bird Club 1978-91 (Sec 1980-90, Chairman 1991, County Records Committee 1988-89). BTO 'C' ringer since 1992. Member of Northumbria Ringing Group 1982-. Special interest: long-term survey of breeding Merlins; also involved in regular survey of Peregrine, Goshawk, Kestrel, Sparrowhawk. During 1994, with Bryan Galloway, set up major nestbox study for MOD on Otterburn Ranges, Northumberland. Author *Lindisfarne's Birds* (1984, rev 1992).

Co-author *Birds in Northumbria* (annual report) 1982-96. Regular contributor on ornithology to *The Northumbrian*. OIR: ambition to live on Holy Island, Northumberland, to carry out round-the-year study of birds. 27 Eddrington Grove, Chapel House, Newcastle upon Tyne NE5 1JG. 0191 267 6974.

KETTLE, Ronald Henry (Ron); *b:* 10 November 1923 in London; w: Irene. BA Mathematics and English Literature (London, 1952). Curator, British Library of Wildlife Sounds (BLOWS) 1972-88. Adult education tutor (part-time) on bird study 1968-93. London NHS Ornithology Section: Field Meetings Sec 1962-69, Hon Sec 1970-73. London NHS: Council 1965-73. Committee, BOC 1988-91. Chairman Wildlife Sound Recording Soc 1988-91. Wimbledon YOC Group Leader 1973-88; in early 1970s ran many YOC holiday courses. Leader of bird tours to Holland, Austria, Cyprus c1968-73. Bird sound discographies published in various journals; chapter on archiving natural history recordings in IASA book (1983); article on BLOWS in *Birdwatcher's Yearbook* 1989; paper 'Common Birds Census results on a woodland plot on Wimbledon Common 1973-1980' in *London Bird Report* 1982. Compiler/editor of tape cassettes *British Bird Songs and Calls* (1987) and *More British Bird Sounds* (1989). Joint compiler/editor of *British Bird Sounds on CD* (1992). Managing Editor *Bioacoustics* from inception in 1988. 75 Dupont Road, London SW20 8EH. 0181 540 0042.

KEY, Rodney William (Rod); *b:* 24 July 1942 in Spondon, Derby; *w:* Margaret. South Shields Grammar-Technical School 1953-59; Long Eaton Grammar School 1959-60; Derby Technical College 1960-63. Grade 1 Teacher's Diploma 1983. Deputy Technical Support Manager, Reckitt Products. Joint County Recorder for Derbyshire since 1980 (responsible for rarity records). Derbyshire Ornithological Society: Committee 1975, Chairman of Records Committee 1980. County co-ordinator for 1993 BTO Winter Gull Roost Count. Part-time teacher on ornithology courses for Derbyshire CC and WEA since 1982. Special interests: migration, identification (esp rarities). Editor of bird notes for DOS monthly bulletins 1968-90. Regular contributor on Derbyshire birds to *Bird Watching*. Articles in *Derbyshire Bird Report*, also compiler of sections on divers to ducks and skuas to terns (and whole of 1970 report). OIR: popular music, playing squash, watching American football. 3 Farningham Close, Spondon, Derby DE21 7DZ. 01332 678571.

KHAN, Robin; *b:* 30 September 1933 in India. Head Ranger (Wildlife and Conservation) Forest Enterprise, S & W England since 1985. Devon

Birdwatching and Preservation Soc: Protection Officer 1970-85, Council member/President 1992-94. Special interests: identification, migration, social pattern and behaviour of raptors. Studies include: raptor migration in Turkey, Israel, Egypt, S Spain, N Africa, esp routes taken by Honey Buzzard, Hobby, Montagu's Harrier and eagle species; Montagu's Harrier over-wintering in Tanzania; Goshawk in SW England; breeding behaviour, food and migration of Honey Buzzard (started 1977); Montagu's Harrier in Devon and Cornwall (1957-69); visits to N India for raptors. Contributions to *BWP* on social pattern and behaviour of Montagu's Harrier and Hobby. Regular articles in *Devon Birds*. Many broadcasts on local radio and both local and national TV on wildlife management in forests. Lectures to wildlife bodies and the general public. BTO 'A' ringer since 1970. Responsible for establishing bird of prey viewpoint in the Haldon Forest (Forest Enterprise) near Exeter. OIR: butterflies and dragonflies (Winston Churchill Travelling Fellowship Award in 1983 for the study of butterfly and dragonfly migration through the Pyrenees), reptiles, photography, travel. Woodlands, Milestone Cross, Chudleigh, Newton Abbot, Devon TQ13 0DR. 01626 854481.

KING, John Michael Buckley (Michael); *b:* 3 April 1924 in Cheshire; *w:* Helen. MA Zoology (Oxford, 1958). Retired. BTO 'A' ringer since c1956 and member of Sponsors Panel from 1989. Chairman Chew Valley Ringing Station 1989-. Special interests: migration, ringing. Participant in several Senegal ringing expeditions. Initiated ringing project in The Gambia 1995. Member: ABC, WAOS. Stonehaven, 16 Marsh Road, Rode, Bath BA3 6PE. 01373 830432.

KING, Vivian Andrew (Andrew); *b:* 28 August 1956 in Winchester, Hants; *w:* Cheryl. Montgomery of Alamein School, Winchester; Barton Peveril College, Eastleigh. BSc Biological Sciences (Westfield College, London, 1977). Claims Inspector, Welsh Office Agriculture Dept. Breconshire Birds Records Committee 1993-. Committee Hampshire & Isle of Wight NT (Winchester Area) 1978-83. RSPB voluntary warden at Dinas. Special interests: 'local patch' studies and contributions to annual reports; population dynamics. 10km square counter for BTO Winter Atlas 1981-84 (Hants); BTO Waterways Bird Survey 1993-; BTO Breeding Bird Survey 1994-. Birding trips to national parks in Norway, Sweden, Finland, Mallorca. OIR: general interest in natural history (esp deer), hill walking, trout and salmon fishing, playing squash. Heddfan, Pennorth, Brecon, Powys LD3 7EX. 01874 658351.

KIRBY, Jeffrey Stephen (Jeff); *b:* 5 March 1961, in Accrington, Lancs. BSc Applied Biology (Liverpool Polytechnic, 1983), MSc Ecology (Durham, 1984), PhD (Open Univ, 1995). Head of Research and Director of Wetlands Advisory Service, WWT since 1993. Prev WWT: Head of Waterfowl Monitoring and Wetland Ecology 1992-93; Head of Counts and Surveys Unit 1991-92; National Wildfowl Counts Organiser 1990. Earlier: Asst Estuaries Officer BTO 1986-90; Ringing Recoveries Officer BTO 1985-86; Asst Ecologist (Ornithologist) Lake District Special Planning Board 1985. Voluntary reserve warden, RSPB Leighton Moss/Morecambe Bay, several occasions 1976-80. Leader, North-east Lancashire Ringing Group 1976-84. Executive Committee member and Membership Secretary, Wader Study Group 1986-90. UK Membership Secretary, Australasian Wader Study Group 1988-90. Special interests: wetland birds, monitoring, methodology, ringing, population dynamics, population ecology, conservation management. Personal projects have included studies of activity and behaviour of diving ducks; Blackbird roost dynamics; coloniality in Black-tailed Godwits; breeding ecology of Ringed and Little Ringed Plovers; wintering ecology of Lapwings and Golden Plovers. BTO 'A' ringer since 1978, trainer and sponsor since 1982. Author of species accounts (Garganey, Ruff, Black-tailed Godwit) in BTO New Breeding Atlas. Author of over one hundred technical reports and scientific papers, and over thirty popular articles, mostly covering aspects of waterfowl ecology, inc seven issues of *Wildfowl and Wader Counts* and annual reports of the Birds of Estuaries Enquiry and National Waterfowl Counts schemes. Experienced lecturer. The Wildfowl & Wetlands Trust, Slimbridge, Gloucester GL2 7BT. 01453 890333; fax 01453 890827.

KIRK, David Anthony; *b:* 2 May 1960 in Gorleston-on-Sea, Norfolk; *p:* Halpin. King Edward VI School Norwich. BSc Zoology (Aberdeen, 1982), MSc Conservation (University College, London, 1983), PhD Ecological separation of small cathartid vultures in South America (Glasgow, 1989). Consulting Research Ecologist to Environment Canada since 1989. Prev: Library Asst, Alexander Library, Edward Grey Institute, Univ Oxford 1988-89. Voluntary posts include rehabilitation of sick and injured birds of prey 1969-78; Norfolk Conservation Corps management on Norfolk NT reserves 1979-82; wardening in vacations on RSPB reserves 1978-83; organiser, North-east Scotland wildfowl counts (Aberdeen Univ Bird Club) 1979; bird census of Loch Muick Nature Reserve for Scottish WT 1979; Beached Bird Survey work 1978-82; banding asst at Long Point Bird Observatory, Ontario 1989. Previous research: feeding ecology of Tawny Owls; effects of introduced hares on endemic birds on Seychelles; management of maquis vegetation in Tunisia; resource partitioning in New World vultures (Venezuela). Special interests: population ecology and conservation biology of diurnal raptors; habitat associations of neotropical migrant songbirds; the role of songbirds in farmland ecosystems; agricultural pesticides and birds. Author of scientific papers in eg *The Auk, Behavioural Ecol and Sociobiol, Can J Zool, J Raptor Research, Wilson Bull*; also in *Current Ornithology* (book series). Illustrations in various publications and exhibitor at eg SWLA annual exhibition (1989), Canadian Museum of Nature (1989,93), and Wildlife Art Gallery, Lavenham, Suffolk. Member: Raptor Research Foundation. OIR: parenting, wildlife and landscape photography, travel, creative writing, vegetarian cooking, organic gardening, alternative healing, music. *Aquila* Applied Ecologists, CP 47, Wakefield, Québec, Canada J0X 3G0. Or c/o National Wildlife Research Centre, Environment Canada, Canadian Wildlife Service, 100 Gamelin Blvd, Hull, Québec, Canada K1A 0H3. +1 819 4592983.

KITCHIN, Charles Edward Fisher; *b:* 26 April 1961 in Bury St Edmunds, Suffolk; *w:* Sue. BSc Environmental Science (Bradford, 1983). Senior Warden RSPB Nene Washes Reserve since 1991. Prev: Warden RSPB Ouse Washes 1991; Asst Warden/Warden RSPB Arne & Garston Wood 1987-91; RSPB contract warden 1985-87; woodland interpreter, Countryside Education Trust, Hants 1984-85; asst reserve officer, Slapton Ley 1981-82. 32 Pinewood Avenue, Whittlesey, Cambs PE7 1EU. 01733 350978.

KNIGHT, John Ernest; *b:* 18 May 1933 in Redcar, Yorkshire; *w:* Zélia. Sir William Turner's School, Coatham. MPhil Environmental Science (Bradford, 1990). Retired development chemist. Ecological consultant and wildlife photographer since 1985. Part-time lecturer in ornithology and natural history, Cleveland Education Dept since 1985. Special interests: moorland birds (esp Merlin), birds of the Spanish Pyrenees, wildlife conservation. Articles published in *The Naturalist*. Member: North Yorks Moors Merlin Study Group. OIR: mammals, watching rugby. 33 North Road, Stokesley, Middlesbrough N Yorks TS9 5DZ. 01642 711933.

KNIGHT, Robert (Rob); *b:* 7 August 1947 in Castleford, Yorkshire; *w:* Janis. Landscape gardener. Supervisor of environmental projects for Manpower Commission Voluntary Services 1982-87. Bird Recorder Castleford & District Naturalists' Society c1970-79. Formerly a warden of Willowgarth Nature Reserve for some twelve years (subsequently Chairman of Management Committee), and voluntary work on other reserves inc Fairburn Ings. Founder-member Pontefract & Castleford Bird Group 1989-, also Secretary. Special interests: 'local patch' work, habitat management, conservation. Instrumental in preventing landowner ploughing up woodland; court order required him to replant the area. Compiler of bird reports for above groups, contributor on local birds to *Birdwatch*. Sketches published in local and county newspapers to illustrate articles on birds. Occasional local radio item, eg on Waxwing invasion. OIR: painting in oils and watercolours, photography, gardening, history (esp local), reading non-fiction, music from traditional folk to classics. 2 Milnes Grove, Airedale, Castleford, W Yorks WF10 3EZ.

KNOX, Alan Glasgow; *b:* 4 December 1950 in Belfast; *w:* Ann-Marie. BSc Zoology (Aberdeen, 1973), PhD Bird Taxonomy (Aberdeen, 1977). Head of Resources, Buckinghamshire County Museum since 1990. Prev: Senior Scientific Officer, British Museum (Nat Hist), Sub-dept of Ornithology, Tring 1981-89; Computer Analyst/Programmer, Dept of Obstetrics and Gynaecology, Univ Aberdeen 1980-81; Research Fellow in Bird Taxonomy, Univ Aberdeen 1977-80. BOU: Council 1990-94, Records Committee 1984- (Chairman 1990-94), Taxonomic Sub-committee 1984-. BTO: Council 1985-89, Finance & Gen Purposes Committee 1988-89. Bird Exploration Fund: Secretary/Treasurer 1984-85, Committee 1985-89. Member of international group reviewing bird taxonomy for European Union. Bird Recorder NE Scotland 1972-81. Past committee member or officer of several local organisations. BTO 'A' ringer since 1969. Special interests: bird taxonomy and evolution, crossbills, Caledonian pine forests, roof-nesting Oystercatchers. Widely travelled in Europe; also Iceland, Russia, Near East, N Africa, USA, Canada, New Zealand, Pacific. Over 100 papers on taxonomy, crossbills, bird records. Compiler *BOU Checklist of Birds of Britain and Ireland* (6th ed 1992). Co-author (with M Walters) *Extinct and Endangered Birds in the Collections of the Natural History Museum* (1994). Editor *North-East Scotland Bird Report* 1974-81. Photographs published in birding and national press. Radio and TV broadcasts. Thomas Henry Huxley Award (Zoological Soc of London) 1977. Developed first computer system for local bird recording in UK in 1975 (*NE Scot Bird Rep* 1977, 25-30). Member: AOU, Assoc Field Orn, Cooper Orn Soc, Wilson Orn Soc. OIR: fishing, boats, books, malt whisky. Buckinghamshire County Museum, Tring Road, Halton, Bucks HP22 5PJ. 01296 696012.

KRAMER, David; *b:* 3 November 1945 in Doncaster, Yorkshire. Bedfordshire NHS: Council 1984-87, Hon Sec 1985-87, Scientific

Committee 1984-92. Bedfordshire Bird Club: Research and Records Committee 1993, 1994; President 1993-96. Regional Organiser for WWT 1986-94. Special interests: migration, behaviour, history of ornithology, effects of recreational activities on wintering wildfowl populations, travel. Long-term study of bird populations at Priory Country Park, Bedford since 1982. Contributed chapter on 'New Waters' to *Bedfordshire Wildlife* (1987). Co-author (with P Trodd) *The Birds of Bedfordshire* (1991). Author *The Birds of Priory Country Park* (1992). Wrote biography of Jannion Steele-Elliott for 1993 reprint of J S-E's *The Vertebrate Fauna of Bedfordshire* (1897-1901). Compiler and publisher of *Priory Park Bird Report* 1990-. Articles on bird behaviour, migration, history, 'local patch' in eg *The Bedfordshire Naturalist, Birdwatch, British Birds, The Hobby* (Beds Bird Club magazine). OIR: blue woolly hats and sweaters; buying bird books instead of clothes; art, but can't paint or draw; sport (ex-basketball, ex-marathon); music. 7 Little Headlands, Putnoe, Bedford MK41 8JT. 01234 349307.

LACK, Peter Christopher; *b:* 17 January 1952 in Oxford; *w:* Diane. BA Zoology (St Johns College, Oxford, 1974), MA 1979, DPhil The habitats and feeding stations of birds in Tsavo National Park, Kenya (Oxford, 1981). Computer Officer BTO since 1990. Prev BTO: Research Officer in Agricultural Birds Unit 1985-90; National Organiser of BTO Winter Atlas 1980-85. BTO 'A' ringer since 1972. Special interests: birds in winter, birds in farmland, birds in Africa, migrants. Several expeditions to various parts of the world and several local projects. Compiler *The Atlas of Wintering Birds in Britain and Ireland* (1986); author *Birds on Lowland Farms* (1992); joint editor *The Birds of Buckinghamshire* (1993). Over thirty scientific papers in various journals, plus many short notes, research reports and more popular articles. Member: ABC (Council). OIR: natural history and countryside, cricket, Suffolk archaeology. Son of late Dr David Lack. BTO, The Nunnery, Thetford, Norfolk IP24 2PU. 01842 750050.

LAINE, Lasse Juhani; *b:* 6 February 1946 in Finland; *w:* Helena. BSc 1976, MSc 1988 Zoology with Botany and Geography (Univ Helsinki). Senior Editor *Eläinmaailma (Animal World)* since 1979. Asst then leader of field courses and lecturer on birds in Dept Zoology, Univ Helsinki 1974-82. Freelance nature photographer since 1964. Finnish Rarities Committee 1976-91 (Chairman 1981-91). Finnish Bird Names Committee 1980-. Officer in Finnish Ornithological Society 1988-92. Survey co-ordinator in 1960s. Special interests: migration (inc watching and counting of visible migration in Finland, Bulgaria, Israel, Turkey); identification (esp birds of tropics, tundra and Siberia, specialising in calls and songs, raptors, warblers, wheatears); censusing (inc studies of transect-line census as a method of evaluating bird densities); breeding biology (inc extensive special studies of Barred Warbler and Red-backed Shrike); photography (wide collection of bird photographs from different parts of the world); ringing (ringed c1,000 Barred Warblers in Finland 1968-86). Widely travelled, inc tour leader, to many parts of former Soviet Union, USA, Argentina, Malaysia, Thailand, Ecuador, Mexico, Turkey etc. Main author and chief editor *Birds of Finland* (in Finnish, 3 vols, 1992-93); author and designer *Suomalainen Lintuopas* (Finnish photographic bird guide, 1996). Editor and translator into Finnish of several English and Swedish bird books eg field guides by Heinzel, Fitter and Parslow (1974) and by Lars Jonsson (1977-83). Compiler and editor of three CDs of songs and calls of birds of Finland (1995). Contributor (inc photographs) to many Finnish and some foreign bird books (eg National Geographic Society's *Field Guide to the Birds of North America* and *Photographic Guide to the Birds of Britain and Europe* by Delin and Svensson). Articles in birdwatching and other popular magazines; also weekly column on birds in *Helsingin Sanomat* (Finnish daily) since 1977. Sub-editor of *Linnut* (prev *Lintumies*) main national Finnish birdwatching magazine 1973-76, and of *Ornis Fennica* 1978; identification consultant *Birding World* since inception. Member: ABA, ABC, NBC, OBC. Started mystery quiz photo series ('probably the first of its kind in Europe') in 1975 in *Lintumies*, which still continues. Since 1989 organiser (through *Eläinmaailma* magazine) of a spring Bird Marathon/Birdwatching Day event in Finland to promote birdwatching and raise funds for nature conservation. OIR: music (esp jazz, rhythm and blues), literature, handball and football (now only on TV). Furuborgintie, 101 60 Degerby Ul. Finland. +358 9 2213539; fax +358 9 2218412; work +358 9 1205471.

LAMB, Eric Thomas; *b:* 16 December 1938 in Folkestone, Kent; *w:* Maurin. BA Mathematics (Open Univ, 1979), MPhil Mathematics (Nottingham, 1985). CEng, MIEE 1974. Consultant mathematician, retired. Trent Valley (now Nottinghamshire) Birdwatchers: Committee member and Secretary in 1960s, also Field Meetings Organiser late 1950s and 60s, now Hon Life Member. Part-time wardening at Gibraltar Point in 1960s and Attenborough NR 1960-80. Working holidays at Tour du Valat reserve, Camargue 1964, 1965. WEA tutor in ornithology and ecology/ conservation since 1960; also some LEA and Nottingham Univ adult education courses. Special interests: identification, migration, songs and

calls, application of statistics to ornithology. Widely travelled for birds in
Europe; also Kenya, USA, Hong Kong. Some notes in *British Birds* and co-
author (with A Dobbs) of paper on weather and migration in TVBW annual
report in 1960s. Member: OBC. OIR: most branches of natural history,
astronomy, watching cricket, political theory, history of science and
mathematics, mathematical research. 38 Clarence Road, Beeston,
Nottingham NG9 5HY. 0115 922 6032.

LANCASTLE, Brian Jeffrey; *b:* 6 January 1953 in Bristol, Avon. ARICS.
Construction industry. Records and Editorial Committees, Avon
Ornithological Group 1983-. Committee Ornithological Section, Bristol
Naturalists' Society c1976-c1984. Special interest: 'local patch' work, inc
counting and recording; regular watching of shoreline of Severn Estuary
from Severn Bridge south to Avonmouth since late 1973 (ie most weekends
and evenings during spring/summer). Section editor of *Avon Bird Report*
1980-. Articles in *ABR* eg 'Seabirds in the Upper Severn Estuary.' Regular
visits to southern Europe (esp Spain); also Israel, The Gambia,
E Africa, E coast of N America. 23 Windmill Lane, Henbury, Bristol
BS10 7XE. 0117 950 9727.

LANGSBURY, Gordon James; *b:* 22 September 1932 in Witney, Oxon;
w: Joy. FRPS 1978. Freelance wildlife photographer, lecturer and author.
Chairman, Nature Group of Royal Photographic Soc 1981-83. Special
interest: waders. Co-author (with M Hill) *Collins Field Guide to
Photographing Birds in Britain and Europe* (1987). Author and presenter of
RSPB video *Photographing Birds* (1996). Leader of birdwatching tours to
Florida for Abercrombie and Kent. OIR: classical music. Sanderlings,
80 Shepherds Close, Hurley, Maidenhead, Berks SL6 5LZ. 01628 824252.

LANGSLOW, Derek Robert; *b:* 7 February 1945 in London; *w:* Helen.
Ashville College Harrogate 1956-63. MA (1966), PhD (1969) Natural
Sciences (Queens' College, Cambridge). Chief Executive, English Nature
since 1990. Chairman Asian Wetland Bureau 1994-. Wetlands International
Executive Committee 1995-. Prev: Nature Conservancy Council Policy
Director 1987-90, Asst Chief Scientist 1984-87, Senior Ornithologist 1978-
84. BTO Ringing and Migration Committee 1975-78. Secretary Edinburgh
Ringing Group 1973-78. Special interests: migration, breeding waders.
Articles published on Blackcap and Black Redstart migration; Golden
Plover and Golden Eagle breeding; breeding census methods; bird
community of Chippenham Fen; conservation of upland breeding birds;
breeding/territory of Dippers; bird conservation in Europe. OIR:

badminton, hill walking, talking. 4 Engaine, Orton Longueville, Peterborough PE2 7QA. 01733 318364.

LANSDOWN, Peter Geoffrey; *b:* 28 March 1947 in Cardiff, Glamorgan; *w:* Christine. Quantity surveyor. Committee Ornithological Section of Cardiff Naturalists' Society 1967-82, inc three years as Secretary, five years as Bird Recorder for Glamorgan, one year as Vice President and one year as President. Glamorgan Bird Records Committee 1970-86. Welsh Records Advisory Group 1976-86. British Birds Rarities Committee 1983-93, inc Chairman 1986-93. Isles of Scilly Records Panel 1984-93. BOU Records Committee 1986-93. *British Birds* Identification Notes Panel 1987-. Council Welsh Ornithological Society 1988-93. Bird tour co-leader for Sunbird 1988-. Special interests: identification, migration, bird recording. Co-editor (with Clive Hurford) of county avifauna *Birds of Glamorgan* (1995). Editor *Glamorgan Bird Report* 1976-80. *British Birds* contributor on identification and bird recording topics 1974-. 197 Springwood, Llanedeyrn, Cardiff CF2 6UG.

LAWN, Michael Richard (Mike); *b:* 3 February 1954 in Godalming, Surrey. Dip and Cert in Field Biology (London, 1990). Analytical chemist. Asst warden Portland Bird Observatory 1984. BTO 'A' ringer since 1975. Special interests: behavioural ecology and population dynamics of woodland passerines, migration, woodland management/conservation, amateur research on Willow Warblers since 1976. Papers in *J Avian Biol, Ornis Scandinavica* and *Ringing & Migration*; also several short notes in *British Birds*. 20 Croft Road, Godalming, Surrey GU7 1BY.

LAWRENCE, Donald Rodney John (Rod); *b:* 12 December 1942 in Crediton, Devon. Cert Ed (London, 1975), Nat Dip in Arboriculture (Surrey Coll of Agric, 1973), Dip in Ecology and Conservation (London, 1975). Freelance naturalist since 1983. Teaching for various bodies inc Exeter Univ, LEA and WEA. Set up Faraway Wildlife Ltd in 1991; organiser and leader of birding/wildlife holidays and expeditions. Special interests: the birds of Australia (several expeditions and birding holidays organised); birds and their ecological niche. Author *The Exe: a river for wildlife* (1991). OIR: wildlife photography (library of over 8,000 slides), playing guitar. 31 Devondale Court, Warren Road, Dawlish Warren, Devon EX7 0PN.

LAWRENCE, Edward Simon (Simon); *b:* 29 October 1957 in Uganda; *w:* Christine. BSc Biological Sciences (Leicester, 1979), PhD Hunting for cryptic prey-evidence for search image in wild passerine birds (Southampton, 1984). Environmental consultant since 1991. Prev: various posts with NCCS/SNH (eg Moorland Bird Survey Team Leader) 1990-91; Post Doctoral Research Fellow, Zoology Dept, Glasgow Univ 1988-90; Lecturer (Bird Ecology), Dept of Adult Education, Southampton Univ 1982-84. Wetland Bird Survey count organiser Loch Gilp 1988-. BTO 'A' ringer since 1985 and Schedule 1 Licence holder. Special interests: behavioural ecology, optimal foraging, predation, crypsis, DNA finger-printing, social organisation, scavenging birds, island endemics, land use, bird conservation, birds and pastoral agriculture, birds and wind farms. Member of Southampton Univ Ornithological Expedition to Ladakh (NW India) 1981, researching trans-Himalayian bird migration. Articles published in *Anim Behav*, *J Animal Ecol*, *New Scientist*, *Oikos*. Contributions (as specialist adviser) to BBC TV programmes in series *World About Us*, *Wildlife on One*, *Natural World*. Churchill Fellow 1988 (studying the endemic birds of Christmas Island). OIR: playing sports (inc rugby, tennis, squash, volleyball, running), angling, riding, Highland cows, wildlife and landscape photography. Quay House, Paterson Street, Lochgilphead, Argyll PA31 8JP. Tel/fax 01546 602468.

LAWSON, Thomas Ritchie (Tom); *b:* 24 November 1935 in Southampton, Hants; *w:* Julia. Highgate School, London. MB, BS (University College and Royal Free Hospital School of Medicine, London Univ, 1960), MRCS, LRCP 1960. Consultant radiologist. Bird tour guide with various organisations, inc Ornitholidays, 1966-. WEA tutor in ornithology 1973-. Lecturer on ornithological topics 1970-. RSPB Hon Local Representative York 1978-88. Member: ABA, AOU. OIR: photography, travel, ornithological literature, bird art. Burton Garth, Main Street, Knapton, York YO2 6QG. 01904 795489.

LAWTON, John Hartley; *b:* 24 September 1943 in Preston, Lancs; *w:* Dorothy. BSc Zoology (Durham, 1965), PhD Zoology (Durham, 1969). Director, NERC Centre for Population Biology and Professor of Community Ecology, Imperial College, Univ London 1989-. Scientific Advisory Committee, Game Conservancy 1984-88. RSPB Council 1987-, Chairman from 1993. Chairman BTO Bird Distribution and Modelling Project Advisory Committee 1991-. Special interests: bird population dynamics, communities and conservation. Author *Red Grouse Populations and Moorland Management* (1990). Joint editor (with A N Lance) *Red Grouse Population Processes* (1990). Piece on Ecology in *A Dictionary of Birds* ed by B Campbell and E Lack (1985). Many scientific papers, those on birds in eg *British Birds, J Animal Ecol, J Zool, Oikos, Ornis Scandinavica*. Witherby Lecture, BTO Annual Conference 1994. OIR: gardening, photography, travel, running, hill walking, music. Centre for Population Biology, Imperial College at Silwood Park, Ascot, Berks SL5 7PY. 01344 294354.

LAZARUS, John; *b:* 24 August 1945 in Harrow, Middlesex; *w:* Dr Rebecca Torrance. BSc Zoology (London, 1967), PhD Psychology (Wales, Cardiff, 1978). Lecturer/Senior Lecturer, Dept of Psychology, Univ Newcastle upon Tyne 1979-. Previous posts in Depts of Psychol of Univ Liverpool, Univ Coll Cardiff, Univ Bristol; also demonstrator in Dept Zool, Newcastle. Assocn for the Study of Animal Behaviour: Council 1981-84, 1991-93; Hon Treas and Chairman of Grants Committee 1985-90. Council member, International Council of Ethologists 1983-92. Field (UK, Iceland and Australia), laboratory and theoretical behavioural research: flocking, vigilance and anti-predator behaviour in passerines and geese; reproductive behaviour, parental care and conservation in waterfowl; egg recognition in noddies. Research published in eg *Anim Behav, Ethology, Ibis, Wildfowl.* Dept of Psychology, University of Newcastle upon Tyne NE1 7RU. 0191 222 6181.

LEA, David; *b:* 3 March 1930 in Orpington, Kent; *w:* Elizabeth. Retired coach tour operator. Prev: Orkney Officer, RSPB 1973-80; Reserves Manager and Deputy Director (Conservation), RSPB 1964-73; Asst Curator, Wildfowl Trust 1952-54; Warden, Lundy Bird Observatory 1950-51. Regional Board Member (part-time), NCCS/Scottish Natural Heritage 1991-96. Conceived and initiated with Derek (now Lord) Barber and Eric Carter the Farming and Wildlife Advisory Group (FWAG) in 1969. Various voluntary posts, most recently eg Committee Orkney Field Club and Orkney FWAG. OIR: pre-history, walking, classical music. Cabby Motorhome, c/o Stackaldbrae, Stromness, Orkney KW16 3EP.

LEACH, Michael; *b:* 9 September 1954 in Tettenhall, Staffs; *w:* Judith. Professional wildlife photographer and author. Special interests: high speed photography of birds in flight, urban bird life, owls. Author of several wildlife books inc *The Complete Owl* (1992). Wildlife articles in a wide range of specialist and popular magazines. Photographs used in over five hundred books throughout the world. Lectures widely and runs wildlife photography courses for the Field Studies Council and other organisations. Brookside, Kinnerley, Oswestry, Shrops SY10 8DB. 01691 682639.

LEES, David Allen; *b:* 14 October 1942 in Worcester Park, Surrey; *w:* Phyllis. Shift supervisor. Co-ordinator of the Hertfordshire Ringing Report and occasionally the Buckinghamshire Ringing Report. Special interest: feather identification. Large collection of feathers, half deposited in the Zoological Museum (Tring) and the other half at the Royal Museum of Scotland (Edinburgh). Advised Museum of Barcelona on the setting up of a feather identification collection. Compiling a database of European bird names in European languages. Co-author (with R Brown *et al*) *Tracks and Signs of the Birds of Britain and Europe* (1988; also transl into French, German and Italian). Author *Birds of the Boxmoor Estate* (1990). Member: Hawk and Owl Trust. OIR: genealogy and history. 183 Northridge Way, Hemel Hempstead, Herts HP1 2AS. 01442 391372.

LEES-SMITH, Derek Thayer; *b:* 21 August 1922 in Shanghai, China; *w:* Anne. Retired British Civil Servant. Organiser and editor of HASA (Holarctic Avian Species Atlas) 1979-86. Special interests: systematics, evolution, biogeography (of mainly the Holarctic avifauna). Author of 'Composition and origin of the south-west Arabian avifauna' in *Sandgrouse* (1986); notes in *Ibis* and *OSME Bulletin*. Member: AOU. OIR: reading thriller fiction; European, American and Russian history; current affairs. 134 The Avenue, Starbeck, Harrogate, N Yorks HG1 4QF. 01423 884068.

LEFRANC, Norbert; *b:* 20 April 1945 in Paris, France. M ès L English (Nancy, 1970), DUniv Sciences (Nancy, 1977). Nature Conservation Officer, Ministry of the Environment, Regional Office, Metz since 1989: responsible for conservation of fauna, flora and habitats in Lorraine, inc national parks, nature reserves, European directives, Ramsar sites, agri-environment measures, etc. Prev: Curator (Natural Sciences), Museum of Saint Dié 1977-88. Secretary of Groupe Tétras Vosges and co-ordinator of Capercaillie population surveys in the Vosges mountains 1975-89. Special interests: shrikes and mountain birds (eg Nutcracker); also keen interest in African birds. Co-ordinator of shrike population surveys in France 1993-95. Worldwide travel, mainly linked with observation of shrikes. Author *Les Oiseaux des Vosges* (1979), *Introductions et Réintroductions Animales en France* booklet for teachers (1985), *Les Pies-Grièches d'Europe, d'Afrique du Nord et du Moyen-Orient* (1993), *Shrikes* (in prep). Articles published in *Alauda, Bulletin de l'Office National de la Chasse, Ciconia, Faune-Sauvage, L'Oiseau et la Revue Française d'Ornithologie, Ornithos.* Member: ABC, LPO, SEOF. Chevalier du Mérite Agricole 1991, for studies and conservation efforts relating to the Capercaillie. 7 Chemin du Bois Basselin, F-88100 Saint Dié, France. +33 29567948; office +33 87399972.

LEGG, Rodney; *b:* 18 April 1947 in Bournemouth, Dorset. Author and publisher. Warden of Steep Holm island in Bristol Channel since 1974. Author of countryside books in the main, with ornithology specifically in *Purbeck's Heath* (1987) and *Steep Holm Wildlife* (1990). Chairman Open Spaces Society from 1988. Council National Trust from 1990. OIR: walking the cat. Kenneth Allsop Memorial Trust, via Wincanton Press, National School, North Street, Wincanton, Somerset BA9 9AT. 01963 32583.

LEONARD, Paul; *b:* 6 December 1957 in Sheffield, Yorkshire; *w:* Christine. Graphic artist with Local Authority (much with natural history emphasis). Sheffield Bird Study Group: General Committee 1984-90, 1996-; Surveys Sub-committee 1986-88; Records Sub-committee 1984- (Sec 1984-86, Chairman 1987-); Recorder 1985-87. Special interests: identification (esp gulls, waders, warblers); 'enigmatic' species (eg snipes and Woodcock, Dunnock, rails and crakes). Self-taught bird artist. Illustrations in bird reports (eg *Sheffield BR, Doncaster BR, Fair Isle BR*); books inc *Birdwatching in the Sheffield Area and Peak District* by J Hornbuckle and D Herringshaw (1985) and *Rare and Scarce Birds in Yorkshire* by A Wilson and R Slack (1996); journals eg *Yorkshire Birding, La Garcilla* (Spanish). OIR: surrealist art, music (esp rock, jazz), collecting old Devon pottery, reading (esp science fiction/fantasy). 12 Rockcliffe Road, Rawmarsh, Rotherham, S Yorks S62 6NA. 01709 525380.

LESLIE, Roderick; *b:* 26 January 1955 in Valetta, Malta. Rugby School. MA Agricultural & Forest Science (Keble College, Oxford, 1976). Fellow, Institute of Chartered Foresters. Regional Environment Manager, Forest Enterprise, SW England since 1988. Prev: National Wildlife and Conservation Officer, Forestry Commission 1985-88. BTO Regional Representative NE Yorkshire 1980-82. RSPB Council 1983-88. Committee Hawk & Owl Trust 1994-. Special interests: ecology of forest birds (main work on re-stocking, esp Nightjar). Assisted with BirdLife International Mt Kupe Forest Project, Cameroon (1992,93). Co-author (with M I Avery) *Birds and Forestry* (1990) and Nightjar text in BTO New Breeding Atlas; articles in *The Naturalist* and *Ornis Scandinavica*, also in other journals and magazines. Member: ABC, Malaysian Nature Society, WAOS. 144 Cranbrook Road, Bristol BS6 7DG. 01272 420041.

LESTER, Martin David; *b:* 12 July 1956 in Melton Mowbray, Leicestershire. Advanced Cert in Ecology & Environmental Management (Leicester, 1992); Dip Applied Ecol (Leicester, 1993). Reserve Warden, Wicken Fen NNR (National Trust) since 1995. Prev: Warden, The Chase

Nature Reserve (London WT) 1993-95; Senior Ranger, Normanby Hall Country Park 1992-93; Asst Warden, Rutland Water NR 1990-93. BTO 'A' ringer since 1989 and member of Trainers Panel. Special interest: monitoring resident and migrant bird populations on reserve as an aid to habitat management. Study on the effects of reedbed management on local Reed Warbler population 1989-91. Five-week surveys in 1990s of the use by resident and migrant species of Hell's Gate National Park, Kenya. Four-week private expedition to the Nepalese Himalaya 1992. Compiler of *Birds of Dagenham Chase* 1993-94, *Birds of Wicken Fen* 1996-. Member: EANHS. OIR: photography, rugby union, hill walking, climbing. c/o Wicken Fen NNR, Lode Lane, Wicken, Cambs CB7 5XP. 01353 720274.

LEVER, Tresham Christopher Arthur Lindsay (Sir Christopher); Bt; *b:* 9 January 1932 in London; *w:* Linda. Eton College. BA History and English (Trinity College, Cambridge, 1954), MA 1957. Retired. BTO: Council 1988-91, Chairman National Centre Appeal 1987-92. Member, IUCN Species Survival Commission 1988-. Chairman, Lever Trust 1988-. Special interest: naturalised species (esp Mandarin). Author *The Naturalized Animals of the British Isles* (1977), *Naturalized Birds of the World* (1987), *The Mandarin Duck* (1990); *They Dined on Eland: the story of the acclimatization societies* (1992), *Naturalized Animals: the ecology of successfully introduced species* (1994). Species account for Budgerigar in *Evolution of Domesticated Animals* ed by I L Mason (1984). Contributor to BTO New Breeding Atlas, to *The Introduction and Naturalisation of Birds* ed by J S Holmes and J R Simons (1996), and to *The European Ornithological Atlas* (in prep). OIR: fishing, golf. Newell House, Winkfield, Berks SL4 4SE. 01344 882604.

LEWINGTON, Ian David (Lew); *b:* 3 December 1964 in Oxford; *w:* Debbie. St Birinus School, Didcot. Bird illustrator. County Bird Recorder Oxfordshire since 1994. Special interests: identification, photography, birding and field sketching at home and abroad. Travelled widely in Europe; also Israel, USA (Texas), China. Illustrated *Rare Birds of Britain and Europe*, text by Per Alström and Peter Colston (1991); *Raptors of Europe*, text by Dick Forsmann and Philip Burton (1996); *Auks of the World*, text by Tony Gaston and Ian Jones (in prep). Illustrations in several books inc *BWP* Vols 6 and 8 and *Handbook of the Birds of the World*. Illus for identification papers in eg *Birding World*, *Dutch Birding*, *Limicola*, *Vår Fågelvärld*. Bird Illustrator of the Year (*British Birds*) 1985 together with the Richard Richardson Award in the same year. Founding member of the South Oxfordshire & District Ornithological Fellowship of Friends 1992. OIR: league badminton, heavy rock drumming, goalkeeper for the birders football team on Scilly. 119 Brasenose Road, Didcot, Oxon OX11 7BP. 01235 819792.

LEWIS, Gary David; *b:* 8 December 1957 in Luton, Beds; *w:* Sue. Government Service. Executive Committee Royal Naval Birdwatching Society 1991-, Hon Treas 1996-. Asst co-ordinator of Min of Defence annual bird survey 1991-. Member of Joint Services Expedition to Brabant Island (Antarctica) with responsibility for bird census and other related scientific recording (results deposited with Scott Polar Research Institute and British Antarctic Survey). Editor of bird section of *Caradon Field & Natural History Society Annual Report* 1988-92. OIR: distance running, family. 40 Pondfield Road, Saltash, Cornwall PL12 4UA. 01752 846723.

LEWIS, Michael John (Mike); *b:* 14 July 1947 in Ilford, Essex; *w:* Jill. Friends School Saffron Walden; College of Estate Management, Kensington. ACIB 1972. Banking internal auditor. Banbury Orn Soc: Treasurer 1980-, Short and Long Day Counts Organiser 1983-91. Wildfowl Counts regional organiser for N Oxfordshire 1985-92, participant 1980-. BTO Regional Representative for Banbury area 1992-95. Special interests: fieldwork and study of relationship between habitat and bird species diversity; participating in annual breeding season studies, eg BTO Garden Bird Feeding Survey since 1991. OIR: mountaineering, gardening, general natural history. Old Mill Cottage, Avon Dassett, Leamington Spa, Warwicks CV33 0AE. 01295 690643.

LEWIS, Victor Charles (Vic); *b:* 24 May 1910 in Leominster, Herefordshire; *w:* Olive. MIEE 1938. Agricultural and landscape contractor, retired 1970. Prev: RAF pilot; flying instructor; commercial aviation. Temporary attachment to BBC Natural History Unit Aug-Dec 1966. Special interest: bird sound recording. 'Produced the first-ever LP commercial record of British bird song to be published in this country' *A Tapestry of British Bird Song* (EMI, 1964); also a further twelve commercial discs for EMI and Pye. In 1981 recorded, compiled, wrote and produced a series of twelve cassettes *British Bird Vocabulary*, a series in six volumes in habitat classification with sets of notes, inc monochrome and colour photographs; 47 species and over 700 examples from their sounds; 1990 supplement added twelve species and 80 examples. In 1988 produced six cassettes of *Sound Guides* arranged in family groups (eg British warblers). Broadcast a number of short radio programmes in 1964 and

1966. Possesses collection of over 400 North American stuffed bird skins. Rosehill House, Lyonshall, Herefordshire HR5 3HS. 01544 340246.

LISHMAN, Gavin Stuart; *b:* 26 July 1958 in Watford, Herts; *w:* Carol. Spalding Grammar School. BSc Zoology (Univ Coll London, 1980), DPhil Ornithology (Wolfson College/Edward Grey Inst, Oxford, 1983). Marketing consultant. British Antarctic Survey: post-graduate studentship 1980-83; contract biologist 1983-84. Co-ordinator London WT Greater London Owl Survey 1985. Local nature reserve work. Special interests: seabird feeding and energetics (fieldwork at Signy Island, South Orkney Islands, Antarctica 1980-82). Papers published in *BAS Bulletin, Ibis, J Zool Soc London*; also in books *Seabirds: feeding biology and role in marine ecosystems* by J P Croxall (1987) and *Handbook of Australian, New Zealand and Antarctic Birds* by Marchant and Higgins (1990). OIR: gardening, walking, badminton. 6 West Road, Bourne, Lincs PE10 9PS. 01778 393200.

LISTER, Steven Michael; *b:* 31 August 1954 in York; *w:* Megan Hall. BSc Chemistry (Hull, 1975). Bird Recorder South Holderness Countryside Society 1983-87. Member Yorkshire Naturalists' Union Ornithological Committee 1983-88. Winter Shorebird Count organiser for N Humbs 1984-85. Birds of Estuaries Enquiry organiser for N Humber Estuary 1985-88. Referees' Sub-committee of Leics and Rutland Ornithological Society 1993-. Special interests: distribution, migration and identification of W Palearctic birds (esp N Africa and Middle East), seawatching. Extensively travelled in Europe, Africa, Asia, N America, Caribbean. Member: ABA, ABC (founder-member), NBC, OBC, OSME. 31 Lisle Street, Loughborough, Leics LE11 1AW. 01509 212952.

LITTLEMORE, Frederick Percival (Fred); *b:* 27 February 1929 in Mickle Trafford, Cheshire; *w:* Marie. Runcorn County Grammar School. Retired. Leics and Rutland Ornithological Society: Committee 1963-93, Chairman 1970-73, Referees' Sub-committee 1963-93. Wildfowl Count organiser for Leicestershire 1969-75, counter at Stanford Reservoir 1963-. Special interests: Palearctic-African and intra African migration, E African birds. Resident in Kenya for two years, with later visits there and to Morocco, Tunisia, Egypt, Sudan; extensive travel in Spain, Cyprus, Crete and N Greece. Long-standing project of monitoring all species recorded at Stanford Reservoir (SP603805) Leics/Northants since 1962. Joint editor *LROS Annual Report* 1979-81. OIR: gardening, botany, entomology, travel, photography, philately. Plemstall, 264 Dunchurch Road, Rugby, Warks CV22 6HX. 01788 812080.

LOATES, Michael John (Mick); *b:* 17 August 1947 in Orpington, Kent; *w:* Liz. Sidcup School of Art 1963-64; Ravensbourne College of Art 1964-66. Wildlife artist and portrait painter. Participant in national low tide counts on Kingsbridge Estuary 1992-94. Special interest: field study of effects of light and shade on wildlife and water for paintings. Illustrator of wildlife books inc *Go Birding* by Tony Soper (1988), *Oceans of Birds* by Tony Soper (1989), *Wildlife of the Salcombe & Kingsbridge Estuary* by Gordon Waterhouse (1992). Vice President Kingsbridge & District NHS 1993-. OIR: study of fishes; coarse, sea and game fishing; conservation of marine and freshwater habitats; travel; reading and collecting books; playing and listening to blues guitar. The Elms, 20 Duncombe Street, Kingsbridge, Devon TQ7 1LR. 01548 853389.

LONG, Adrian James; *b:* 7 March 1965 in St Johnstone, Scotland. BSc Biological Sciences (East Anglia, 1987). Researcher, BirdLife International 1991-. Prev: fieldwork in Chiapas, Mexico 1989-90; joint project between Univ E Anglia, Univ Kyung Hee and Asian Wetland Bureau surveying South Korean coastal wetlands 1988. Voluntary work for AWB (then Interwader) in Thailand, Malaysia and Singapore 1984-85. UEA expeditions in Java (1984) and Mexico (1986). Council Oriental Bird Club 1988 and 1992-95. Special interests: conservation of threatened species, identifying conservation priorities for birds, gathering data on poorly known species, mapping bird distributions. Editor *OBC Bulletin* 1992-95. Articles on bird conservation in eg *Bird Cons Internat, Condor, Cons Biol, Forktail, Nature*; also contributions to books. Member: NBC (founder-member), OBC. BirdLife International, Wellbrook Court, Cambridge CB3 0NA. 01223 277318.

LONGLEY, Paul Martin; Major; *b:* 10 September 1958 in Bolivia. Chatham House Grammar School 1970-78. BA Chemistry (Lincoln College, Oxford, 1981), MA 1985. Army Staff College 1990. Army Officer. Army Ornithological Society: Regional Representative (various areas in N Ireland). AOS bird counts in Lydd (Kent) 1988, Shrivenham (Wilts) 1989, Camberley (Surrey) 1990, Ballykinler (Co Down) 1993. Member of Oxford University Exploration Society Committee 1979-81. Special interest: W African birds. Travelled widely in W and N Africa. Military service and travel in Hong Kong, Brunei, Malaysia, Cyprus, Germany. Oxford Univ Expedition to Tanzania (Usambaras and Kilimanjaro) 1980. OIR: classical music, windsurfing, riding, watercolour sketching, photography, philately. c/o C J Longley, 251 Oakwood Drive, Southampton SO16 8DG.

LORAND, Stephen (Steve); *b:* 1 June 1944 in Grimsby, Lincs; *w:* Valerie. Wintringham Boys Grammar School, Grimsby. Garden centre proprietor. Lincs & S Humberside TNC: Little Tern warden at Donna Nook, Lincs 1984; Warden of Snipe Dales NR, Lincs 1985-87. BTO 'A' ringer 1961-76. Ringing Secretary Cleethorpes Ringing Group 1967-76. Voluntary warden at Donna Nook NR 1979-. Special interests: identification, migration, populations and census work, distribution, seabirds. Author *Birds of Lincolnshire and South Humberside* (1989). Compiler *Cleethorpes Ringing Group Annual Report* 1965-70. Contributor of coastal migration reports to *Lincolnshire Naturalists' Union Transactions* Vols 17-19 (1969-71). Other reports, inc checklist of the birds of Donna Nook, during 1965-79. OIR: botany, writing, traditional jazz. Willow Holt, Marsh Lane, North Somercotes, Louth, Lincs LN11 7PD. 01507 358145.

LORD, Michael Henry; MBE 1993; *b:* 3 March 1939 in Hove, Sussex; *w:* Alix. Journalist. Bristol Ornithological Society Committee, inc Secretary and Chairman at various times 1970-93. Avon Ornithological Group Secretary and Chairman at various times 1987-93. Hon Life Fellow WWT since 1993. General Secretary, Cornwall Birdwatching and Preservation Society 1995-. Voluntary warden for English Nature (Avon Gorge and Lizard NNRs) since 1987. Leader of E African wildlife holidays for Papyrus Tours since 1993. Organiser of Avon Gorge Peregrine protection project 1993. Articles in eg *Cornwall Today, Country Life*. Member: EAWS. OIR: music, malt whisky and walking (not simultaneously). Gue Gassel, Church Cove, The Lizard, Cornwall TR12 7PH. 01326 290981.

LOSEBY, Timothy (Tim); *b:* 29 April 1950 in Doncaster, Yorkshire; *w:* Irene. Insurance surveyor. Special interests: identification, migration, photography (pioneer of rare bird photography in early 1980s). Travel abroad inc Indian subcontinent and former USSR. Comprehensive slide collection from these regions and the W Palearctic, inc common British birds as well as rare and uncommon species. Photographs published in most main birdwatching and ornithological publications in Britain and Europe eg *Birding World, Birdwatch, British Birds, Dutch Birding, Limicola, Vår Fågelvärld*; also in books. Occasional articles for magazines eg *Bird Watching, Birds*. Illustrated talks to RSPB and other natural history groups. Member: OBC, OSME. OIR: music, sport. 34 Meteor Road, West Malling, Kent ME19 4TH. 01732 870283.

LOVE, Dudley Mark (Mark); *b:* 31 August 1953 in Croydon, Surrey; *w:* Lucy. BSc Chemistry (Univ Coll London, 1976), Barrister-at-Law

(Council of Legal Education, 1979), Called to the Bar Gray's Inn 1979. Barrister in private practice. Since 1982 has represented RSPB in matters relating to the Wildlife and Countryside Act 1981, principally in prosecuting offences concerning wild birds in England and Wales. Has undertaken similar work for a number of Local Authorities in all aspects of environmental law; also Legal Director of the RSPCA 1989-91. An informal legal adviser to the BTO Ringing Scheme since 1987. Occasional wildlife guide with Canvas Holidays in the Pyrenees and Brittany. Both he and wife Lucy BTO 'C' ringers since 1983 and were joint 10km square stewards for the BTO Winter Atlas and New Breeding Bird Atlas. Their ringing principally involves a continuing project on the movement of passerines through St Martins, Isle of Scilly in autumn and the resident and migrant populations at a site on the slopes of the North Downs in W Kent. They also run a YOC Group and a WATCH Group. OIR: Lepidoptera and general natural history; opera and drinking malt whisky 'not invariably at the same time'. Coldrum House, Coldrum Lane, Trottiscliffe, Kent ME19 5EG. 01732 822225; office 0171 936 2613.

LOWES, John Peter (Peter); *b:* 20 December 1945 in Barnard Castle, Co Durham; *w:* Eva. Austin Friars School, Carlisle. Self-employed photographer. Photographs published in eg *Bird Watching, Birds, British Birds*. Winner of Bird Photograph of the Year (*British Birds*) 1977. Illustrated lectures on birds of the British Isles to schools, clubs and the general public. 43 Millfield Avenue, Northallerton, N Yorks DL6 1AT. 01609 774589.

LUSMORE, Neville; *b:* 5 September 1939 in Dursley, Glos. Dursley Grammar School 1951-58. Semi-retired. Dursley Birdwatching and Preservation Society: former Committee member for over twenty years, Hon Sec 1967-73, organiser of Garden Bird Feeding Survey for DBPS since 1979. Special interest: Rook populations in south Gloucestershire. OIR: botany, foreign travel, nature conservation, photography, gardening, walking, books. 6 Canal Cottages, Upper Framilode, Gloucester GL2 7LJ. 01452 741219.

MACDONALD, Donald (Donnie); *b:* 1 May 1911 in Dornoch, Sutherland; *w:* Joan. Dornoch Academy. Sheriff Clerk, retired. Bird Recorder Sutherland and Ross-shire 1969-76. BTO Representative E Sutherland 1974-84. Wildfowl Trust Counts 1955/56 to 1981/82. Papers on Corn Bunting, Whitethroat and Collared Dove published in *Scottish Birds*; also articles in *Birds* and *Scottish Wildlife*, and short notes in *Scottish Birds* and

British Birds. Contributed section 'The East Coast and Eastern Lowlands' to *Sutherland Birds* ed by Stewart Angus 1983. Detailed wildlife journal kept from 1 January 1933. OIR: 'now reduced to bowls'. Elmbank, Castle Street, Dornoch, Sutherland IV25 3SN. 01862 810275.

MACFARLANE, Arthur Maxwell (Maxwell); Lt Col Retd; *b:* 16 November 1930 in London; *w:* Cathy. Mill Hill School 1944-48. RMA Sandhurst 1949-50; Staff College, Camberley 1962. Commissioned Royal Artillery 1950-85. Civil Servant 1985-96. Recorder Hong Kong Bird Watching Society 1957-60. Army Birdwatching Society: Committee 1968-85, Editor 1977-85. Special interests: identification, migration and status, esp Hong Kong, Lebanon and Syria. Co-author (with A D Macdonald) *An Annotated Check-list of the Birds of Hong Kong, 1960* (1966). Field notes on the birds of Korea (1953-54) published in *Ibis*; field notes on the birds of Lebanon and Syria (1974-77) published by ABWS. Correspondent for Lebanon and Syria for *BWP*. Member: HKBWS. OIR: military history, esp campaign medals. 60 Holden Park Road, Southborough, Tunbridge Wells, Kent TN4 0EP. 01892 532708.

MACKAY, Andrew John; *b:* 8 May 1965 in Bristol, Avon. Groby Community College; Loughborough College of Art and Design. Freelance wildlife artist/illustrator since 1988. Asst warden Sandwich Bay Bird Observatory 1986-87. Leics & Rutland Ornithological Society: Committee 1988-, Records Committee 1992-. County Bird Recorder Leicestershire 1994-95. Special interests: identification, migration, rarities, gulls. Editor *Leics & Rutland Bird Report* 1991-. Illustrations in *Rare Birds in Britain 1800-1990* by Lee Evans (1994) and the *Concise BWP* (in prep); in journals eg *Birding World*, *British Birds*, *Ringing & Migration*; also in various JNCC publications. Paintings regularly exhibited at RSPB, BTO and Leics and Rutland TNC. OIR: moths, butterflies, dragonflies, watching sport, music. 68 Leicester Road, Markfield, Leicester LE67 9RE. 01530 243770.

MACKENZIE-GRIEVE, Colin John; *b:* 28 January 1951 in Chelmsford, Essex; *w:* Monica. Shrewsbury School. MA Law (Magdalene College, Cambridge, 1972). Solicitor of the Supreme Court, admitted 1975. Solicitor (Partner, Head of Commercial Property Dept, Stephenson Harwood). Essex Birdwatching Society: Executive Committee 1975-77, Recording Committee 1975-88. Special interests: migration, passerine identification. Cambridge Univ first expedition to the Shiant Islands 1970. Ornithological travel inc Uganda, Iran, Sri Lanka, Israel, Morocco, Australia, Thailand, Indonesia, Hong Kong. Editor *Cambridge Bird Club Bulletin* 1970-71, and

Essex Bird Report 1975-77; also article in latter on the birds of Old Hall Marshes. OIR: family, opera, Arsenal FC. 7 Sunset Avenue, Woodford Green, Essex IG8 0ST. 0181 504 0129.

MACKLIN, Robin Nigel (Rob); *b:* 2 March 1950 in Winchester, Hants; *p:* Kathleen Archibald. Peter Symond's Grammar School, Winchester. Warden/Site Manager RSPB North Warren since 1990. Prev RSPB: Warden Minsmere 1986-90; contract warden at various sites 1983-86. Council Suffolk Ornithologists' Group 1990-. Council Suffolk Naturalists' Society 1996-. Special interests: habitat requirements of breeding waders of lowland wet grassland. RSPB co-ordinator for survey of breeding Woodlarks on Suffolk Sandlings. Six-week study of Magpie Robins for ICBP in Seychelles Dec 1991-Jan 1992. Compiler of finches to buntings section of *Suffolk Bird Report* since 1990. OIR: butterflies; playing village cricket for Sweffling, Suffolk. Racewalk, Priory Road, Snape, Saxmundham, Suffolk IP17 1SD. 01728 688481.

MACLURE, Edward Stanley Winton (Winton); Lt Cdr RN Retd; *b:* 11 April 1909 in Winchester, Hants; *w:* Jeanette (deceased). Royal Navy 1926-54 then Admiralty Surface Weapons Establishment, retired 1975. Hon Secretary and Treasurer, Royal Naval Birdwatching Society 1957-85. Articles published in the Society's journal *Sea Swallow*. 'I sometimes wonder if my interest in natural history stems from the fact that...I can claim relationship with Frank Buckland the Victorian naturalist and founder of the Zoological Society of London.' Flat No 1, Hinton House, Jubilee Road, Waterlooville, Hants PO7 7QX. 01705 268960.

MACMAHON, Clare; OBE 1982; *b:* 26 November 1924 in Downpatrick, Co Down. BSc Botany and Zoology (Queen's Univ Belfast, 1946). AMA 1951, MIBiol 1954, Member of Linnean Soc 1982-. Retired Deputy Principal, Stranmillis College of Education. Pro-Chancellor (honorary), The Queen's Univ of Belfast 1988-. Belfast Naturalists' Field Club: Secretary of Zoology Section and Leader of Bird Group 1954-57. Chairman, Wildbird Advisory Committee to the DoE (NI) 1973-77. Chairman, RSPB Northern Ireland Region Committee 1987-93. OIR: field botany, walking, music, reading. 7 Kimscourt, 21 Kensington Road, Belfast BT5 6NH. 01232 792665.

MACMILLAN, Andrew Thomas; *b:* 21 January 1933 in Edinburgh; *w:* Helen. CA (Inst of Chartered Accountants of Scotland) 1956. Finance director, retired. President SOC 1975-78, Hon Member from 1986.

Chairman RSPB Scottish Committee 1973-75. Member of Secretary of State's Advisory Committee on the Protection of Birds for Scotland 1970-81, and of NCC Advisory Committee on Birds 1981-84. Former Trustee George Lodge Trust; Fair Isle Bird Observatory Trustee and Management Committee Member 1970-86. Editor *Edinburgh Bird Bulletin* 1957-58. Asst editor *Scottish Birds* from start in 1958, Editor 1962-70; set up organisation for modern series of *Scottish Bird Reports* and compiled those for 1968 and 1969. OIR: hill walking; collecting Scottish tokens and banknotes, and all communion tokens. 20 Garscube Terrace, Edinburgh EH12 6BQ. 0131 337 5575.

MADGE, Stanley Graham (Graham); MBE; *b:* 20 February 1920 in Stockleigh English, Devon; *w:* Dora (deceased). Retired teacher. Hon Sec Devon Birdwatching & Preservation Society 1965-67, President 1973-81. Special interest: birds of prey (Accipitriformes and Falconiformes, 148 species on life list); bird photography ('most memorable photo, a juvenile Taita Falcon'); sound recording. Travel: lived in Malaya 1965-67, and in Zambia 1970-73; countries visited for birds inc Spain, France, Germany, Switzerland, former Yugoslavia, Bulgaria, Greece, India, Australia, South Africa, Kenya, USA, Belize, Venezuela. Numerous notes and articles in *Devon Birds*; notes in *British Birds* and *Bull E African NHS*; many articles in *Bull Zambian Orn Soc*; papers in *Bull BOC* and *Malay Nature Journal*. Recorded songs of many species included in *Bird Songs of SE Asia* compiled and edited by Terry White (1984); also calls of Taita Falcon in *South African Bird Sounds* by Guy Gibbon (1991). 'Has strived for many years to draw attention to environmental problems and damage to wildlife resulting from human over-population; author of *Commonsense & the Population Problem* (1984)'. OIR: bee-keeping, botany, butterflies, church work. 8 Lame John's Field, Crediton, Devon EX17 1EB. 01363 772175.

MADGE, Stephen Charles (Steve); *b:* 15 January 1948 in Torpoint, Cornwall; *w:* Penny. Saltash Grammar School. Freelance writer and tour guide since 1979 (Sunbird 1979-81, Birdquest 1982-95, partner in Limosa Holidays from 1995). Prev: RSPB Warden Bempton Cliffs and Fairburn Ings 1973-79; asst warden Calf of Man Bird Observatory 1972. Served on various committees and councils inc Ornithological Society of Turkey and its successor OSME. British Birds Rarities Committee 1977-88 (and its Seabird Advisory Panel 1989-). East African Rarities Committee 1986-. President, Cornwall Birdwatching and Preservation Society 1994-. Special interests: identification and conservation; Palearctic and Oriental birds. Widely travelled in all continents, with favourite areas Palearctic Asia and the Middle East. Led the first organised bird tours to Israel, Yemen and Central Asia. Author *Birdwatching* (1980); *Wildfowl: an identification guide to the ducks, geese and swans of the world* (1988); *Crows and Jays: a guide to the crows, jays and magpies of the world*, illus by Hilary Burn (1993); Afghanistan section in *Important Bird Areas of the Middle East* by M I Evans (1994). Many papers on identification topics, chiefly *Birding World* and *British Birds*, but also in many other journals inc *Courser, Dutch Birding, Forktail, Limicola, Scopus*. Compiler (with Keith Allsopp) of 'Recent Reports' for *British Birds* c1977-82. Member of Identification Notes Panel of *British Birds* 1989-. British representative on editorial panel of German journal *Limicola* 1992-. Editor *Caradon Field and Natural History Club Annual Report* 1984-95. Member: ABC, NBC, OBC, OSME. OIR: wildlife surveys and conservation issues in Cornwall, specialising in botany and moths. Seawinds, Downderry, Torpoint, Cornwall PL11 3LZ. 01503 250432.

MAGEE, John Desmond; *b:* 10 September 1923 in Watford, Herts; *w:* Maureen. ACII 1953. Retired underwriting superintendent. London NHS: Chairman of Ornithological Section for two years in 1970s, Records Committee 1972-80, many years on General Ornithological Committee and Field Meetings Sec. Herts NHS: Council for two years in 1960s, Life Member (1984). Special interests: BTO surveys, Golden Oriole Group, photography, occasional tour leader. Wrote section of *London Bird Report* 1972-80; articles published in *LBR, Herts NHS Trans* and *Bird Study*. Author *Guide to the Birds of Tring Reservoirs* (1978). Lecturer on birds over many years, including Local Authority classes. OIR: Lions International. 12 Russell Close, Wells-next-the-Sea, Norfolk NR23 1BX. 01328 711337.

MANNS, Leonard; *b:* 15 September 1931 in Portsmouth, Hants. Government Service, retired. Sussex Ornithological Society: Council, Surveys and Projects Officer, Secretary of Scientific Committee, all 1992-. Co-ordinator for Sussex of BTO Farmland Bunting Survey 1992-93; organiser Corn Bunting and Grey Wagtail breeding surveys in Sussex for Sussex Orn Soc 1993-94. BTO 'A' ringer since 1961. Special interests: ecology, conservation, populations, woodland species. Current projects: effects of storm damage on bird communities in two Sussex Wealden woodlands (linked with BTO habitats research study); bird communities in broad-leaved woodlands in the Sussex Weald. OIR: photography, practical conservation work, tree growing, gardening, reading, classical music. 5 Downsview Avenue, Storrington, Pulborough, W Sussex RH20 4PS. 01903 744231.

MANTON, Brian Joseph; *b:* 30 March 1942 in Dumfries; *w:* Lisa. Westcliff High School for Boys. ACIB, PIIA. Banker: chief internal auditor. BTO 'A' ringer since c1975 and sponsor. Tutor for various BTO ringing courses. Holder of cannon-netting endorsement. Senior ringer, Basildon Ringing Group 1978-. Special interests: training of bird ringers; operation of a Constant Effort Site 1984-94; migration, esp gulls; ringing and training of local ringers in Mallorca, Portugal, Spain and Israel; birdwatching abroad. Articles published in *Ringers Bulletin*. Participation in three TV programmes involving bird ringing, inc two relating to cannon-netting of gulls. 72 Leighcliff Road, Leigh-on-Sea, Essex SS9 1DN. 01702 75183.

MARCHANT, John Hatlee; *b:* 12 June 1951 in Gosport, Hants; *w:* Jane. Portsmouth Grammar School. MA Applied Biology (Sidney Sussex College, Cambridge, 1972). Research Officer for BTO since 1973, Team Leader in the Census Unit from 1990. BTO staff co-ordinator for Common Birds Census and Waterways Bird Survey, and previously for various surveys inc Birds of Estuaries Enquiry. Bird Recorder for Buckinghamshire 1982-88. Committee Bird Exploration Fund 1982-. British Birds Rarities Committee 1986-93. BOU Records Committee 1990-. Wader consultant Seychelles Bird Records Committee 1992-. BTO 'A' ringer since 1972. Special interests: writing, photography, identification topics, occurrence patterns, migration studies, record assessment, waders, kinglets. Extensive research on the world's waders in library, museum and field. Census studies, inc monitoring breeding Firecrests, 1981-90. Bird ringing expeditions to Scottish islands, Morocco, Portugal and Australia. Ringing studies, inc Constant Effort Site 1986-90. Co-author (with A J Prater and J Vuorinen) *Identification and Ageing of Holarctic Waders* (1977, in Finnish 1979, in Chinese 1991); (with P J Hayman and A J Prater) *Shorebirds: an identification guide to the waders of the world* (1986); (with R Hudson et al) *Population Trends in British Breeding Birds* (1990). Over one hundred papers and articles in *Bird Study*, *BTO News*, *British Birds*, *Ibis*, other journals, books and reports. Photographs published in *British Birds*, *Birding World*, books and reports. The Patch, Mill Road, Winfarthing, Diss, Norfolk IP22 2DZ. 01379 640502.

MARGOSCHIS, Richard; *b:* 31 March 1921 in Shawbury, Shrops; *w:* Vivien (deceased). Retired chief public health officer. Special interest: sound recording. Director of weekend courses on natural history sound recording for Field Studies Council at Preston Montford Field Centre annually since c1974. Author *Recording Natural History Sounds* (1977). Recordist and publisher of six stereo cassettes entitled *British Wildlife Habitats* (1976-85).

Numerous articles in various magazines since mid 1960s. Large library of recordings used for radio, TV, cinema films, atmosphere for exhibitions and elsewhere. Co-founder Wildlife Sound Recording Society (1968). As tape editor to the Society, produced ninety-five circulating tape programmes, each forty-five minutes. OIR: work with local 'talking newspaper' for the blind. 80 Mancetter Road, Atherstone, Warks CV9 1NH. 01827 712925.

MARR, Benjamin Anthony Edward (Tony); *b:* 16 December 1939 in Glasgow. Steyning Grammar School. Customer Service Manager, HM Land Registry. Sussex Ornithological Society: Hon Sec 1962-71, Vice Pres 1976-81, President 1990-. RSPB Council 1970-75, 1988-93. BOU Records Committee 1992-. Seabirds Advisory Panel of British Birds Rarities Committee 1986-. Special interests: identification, migration, seabirds. Some forty days at sea on 'pelagics' in eastern N Atlantic between Portugal and Senegal 1986-93. Articles published in *Birding World, Birdwatch, British Birds*. Salzman Prize of Junior Bird Recorders' Club 1954, 1955, 1956. Member: ABC, OBC, OSME, Seabird Group. OIR: listening to music, driving fast, eating and drinking. Two Hoots, Old Hall Farm Barns, Cley next the Sea, Norfolk NR25 7RY. 01263 741313.

MARSTON, Keith; *b:* 2 July 1955 in Northern Rhodesia (Zambia). BA Geography (Leeds, 1976), PGCE (Exeter, 1977). Senior Field Studies Tutor, Medina Valley Centre since 1986. Voluntary warden on various RSPB reserves 1976-78. Wetland Bird Survey counter for Medina Valley (Isle of Wight) 1986-. Leader of bird identification courses on IoW. OIR: paragliding, backpacking in Swiss Alps. Medina Valley Centre, Dodnor Lane, Newport, Isle of Wight PO30 5TE. 01983 522195.

MARTIN, Alan John; *b:* 12 October 1953 in Feltham, Middlesex; *w:* Amanda. BA Business Studies (Kingston Polytechnic, 1976). FCMA 1982. Financial Controller Rank Xerox (UK) Ltd. Founder-member and Treasurer Stour Ringing Group 1981-. BTO Council and Hon Treasurer 1994-98. BTO 'A' ringer since 1981. Special interests: study of wintering Siskins in Surrey; owl and Kestrel nestbox scheme on Salisbury Plain; operation of two autumn migration ringing sites in Dorset. Overseas ringing activities inc participation in expeditions to Senegal in 1991,92,93, Thailand in 1995 and ringing in Eilat, Israel 1986. Articles in *Ringing & Migration* and *Ringers Bulletin* on ageing Siskins and capture techniques for House Martins. Editor *Stour Ringing Group*

Annual Report 1982-95; also regular articles eg on use of tape lures. Orchard House, 44 Chertsey Road, Windlesham, Surrey GU20 6EP. 01276 476739.

MARTIN, Brian; *b:* 4 March 1940 in Liverpool; *w:* Rosalind. Toxteth High School, Liverpool 1951-58. Cert in Social Studies (Southampton, 1966). Probation officer, retired. BTO Representative North Cheshire 1980-88. Projects Sub-committee Cheshire and Wirral Ornithological Society 1992-. Founder-member and Recorder, Woolston Eyes Conservation Group 1980-. Wildfowl Count organiser for a number of N Cheshire sites; also organiser of counts at Woolston Eyes, Warrington 1980-. BTO Heronries Census co-ordinator for Cheshire 1980-. BTO 'A' ringer to 1994. Special interests: wetlands and their conservation; study of colony of Black-necked Grebes over several years, esp breeding success and habitat requirements; summering populations of Swifts in Warrington and Cheshire (personal data collection since 1992 and organiser of county survey 1995-96); monitoring of House Martin colonies in Warrington study area. Articles published in *Cheshire Bird Report.* Editor *Woolston Eyes Conservation Group Annual Report* since 1979; also compiler of sections of systematic list and author of papers, eg on the food of Short-eared Owls wintering on the reserve. OIR: classical music, reading, gardening (esp alpines and orchids). 45 Albert Road, Grappenhall, Warrington WA4 2PF. 01925 264251.

MARTIN, Graham Richard; *b:* 14 November 1948 in Ilford, Essex; *w:* Marie-Anne. BSc Human and Physical Sciences (Surrey, 1970), PhD Psychology (Exeter, 1974), DSc Biology (Birmingham, 1995). Professor of Avian Sensory Science, Univ Birmingham 1996-. Prev: Lecturer/Senior Lecturer/Reader in Biology, Univ Birmingham 1977-96; Research Fellow, Univ Sussex 1974-76. Worcestershire WT: Conservation Committee, Council. Special interests: avian senses (esp vision and hearing), sensory aspects of foraging and noctural behaviour, owls, herons, ducks, waders, ostriches, albatrosses. Author *Birds by Night* (1990) and various chapters in edited works. Over fifty articles in eg *Brain, Behaviour, and Evolution*; *Ibis*; *J Comparative Physiol*; *Vision Research.* School of Continuing Studies, University of Birmingham, Edgbaston, Birmingham B15 2TT. 0121 414 5598.

MARTIN, John Peter; *b:* 9 July 1959 in Stoke-on-Trent, Staffs; *w:* Janette. BSc Applied Biology (UWIST, Cardiff, 1980). Conservation Officer, Bristol, Bath and Avon WT since 1993. Prev: Countryside Officer Walsall MBC 1989-92; Scientific Officer NCC 1987-89; research asst RSPB 1982-85. West Midland Bird Club: Staffordshire Records Committee from c1991 and assisted with writing bird report each year since. Special interests:

migration, identification, conservation, gulls, drawing birds. Travel for birds inc numerous Mediterranean trips, Morocco, Turkey, Israel, USA (California), The Gambia, India. Some letters in *British Birds*; illustrations for *An Atlas of the Breeding Birds of Shropshire* by P Deans *et al* (1992) and *Birds of Glamorgan* by Clive Hurford and Peter Lansdown (1995), plus regular line drawings in WMBC reports. OIR: playing and watching football, cricket, music, cinema. 34 Cranmore Green, Pilning, Bristol BS12 1MM.

MARTINS, Rodney Paul (Rod); *b:* 22 January 1957 in Norwich, Norfolk. BSc Geography (Leicester, 1979). Ornithological tour leader since 1986. Extensive experience in the design and development of tours to 'pioneer' areas eg in Asia, Central America, West Africa and South Atlantic; architect and developer of birdwatching tourism to Yemen since 1986. Norfolk NT Survey Officer 1993-94. Oriental Bird Club: member of launch committee, member of Council 1984-87. OSME Council 1986-96. Special interests: Palearctic bird distributions (esp Turkey and Middle East), conservation. Editor *Turkey Bird Report* 1986-94. Editorial Committee OSME 1990-96. Turkey correspondent for *BWP*. Member: ABA, ABC, EAOS, Falklands Conservation, NBC, OBC, OSME, WAOS. 6 Connaught Road, Norwich NR2 3BP. 01603 661964.

MASON, Nicholas James; *b:* 22 June 1946 in Bury St Edmunds, Suffolk; *w:* Vivien. BSc Life Science (Liverpool, 1972). Schoolteacher. Asst warden Blakeney Point Apr-Aug 1972. Warden Winterton Dunes Apr-Aug 1973. Voluntary warden Sutton and Hollesley Commons 1984-. Wetland Bird Survey organiser for Deben Estuary 1985-. 10km square organiser for BTO New Breeding Atlas 1990-92 and raptor survey. Special interests: heathland birds, annual wildlife trips with school children to Cairngorms or Scottish islands. OIR: dragonflies, cricket, volleyball. Evening Hall, Hollesley, Woodbridge, Suffolk IP12 3QU. 01394 411150.

MASSEY, Keith Gordon; *b:* 6 November 1947 in Warrington, Lancs (now Cheshire). Penketh and Sankey Secondary Modern School 1959-62. Warden, Fiddlers Ferry Reserve since 1993. Prev: Ranger, Risley Moss Reserve 1985-86. Voluntary surveys and monitoring birds at Fiddlers Ferry and preparation of monthly bird reports 1980-93. Wildfowl Count organiser from winter 1979/80 and waders from 1990/91. Participant in many other national and local censuses and surveys, inc atlas schemes and single-species projects. Personal studies inc nestbox (and ledge) scheme for Peregrines 1994-; sex ratio of Pochard and Tufted Duck from winter 1979/80; Yellow-legged Gull occurrences, *cachinnans/michahellis* from

1984 and *omissus* from 1986. Overseas: Hungary, Mallorca. 'Energy for Wildlife' report to CEGB (1987, Year of the Environment); ornithological reports for Mersey Valley Partnership and Groundwork Trust with the CEGB 1980-87. Monthly bird reports in *Bird Watching*. Participant in RSPB film 1985 and Powergen wildlife awareness commercial 1992. OIR: local and county surveys of butterflies, dragonflies and damselflies; fine art, painting and drawing, model making for castings. 4 Hall Terrace, Great Sankey, Warrington, Cheshire WA5 3EZ. 01925 721382.

MATHER, John Robert; *b:* 5 December 1930 in Summerbridge, Yorkshire; *w:* 'Bunty'. Harrogate College of Art 1946-50. Retired company director (advertising). Past President Harrogate and District Naturalists' Society. Yorkshire Naturalists' Union: Ornithological Recorder (VC64) 1964-79, Chairman of Records Committee 1979-93, President 1982. Council Yorkshire WT 1991-96. Spurn Bird Observatory Committee 1965-87. British Birds Rarities Committee 1976-84. BOU Records Committee 1986-93 (three years as Chairman). BTO Ringing and Migration Committee in 1970s. Chairman Bird Observatories Council 1980-83. BTO 'A' ringer since 1953. Owner and director of Knaresborough Ringing Station from early 1950s. Special interests: taxonomy, divers, auks. Worldwide travel for birds inc South Africa, E Africa, Morocco, India, Nepal, E and W USA, Canada and most of Europe. Author *The Birds of Yorkshire* (1986) and *Where to Watch Birds in Yorkshire* (1994). Editor *Yorkshire Bird Report* 1970-79. Article (with D M Burn) on the White-billed Diver in Britain in *British Birds* 1974. OIR: breeding ornamental pheasants, pigeon racing, general interest in mammals and molluscs, good food and wine, appreciating good music (some classics and modern jazz). Founder-member ABC. Eagle Lodge, 44 Aspin Lane, Knaresborough, N Yorks HG5 8EP. 01423 862775.

MATTHEWS, Geoffrey Vernon Townsend; OBE 1986; Order of the Golden Ark (Netherlands) 1987; *b:* 16 June 1923 in Norwich, Norfolk; *w:* Mary. Bedford School. Christ's College, Cambridge: BA Natural Science 1947, MA 1950, PhD Bird navigation 1950, post-doctoral research on bird navigation 1950-55. CBiol, FIBiol 1974. Professorial Fellow, Dept of Zoology, Univ College Cardiff 1970-90 and Special Lecturer, Dept of Zoology and Psychology, Univ Bristol 1965-88. Wildfowl (& Wetlands) Trust: Asst Director (Research) 1955-63, Director of Research and Conservation 1964-88, Deputy Director 1973-88. Director International Waterfowl (and Wetlands) Research Bureau 1969-88. BOU: Council 1964-75, Vice President 1972-75, member and later Chairman Research and Special Publications Committee 1960-75, Chairman Criteria for Medals Committee 1964-65. BTO Scientific Advisory Committee 1958-80. Edward Grey Institute (Univ Oxford) Council for Ornithology 1969-91. Assocn for the Study of Animal Behaviour: Council 1961-76, President 1971-74. Game Conservancy Scientific Advisory Committee 1970-83. Royal Society Government Grant Board 1983-84. British Section, ICBP 1956-68. British Delegate, IWRB 1956-68. International Ethological Committee 1968-74. International Ornithological Committee 1974-90. Advisory Committee on Birds (Dept of Environment, then NCC) 1978-90. Wildfowl Conservation Committee (Nature Conservancy) 1956-88; Chairman Cold Weather Shooting Bans Committee; Chairman Specialist Group on Wildfowl. Anglo-Soviet Environmental Protection Agreement Committee (Dept of Environment) 1976-80. Severn Barrage Committee (Dept of Energy) 1978-81. Severn Tidal Power Group (Dept of Energy and CEGB) Chairman Environmental Panel 1987-89. EEC Commission's Advisory Group on the Bird Conservation Directive 1976-85. Special interests: behaviour of birds, esp migratory behaviour with a specialisation in bird orientation and navigation; conservation of birds, esp waterfowl and their habitats. Author *Bird Navigation* (1955, 2nd ed 1968 also in German 1971); *Orientation and Position-finding in Birds* (1971), *The Ramsar Convention on Wetlands: its history and development* (1973; extended German ed 1993; Japanese ed 1995). Editor *Wildfowl* 1968-88 (with M A Ogilvie 1968-86); (with Yu A Isakov) *Proc Internat Regional Meeting on the Conservation of Wildfowl Resources, Leningrad* (1970); (with M Smart) *Proc Second Internat Swan Symposium, Sapporo, Japan* (1981); (with Yu A Isakov) *Proc Symposium on the Mapping of Waterfowl Distributions, Migrations and Habitats, Alushta, Crimea* (1981); *Proc IWRB Symposium on Managing Waterfowl Populations, Astrakhan, Russia* (1990). Author of sixteen chapters on bird navigation and twenty-seven on conservation and bird biology in multi-authored books. Forty-four research papers on bird navigation in eg *The Auk, Ibis, Wildfowl* and conference procs; 104 research papers and general articles on waterfowl and wetland conservation and general bird biology in eg *Birds, British Birds, The Times*. Union Medal of BOU 1980; Medal of RSPB 1990. Corresponding Fellow of American Ornithologists' Union 1969, and of Schweizerische Gesellschaft für Vogelkunde und Vogelschutz 1975. Honorary Member Hungarian Ornithological Society 1981. Counsellor of Honour IWRB 1988. OIR: collecting zoological and botanical stamps, fossil hunting, walking, listening to music. 32 Tetbury Street, Minchinhampton, Stroud, Glos GL6 9JH. 01453 884769.

MATTINGLEY, Wendy Ann; *b:* 6 May 1954 in Aberfeldy, Perthshire; *h:* John. Breadalbane Academy, Aberfeldy; Duncan of Jordanstone College of Art; Dundee College of Education. Dip in Home Econ, Dip in Secondary Education. Garden manager. Contract seasonal fieldworker RSPB Tayside 1991-95. BTO Representative Fife 1981-87. Committee SOC St Andrews Branch mid 1980s. SOC Recorder Perth & Kinross 1987-95. SOC: Council 1991-, Surveys and Research Committee 1991-. Merlin co-ordinator Tayside Raptor Group. Member of Tay Ringing Group. Special interests: raptors and upland species generally; monitoring of Merlin and Hen Harrier breeding sites and winter roosts of Raven and Hen Harrier within Perth & Kinross; wildfowl counts. Joint editor *Perth & Kinross Bird Report* 1988-94. OIR: dragonflies, horticulture, W African music. Cluny House, Aberfeldy, Perthshire PH15 2JT. 01887 820795.

MAWSON, Geoffrey (Geoff); *b:* 23 February 1948 in Sheffield, Yorkshire; *w:* Gill. BTO Representative Derbyshire 1982-92. BTO 'A' ringer since 1972. Secretary Sorby-Breck Ringing Group since 1972. Rehabilitator of wild birds. Special interests: migration, raptors, ringing at home and abroad (Australia, Greece, Cyprus, USA). Compiler of local ringing reports. OIR: botany (esp alpines and orchids), butterflies, bats, beetles, wildlife gardening. Moonpenny Farm, Farwater Lane, Dronfield, Sheffield S18 6RA. 01246 415097.

MAY, Derwent; *b:* 29 April 1930 in Eastbourne, Sussex; *w:* Yolanta. MA English (Lincoln College, Oxford, 1952). Author and journalist. Literary Editor *The Listener* 1965-86. Literary and Arts Editor *The Sunday Telegraph* 1986-90. Four novels. Research asst Edward Grey Institute, Univ Oxford 1948. Contributor of weekly 'Nature Notes' to *The Times* since 1981, and weekly 'Feather Report' since 1992. Author *The Times Nature Diary* (1983), *The New Times Nature Diary* (1993), *Feather Reports* (1996). OIR: travel, opera. 201 Albany Street, London NW1 4AB. 0171 387 0848.

MAYHEW, Peter Watts; *b:* 30 June 1959 in Glasgow; *w:* Erica. BSc Zoology (Glasgow, 1980), PhD Feeding ecology and behaviour of Wigeon (Glasgow, 1985). RSPB Reserves Manager North Scotland since 1989. Prev: Head of Conservation, British Association for Shooting and Conservation 1984-89. Special interests: ecology of wildfowl and waders, habitat management for birds, shooting and conservation. A number of scientific papers on ecology of Wigeon published in eg *Ibis* and *Ornis Scandinavica*. OIR: mountaineering. RSPB North Scotland Office, Etive House, Beechwood Park, Inverness IV2 3BW. 01463 715000.

McCARTNEY, Paul; *b:* 29 December 1944 in Redruth, Cornwall; *w:* Sarah. BSc Chemistry (Birmingham, 1966), BA Mathematics (Open Univ, 1988). Project Officer and Data Manager Cornwall WT since 1988. Ornithological consultant for environmental impact assessments, in particular a number of wind-farm applications; also work for former National Rivers Authority on waders and wildfowl. Voluntary warden Cape Clear Bird Observatory 1970-72. Contract and voluntary work for RSPB 1972. Study of avifauna of Lizard Peninsula, Cornwall for Bristol University 1983-84. Special interests: population numbers and distribution. Pixie Cottage, High Road, Zelah, Truro TR4 9HL. 01872 540463.

McCURLEY, Robert (Bob); *b:* 10 January 1934 in Consett, Co Durham; *w:* Margaret. Leisure and sportswear buyer. RSPB Tayside Members' Group Committee 1985-. SOC Tayside Branch Committee 1986-, Chairman 1988-91. Founder-member Fife Bird Club and Committee 1985-88. Special interest: census and survey work. Active in Common Birds Census, also high and low water surveys; voluntary monitoring of Schedule 1 species in Tayside for RSPB 1984-; monitoring Little Tern colonies in Tayside for East Coast Tern Conservation Group 1992-. Several visits to Fair Isle and North Ronaldsay to study migration. Author *Checklist of Birds of Angus* (1993); occasional local radio. OIR: golf, chess, snooker, walking. 22 Kinnordy Terrace, Craigiebank, Dundee DD4 7NW. 01382 462944.

McFAUL, Liam Joseph; *b:* 12 October 1962 on Rathlin Island, Co Antrim. Fisherman and farmer. RSPB Warden Rathlin Island 1990-. Special interest: birds of Rathlin Island. Keen interest developed from young age in the island bird life and ecology, inspired by knowledge passed down from forefathers who were involved in the harvest of seabirds and eggs as part of their staple diet and local economy. Contributor to programme *Natural Selection* on Ulster TV, also broadcasts on BBC World Service and RTE Radio. OIR: auxiliary coastguard, volunteer fireman, trustee of Rathlin Island Trust. South Cleggan, Rathlin Island, Ballycastle, Co Antrim BT54 6RT. 01265 763935.

McGEOCH, John Alexander; *b:* 20 November 1928 in Gosforth, Northumberland; *w:* Joan. Newcastle upon Tyne Royal Grammar School 1937-46. BDS (Durham, 1951). General dental practitioner, retired. Somerset Ornithological Society: Vice President 1963-88, Editorial Committee 1960-85. County Bird Recorder 1980s. Founder-member Somerset TNC (1964), and member of several committees. Special interests: intensive and detailed recording within R Brue valley over many years (subject of Radio 4 *Living World* broadcast 1977); Water Rail and Snipe and improvement of habitats for their year-round use. In Middle East during early 1950s. Author (with E A Chapman) 'Recent Field Observations from Iraq' in *Ibis* 1956; also 'Observations from Ser Amadia, Kurdistan, Iraq' in *Ardea* 1963. Numerous surveys and reports for Somerset TNC and regular contributor to *Somerset Birds* (annual report) since 1955. Member: OSME. OIR: travel, theatre, wines. 4 Kippax Avenue, Wells, Somerset BA5 2TT. 01749 672054.

McGOWAN, Philip; *b:* 6 March 1964 in Milnethorpe, Cumbria. BSc Biology of Plants and Animals (Newcastle, 1987), PhD Social organisation in the Malaysian Peacock Pheasant (Open Univ, 1992). Post-doctoral Research Fellow, Open Univ since 1992 inc World Pheasant Association Conservation Officer 1992-93. Member of core committees of BirdLife International/WPA Species Survival Commission Partridge, Quail and Francolin Specialist Group (1992-) and Pheasant Specialist Group (1993-); member Megapode Specialist Group (1992-), also WPA Scientific Advisory Committee (1991-96) and its successor Conservation Policy and Programmes Committee (1996-). WPA Council 1994-. Special interests: distribution, ecology and conservation of Asian Galliformes. Himachal Wildlife Project 1983; Newcastle/Aberdeen Univs NW Himalaya Expedition 1985; Newcastle Univ Philippine Expedition 1987; Royal Geog Soc/Universiti Brunei Darussalam Brunei Rainforest Project 1992; project on conservation assessment of Galliformes 1992-93. Study of habitat use and management of the Swamp Francolin in India (collaboration with Aligarh Muslim Univ) 1993-, and identification of key areas for conservation of Asian Galliformes 1994-. Two expedition reports produced. Publications on methodology in WPA symposium proceedings; others, mostly on pheasants in *Bull BOC, Forktail, J Tropical Ecol, J WPA*; also action plans co-compiled under the auspices of the above Specialist Groups. Some 150 species accounts for Phasianidae section of *Handbook of the Birds of the World*. Member: AOU, OBC, Soc for Conservation Biol, WPA. Biology Dept, Open University, Walton Hall, Milton Keynes MK7 6AA. 01908 654071; fax 01908 654167.

McKEE, Neville Desmond; MBE 1996; *b:* 25 March 1945 in Belfast; *w:* Pat. Royal Belfast Academical Institution. BSc Botany (Queen's Univ Belfast, 1968), MSc Zoology (Ulster, 1982). Teacher of biology at the Belfast Royal Academy. Committee Copeland Bird Observatory 1962-. Wildfowl counter with NI Ornithologists' Club on Loughs Neagh, Foyle, Carlingford 1964-75. Co-ordinator of Operation Seafarer around N Ireland for NIOC 1966-70.

Member of NI Advisory Committee to RSPB for ten years since 1965. BTO Ringing and Migration Committee 1979-81. Bookings Secretary for Copeland Bird Obs since 1971. BTO 'A' ringer since 1962 and member of Sponsors Panel. Secretary Antrim and Ards Ringing Group 1983-. Advisory Committee Ulster WT 1983-88. Special interests: migration, breeding biology, Storm Petrel, Manx Shearwater, passerines (esp Dipper, Wood Warbler, nomadic finches), habitat creation and woodland management. Leader of several expeditions to Inishglora, Co Mayo and Roaninish, Co Donegal on which 25,000 Storm Petrels ringed. Monitoring breeding of Wood Warbler in Co Antrim since 1983. Author of Copeland chapter in *Bird Observatories in Britain and Ireland* ed by Roger Durman (1976). Regular articles in *Copeland Bird Observatory Annual Report*. Many radio and TV appearances. Unpublished MSc thesis on estimation of colony size of Storm Petrels lodged at Univ Ulster Coleraine Campus. Part-time lecturer in ornithology and arboriculture at Inst of Continuing Education Queen's Univ Belfast and Univ Ulster; also talks on birds and trees to local groups. OIR: operating native tree and shrub nursery, commercially supplying transplantable native source stock for woodland planting. 67 Temple Rise, Templepatrick, Ballyclare, Co Antrim BT39 0AG. 01849 433068.

McLOUGHLIN, John; *b:* 17 December 1959 in Doncaster, S Yorks. BSc Ecology (Leeds, 1987). Professional ornithologist. Organiser, Birdline North East since 1989. Research asst on several conservation contracts for RSPB, English Nature and BirdLife International since 1982 (eg Mid Wales River Bird Survey 1982-83, Lowland Rainforest Survey Peninsular Thailand 1988, RSPB/GCT Black Grouse Survey 1996). Bird Recorder for VC63 (S Yorks) 1994-. British Birds Rarities Committee 1996-. Special interests: identification and migration (travelled widely through Europe, to the Far East, Central and S America); upland bird conservation (involved with Yorkshire Dales Upland Bird Study Group and organised North York Moors Merlin Study Group, 1985). Regular contributor to popular magazines, eg *Bird Watching, Birding World, Birdwatch, Yorkshire Birding*. Illustrated talks on all aspects of birdwatching. OIR: Leeds United supporter. 8 Harrison Grove, Harrogate, N Yorks HG1 4QJ. 01423 881630.

McMAHON, Eleanor Kathleen; *b:* 14 October 1960 in Walgrave, Northants; *h:* Neil. SRN 1981, Dip Nursing Studies 1985, BSc Health Studies (Nene College, Northampton, 1991). Ward Sister Kettering General Hospital. Secretary Northamptonshire Bird Club c1986-. Wildfowl counter on local waters. Constant involvement in BTO survey work. Special interests: 'local patch' work, photography, foreign birding trips. Member:

OSME. OIR: church, jogging, cycling, walking, gardening, reading poetry, classical music, cookery. Oriole House, 5 The Croft, Hanging Houghton, Northants NN6 9HW. 01604 880009.

McMAHON, Sara; *b:* 5 April 1953 in Coventry, Warwicks. HND Applied Biology (Plymouth Polytechic, 1973), LIBiol (Bristol, 1975). Scientific officer, ecotoxicology research. BoEE/WeBS Organiser for Tamar Complex 1988-95. Hon Sec Devon Birdwatching & Preservation Society 1996-. Special interest: birds of the Tamar Complex 1969-93, the changes taking place and the reasons for them. Paper on a new approach to describing estuarine wader communities in *Wader Study Group Bulletin* 1993; also articles on Tamar Estuary wildfowl and wader counts for *Caradon Field Club Annual Report* 1990-. Conference papers given on computer analysis of wildfowl and wader data. 72 Underwood Road, Plympton, Devon PL7 3SZ. 01752 343900.

McNEIL, Duncan Alexander Crichton (Mac, Doc, Don etc); *b:* 23 March 1940 in Epsom, Surrey. Sutton County Grammar School. BSc Special Chemistry (Leicester, 1962), PhD Spectroscopy (Leicester, 1966), Cert in Ecology (Leicester, 1975). Lecturer in Computer Programming, Charles Keene College of Further Education since 1973. Various night school classes run for Leicester Univ and for WEA since 1973. Official Observer, Hampton Court Park, for the Bird Sanctuaries Committee DoE from 1971 until Committee abolished in 1981. Committee Surbiton and District Birdwatching Society 1970s, also Sec of Surveys Sub-committee. Committee Leicester Lit and Phil Soc, Nat Hist Section 1970s. Co-ordinator of surveys in Surbiton: annual nesting records for swallow family, Carrion Crow and Spotted Flycatcher, also set up Common Birds Census work; in Leicester: churchyard natural history survey, Carrion Crow in relation to Dutch elm disease, survey of area to be used as waste tip by NCB, riparian species on stretches of endangered waterways. Special interests: House Martins and their parasites (subject of ecology certificate project, winding down after twenty years additional work). Notes on House Martin and other subjects in eg *Bird Study* and *British Birds*; also papers with Frank Clark on martin fleas in various ecological and entomological journals. Monthly column on natural history in local free newspaper. Interviewed about flea studies on local radio. OIR: railway history, books, photography. 721 Loughborough Road, Birstall, Leics LE4 4NN. 0116 267 6946.

MEAD, Christopher John (Chris); *b:* 1 May 1940 in Hove, Sussex; *w:* Verity ('V'). Aldenham School, Herts 1952-59. Mathematics at Peterhouse

College, Cambridge 1959-61. CBiol, MIBiol c1970. BTO 1961-95, mainly in Ringing Office, latterly combined with press work. Since retiring in 1995 (following a stroke in 1994) continued as press and publicity consultant with BTO but expanded writing (inc text for internet site) and other activities (eg promoting annual National Nest Box Week). Past Council member of Bardsey Island Trust and BOU. Former Chairman of Seabird Group and long-standing member. Was member of European Union for Bird Ringing for approx 15 years, Gen Sec and Board member 1983-85. Founder-member and Committee Sussex Ornithological Society ('spawned in my parents' house in Brighton'). Committee Hertfordshire NHS Bird Group c1970. President Suffolk Naturalists 1994. BTO 'A' ringer since 1960, trainer and sponsor. Atlas work in Scotland 1971 and 72. BTO Breeding Atlas organiser (with wife) 1968. Hertfordshire Atlas organiser 1967-73. Ringing partnership leader (with Boddy, with Benyon, and with Ponting 1961-). Member Wash Wader Ringing Group. Founder-member and ringer-in-charge Wissey RG 1994-. Special interests: bird ringing and training ringers; migration; longevity and population dynamics; birds of Ashridge Estate (ringing 1965-91); Sand Martin, Pied Flycatcher (ringing in Hereford and Wales since 1967), tits, owls, Robin; photography in hand; radio, TV and writing for specialist magazines. Constant Effort Site in Norfolk 1993-. Expeditions to Iberia, esp Portugal (Iberian Ringing Group leader 1967-77). Other countries inc USA (Texas), Belize, Zimbabwe. Author *Bird Ringing* (1974), *Robins* (1984), *Owls* (1987); *Hertfordshire Breeding Bird Atlas* with Ken Smith (1982), *Bird Migration* (1983). Contributions to many other books eg *Atlas of Bird Migration*, *Bird Families of the World*, *BWP*, *Birds of the World*, *Birdwatcher's Yearbook*, *A Dictionary of Birds*, *The Living Countryside*, *The Peregrine Falcon*, *The Wildlife Year*; also species texts in both BTO Breeding Atlases and Winter Atlas. Many papers in journals and magazines eg *Ardeola*, *Bird Study*, *Bird Watching*, *Birds*, *British Birds*, *British Wildlife*, *Bull BOC*, *Ringing & Migration*. Much radio and TV. Union Medal, BOU 1996. Member: OTOP (Polish Bird Society), Seabird Group, Wader Study Group. OIR: listening to jazz (esp Duke Ellington); watching rugby and motor racing on TV; local history; looking at natural history rather than birds; tearing up £5 notes on a dung heap (rest of family own five horses and ponies). The Nunnery, Hilborough, Thetford, Norfolk IP26 5BW. Tel/fax 01760 756466.

MEADOWS, Brian Stanley; *b:* 8 February 1939 in London; *w:* Ann. BSc Geology and Zoology (London, 1969). MIBiol 1970, FCIWEM 1988. Manager, Environmental Control for Yanbu (1983-95) then Jubail (1995-), Government of Saudi Arabia (inc population studies of shorebirds and mangrove warblers as part of Red Sea Ecology Investigations). Recorder for Metropolitan Essex and member of Records Committee for *Essex Bird Report* and *London Bird Report* 1962-71. Organiser of London NHS Black Redstart Survey 1964-70. Count organiser for Palearctic wildfowl in E Africa 1976-82. Ornithological Sub-committee of East African NHS 1976-. Preparatory committee for *A New Guide to the Birds of Essex* 1982-83. Special interests: birds of central Hejaz, western Arabia ('definitely now the world's expert on this hitherto ornithologically unexplored region'); wildfowl and wader populations in Arabia; biology of African Reed Warbler; Kingfisher ecology ('probably first author, back in early seventies, to draw attention to correlation of river pollution and numbers, eg *Ibis* 114, 433); raptor migration in Middle East; status of migrant shrikes in Arabia. An author for *Birds of East Africa* (1980); author *Birds of Madinat Yanbu Al-Sinaiyah and its Hinterland* (1988); editor/co-author *Ecology of the Red Sea: investigations at Yanbu Al-Sinaiyah 1982-91* (1993). Papers in conference proceedings and articles in eg *Bulletin de la Société des Sciences Naturelles et Physiques du Maroc, London Naturalist, Sandgrouse, Scopus*; also in *Essex Bird Report* and *London BR*. Member: Ethiopian NHS, EANHS, OSME. OIR: English landscape history. 9 Old Hall Lane, Walton-on-the-Naze, Essex CO14 8LE. 01255 678735.

MEARNS, Barbara Crawford; *b:* 12 May 1955 in Greenock, Renfrewshire; *h:* Richard. Dip Brit Assocn of Occup Therapists 1975. Organiser of the A Rocha Network (international Christian conservation organisation) since 1993. Special interests: ornithological biography, history of ornithology. Co-author (with Richard Mearns) *Biographies for Birdwatchers: the lives of those commemorated in Western Palearctic bird names* (1988) and *Audubon to Xantus: the lives of those commemorated in North American bird names* (1992); also *The Bird Collectors* (in prep). OIR: moths, butterflies, dragonflies. Connansknowe, Kirkton, Dumfries DG1 1SX.

MEARNS, Richard James; *b:* 4 June 1950 in Malaya; *w:* Barbara. BSc Biology (Edinburgh, 1971). Senior Countryside Ranger, Dumfries and Galloway Council since 1986. Study of Peregrines in SW Scotland 1974-82 (under direction of Ian Newton). Short contract work for NCC on Solway waders (1977-78) and for RSPB on Corncrakes on South Uist (1986). Special interests: ornithological biography, history of ornithology. Co-author (with Barbara Mearns) *Biographies for Birdwatchers: the lives of those commemorated in Western Palearctic bird names* (1988) and *Audubon to Xantus: the lives of those commemorated in North American bird names* (1992); also *The Bird Collectors* (in prep). Papers on SW Scotland

Peregrines in *Bird Study, Ibis, Ornis Scandinavica, Scottish Birds*; and on Ravens in S Scotland in *Scottish Birds*. OIR: moths. Connansknowe, Kirkton, Dumfries DG1 1SX.

MEDLAND, Julian Michael; *b:* 9 October 1959 in Leicester; *w:* Audrey. BSc Zoology (Wales, Swansea, 1981). ACIB 1992. Offshore finance. Secretary Ornithological Section of La Société Guernesiaise since 1993. Bird Recorder for Guernsey since 1993. Special interests: visible migration, seawatching, specific site study (Jerbourg, St Martins). Articles in *Guernsey Bird Report* and *Trans Soc Guernesaise*. Clyne, Rue de la Ronde Cheminée, Castel, Guernsey GY5 7GE. 01481 55411.

MEEK, Eric Richard; *b:* 19 June 1947 in Newcastle upon Tyne, Northumberland; *w:* Christine. Gosforth Grammar School 1958-65. MA Geography (Fitzwilliam College, Cambridge, 1968), PGCE (Durham, 1969). RSPB Orkney Officer since 1981. National Trust warden Farne Islands summer 1964 and 1965. Asst warden Fair Isle Bird Observatory 1972. BTO Ringing and Migration Committee mid 1970s. BTO 'A' ringer since 1965 and Sponsors Panel since its inception. Co-ordinator Northumberland Merlin Survey 1973-80. Sec Northumbria Ringing Group 1970-80 and Sec Orkney RG 1982-. Northumberland Rarities Committee 1970-80. Scottish Rarities Committee 1990-. Wetland Bird Survey co-ordinator Orkney 1990-. WEA tutor in ornithology 1970-80. Trustee North Ronaldsay Bird Observatory 1987-. Special interests: raptors, esp Merlin and Hen Harrier (ongoing studies in Orkney); Goosander (in Northumberland 1970s); study of Orkney breeding Pintail population; studies of Orkney Great and Arctic Skua populations; migration; rarities. Travel for birds in N America, Africa and Asia. Author/co-author of papers on study interests in *Bird Study, British Birds, Scottish Birds, Seabird*; also on other topics eg effects of aero-generators on moorland birds and Orkney Mute Swan numbers in relation to Canadian pondweed invasion. Joint editor *Birds in Northumbria* (annual report) 1970-77 and *Orkney Bird Report* 1987-95. Co-author (with B Galloway) 'Northumberland's Birds' in *Trans Nat Hist Soc of Northumbria* 1978 (most recent county avifauna). Scientific adviser for RSPB film *Northern Flights* on the birds of Orkney. Numerous radio broadcasts. Winner of 1988 Boddy & Sparrow Award presented by BTO for paper 'The breeding ecology and decline of the Merlin in Orkney' *Bird Study*. Member ABC, OBC. OIR: all aspects of natural history and conservation (esp botanising), travelling abroad, drinking real ale. Smyril, Stenness, Orkney KW16 3JX. 01856 850176.

MELDRUM, John Alexander Kenneth; *b:* 2 April 1928 in Inverness; *w:* Christobel. Stonyhurst College 1941-45. MB (Trinity College, Dublin, 1951), MA (Trinity, 1952). Consultant Anaesthetist, Birmingham Area Health Authority, retired. Chairman Wildlife Sound Recording Society 1983-86. International Bioacoustics Council c1980. Several articles published on sound recording in eg *Doctor Magazine*, *Hobby Doctor*. Sound recordings: *British Bird Songs and Calls* (cassette) (1990) and *British Bird Sounds on CD* (1991). Winner 3M Tape Recording Contest 1974 (atmospheric recording on Cley Marshes, Norfolk). Winner British Amateur Tape Recording Contest 1975 (Lapwing and Redshank in high wind on Mawddach Estuary). Winner European Tape Recording Contest 1975. Winner Tandberg Trophy and CIMES International Cup 1975 (Fulmars on Bamburgh Castle Walls). OIR: rifle shooting, music and opera. Heath House, 1 Millgate, Lisvane, Cardiff CF4 5TY. 01222 758809.

MERNE, Oscar James; *b:* 6 November 1943 in Dublin, Ireland; *w:* Margaret. MSc Environmental Sciences (Trinity College, Dublin, 1985). Wildlife Research Officer (Ornithology) National Parks & Wildlife Service since 1978. Prev: Warden Wexford Wildfowl Reserve 1968-77; producer of wildlife films for Irish TV 1966-67 (inc cinephotography, sound recording, script-writing). Hon Sec Bird Group, Dublin Naturalists' Field Club late 1950s. Hon Sec Irish Ornithologists' Club early 1960s. Founder-member Irish Wildfowl Committee (1966), later to merge (1969) with IOC and Irish Soc for the Protection of Birds to form the Irish Wildbird Conservancy; Hon Sec, Hon Treas, Council, Exec Committee and other posts in IWC at various stages in late 1960s and early 1970s; Trustee of IWC since 1969. BOU Council 1972-74. BTO Ringing and Migration Committee (NP&WS permanent representative) since 1975. Co-ordinator (with T R E Devlin) Malin Head Bird Observatory 1961-65. Co-ordinator Great Saltee Ringing Station 1977-. International Ornithological Committee 1991-. Member of ORNIS Committee and Scientific Working Group of European Union since 1987. Special interests: colonial breeding seabirds; passage and wintering waterfowl, their status, distribution and conservation (inc habitats); ringing and migration studies. Travelled widely in W Palearctic (Iceland to Russia, Portugal to Romania, N Africa, Canaries; also E Africa). Author *Ducks, Geese and Swans* (1974), *Irish Wading Birds* (1979). Co-author (with R Roche) *Saltees: islands of birds and legends* (1977, 2nd ed 1987). Contributor to eg *Birds of Galway and Mayo* ed by T Whilde (1977), *The Irish Wildlife Book* ed by F O'Gorman (1979), BTO Winter Atlas (3 species accounts), *Important Bird Areas in Europe* ed by R F A Grimmett and T A Jones (1989). Author or co-author of papers and notes in eg *Bird Study, British Birds, Irish Birds, Irish Naturalists' J, Irish Ringers' Bulletin, Seabird Group Newsletter, Wildfowl*; also in annual reports inc *Irish East Coast Bird Report* and *Wexford Bird Report*. Member: EAWS, European Bird Census Council, IWRB, LPO, Seabird Group, Société pour l'Etude et la Protection de la Nature en Bretagne, Wader Study Group. OIR: travel, photography (wildlife and landscape), island-going, wine, gardening, walking, reading. National Parks & Wildlife Service, 51 St Stephen's Green, Dublin 2, Ireland. +353 (0)1 6613111.

MERRIE, Thomas David Hepburn (David); *b:* 8 October 1935 in Bristol; *w:* Heddy. Clifton College. BA Mech Eng Tripos (Peterhouse College, Cambridge, 1957). MIMechE 1969, CEng. Consultant engineer. SOC Council 1968-77. SOC Stirling Branch: founder (1967), Secretary, Vice-chairman, Chairman 1967-77. Chairman SOC Clyde Branch 1994-. Co-founder and first Chairman North Sea Bird Club 1979-84. Organiser of survey into distribution and breeding success of Black-throated and Red-throated Divers in Scotland 1973-78. Special interests: divers, raptors, birds of Scotland, conservation. Personal project since 1976 to provide floating nest-rafts for divers in Scotland (significantly improved breeding production in the study population). Papers on Golden Eagle and diver studies published in journals; articles on other topics, inc North Sea Bird Club, in Scottish popular magazines. Observations contributed to *Birds of Egypt* by Goodman et al (1989). Worked in Egypt 1984-86; also travel for birds in Kenya, South Africa, Australia, New Zealand, USA and Europe. Member: OSME, Scottish Raptor Study Group. OIR: hill walking, travel, photography, gardening, community projects. Craigie House, Craigie, Clunie, Blairgowrie, Perthshire PH10 6RG. Tel/fax 01250 884273.

MERRITT, Anthony John; *b:* 23 August 1958 in Bristol; *p:* Dr Sarah Webster. BSc Zoology (Durham, 1980). Research Officer (Industrial Wetlands) WWT 1992-94. Prev: Avon WT Conservation Officer 1986-92; Senior Superviser (Conservation) 1985-86; Surveys Officer 1983-85. Earlier: contract work for NCC, Avon CC, RSPB 1977-83. Chairman Chew Valley Lake Conservation Committee 1984-. Voluntary warden Chew Valley Lake 1976-. Records Committee *Avon Bird Report* 1983-, also Editorial Committee 1983-87. Special interests: wetland birds and their ecological requirements, Palearctic birds, migration/movements and weather, conservation. Bird-related travel to Belgium, Canary Islands, France, Hungary, Israel, Madeira, Morocco, Netherlands, N Cyprus, Spain, Turkey, The Gambia, Guatemala, Mexico, USA, China, Hong Kong,

Thailand. Author *Wetlands, Industry and Wildlife: a manual of principles and practices* (1994). Contributions to other books inc *The Natural History of Chew Valley* ed by R Janes (1987). Articles in *Avon Bird Report, Avon Wildlife* and *Nature in Avon*. Illustrations in Avon and Kent bird reports and elsewhere. OIR: other forms of natural history (esp butterflies), nature conservation (esp wetlands), photography (inc birds), travel, cinema, football. 16 Berkeley Road, Westbury Park, Bristol BS6 7PJ. 0117 974 1486.

MESSAGE, Stephen James (Steve); *b:* 9 April 1968 in Benenden, Kent. Hastings College of Art & Technology 1984-86; Bournemouth & Poole College of Art & Design (HND in Wildlife Illustration 1988). Bird and wildlife illustrator. Artwork in wide range of publications inc covers of eg *Birding World, British Birds*; in books eg *Birds of Greece* by G Handrinos and T Akriotis (1996) and bird reports. Work exhibited at SWLA (Mall Galleries) and elsewhere. Winner Richard Richardson Award (*British Birds*) 1989. OIR: cricket, football, badminton, snooker. Greenview, Benenden, Cranbrook, Kent TN17 4DD. 01580 240564.

MILLINGTON, Hazel Merion; *b:* 26 July 1955 in Shrewsbury, Shrops; *h:* Richard. Cert Ed (Brighton Coll of Ed, 1976). Circulation Manager *Birding World* since 1987. Co-founder of Bird Information Service 1986. Partner in Birdline 1986-. Special interest: foreign travel. Author *Confessions of a Twitching Widow* (1988). OIR: appreciation of theatre; fine cuisine. Stonerunner, Coast Road, Cley next the Sea, Holt, Norfolk NR25 7RZ. 01263 741139; fax 01263 741173.

MILLINGTON, Richard Graham; *b:* 28 May 1954 in Crondall, Hants; *w:* Hazel. BA Visual Communication (Brighton Coll of Art, 1976). Voice of Birdline since 1986. Asst Editor *Birding World* since 1987. Co-founder of Bird Information Service 1986. Norfolk Records Committee 1986-94. Special interests: field identification skills and sociology of birdwatchers. Freelance identification consultant. Bird artist (exhibited at numerous venues) and illustrator of bird books (twenty titles). Author and illustrator of *A Twitcher's Diary* (1981). Ornithological journalist: numerous publications, inc monthly articles in *Bird Watching* since 1986. Stonerunner, Coast Road, Cley next the Sea, Holt, Norfolk NR25 7RZ. 01263 741139; fax 01263 741173.

MILLS, Richard T; *b:* 8 August 1947 in Salon de Provence, France; *w:* Monica. Studied science at Univ College, Cork. Senior staff press photographer with the *Examiner* group of newspapers since 1968.

Committee IWC Cork Branch 1985. Special interests: bird and general wildlife photography. Travel in Europe, Somalia, Kenya, South Africa, Peru. Photographs published in wide range of books, journals and magazines; also in several permanent environmental display centres. Many public lectures, talks and slide shows inc all-Ireland conferences and BTO annual conference. Featured on RTE (Irish TV). Bird Photograph of the Year (*British Birds*) 1981; IWC/McSweeny cup for Irish Bird Photographer of the Year 1988,89,90 (judge thereafter). OIR: travel, computing and electronics. Redwing, 44 Halldene Avenue, Bishopstown, Cork, Ireland. +353 (0)21 341836; fax +353 (0)21 341611.

MILLS, Terry Robert; *b:* 13 October 1945 in Oxford. MA Lit Hum (Oxford, 1967), Dip BA (Manchester Business School, 1970). Banker. Voluntary warden for Nature Conservancy, Waterperry Forest NR 1963-67 (inaugurated nestbox scheme to increase diversity). Field Secretary Nigerian Field Soc, Lagos 1978-80. Wildlife tour leader Royal Asiatic Soc, Seoul 1981-83. Special interests: migration (studies in Middle East, W Africa, SW Spain). Leader of small ornithological expeditions in Europe (inc establishment of regional park at Montenach, Lorraine, France 1984-87), Africa, Asia and Americas. Author of report *Birds of the Danube Delta* (1966); BBC World Service broadcasts on wildlife in Nigeria (1979); co-author 'Birds of the Lagos Region' in *Malimbus* (1984). Member: OSME. OIR: shooting, fishing, canoeing, hiking. 36 Chartfield Avenue, Putney, London SW15 6HG. 0181 789 0997.

MILLS, Thomas Ian (Ian); *b:* 24 April 1950 in Sunderland, Tyne and Wear; *w:* Dorothy. St Aidan's Grammar School. Teaching Cert (Sunderland Coll of Education, 1973), BA Psychology (Open Univ, 1976). Head teacher, junior school since 1993. Durham Bird Club: Committee 1978-85, Records Committee 1978-. Committee Whitburn Bird Observatory 1990-. BTO 'C' ringer 1978-90 and member Durham Ringing Group until 1990. Carried out BTO Common Birds Census 1976-80. Special interests: migration (esp seabirds), identification, foreign birding trips. Section author *Birds in Durham* (annual report) 1980-. OIR: computers, music, reading, theatre. Holly Lodge, 24A Moor Lane, Cleadon, Sunderland SR6 7TT. 0191 536 3628.

MILTON, Nicholas David (Nick); *b:* 25 December 1966 in London. Old Buckenham High School, Diss 1980-83; Diss Sixth Form Centre 1983-85. BSc Environmental Studies (Hatfield Polytechnic, 1989). Campaigns Officer for The Wildlife Trusts since 1994. Prev: Farm Conservation

Adviser, Farming and Wildlife Advisory Group 1993-94; various RSPB posts 1990-93, inc advisory officer; also ranger for States of Jersey Planning Dept in 1988 and researcher in BBC Nat Hist Unit 1987-88. Birds of Estuaries Enquiry counter on Stour Estuary, Essex 1990-93. Voluntary warden RSPB Strumpshaw Fen Reserve 1986-88. Special interests: the effects of agricultural policy on birds in the wider countryside; habitat creation on land coming out of agricultural production; *Red Data Book* species in Channel Islands (Dartford and Cetti's Warblers, Cirl Bunting, Serin). Co-author (with G Williams) of Channel Islands entry in *Important Bird Areas in the United Kingdom including the Channel Islands and the Isle of Man* ed by D E Pritchard *et al* (1992). Paper on Cirl Bunting in Jersey in *Société Jersiaise Annual Bulletin* (1993); also articles in *British Wildlife* and *Farmers Weekly*. OIR: scuba diving, collecting surrealist art, oenology, adders and dragonflies. Bogallan Lodge, Artafallie, North Kessock, Ross-shire IV1 1XF. 01463 731752.

MINTON, Clive Dudley Thomas; *b:* 7 October 1934 in Bramhall, Cheshire; *w:* Patricia. MA Natural Sciences (Cambridge, 1957), PhD Metallurgy (Cambridge, 1960). Retired management consultant. Part-time tutor in ornithology Birmingham Extra-mural Dept 1961-77. Hon Vice President Royal Australasian Ornithologists' Union 1989-95, also Research Committee 1980-88. Trustee WWF Australia 1991-, and Scientific Advisory Committee 1984-91. BTO Council 1973-78. RSPB Council 1974-78. BTO 'A' ringer since 1948. Founder Chairman Wader Study Group 1970-74. Founder Chairman Australasian Wader Study Group 1980-85. Founder Wash Wader Ringing Group (1959). Special interests: long-term species and population studies, esp ringing and migration. Particular studies in UK inc waders, Mute Swan, Swallow, Sand Martin, thrush and finch roosts, Wigeon, Canada Goose. Since 1978 resident in Australia, where detailed study of waders inc leading seventeen expeditions to study them in NW of country since 1981. Many published scientific papers in eg *Bird Study*, *Wildfowl*; also articles in *Wader Study Group Bulletin* etc. Photographs in many publications. Regular broadcasts with BBC over twenty-year period and some TV; occasionally with ABC in Australia since 1978. Technical adviser on several TV documentaries on eg Mute Swan and waders in UK and Banded Stilts in Australia. BTO Tucker Medal 1975. Member: as above, also Bird Observers' Club of Australia and Wader Study Group. Non-government representative at inaugural Japan/Australia Migratory Birds Agreement Meeting 1983. OIR: sport (participating and watching), photography, travel. 165, Dalgetty Road, Beaumaris, Victoria 3193, Australia. Tel/fax +61 3 95894901.

MITCHAM, Terry; *b:* 30 August 1948 in Branston, Lincs; *w:* Patricia. North Kesteven Grammar School 1959-66. Cert Ed 1969, BEd 1970 (Sheffield City Coll of Education). Schoolteacher, head of humanities. Bird Recorder Rutland NHS 1982-. Adult education tutor in ornithology Casterton Community College 1985-. Management Committee Rutland Water NR 1983-. Special interest: local fieldwork. Participant in surveys inc BTO Common Birds Census, Garden Bird Feeding Survey, Wetland Bird Survey, atlas recording. Author *The Birds of Rutland and its Reservoirs* (1984), *Birdwatching in Rutland* (1987), *Rutland Breeding Bird Atlas* (1992). Contributor of bird report to *Rutland NHS Annual Report* since 1982, and local correspondent for *Bird Watching* 1986-. OIR: gardening, reading. 30 Sutherland Way, Stamford, Lincs PE9 2TB. 01780 51268.

MITCHELL, Dominic Francis John; *b:* 21 September 1959 in London. Founding director of Solo Publishing Ltd 1990-. Founding publisher and editor of *Birdwatch* magazine, launched January 1992. Committee North London RSPB Members' Group 1978-79. Volunteer fieldworker in the London area for BTO New Breeding Atlas 1988-91. Special interests: identification (esp passerines), photography, W Palearctic birds. Author *Where to Watch Birds in the London Area*, *The Photographic Handbook of Rare Birds in Britain and Europe*, and consultant editor of *Birdwatching* (in prep). Numerous features and photographs published in *Birdwatch*. Frequent commentator for local and national media (esp radio) on topical ornithological matters. Member: OBC, OSME. Collector of all forms of ornithological literature, with extensive personal library. OIR: current affairs, world travel, music, cinema, good food. c/o *Birdwatch*, Bow House, 153-159 Bow Road, London E3 2SE. 0181 983 1855.

MITCHELL, Margaret; *b:* 22 March 1934 in India; *h:* John. BA English and Latin (Natal, 1953), MA Philosophy, Politics and Economics (Lady Margaret Hall, Oxford, 1957). Teacher. Executive Committee Essex Birdwatching Society 1989-, Vice Chairman 1991-93, Chairman 1993-96. Participant in BTO surveys and Wetland Bird Survey counter on Blackwater Estuary. Special interests: identification, esp raptors and shorebirds. Bird-related travel inc N America (particularly Alaska), Belize and Venezuela, S Argentina, The Gambia, South Africa, N India, Ethiopia. One of sub-editors of *The Essex Bird Report* since 1991. OIR: geology, identification of fungi, general natural history, travel. 61 Weald Road, Brentwood, Essex CM14 4TN. 01277 212316.

MITCHELL, Owen; *b:* 6 April 1950 in Rustington, W Sussex; *w:* Marian. Steyning Secondary School. Police officer. Sussex Ornithological Society: Council 1978-82, 1994-95; Records Committee 1982-90, 1994-; Recorder 1994-95. Co-ordinator of records for Selsey Bill 1979-93. Special interests: migration, seawatching. Author *The Birds of Selsey Bill, West Sussex: a checklist with notes* (1991). Co-compiler *Selsey Bill, West Sussex* (annual bird report) 1979-83. Articles in *Sussex Bird Report* and *Sussex OS Newsletter.* 'Part-time twitcher.' OIR: keep fit, music, travel. 21 Trundle View Close, Barnham, Bognor Regis, W Sussex PO22 0JZ.

MONK, James Francis; *b:* 8 October 1915 in India; *w:* Diana. Winchester College 1929-34. BA Physiology (Trinity College, Oxford, 1937), BM (Oxford, 1941), DM (Oxford, 1949). General practitioner, retired. BTO Council 1958-c60. BOU: Council 1966-67, Hon Sec 1967-72, Vice President 1978-82, President 1983-87. BOC: Vice Chairman 1965-68, Chairman 1968-71. Special interests: migration and astro-navigation. Papers on Wryneck Survey for BTO and breeding biology of the Greenfinch published in *Bird Study.* Editor of *Ibis* 1960-66 and *Bull BOC* 1976-90. BOU Medal 1988. OIR: gardening. Bridge Cottage, Goring, Reading RG8 9AN. 01491 872500.

MONTGOMERY, George Peter Ferris (Peter); MBE 1989; Sqn Ldr Retd; *b:* 9 June 1939 in Cranwell, Lincs; *w:* Phyl. HNC Electrical & Electronic Engineering. Committee Rheindahlen (Germany) Bird Watching Group 1983-86. Royal Air Force Ornithological Society: General Secretary 1982, Field Activities Liaison Officer 1987-90. Ornithological conservation projects in Germany and Holland 1973-76 and 1983-86, with emphasis on wetlands and regeneration of habitat for breeding Bluethroat. Ornithological expeditions: Arctic Norway 1976; S Norway (survey for British Outward Bound Centre) 1980; Benbecula 1981; Cyprus 1982; Austria (detailed survey of wetlands for Dr Grull of Illmitz Biol Station) 1985; Scottish Highlands (surveys for BTO New Breeding Atlas, 341 tetrads) 1989 and 1990; Hungary (Great Bustard surveys for MME/BLI, Budapest) 1994. Editor *RAFOS Journal* 1993-96. Numerous articles and reports in *RBWG Newsletter, RAFOS Newsletter* and *RAFOS Journal* 1973-96. Various reports inc 'Report on Ornithological Surveys in 101 RAF Stations in UK' (1991). Honorary Life Membership of RAFOS 1991. Special interest: investigating ornithological activity open to wheelchair-bound people. OIR: artist, specialising in landscapes, in oils; active participant involved in improving accessibility, generally, for people with disabilities. Beech Cottage, Church Street, Scothern, Lincoln LN2 2UA. 01673 861556.

MOON, Stephen John (Steve); *b:* 29 September 1949 in Alton, Hants; *w:* Madeleine (Mayor of Porthcawl 1995-96). BSc Environmental Sciences (East Anglia, 1973), MSc Ecology (Durham, 1974). MIEEM 1993. Principal Planning Officer (Environment) for Bridgend CBC since 1996. Prev: Warden Kenfig NNR (Mid Glam) 1976-94. Formerly: Bristol Naturalists' Society (Junior Section), Bristol Orn Club (founder-member and junior editor of *Bird News* in 1960s), Glamorgan WT (Council, Mid Area Committee and Scientific Committee, then Glamorgan Watch Clubs Organiser 1979-89), Cardiff Naturalists' Soc (Council, President, Treasurer and Programme Secretary of Ornithological Section), Glamorgan Bird Club (Treasurer and Membership Secretary 1990-95), briefly BTO Rep, Gower Orn Soc. Currently (1996): Welsh Ornithological Society (Council), Glamorgan Bird Club (Mid & South Glamorgan Bird Recorder, WeBS Organiser for Mid & South Glam). BTO 'A' ringer since 1986. Kenfig Ringing Group Treasurer. Special interests: ringing, identification, all aspects of conservation. Editor *Mid & South Glamorgan Bird Report* since 1991. Short identification notes in *British Birds*. Winner of Slimbridge Wildfowl Trust's Identification Competition for Schools in c1967. Member: DoE Canada Goose Working Party. Found Britain's first Little Whimbrel (1982). Glamorgan list 251, best day tally in Mid Glam 111. OIR: playing acoustic guitar; yo-yo; moth recording and dragonfly hunting; fan of BBC weather show. 36 Rest Bay Close, Porthcawl, Glamorgan CF36 3UN. 01656 786571.

MOORE, Allen Stewart; *b:* 22 May 1957 in Douglas, Isle of Man; *w:* Ruth. BPharm (Bradford, 1979). Hospital pharmacist. Committee Manx Ornithological Society 1984-. Manx Bird Records Sub-committee 1993-. Trustee of Manx Chough Project 1991-. Organiser for Isle of Man of Seabird Colony Register 1985-87; subsequently contributor of IoM data for Seabird Monitoring Programme. Member of Calf of Man Consultatory Committee 1992-94 (ornithological input to this body set up to protect marine environment). Organiser (with Aron Sapsford) of 1992 and 1995 Chough Surveys in Isle of Man. Special interests: Choughs (all aspects of ecology), seabirds (breeding population monitoring), raptors (esp monitoring of breeding Peregrines in Isle of Man). Joint editor *Peregrine: a Journal of Manx Natural History* since 1989, sole editor from 1993. Author or co-author of Manx Ornithological Report since 1982 (published in *Peregrine*) and articles therein. OIR: Manx language and culture. Lyndale, Derby Road, Peel, Isle of Man IM5 1HH. 01624 843798.

MOORE, Amberley Mary; *b:* 23 August 1931 in Harrow-on-the-Hill, London; *h:* Peter James Moore MBE. Perse School for Girls, Cambridge; Guy's Hospital School of Radiography. Diploma, College of Radiographers 1952. The Gambia Ornithological Society: Committee 1978-79, Hon Sec 1981-83. British Ornithologists' Club: Committee 1987-, Hon Sec 1989-95. West African Ornithological Society, Sec to Council 1984-95. Special interests: the history of ornithology, ornithological exploration of West Africa. Co-author (with J H Elgood *et al*) *The Birds of Nigeria: an annotated check-list* (2nd ed, 1994). Ornithological field notes published in *Malimbus*; natural history and travel in West Africa in *Bull BOC*, *The Guardian* and *Nigerian Field*. Member: WAOS. 1 Uppingham Road, Oakham, Rutland, Leics LE15 6JB.

MOORE, Derek Raymond; *b:* 1 January 1943 in Beccles Suffolk; *w:* Beryl. Sir John Leman School, Beccles. Director Suffolk Wildlife Trust since 1985. Suffolk Bird Recorder 1978-84. Chairman Suffolk Naturalists' Society 1982-84. Chairman and founder Landguard Bird Observatory 1983-85. BTO Research and Surveys Committee 1985-89, Council member and Chairman of Membership and Development Committee 1993-97. Suffolk Ornithological Records Committee 1978-93, Chairman 1988-91. Suffolk Ornithological Atlas Group 1989-93. BTO 'A' ringer since 1984. Special interests: migration, distribution, conservation, communicating. Leader of wildlife tours at home and abroad, also private expeditions to Netherlands, France, Spain, Crete, Cyprus, Poland, Russia, Morocco, The Gambia, USA. Co-author (with Steve Piotrowski and Malcolm Bowling) *Easy Birdwatching* (1990); (with Bill Oddie) *A Birdwatcher's Guide to the Birds of Cyprus* (1993); (with Hilary Welch *et al*) *Where to Watch Birds in Turkey, Greece and Cyprus* (1996). Editor *Suffolk Birds* (annual report) 1978-84. Numerous articles in eg *Bird Watching*, *Birdwatch*, *Birdwatcher's Yearbook*, *British Birds* (with Steve Piotrowski), *Country Life*, *Suffolk Birds*. Local radio and TV broadcasts. OIR: watching soccer (Norwich City) and cricket; music; travel. Crosslands, Cage Lane, Boxted, Colchester CO4 5RE. 01206 272594. Office: 01473 890089; fax 01473 890165.

MOORE, Norman Winfrid; *b:* 24 February 1923 in London; *w:* Janet. BA Natural Sciences (Cambridge, c1942), MA (Cambridge), PhD Behaviour and ecology of adult dragonflies (Bristol, 1953). FIBiol 1965. Retired. Chief Advisory Officer, NCC 1974-83; also Visiting Professor, Wye College Univ London 1978-83. Prev: Head, Toxic Chemicals and Wildlife Division, Monks Wood, Nature Conservancy 1960-74; Regional Officer for SW England, NC 1953-60; Asst Lecturer and Lecturer Univ Bristol 1949-53.

BOU Council 1960-63, Vice President 1977-81. Past Council member and Vice President, British Ecological Society. Co-ordinator BTO Buzzard Survey 1953-56. Special interests: direct and indirect effects of human activities on bird populations (habitat reduction, myxomatosis, pesticides, PCBs, urban development). Author *The Bird of Time* (1987). Numerous scientific papers and articles, mainly on effects of pesticides. Occasional radio and TV broadcasts on ornithology-related subjects. Union Medal of BOU 1972. Hon Fellow of Linnean Society 1993. Much of scientific and conservation work on Odonata, often related to ornithological work. OIR: travel (esp to remote islands), practical nature conservation, walking, oil and watercolour painting. The Farm House, 117 Boxworth End, Swavesey, Cambridge CB4 5RA. 01954 230233.

MORAN, Richard John McMoran (John); Lord (2nd Baron, 1943); KCMG 1981 (CMG 1970); Grand Cross, Order of the Infante (Portugal) 1978; *b:* 22 September 1924 in London; *w:* Shirley (The Lady Moran). Eton College. King's College, Cambridge. RNVR 1943-45. Diplomatic Service 1945-84 (Ambassador to Chad, Hungary and Portugal, High Commissioner in Canada); Cross Bencher in House of Lords. RSPB Council 1989-94. Chairman, Regional Fisheries Advisory Committee, Welsh Region, National Rivers Authority 1989-94. Chairman, Wildlife and Countryside Link 1992-95. Chairman of All Party Conservation Group of both Houses of Parliament. President, Radnorshire Wildlife Trust. House of Lords, Westminster, London SW1A 0PW.

MORGAN, Nicholas John (Nick); *b:* 10 April 1961 in Eckington, Worcs; *w:* Sandra. Prince Henry's High School, Evesham. BA Economics (Sheffield, 1982). Accountant. Bird Recorder for NW Yorkshire 1989-. Secretary Yorkshire Naturalists' Union Ornithological Records Committee 1991-94. Special interests: birds of gravel pits, rarities, bird distribution. Author *The Birds of Swale Lakes* (booklet, 1991). Regular birdwatching column for local press. Site guides and articles on birdwatching in NW Yorks published in eg *Yorkshire Birding, Yorkshire Naturalist*. OIR: art, pub quizzes, cryptozoology. Linden, Church View, Ainderby Steeple, Northallerton, N Yorks DL7 9PU. 01609 770168.

MORLEY, Elliot Anthony; MP; *b:* 6 July 1952 in Liverpool; *w:* Patricia. St Margaret's High School Liverpool. Cert Ed, BEd (Hull College of Education, 1975). RSPB Council 1989-93. BTO Council 1991-95. Trustee, Birds of the Humber Trust 1992-. BTO 'A' ringer since 1971. Special interests: waders, agro-environmental policy, nature conservation. Wildlife photographs in Kodak House of Commons Photographic Society exhibition 1994. Contributor to *The New Waterlands*, joint Sussex WT, RSNC, Water for Wildlife publication. Various illustrated talks. Vice President, Wildlife and Countryside Link. Opposition spokesperson on Food, Agriculture, Rural Affairs and Animal Welfare. 9 West Street, Winterton, N Lincs DN15 9QG. 01724 734510/842000.

MORRIS, Glenn Eric; *b:* 20 March 1947 in Brierley Hill, W Midlands; *w:* Dr Nguyen thi Man. BA Natural Sciences (Biochemistry) (Downing College, Cambridge, 1967), DPhil Biochemistry (Sussex, 1970). Professor of Biochemistry (see address). Member of Clwyd Bird Recording Group 1989-94. Wetland Bird Survey organiser for Clwyd (inland) 1992-. Special interest: birds of Vietnam. Editor *Garrulax* (newsletter on biology and conservation in Vietnam published by RSPB) 1985-92. Editor of wildfowl section of *Clwyd Bird Report* 1989-94. Editor *Connah's Quay Nature Reserve Report* 1985-90. Member: OBC. OIR: research into genetic and infectious human diseases. MRIC, NE Wales Institute, Wrexham LL11 2AW. 01978 293330.

MORTLOCK, Barbara Mary; *b:* 27 March 1935 in Margate, Kent; *h:* Derek. Maidstone Girls' Grammar School. BSc Mathematics (Royal Holloway College, Univ London, 1957), Retired local government officer. Wetland Bird Survey counter since 1985. Recorder for Weir Wood Reservoir (Sussex Orn Soc) since 1992. Author *Birds of Weir Wood Reservoir 1954-89* (priv print, 1993). Special interest: computerisation of bird records and bird studies. OIR: photography, mineral collecting. 37 Barnmead, Haywards Heath, W Sussex RH16 1UY. 01444 412641.

MORTON, Robert (Rab); *b:* 1 June 1943 in Blantyre, Strathclyde. Warden Sandwich Bay Bird Observatory and member of Kent Ornithological Society Rarities Committee since 1991. Special interests: migration, photography. Member: Seabird Group. SBBO, Guilford Road, Sandwich Bay, Sandwich, Kent CT13 9PF. 01304 617341.

MOSER, Michael Edward; *b:* 16 July 1956 in Kendal, Cumbria; *w:* Joanna Stewart-Smith. Shrewsbury School 1969-74. BSc Ecology (Durham, 1978), PhD Resource partitioning in a community of herons and egrets (Durham, 1983). Director Wetlands International (formerly IWRB) since 1988. Prev: Director of Development BTO 1986-88; Estuaries Officer BTO 1982-86; research asst at Station Biologique de la Tour du Valat in Camargue, France (doctoral research also in Camargue 1979-82). WWT Council

1993-. Scientific Council of Bonn Convention on the Conservation of Migratory Species 1988-. Special interest: wetlands and wetland birds. Extensive travel worldwide. Board member of Station Biologique de la Tour du Valat since 1989. Joint compiler (with D G Salmon) *Wildfowl and Wader Counts* covering 1982/83-1985/86. General editor (with C M Finlayson) *Wetlands* (1991). Many scientific papers in eg *Ardea, Biol Cons, Bird Study, Ibis, Irish Birds, J Appl Ecol, Scottish Birds, Wader Study Group Bulletin, Wildfowl*; also many research reports, conference proceedings and popular articles. Asst editor *Wader Study Group Bulletin* 1985-87. Editorial Board *Bird Study* 1986-88. Lectures, esp on wetlands and waterfowl. Frequent radio and TV appearances. OIR: travel, good food and wine, fly-fishing, people. Wetlands International, PO Box 7002, 6700 CA Wageningen, The Netherlands.

MOSS, Dorian; *b:* 16 October 1948 in Woking, Surrey. BA Mathematics (Oxford, 1970), MSc Statistics (Oxford, 1972), PhD Ecology (Edinburgh, 1976). Principal Scientific Officer, Environmental Information Centre, Institute of Terrestrial Ecology, Monks Wood since 1978. Prev: Research Asst Univ Edinburgh 1975-77. Chairman Univ Coll of North Wales Bird Group 1981-88. BTO Research and Surveys Committee 1982-86, Ringing Committee 1987-90, Integrated Population Monitoring Working Group from 1991. Treasurer SCAN Ringing Group (Conwy and Anglesey) since 1982, Secretary from 1992. Birds of Estuaries Enquiry counts organiser N Wales 1981-88. Fieldwork for BTO Breeding Atlas. BTO 'A' ringer since 1975, trainer and sponsor. Constant Effort Site operator. Special interests: Kestrel, estuarine waders, Pied Flycatcher in N Wales. MSc thesis: 'A statistical analysis of clutch size in the Great Tit'; PhD thesis: 'Woodland song-bird populations and growth of nestling Sparrowhawks'. Many scientific papers published in eg *Bird Study, Forestry, Ibis, J Animal Ecol, J Forestry, J Zool*. Also contributions to books. OIR: worldwide travel, classical music. 16 High Street, Stilton, Peterborough PE7 3RA. 01733 244373.

MOSS, Stephen; *b:* 26 April 1960 in London; *w:* Jane. MA English Literature (Cambridge, 1982). Television producer. Special interest: birds and weather. Regular contributor to *Birdwatch*; monthly column on birds for *The Guardian*, also contributor to Science and Environment sections. Author *Birds and Weather* (1995); co-author *Birding with Bill Oddie* (1996), *The Complete Garden Book* (1996). OIR: family life. 40 Gilpin Avenue, London SW14 8QY. 0181 878 2491. Or BBC White City, 201 Wood Lane, London W12 7TS. 0181 752 4803.

MOUNTFORD, Peter Joseph; *b:* 12 December 1934 in Birmingham; *w:* Margaret. Site Manager, English Nature, Mendip and South Somerset Reserves 1988-94, retired. Prev: Warden/Site Manager Avon Gorge and Gordano NNRs 1983-88; Warden (first) Stodmarsh NNR 1965-83; Warden (first) Tring Reservoirs and Knocking Hoe NNR 1963-65; Warden (first) Spurn Bird Observatory and Spurn Point NR 1960-63; scientific asst Nature Conservancy East Anglian Region (compiling card index of birds of Scolt Head, autumn 1959); asst warden Scolt Head Island NNR 1958, 1959. Executive Committee Kent Ornithological Society 1965-68. Organiser, National Wildfowl Count, East Kent 1965-68. BTO 'A' ringer since 1958; also training ringers when Warden Spurn Bird Obs. Special interests: identification, coastal and sea migration, wildfowl and waders. Common Birds Census set up on reserves. Occasional magazine articles; records to several county bird reports. OIR: reading, book collecting, classical music, walking. 6 Prior Place, Wells, Somerset BA5 1SP.

MOUNTFORT, Guy Reginald; OBE 1970; Commander, Order of the Golden Ark, Netherlands 1980; *b:* 4 December 1905 in London; *w:* Joan. Retired Managing Director, Ogilvy & Mather Ltd. BOU: Hon Sec 1952-62, President 1970-75. Ex Council Member of Charles Darwin Foundation. On behalf of WWF helped to create wildlife reserves in The Gambia, Spain, Bulgaria, Jordan, Pakistan, India, Bangladesh and Nepal. Scientific expeditions made to all except The Gambia. Books: *A Field Guide to the Birds of Britain and Europe* with Roger Peterson and P A D Hollom (1954, 5th edn 1993); *The Hawfinch* (1957); *Portrait of a Wilderness* (1958); *Portrait of a River* (1962); *Portrait of a Desert* (1965); *The Vanishing Jungle* (1969); *Tigers* (1973); *So Small a World* (1974); *Back from the Brink* (1977); *Saving the Tiger* (1981); *Wild India* (1985); *Rare Birds of the World* (1988); *Memories of Three Lives* (1991). Contributions to ornithological and other scientific journals. Radio and TV broadcasts on ornithology and exploration. Medal of the Société d'Acclimatation 1936; Union Medal, BOU 1967; Stamford Raffles Award of the Zoological Society 1969; Gold Medal, WWF 1978. Member: AOU, ICBP, SOF, WWF (Vice President). OIR: travel, gardening, photography. 8 Park Manor, St Aldhelms Road, Poole, Dorset BH13 6BS. 01202 768815.

MOYSER, Geoffrey; *b:* 12 February 1951. HND Mathematics, Statistics and Computing (Cheltenham College of Technology, 1972). Computer analyst/programmer. Gloucestershire Bird Records Committee 1987-94. Special interests: identification, migration, continuous study of one site (R Severn at Berkeley, Glos) since 1974. Co-author (with R M Sellers) *The*

Birds of Berkeley (1985) also 20-year edition in prep. OIR: performing traditional folk songs and music; karate. 57 Shakespeare Road, Dursley, Glos GL11 4QG.

MUDGE, Gregory Philip (Greg); *b:* 2 October 1950 in Paignton, Devon; *w:* Denise. BSc Zoology (Wales, Cardiff, 1972), PhD Avian Ecology (Wales, Cardiff, 1978). Senior Ornithologist, Scottish Natural Heritage since 1992. Secretary Sea Eagle Project Team 1992-. Chairman Capercaillie Working Group 1992-. Special interests: seabirds (esp divers, ducks). Co-author (with D Stroud and M W Pienkowski) *Protecting Internationally Important Bird Sites* (1990) and (with D E Pritchard *et al*) *Important Bird Areas in the United Kingdom* (1992). Scottish Natural Heritage, 2 Anderson Place, Edinburgh EH6 5NP. 0131 446 2424.

MUNNS, Geoffrey Ferrers Altham; Major Retd; *b:* 25 July 1920 in Darjeeling, India; *w:* Sheila. St Albans School. Royal Military Academy, Woolwich; commissioned into Royal Regiment of Artillery, November 1939. BTO Council 1974-82, Hon Secretary 1978-82, Regional Representative Kent since 1967. Executive Committee Kent Ornithological Society 1964-81, ex officio 1982-. Regional organiser for BTO Breeding Atlas 1968-72, Winter Atlas 1981-84, New Breeding Atlas 1988-91. Organised first and third BTO one-day conferences in Tunbridge Wells, in 1971 and 1973 respectively. Special interests: changes in the distribution and abundance of British birds, welfare of resident and migratory birds in Cyprus. Was Hon Sec of BTO when 10km square of the National Grid became the standard unit for most surveys; suggested that BTO Regional Representatives should appoint a volunteer 'steward' in each square to act as the local fieldwork organiser (hence the term '10km square steward', see *Birdwatcher's Yearbook* 1982). Attended conferences of European Section of ICBP in Visegrad (Hungary) 1987, Adana (Turkey) 1989, and Aachen (Germany) 1992 as an active observer for the Cyprus Ornithological Society (1957) in the absence of any official delegate from the island. Bernard Tucker Medal, BTO 1985. Member: Cyprus OS (1957). OIR: rugby union (played for RMA and RA in earlier years, also represented the Gunners in athletics and tennis). Spring Place, St Aubyns Close, Orpington, Kent BR6 0SN. 01689 835325.

MURPHY, Christopher William (Chris); *b:* 26 August 1954 in Waterloo, Lancs; *w:* Doris. Ornithologist and proprietor Murphy's Wildlife Holidays since 1992. Prev: freelance ornithologist, writer and tour leader 1989-91, working full-time on BTO/IWC Euro-Atlas in 1990; RSPB Asst Regional

Officer (N Ireland) 1984-88. YOC Leader 1969-74. Committee Liverpool RSPB Members' Group and Liverpool Naturalists' Field Club 1971-76. Co-founder Oriental Bird Club (1984) and OBC representative in Ireland 1985-. Organiser of NI Breeding Wader Survey 1985-86 and NI Corncrake Survey 1986. Co-founder of Belfast Lough Nature Conservation Committee 1987 and several other conservation groups in Northern Ireland. Queen's Univ Belfast tutor in ornithology 1989-. Co-founder and Council member Northern Ireland Birdwatchers' Association 1991-, Hon Sec since 1993. Special interests: *Phylloscopus* warblers, identification, seabirding, migration, breeding waders, islands, Nepal and the Oriental region in general, also Turkey, France and Ireland. Twelve-month overland expedition to India 1978/79. Three-month expedition to Turkey (summer 1983) where highlights inc finding two new species for the country, both breeding. Notes, articles and papers published in many journals and magazines inc *Bird Watching, Birdwatch, British Birds, Irish Birding News, Irish Birds*. Co-editor *Northern Ireland Bird Report* 1991-. Numerous radio and TV broadcasts on birdwatching and conservation. Co-organiser and founder of Irish Birdwatching Fair, 1994. Holder of Irish 24-hr record of 133 species (1993). OIR: butterflies, dragonflies, all mammals (esp carnivores, bats, cetaceans), some local cricket, also golf and other sports. Larches, 12 Belvoir Close, Belvoir Park, Belfast BT8 4PL. 01232 693232.

MURRAY, John Bishop; *b:* 9 February 1937 in Milngavie, Dunbartonshire; *w:* Suzanne. Bearsden Academy. Museum Association's Technical Cert (Taxidermy) 1964. Village subpostmaster and shopkeeper. Prev: Taxidermist Royal Scottish Museum Edinburgh (1964-77), Nottingham Nat Hist Museum (1961-64), Glasgow Museum and Art Gallery (1959-61). British Falconers' Club: member 1959-88, Council 1974-86, founder of Scottish contingent 1973 and Chairman thereof until 1978. Secretary of State for Scotland's Advisory Committee on Bird Protection 1970-77. Home Office Specialist Raptor Group 1977-80. Co-founder Foulshiels Bird Study Group 1990. Trained and flown all raptors on British list except Hobby. Granted first-ever licence in Britain to take a Golden Eagle from the nest for falconry (1972). Studied relationship between hunting ability and daily food intake of a trained adult male Golden Eagle over 18 months. Interest in bird photography. Leader of many groups of birdwatchers all around Scotland, inc the islands. Participant in several 'Natural History Question Times' on Scottish Radio. OIR: local history (book on village of Stoneyburn), military aircraft (esp aerobatic teams), building and collecting model aircraft, philately, tracing family history. Woodville, 59 Main Street, Stoneyburn, Bathgate, W Lothian EH47 8BY. 01501 762258.

MURRAY, Raymond David (Ray); *b:* 18 January 1950 in Edinburgh; *w:* Sheila. MA Geography (Edinburgh, 1972). Secondary Teacher Qualification (Moray House College, Edinburgh, 1977). Visiting teacher of environmental education. Bird Recorder for Borders 1979-. Chairman Scottish Local Bird Recorders Conference 1989-93. SOC: Council 1986-, Vice President 1990-93, President 1993-96. Organiser SE Scotland Tetrad Atlas 1988-. Special interests: atlasing, Goosander, taxonomy. Author *Birds of the Borders* (1986). Editor *Borders Bird Report* 1980-, and *Scottish Bird Report* 1990-. Articles, inc several on Goosanders in Borders, also on colonisation of Scotland by continental species in twentieth century and Scottish influxes of Quail (1989) and Bluethroat (1986), mostly in *Borders Bird Report* or *Scottish Birds*. OIR: skiing, reading science fiction/fantasy. 4 Bellfield Crescent, Eddleston, Peebles EH45 8RQ. 01721 730677.

NAIRN, Richard George Wilson; *b:* 28 March 1952 in Dublin, Ireland; *w:* Wendy. BA Mod (Natural Sciences) (Trinity College Dublin, 1973), MA Natural Sciences (Trinity College, Dublin, 1979). MIEEM 1991, MIBiol 1991. Environmental consultant and writer. Director Natural Environment Consultants since 1990. Prev: National Director IWC 1981-90; Scientific Editor Royal Irish Academy 1979-80; Nature Reserve Warden National Trust 1974-79. Wildlife Advisory Council 1981-84. Praeger Committee, Royal Irish Academy 1988-94. Green 2000 Advisory Group 1991-92. Special interests: breeding wader surveys, factors affecting winter roost selection by waders, bird/habitat relationships, bird and habitat conservation. Contributor to books eg *Birds and Pastoral Agriculture in Europe* ed by D J Curtis *et al* (1991) and *Ireland's Wild Countryside* by É de Buitléar (1993). Ornithological papers in *Irish Birds*, and articles in *IWC News* etc. Member of study team which prepared coastal zone management policy for Ireland; extensive experience since 1990 of environmental impact assessments of eg roads, pipelines. Runs natural history courses. OIR: hill walking, sailing, photography, organic gardening. Natural Environment Consultants, Glanmore, Ashford, Co Wicklow, Ireland. +353 (0)404 40261; fax +353 (0)404 40800.

NEAL, Michael Geoffrey (Geoff); *b:* 25 March 1952 in Mancot, Flints. Quality assurance manager. Clwyd (later Flints & Denbighs) Bird Recorder 1993-. Spurn Bird Observatory Committee 1986-95. Author *The Birds of Spurn: a comprehensive checklist* (1996). Co-author *Spurn Bird Observatory Report* 1986-. Co-editor *Clwyd Bird Report* 1989-.

Compiler of various quizzes and competitions in early issues of *Birding World* and *Yorkshire Birding*. OIR: moths, collecting 1960s records, drinking real ale (member of CAMRA since 1977). 36 The Ridgeway, Hawarden, Deeside, Flints CH5 3ER. 01244 533622.

NELSON, Joseph Bryan (Bryan); *b:* 14 March 1932 in Shipley, Yorks; *w:* June. BSc Zoolgy (St Andrews, 1959), DPhil Animal Behaviour/Ecology (Oxford, 1963). FRSE 1982. Retired. Lecturer, Senior Lecturer, Reader in Zoology, Aberdeen Univ 1969-85; Director (first) Azraq Desert Research Station, Jordan 1968-69; Leverhulme Post Doctoral Research Fellowship 1966. Chairman SOC Stewartry Branch 1987-92. Member, Expert Panel, Abbott's Booby Research Programme (Christmas Island). Hon Vice President Galapagos Conservation Trust. Special interests: seabird ecology and behaviour, esp all families of the order Pelecaniformes ('particularly the North Atlantic Gannet, of which I am the major biographer'). Author *Galapagos: islands of birds* (1968), *Azraq: desert oasis* (1974), *The Sulidae: gannets and boobies* (1978), *The Gannet* (1978), *The Biology and Ecology of Seabirds* (1980), *Living with Seabirds* (1986), *The Gannet* (1988), *The Pelecaniformes* (in prep). Numerous scientific papers, mostly on gannets, boobies and frigatebirds, in eg *Ardea, British Birds, Ibis, J Animal Ecol, The Living Bird, Natural History, Proc Linn Soc, Scottish Birds*. Articles in eg *American Nat Hist Magazine, The Countryman, The Field, Scottish Field*. Editor *RSPB Galloway Newsletter* 1988-96. Films (photographer) *Gannet Behaviour* (1963), *Galapagos Seabirds* (1966), *Abbott's Booby* (1970). Occasional radio and TV broadcasts. OIR: hill walking, reading, islands, boating. Mine House, Auchencairn, Castle Douglas, Kirkcudbrightshire DG7 1RL. 01556 640320.

NEWMAN, Errol Christopher Bernard (Lew); *b:* 11 February 1942 in Guildford, Surrey; w: Ann. Royal Grammar School, Guildford. RICS Land Surveying (SW Essex Tech Coll, 1963), LIEnvSc (1993). Country Park Warden. Prev: Asst Reserves Manager RSPB 1973-74. Surrey Bird Club Committee/Conservation Officer 1970-75. BTO Regional Representative and Development Officer, Bedfordshire 1988-95. Bedfordshire NHS Scientific Committee 1988-, Secretary 1994-. Founder-member and Research Officer Bedfordshire Bird Club 1992-96. BTO 'A' ringer since 1982, Trainers Panel 1990-. Two Constant Effort Sites 1988-. Founder-member and Secretary Ivel Ringing Group 1990-. Cambridge Gull Group 1985-. Regional organiser for major BTO projects, inc atlases and surveys (both Surrey and Beds); also consultee for WWT Goose Survey 1990-91. Special interests: ringing and migration studies; Whitethroat, Reed

Bunting, Lady Amherst's Pheasant, Nightingale, Mute Swan; high-power tape luring. Editor *Ivel RG Report* 1990-. Articles and other contributions, mainly in bird reports. Occasional radio. 15 Birchmead, Gamlingay, Sandy, Beds SG19 3ND. 01767 651250.

NEWNHAM, John Alan; *b:* 11 November 1948 in Worthing, Sussex; *w:* Denise. Steyning Grammar School 1960-67. BSc Medical Science (Edinburgh, 1970), MB, ChB (Edinburgh, 1973). Principal in general medical practice. Shoreham District Ornithological Society: Hon Recorder 1975-81, Council 1973-88, Chairman 1982-85. Sussex Ornithological Society: Council intermittently from 1977, Scientific Committee 1979-, Hon Scientific Officer 1983-88, Hon Vice President 1991-; also since 1989 responsibility for developing and maintaining the computerised database of bird records in Sussex. BTO 'A' ringer since 1960s and sponsor. Special interest: migration. Editor *The Birds of Shoreham* (1988). Asst editor *Birds of Sussex* ed by Paul James (1996). Papers on Nightingales, gulls and migration in *Sussex Bird Reports* 1980-93; wide range of articles annually in *SDOS Annual Report* since 1968. Walton House, 61 Grand Avenue, Worthing, W Sussex BN11 5BA. 01903 247596.

NEWTON, Ian; Professor; FRS 1993, FRSE 1994; *b:* 17 January 1940 in Chesterfield, Derbys; *w:* Halina. BSc Zoology (Bristol 1961), DPhil Ecology of finches (Oxford, 1964), DSc Zoology (Oxford, 1982). Avian ecologist. Since 1971: research on bird-of-prey and other bird populations, monitoring pesticide residues in certain bird species and assessing effects on populations; known particularly for long-term study of the Sparrow-hawk. 1967-70: research on waterfowl, examining breeding biology of ducks and geese and agricultural damage by wintering geese. 1961-67: research on the comparative feeding ecology of British finches, inc ecology of the Bullfinch in relation to bud damage in fruit orchards. Committee work: British Ecological Society (President 1994-95, Council 1993-96); BOU (Vice President 1989-92); Wildfowl & Wetlands Trust (Council, Chairman Research Advisory Committee 1988-96); BTO (Populations and Surveys Committee 1994-96); Game Conservancy (Research Advisory Committee 1982-85); North American Peregrine Fund (Board Member and Chairman of Programme Committee 1988-96); JNCC (Steering Group on Red Kite and White-tailed Eagle reintroductions). Author *Finches* (1972), *Population Ecology of Raptors* (1979), *The Sparrowhawk* (1986). Editor *Lifetime Reproduction in Birds* (1989), *Birds of Prey* (1990). Co-editor (with R D Chancellor) *Conservation Studies on Raptors* (1985). Over 200 scientific papers. Asst Editor *Ibis* 1965-67; Editorial Board *J Animal Ecol*

1992- and *Proc Roy Soc B* 1993-. Contributions to several radio and TV programmes. Union Medal of BOU 1988 (eminent services to ornithology); Gold Medal of BES 1989 (excellence in ecology); RSPB Medal 1991 (exceptional services to ornithology and conservation); President's Award of Raptor Research Foundation 1993 (insightful leadership in raptor research); Marsh Award for Conservation Biology of the Zoological Society of London 1995 (contributions of fundamental science and its application to the conservation of animal species and habitat); Elliot Coues Award of the AOU 1995 (meritorious contributions, having an important influence on the study of birds in the Western Hemisphere). OIR: apple growing, breeding of rare breeds of domestic fowl. Institute of Terrestrial Ecology, Monks Wood, Abbots Ripton, Huntingdon, Cambs PE17 2LS. 01487 773381; fax 01487 773467.

NICHOLSON, Edward Max (Max); Hon LLD Aberdeen 1964, Hon DL Birmingham 1983, CB 1948, CVO 1971, Commandeur, Order of the Golden Ark (Netherlands) 1973; *b:* 12 July 1904 in Ireland; *w:* Marie-Antoinette. Sedbergh School. Hon Fellow, Hertford College, Oxford, 1993. Administrator in public service and voluntary bodies; consultant. Director General, Nature Conservancy 1952-66. Director, Oxford Bird Census 1927-29 and National Census of Heronries 1928. BTO: Hon Sec 1932-39, Chairman 1947-49. Wildfowl Trust Vice President 1949-. Advisory Council on Scientific Policy 1948-64. Senior Editor *British Birds* 1950-60. International Ornithological Committee from 1950. BOU Vice President 1958-61. BOC Vice Chairman 1955-56. AOU: Corresponding Fellow 1953, Hon Fellow 1991. First Chairman and Chief Editor West Palaearctic Birds Ltd 1964-66, then Board Member to 1993; editor for habitat sections of *BWP* throughout and for voice sections until 1982. Founder-member 1937 Bird Club, later President. Convenor for Conservation, International Biological Programme 1963-74. Special interests: habitat and population, voice and bird song. Expeditions inc Spain and Mediterranean, Baluchistan, Greenland, Guyana, Jordan, Tunisia. Co-ordinator S'Albu-fera Project, Mallorca 1989-. Author *Birds in England* (1926), *How Birds Live* (1927), *British Birds Census of Heronries Report* (1929), *The Study of Birds* (1929), *The Art of Birdwatching* (1931), *Songs of Wild Birds* (with Ludwig Koch) (1936), *More Songs of Wild Birds* (1937), *Birds and Men* (1951), *Britain's Nature Reserves* (1958), *The Environmental Revolution* (1970), *The New Environmental Age* (1987), *Bird-watching in London: a historical perspective* (1995). Papers published in *British Birds*, *Ibis* and many other journals. Awards: Geoffroy St Hilaire Gold Medal, Société Nationale de Protection de Nature de France 1956; Tucker Medal, BTO

1956; First Phillips Medallist 1963 and Member of Honour International Union for Conservation of Nature and Natural Resources; Godman-Salvin Medallist, BOU 1962; Premio Europeo Cortina-Ulisse (Italy) 1971; Europa Preis für Landespflege 1972; Gold Medallist, WWF 1982; Founder's Medallist, BTO 1991. 13 Upper Cheyne Row, London SW3 5JW. 0171 3527208.

NIGHTINGALE, Barry James; *b:* 4 April 1947 in Luton, Beds; *w:* Wendy. HNC Business Studies (Luton Coll of Tech, 1967). Marketing manager (engineering). Bird Recorder for Bedfordshire 1978-85. Council Beds NHS 1981-87, 1996-; Scientific Committee 1978-88. Founder-member and Committee Bedfordshire Bird Club since formation in 1992, Chairman 1996-. Special interest: population and distribution surveys. Participant in both BTO Breeding Atlases, both Beds Breeding Atlases, BTO Winter Atlas, various BTO species surveys, wildfowl counts in Beds since 1970s and Common Birds Census 1979-94. Editor *Bedfordshire Bird Report* 1977-85; co-author (with Keith Allsopp) monthly, recent and seasonal reports in *British Birds* 1989-, also articles. Compiler of 'Bedfordshire Bird List' in *Bedfordshire Bird Atlas* ed by B D Harding (1979) and of 'Species Checklist: Birds' in *Bedfordshire Wildlife* by Nau, Boon and Knowles (1987). Added Arctic Redpoll and Sabine's Gull to county list. OIR: gardening, cooking, general natural history (esp butterflies and flowering plants). 7 Bloomsbury Close, Woburn, Beds MK17 9QS. 01525 290314.

NOBLE-ROLLIN, Calvert; *b:* 23 January 1906 in Jarrow, Co Durham. Durham School. Gave up work as metallurgical chemist in 1930 to found the Bird Research Station at Glanton. In 1932 the Station originated and organised annual worldwide synchronised dawn chorus study; by 1952 this had expanded to spring and autumn recording. Introduced all-day watching of daily behaviour, either of a single bird or a group; and sound recording was added when it became available. Study of abnormal plumage: 'it has been shown that the unusual white seen in wild birds in gardens and parks is due to feeding and breeding tests showed that, contrary to opinion, it is not inherited.' Papers published in eg *British Birds, Bull BOC, Canadian Field Naturalist, The Naturalist* and *Scottish Naturalist*, as well as in the Station's own publications (inc journal, *Bird Research*). The Station has a museum with early field study apparatus, a series of early to modern field cameras, and a range of recording equipment. There is also 'an electro-photographic pre-computer, invented in the station, which can identify species and present, at the end of the day, a worked out image of a bird's daily feeding pattern. In contrast there is in the Station a ringing room dating back to the rural pre-electric days of oil lamps.' OIR: photography, trees (related to study of the dawn chorus). Bird Research Station, Glanton, Alnwick, Northumberland NE66 4AH. 01665 578257.

NORMAN, David; *b:* 23 June 1949 in Leicester; *w:* Maureen. BA Physics (Cambridge, 1970), MA 1975, PhD Physics (Leicester, 1977). CPhys, FInstP. Assistant Director, Daresbury Laboratory; Visiting Professor in Surface Science, Univ Liverpool. BTO Ringing Committee 1986-90. Ringing Recorder Cheshire and Wirral 1988-. Chairman Mersey Estuary Conservation Group 1987-. Vice Chairman Woolston Eyes Conservation Group 1986-95. BTO 'A' ringer since 1981 and Sponsors Panel 1986-. Member Merseyside Ringing Group 1978-. Chairman Research Committee Liverpool Bay Wader Study Group 1995-. Special interests: study of various aspects of birds' lives through ringing (esp migration and weight changes of free-flying birds, and growth curves of chicks); particular study species inc Fieldfare, Sand Martin, Grey Heron, Little Tern. Four visits made to Senegal 1991-96 with ringing expeditions. Author *The Fieldfare* (1994). Co-author (with J P Guest *et al*) *The Breeding Bird Atlas of Cheshire & Wirral* (1992). Species accounts for Chaffinch and Brambling in BTO Winter Atlas. Papers in *Ringing & Migration* (also Editorial Panel 1992-) and notes in *British Birds*. Articles and Ringing Report in *Cheshire & Wirral Bird Report* since 1988. Numerous talks given to local societies on British birds in Senegal, Fieldfares, and the wildlife of the Mersey Estuary. Member: ABC. OIR: travel, completing *Times* crosswords. Rowswood Cottage, Ridding Lane, Sutton Weaver, Runcorn, Cheshire WA7 6PF. 01928 711064.

NORMAN, David Martin (Dave); *b:* 30 May 1950 in Reading, Berks; *w:* Karen. BA English and American Literature (Kent, 1971), Dip Career Guidance (Bristol Polytechnic, 1975), RSA Counselling Cert 1992. Area manager of career guidance service. Founder of Kent Univ NHS 1971, and South Devon Bird Group 1983. Member of Devon Birds Record Adjudication Panel 1985-95, and of Prawle Point Reserve Committee since 1985. Council Devon Birdwatching & Preservation Society 1985-89. Leader of YOC Torbay 1975-89. Special interests: migration studies on Devon coast and long-term record keeping at Prawle Point. Overseas travel inc central Spain, Egypt, Israel, India, USA (Florida), Nepal, Lapland, The Gambia, Kenya. Co-author (with Vic Tucker) *Where to Watch Birds in Devon and Cornwall* ('forerunner of national series') (1984, 2nd ed 1991). Various articles published in *Devon Birds*. 18 Milton Crescent, Brixham, Devon TQ5 0BD. 01803 882630.

NORMAN, Stephen Charles (Steve); *b:* 30 November 1945 in Middlesbrough, Cleveland; *w:* Florence. Steel scheduler (finishing mills). Warden South Gare Observatory 1978-80. BTO 'A' ringer since 1976. Member of South Cleveland Ringing Group since 1976 and Isle of May Bird Observatory since 1986. Special interests: post-juvenile and post-nuptial moult in relation to other events in the biological cycle, esp within the Sylviidae. Ongoing studies: moult in thirty-five species of Sylviidae breeding in Europe and its relationship to migration and any species/genus differences; annual studies on extent of post-juvenile moult in resident passerines in Britain and any geographical/altitudinal variations. Two weeks working at the Heligoland Bird Observatory in September 1979. Papers on study topics in *Ibis* and *Ringing & Migration*. BTO Boddy and Sparrow Prize 1987. OIR: military history, botany. 62 Birkdale Road, Errington Park, New Marske, Cleveland TS11 8JB. 01642 476275.

NORMAN, Wilfred; *b:* 5 September 1943 in Middlesbrough, Cleveland; *w:* Jean. Acklam Hall Grammar School, Middlesbrough. Executive Officer Employment Service, retired. Records Sub-committee Teesmouth Bird Club 1978-, Ringing Officer 1979-, main Committee earlier. BTO 'A' ringer since 1975. Founder-member/Secretary South Cleveland Ringing Group 1976-. Special interests: birds of prey (esp Merlin), migration. Founder-member North York Moors Merlin Study Group 1985-, member North York Moors Forest Bird Study Group 1992-. Lectures to clubs and societies, mainly on ringing; also ringing demonstrations with SCRG colleagues. Compiler of County of Cleveland Ringing Report 1978- (publ in *County of Cleveland Bird Report*). Papers published in *South Cleveland Ringing Group Report* and *Ringing & Migration*. 'Personally added Wilson's Phalarope to Yorkshire list, also Thrush Nightingale and Black-billed Cuckoo jointly with others.' OIR: keen macrolepidoperist (recording moth occurrences virtually nightly at Grosmont since 1979 and founder-member North Yorks Lepidoptera Study Group 1986-); watching most sports, esp rugby union, soccer, athletics; cryptic crossword addict. 2 Station Cottages, Grosmont, Whitby, N Yorks YO22 5PB. 01947 895226.

NORRIS, Cuthbert Antony (Tony); *b:* 9 January 1917 in Cradley Vicarage, W Midlands; *w:* Barbara. Monkton Combe School. London School of Printing. Printer. West Midland Bird Club: Hon Sec, Hon Chairman, President 1937-94. Special interest: factors determining the distribution and status of birds with special reference to changes in agricultural practices. Current research involves weekly bird counts in ten 1km x 1km squares in S Worcs. Author *The Birds of Warwickshire* (1947) and *The*

Distribution and Status of the Corncrake (1949). Editor and contributor *West Midland Bird Club Report* 1936-. RSPB Gold Medal 1964; BTO Tucker Medal 1959; BTO Jubilee Medal 1994. OIR: horticulture, archery. The Lodge, Gilvers Lane, Hanley Castle, Worcs WR8 0AT. 01684 310817.

NORRIS, Kenneth John (Ken); *b:* 17 November 1963 in Birmingham; *w:* Tracy. BSc Environmental Biology (Wales, Aberystwyth, 1985), DPhil Significance of plumage characteristics in Blue Tits (EGI, Oxford, 1989). Research Biologist (estuaries and other wetlands) RSPB since 1993. Prev: post-doctoral research asst Edward Grey Institute, Oxford Univ 1989-92. BTO 'C' ringer since 1987. Member Wytham Ringing Group 1985-92. Special interests: visual communication, host/parasite ecology, conservation biology and ecology of migrant waterbirds. Topics inc modelling dispersion patterns of wintering waders; the impacts of commercial shellfisheries on wintering waders; management of saltmarsh for wintering waders; conservation of Arctic breeding waterfowl (visit to Taymyr Peninsula, Siberia summer 1993). Author or co-author of papers in eg *American Naturalist, Behavioural Ecol and Sociobiol, J Animal Ecol, Nature.* Member: Wader Study Group. OIR: football, travel, food and drink, walking, antique furniture, opera. RSPB, The Lodge, Sandy, Beds SG19 2DL. 01767 680551.

NURNEY, David Ian (Dave); *b:* 28 May 1959 in Edmonton, London; *w:* Jackie. Dip in Communication Design (Graphics and Illustration) (Epsom School of Art, 1981). Bird illustrator. Published artwork includes the illustrations for *Woodpeckers: a guide to the woodpeckers, piculets and wrynecks of the world* by H Winkler and D A Christie (1995) and line drawings in three volumes of *BWP.* Author of identification articles in *Bird Watching.* OIR: badminton, listening to music, playing the bass, old movies. 43 Abington Grove, Elm, Wisbech, Cambs PE14 0BL. 01945 860786.

O'BRIEN, Mark Gregory (OB); *b:* 27 October 1960 in Gloucester; *w:* Anne. BSc Ecology (Loughborough, 1982). Research Biologist RSPB 1990-. Prev: research asst BTO 1988-90; research asst RSPB 1986-88; scientific officer NCC 1985-86; research asst RSPB Apr-Sep 1985; Suffolk WT (various posts) 1983-85. Projects range from the breeding biology of Red-necked Phalarope on Shetland to population estimates of breeding waders in the UK. BTO 'C' ringer since 1991. Co-author of articles on breeding waders in *Bird Study* and *RSPB Conservation Review.* Member: Wader Study Group. OIR: 'keen rugby player at mediocre level.' RSPB 17 Regent Terrace, Edinburgh EH7 5BN. 0131 557 3136; home 0131 657 4220.

O'CONNOR, Raymond Joseph; *b:* 20 January 1944 in Dublin, Ireland; *w:* Deirdre. BSc Physics (National Univ of Ireland, 1965), DPhil Zoology (Edward Grey Institute, Oxford, 1973). FIBiol 1983. Professor of Wildlife Ecology, Univ Maine, Orono (USA) 1987-. Prev: Director BTO 1978-87; Lecturer in Zoology, Univ Coll North Wales, Bangor 1975-78; Lecturer in Zoology, Queen's Univ, Belfast 1972-75. Voluntary posts inc Advisory Committee on Birds (N Ireland Govt); American Ornithologists' Union: *Birds of North America* Advisory Committee; BOU: *Dictionary of Birds* Editorial Committee, Research Committee, Council; Conservation Foundation (Washington DC, USA) Avian Effects Dialogue Group; Cornell Univ: Admin Board, Laboratory of Ornithology; International Ornithological Committee; IWC Fieldwork Committee; Manomet Bird Observatory: Landbird Research Advisory Board; NCC Wild Birds Advisory Council; RSPB Research Advisory Committee; Wildfowl Trust Scientific Advisory Committee. Special interests: growth and development of birds; birds and agriculture; population dynamics. Author *The Growth and Development of Birds* (1984). Co-author (with M Shrubb) *Farming and Birds* (1986). Over one hundred papers and articles. National Research Council Fellowship 1993-94. Member: AOU (elective member 1988), Cooper Ornithological Society. Dept of Wildlife Ecology, 238 Nutting Hall, University of Maine, Orono, Maine 04469, USA. +1 207 5812880.

ODDIE, William Edgar (Bill); *b:* 7 July 1941 in Rochdale, Lancashire. Halesowen Grammar School, King Edward's School Birmingham. BA English Literature (Pembroke College, Cambridge, 1963). Script writer, actor, song writer, singer, broadcaster, record producer, director etc etc. Served on various councils of conservation groups inc OSME, RSPB, WWT, WWF. President of Northumberland WT and Sandwich Bay Bird Observatory. Considerably involved in the problems of migrant-bird killing in the Mediterranean area, particularly in Cyprus. Travelled widely throughout the world in pursuit of birds, inc India, Africa, USA, Australia, New Zealand, Papua New Guinea, Thailand, Hong Kong, Seychelles, Galapagos, Iceland, Middle East and Europe. Avid 'bird racer'; taken part in such events throughout Britain and also in Australia, Kenya and Hong Kong. Author and illustrator of *Bill Oddie's Little Black Bird Book* (1980), *Gone Birding* (1983), *Birdwatching with Bill Oddie* (1988), *Bill Oddie's Colouring Guides* (1991), *Birdwatching for the Under Tens* (1991), *Follow that Bird* (1994). Co-author (with David Tomlinson) *The Big Bird Race* (1983); (with Peter Holden) *Bird in the Nest* (1995); (with Hilary Welch *et al*) *Where to Watch Birds in Turkey, Greece and Cyprus* (1996). Contributor to various magazines inc *Bird Watching, Birding World, Birdwatch, British*

Birds. Presenter of TV programmes inc *Oddie in Paradise* (Papua New Guinea), *The Great Kenyan Bird Safari*, *Favourite Walks* (Fair Isle), *Bird in the Nest* (1994,95) all for the BBC; *Wild Weekends* for TV AM; *The Bird Business*, *Flight to Eilat* and *The Big Bird Race* for Channel 4; *For the Birds* for American Cable. Also *Ask Oddie* (ecological series for HTV) and several ornithological 'reports' for news and travel programmes. 'Voice overs' for various videos, from identification to birding games. OIR: 'an obsessional (non classical) music listener and amateur musician; an avid sports fan.'

ODIN, Nigel; *b:* 14 October 1958 in Nottingham. BSc Earth and Life Studies (Derby, 1980). Ranger Landguard Reserve and Warden Landguard Bird Observatory 1989-95. Prev: asst warden Dungeness Bird Observatory 1987-88 and Sandwich Bay Bird Obs 1985-87; research asst Univ Wales Inst of Sci and Tech 1981-82; species protection officer RSPB 1981. Special interest: migration studies. Numerous articles in eg *Biol Cons*, *Bird Watching*, *Birding World* (and former *Twitching*), *British Birds*, *Devon Birds*, *The Harrier*, *White Admiral*. Compiler of systematic lists and contributor of articles to Glamorgan, Suffolk, Sandwich Bay, Landguard and Kenfig bird reports. Author of booklet *Llanishen/Lisvane Reservoirs Ornithological Report* (1983). OIR: Lepidoptera, Odonata, esp migrants. c/o Landguard Bird Observatory, View Point Road, Felixstowe, Suffolk IP11 8TW. 01394 673782.

OGILVIE, Colin; *b:* 4 January 1922 in Warrington, Cheshire. Marlborough College. MB, ChB (Liverpool, 1944), MD 1954, FRCP 1967. Consultant physician. Regular annual contributor to BTO Common Birds Census since 1989. Special interests: behaviour and census work. Author of series of articles on Rook behaviour in *British Birds*. 1 The Riffel, Woolton Park, Liverpool L25 6DR. 0151 428 3472.

OGILVIE, Malcolm Alexander; *b:* 5 September 1939 in Streatley, Berks; *w:* Carol. Brentwood School, Essex 1948-58. PhD Migration of Teal (Bristol, 1983). MIBiol, CBiol 1977. Freelance ornithological and botanical consultant, natural history writer and editor since 1986. Prev: Research Officer WWT 1960-86. Gloucestershire Ornithological Advisory Committee 1963-86. BTO Ringing Committee 1970-85. BTO Regional Representative for Islay, Jura & Colonsay 1989-. Argyll Bird Records Committee 1990-. National Wildfowl Counts/Wetland Bird Survey organiser for Argyll 1991-. Scottish Natural Heritage: SW Regional Board 1991-, Scientific Advisory Committee 1994-. Secretary Rare Breeding Birds Panel 1993-.

Special interests: wildfowl (esp numbers, distribution and migration of geese, also impact on agriculture); birds of Islay (esp birds of prey and owls); bird ringing (BTO 'A' ringer since 1958). Expeditions to E Greenland, Iceland and Svalbard, studying and ringing geese. Author *Ducks of Britain and Europe* (1975), *The Winter Birds* (1976), *Wild Geese* (1978), *The Bird-watcher's Guide to the Wetlands of Britain* (1979), *Birdwatching on Inland Fresh Waters* (1981), *The Wildfowl of Britain and Europe* (1981), *Flamingos* (1986), *The Birds of Islay* (1992, 2nd ed 1994), *Wildfowl Behaviour Guide* (1994). Editor *Symposium on Current Research in Arctic Geese* (1984), *Best Days with British Birds* co-editor with Stuart Winter (1989). Contributor to many other books inc *BWP* Vols 1-6 (1977-92), *The Encyclopedia of Birds* (1985), *Wildfowl in Great Britain* (2nd ed 1986), BTO Winter Atlas, *The Illustrated Encyclopedia of Birds* (1990), *The Hamlyn Photographic Guide to Birds of the World* (1991), BTO New Breeding Atlas, *Atlas of Bird Migration* (1995). Over 70 papers and articles published in eg *Aquila, Bird Study, British Birds, Condor, Ibis, J Wildlife Management, Scottish Birds, Wildfowl*. Editor (with C M Swaine) *Gloucestershire Bird Report* 1968-78. Editor (with Geoffrey Matthews) *Wildfowl* 1968-86. Editorial Board *BWP* 1976-88. Editor *Islay Bird and Natural History Report* 1986-. Editorial Board *British Birds* 1972-. Editor *BWP Journal* 1997-. Occasional TV and radio programmes and interviews. Lecturing and occasional tour leader. OIR: botanical studies, collecting books on polar regions and mountaineering, listening to classical music (esp opera), reading, gardening, trustee of local museum, computing. Glencairn, Bruichladdich, Isle of Islay PA49 7UN. Tel/fax 01496 850218.

O'HALLORAN, John; *b:* 8 January 1962 in Cork, Ireland; *w:* Deirdre. BSc Zoology (National Univ of Ireland, Univ College Cork, 1984), PhD Lead toxicity in Swans (Cork, 1987). MIBiol. Lecturer in Zoology, Univ College Cork since 1989. Prev: post-doctoral research, Univ of Wales College of Cardiff, working on Dippers 1987-89. Chairman IWC Cork Branch 1985-87. Co-ordinator of a range of surveys inc waterfowl survey of Cork Harbour 1978-81. Kilcolman Wildfowl Refuge Scientific Advisory Committee 1989-. BTO 'A' ringer since 1990. Special interests: aquatic birds (swans and Dipper) and the effects of pollutants on their ecology, physiology and biochemistry; avian ecology and biology; ringing. Many scientific articles on principal interests in eg *J Appl Ecol, J Zool, Oecologia*. Editor *Cork Bird Report* 1978-90, also editor of a range of booklets and reports on birds. Organised two national ornithological research conferences (1985,92) and produced complete list and book of abstracts on research on birds in Ireland. Member: Wader Study Group. Dept of Zoology, University College, Cork, Ireland. +353 (0)21 276871.

OKILL, John David (David); *b:* 26 May 1949 in Bebbington, Wirral, Cheshire; *w:* Gillian. Dip in Public Health (Liverpool Univ/Liverpool Poly, 1971). Shetland Islands Council, Divisional Manager - Environmental Health 1975-96; Scottish Environment Protection Agency, Pollution, Protection and Control 1996-. Committee member of Shetland Bird Club (1976-), Shetland Crofting and Farming Wildlife Advisory Group (1979-) and Seabird Group (1994-). Vice Chairman Fair Isle Bird Observatory Trust 1985-. Representative on Bird Observatories Council 1988-. Secretary Shetland RG 1993-. Chairman Shetland Conservation Volunteers 1988-93. BTO Regional Representative Shetland 1983-. Member of Shetland Oil Terminal Environmental Advisory Group (SOTEAG) Monitoring Committee 1990-. Wildfowl counter, also organiser of annual Whooper Swan count throughout Shetland 1978-. Special interests: migration studies, ringing (esp Red-throated Diver, seabirds, Merlin, waders). Ringing expeditions to Morocco, Spain, Senegal; also ringed in Holland, France, Portugal. Other travel inc Thailand, USA (Florida), Africa (N, E & W), Israel, Iceland, Europe. Author or co-author of papers and shorter items on various species (esp Red-throated Diver, Cormorant, Merlin) in eg *Bird Study*, *Ringing & Migration*, *Scottish Birds*, *Seabird*. Editor *Shetland Bird Report* 1977-83. OIR: boating, reading. Heilinabretta, Trondra, Shetland ZE1 0XL. 01595 880450.

OLD, Alan Bryan; *b:* 13 February 1933 in Cardiff, South Glamorgan. Cardiff High School 1944-50. National College of Rubber Technology 1950-53. Works accountant. Treasurer Cumbria Naturalists' Union 1986- and Maryport NHS 1984-. BTO 'A' ringer since 1956. Special interest: nestbox study of Pied Flycatcher (provided most British data for *The Pied Flycatcher* by A Lundberg and R J Alatalo, 1992) and boxes also used for doctoral research by British and foreign universities. Member: Wader Study Group. OIR: rugby union. Kalinka, Flimby Brow, Flimby, Maryport, Cumbria CA15 8TD. 01900 67071.

OLDFIELD, Brian; *b:* 26 March 1936 in Rawtenstall, Lancs; *w:* Edna. Textile worker. Founded Rossendale Naturalists' Field Club in 1983 and Chairman to 1989. Special interest: bird photography, esp local birds of prey. 'Strongly believe I am the first man ever to photograph Kingfishers feeding their young on the River Irwell.' Many articles published in

Rossendale Free Press 1981-86, also in various journals eg *Countryside*. Photographs published in *British Birds and their Habitats* by Ron Freethy (1983) and other books, inc cover shot for Freethy's *Owls: a guide for ornithologists* (1993) dedicated to the memory of Eric Hosking. Contributions to several TV and radio programmes inc *Down to Earth* and BBC Radio Lancashire's *Country Ways* during 1980s. Illustrated lectures to local organisations and schools. OIR: general photography, other aspects of natural history (esp mammals such as the badger). 1 Fairfield Avenue, Edgeside, Waterfoot, Rossendale, Lancs BB4 9TG. 01706 224642.

OLSSON, Martin Urban (Urban); *b:* 7 March 1954 in Göteborg, Sweden; *p:* Eva Edwartz. BSc Biology, Chemistry (Göteborg, 1981). Co-founder of Regulus Travel (1988) and co-owner with Per Alström. Swedish Ornithological Society: Rarities Committee 1991-, Nomenclature Committee 1991-. Special interests: phylogenetic systematics and biogeography, identification, photography, sound recording. Co-author (with C Byers and J Curson) *Buntings and Sparrows: a guide to the buntings and North American sparrows* (1995). Co-editor (with N Kjellén) of official list of Swedish names for Holarctic birds (1995). Author or co-author of over 30 papers on identification, conservation, taxonomy and systematics in eg *Birding World, British Birds, Bull BOC, Bull OBC, Dutch Birding, Forktail, Ibis* (describing three new *Phylloscopus* species), *Limicola, Strix, Vår Fågelvärld*. Editorial Board *Vår Fågelvärld* 1991-95. Identification consultant *Limicola*. Co-author of regional bird reports 1979 and 1981. Member: ABC, OBC, Swedish OS. Lectures on identification and taxonomy in several countries. Morphology and Systematics Section, Dept of Zoology, University of Göteborg, Medicinaregatan 18, S-413 90 Göteborg, Sweden. +46 (0)31 7733892; home +46 (0)31 3312110; fax +46 (0)31 3314184.

O'NEILL, Anthony James (Tony); *b:* 15 August 1953 in Knutsford, Cheshire; *w:* Janet. Licensed conveyancer. Stockport RSPB Members' Group: Committee 1980-89, Chairman and Group Leader 1989-. Committee Cheshire Ornithological Assocn 1981-86. National Wildfowl Count co-ordinator (Cheshire) 1981-. Special interests: conservation, identification, survey work. Compiler *Cheshire Bird Report* 1983-87. OIR: travel. 285 Marsland Road, Sale, Cheshire M33 1UN. 0161 962 2449.

ORMEROD, James (Jim); *b:* 10 December 1948 in Rawtenstall, Lancs. Bacup and Rawtenstall Grammar School. BSc Biological Sciences (Leicester, 1970). Computer programmer/analyst. Secretary/Treasurer

Rossendale Ornithologists' Club since 1983. Special interests: atlas work, computers for bird data storage. Co-editor *ROC Bird Report* annually since 1976. OIR: butterflies, dragonflies, bumblebees, general natural history, computers, reading, listening to music. 17 Robert Street, Piercy, Rossendale, Lancs BB4 9JF. 01706 227672.

ORMEROD, Stephen James (Steve); *b:* 24 January 1958 in Burnley, Lancs. BSc Human Ecology (Huddersfield Polytechnic, 1980), MSc Applied Hydrobiology (UWIST, Cardiff 1981), PhD River Ecology (Cardiff, 1985). MIEEM (founder-member) 1991. Head, Catchment Research Group, UWCC since 1984. Council Member, Countryside Council for Wales 1991-95. BTO Research and Surveys Committee 1992-95; Working Group on the Scientific Strategy of the BTO Ringing Scheme 1995-. JNCC Science Review Panel on Offshore Animals (Seabird Monitoring Programme and Seabirds at Sea Team) 1993. BirdLife International/IWRB International Workshop on Wetland Habitats 1994. BTO 'A' ringer since 1988. Special interests: research into the ecology of river and wetland birds worldwide; acidification, land-use change and the conservation of rivers and wetlands; birds as indicator organisms; coastal ringing studies of warblers, Swallows and Oystercatchers. Joint author (with Stephanie Tyler) *The Dippers* (1994). Author of over one hundred scientific papers on the ecology of rivers and wetlands, esp Dipper, Grey Wagtail, Kingfisher and Nepalese river birds. Editorial Boards of *Ringing & Migration* 1989-92, *Environmental Pollution* 1988-, *Freshwater Biol* 1992-, *J Appl Ecol* 1995-. Winston Churchill Travelling Fellowship 1987 for study of the ecological impact of acid rain in the USA and Canada. Founder-member of OBC. OIR: the arts; reading, writing and publishing poetry; music (guitar); travel; sport; diving. School of Pure and Applied Biology, University of Wales College of Cardiff, PO Box 915, Cardiff CF1 3TU. Tel/fax 01222 874305.

ORR, Brian; *b:* 8 March 1961 in Glasgow. Ranger, Irvine Beach Park since 1986. Birds of Estuaries Enquiry and Wetland Bird Survey co-ordinator for Ayrshire since 1990, with all Ayrshire figures stored on computer. Ayrshire Bird Rarities Committee 1994-. SOC Ayrshire Branch Committee 1994-. RSPB North Ayrshire Members' Group Committee 1985-. Special interests: 'local patch' work; wildfowl and waders. Member of organising group for Ayrshire Breeding Birds Atlas Project. Travel for birds inc Europe and the Middle East. Compiler of sightings sections in local SOC and RSPB newsletters. Some photographs published in *Bird Watching* and *Birding World.* 14 Monach Gardens, Dreghorn, Irvine, Ayrshire KA11 4EB. 01294 216907.

ORR, Norman William (Norrie); Sqn Ldr RAF Retd; *b:* 9 February 1918 in Scotland; *w:* Pat. RAF Flying College, graduated Specialist Navigator 1953. RAF Regular Officer followed by Min of Aviation/Civil Aviation Authority. Retired 1978. RSPB Council 1960-66. Also Council of SPNR (now RSNC) and Council for Nature in 1960-70s. Founder Chairman Hampshire TNC 1960-64, Vice President. Special interests: conservation, distribution, breeding biology, bird voices and sound recording (since mid 1950s), nest finding (though never egg collector), bird navigation, photography (ARPS 1972), lecturing. Study species include Red-necked and Black-necked Grebes, White-fronted Goose, White-tailed Eagle, Montagu's and Marsh Harriers, Hobby, Peregrine, Stone Curlew, Kentish Plover, Little Tern, Long-eared Owl, Woodlark, Nightingale, Thrush Nightingale, Bluethroat, Marsh and Dartford Warblers, Penduline Tit, shrike spp, Chough, Cirl and Ortolan Buntings. Widely travelled in W Europe and most other parts of the world. During operational service in N Africa and Italy 1941-45 took opportunities to study the birds of those areas; postings in Malaya (1947-50) and north Germany (1956-58) provided further opportunites. Later participated in the making of a BBC 'Look' TV programme on the Shelduck which included aerial sequences of the moulting areas in the North Sea reconnoitred previously when low flying over the region. Member of German/Spanish ornithological expedition to Spain 1960; participant in survey of birds of the Cevennes, France 1988-94. First article was 'Terns of Dungeness' in *Sussex Magazine* (late 1930s), followed by many more in eg *Birds*, *Birdwatch*, *British Birds*; also in county bird reports and other publications. Contributions to books (notes, records, photographs) inc *Birds of Sussex* by J Walpole-Bond (1938), *Collins Guide to Bird Watching* by Richard Fitter (1963), *Birds of Hampshire and the Isle of Wight* by E Cohen (1963), *Field Guide to Birds' Nests* by B Campbell and J Ferguson-Lees (1972), *Birds of Hampshire* ed by J M Clark and J A Eyre (1993), also notes on breeding of Little Tern and on Thrush Nightingale in *BWP*. Photographs exhibited nationally (mainly RPS exhibitions) and internationally. Sound recordings broadcast by BBC ('was first to record Dartford Warbler's song, in 1958, broadcast by BBC in 1960'), published on commercial discs and tapes (eg in *The Peterson Guide to the Bird Songs of Britain and Europe*, 1974), and deposited in the British Library of Wildlife Sounds (now part of National Sound Archive) since its foundation in 1969. Member: Verein Jordsand zum Schutze der Seevögel since 1956. One of UK's representatives in 1960-70s on the European and ICAO Aircraft Bird-Strike Committees. OIR: Lepidoptera, herpetology, botany, meteorology, opera, European art and architecture, Scotland's history, private flying. 4 Denham Drive, Christchurch, Dorset BH23 5AT. 01425 273361.

ORR-EWING, Duncan Charles; *b:* 19 January 1964 in Redhill, Surrey. BA French and German (Durham, 1986). ARICS 1990. RSPB Conservation Officer for South Strathclyde and Central Regions since 1993. Prev: RSPB project officer (Scottish Red Kite reintroduction project) 1991; Deutscher Bund für Vogelschutz Eagle Owl reintroduction project 1985. Secretary SOC Clyde Branch 1995-. Special interests: Scottish breeding, passage and wintering birds (esp raptors). Birdwatching overseas inc Ecuador and Venezuela (Durham Univ expedition to NW Ecuador 1986), The Gambia, USA (Texas), Bolivia, Australia and New Zealand, Kenya, Nepal. OIR: tennis, swimming, rugby, photography, real ale. Member: Central and South Strathclyde Raptor Study Groups. RSPB South and West Scotland Office, Unit 3.1 West of Scotland Science Park, Kelvin Campus, Glasgow G20 0SP. 0141 945 5224.

OSBORN, Kevin Philip; *b:* 12 August 1960 in Chadwell-St-Mary, Grays, Essex; *w:* Karen. Pollution control officer, Scottish Environment Protection Agency 1996-. Experience between 1983 and 1987 includes asst warden at Dungeness and Fair Isle Bird Observatories, research officer at RSPB East Anglia and NCC East Anglia, and seabird monitoring officer at Fair Isle Bird Obs. BTO 'A' ringer since 1974, also trainer and sponsor since 1986. Shetland Bird Club: Committee 1990-, Bird Rarities Committee 1993-. Scottish Birds Records Committee 1994-. Bird Recorder for Shetland 1995-. Special interests: identification (esp gulls and warblers), migration, seabird research (eg breeding productivity of Razorbills in Shetland), photography. Editor *Shetland Bird Report* 1990-. Co-editor *Shetland Bird Club Newsletter* 1993-. Short notes and papers on identification published in eg *Birding World, Birds, British Birds, Scottish Birds*; also photographs in *Birding World* and *British Birds*. OIR: cetaceans, use of personal computers, playing pool. 20 Nederdale, Lerwick, Shetland ZE1 0SA. 01595 695974.

O'SULLIVAN, Oran; *b:* 4 October 1955 in Ireland; *p:* Mairead Wynne. General Manager IWC/BirdWatch Ireland since 1993; prev: fieldworker IWC 1992. Council member and Secretary, Cape Clear Bird Observatory 1977-. Special interests: seabird migration off western Ireland, bird photography. Co-editor *Irish Bird Report* 1986-. Editor *Wexford Bird Report* 1977-82. Travel articles and photographs published in eg *Birdwatch, British Birds, Dutch Birding, Irish Birds*. Ireland correspondent *British Birds* 1994-. OIR: New World wines, cooking, music. c/o 8 Longford Place, Monkstown, Co Dublin, Ireland. +353 (0)1 2804322.

OWEN, Denis Frank; *b:* 4 April 1931 in London. MA Zoology (Oxford, 1958), PhD Zoology (Michigan, 1961). Zoologist (some teaching, but mainly research), Oxford Brookes Univ since 1973. Prev: researcher, Museum of Zoology, Univ Michigan 1958-61; field asst Edward Grey Institute of Field Ornithology, Oxford Univ 1951-58; assistant in Bird Room, Natural History Museum, London 1947-49. RSPB Council in 1950s. Special interests: ecology and genetics, esp tropical species. Approx ten per cent of published work is concerned with some aspect of ornithology, inc *What is Ecology?* (1974, also in Japanese, Dutch, Hebrew, Russian and Chinese) and some twenty-five scientific papers. At one time a regular broadcaster on BBC Radio 4, including many ornithological contributions. OIR: moth collecting, gardening, reading. 42 Little Wittenham Road, Long Wittenham, Abingdon, Oxon OX14 4QS. 01865 407654. Or School of Biological and Molecular Sciences, Oxford Brookes University, Headington, Oxford OX3 0BP. 01865 819244. **Deceased** (3 October 1996).

OWEN, Myrfyn; *b:* 8 April 1943 in Bangor, Gwynedd; *w:* Marian. BSc Agriculture (Wales, Aberystwyth, 1964), PhD Agricultural Botany (Leeds, 1967). Director General WWT since 1992. Prev WWT posts with year of appointment: Director of Research and Conservation 1992, Head of Research 1988, Asst Director (Research) 1979, Conservation Research Officer 1974, Ecologist 1967. Earlier: research asst Univ Leeds 1964-67. Current or former committee positions: BASC Conservation and Research Committee, BOU Council, BTO Research and Surveys Committee, DoE Lead Poisoning in Waterfowl Working Group, IWRB Threatened Waterfowl Research Group (Co-ordinator), NCC Advisory Committee on Birds, Specialist Group on Waterfowl, NERC (Arctic Programme Steering Committee), RSPB Research Advisory Committee, Severn Estuary Conservation Group (Chairman). Special interests: ecology, population dynamics. Major project over twenty years has been a study of the ecology and population dynamics of the Barnacle Geese breeding in Svalbard (Spitsbergen) and wintering on the Solway Firth. This has involved several major expeditions to Svalbard for ringing and annual trips to Norwegian staging areas. Developed the National Waterfowl Counts Scheme (now part of the Wetland Bird Survey), including the major review of the results leading to publication of *Wildfowl in Great Britain* (co-author with G L Atkinson-Willes and D G Salmon, 1986). Author of *Wildfowl of Europe* (1976), *Wild Geese of the World* (1980), *The Barnacle Goose* (1990), *Waterfowl Ecology* (1990); also chapters in other books. More that one hundred scientific papers published in most ornithological and ecological journals in Europe and North America, inc *Anim Behav, Aquila, Ardea,*

Biol Cons, Bird Study, Ibis, J Animal Ecol, J Appl Ecol, J Ecol, J Wildlife Management, J Zool, Ornis Scandinavica, Wildfowl, and in proceedings of symposia; also numerous shorter pieces and popular articles. Writer of shooting script and commentary for RSPB film on the Pink-footed Goose, consultant on BBC *Wildfowl* video, numerous TV and radio appearances. Wildfowl & Wetlands Trust, Slimbridge, Gloucester GL2 7BT. 01453 890333; fax 01453 890827.

PAGE, Douglas (Doug); *b:* 18 June 1949 in Rotherham, Yorkshire; *w:* Jackie. HND Construction. Director of construction company. British Birds Rarities Committee 1995-. Isles of Scilly Rarities Panel 1984-. Special interest: identification. Worldwide travel in most European countries, USA, SE Asia, Middle East, N Africa, S and Central America, Australia. OIR: squash, music, food and drink. 11 Ashley Court, Finningley, Doncaster, S Yorks DN9 3RA. 01302 770319.

PAIN, Deborah Jean (Debbie); *b:* 28 April 1962 in Ramsgate, Kent. BSc Environmental Chemistry (Wye College, London, 1983), DPhil Lead poisoning in waterfowl: an investigation of sources and screening techniques (Edward Grey Institute, Oxford, 1987). Research Biologist RSPB since 1992. Prev: Research Biologist, Station Biologique de la Tour du Valat, Camargue (France) 1988-91. Special interests: lead poisoning in waterfowl and raptors; birds and farming systems in the EC. Extensive research work in the EC and some work with the US Fish and Wildlife Service. Joint editor (with M W Pienkowski) *Farming and Birds in Europe* (in press). Articles on lead and other metal pollution and birds in eg *Biol Cons, Bull Environmental Contamination and Toxicology, Ecotoxicology and Environmental Safety, Environmental Pollution, Gibier Faune Sauvage, Ibis, Internat J Environmental Analytical Chem, Wildfowl*. Review paper on lead poisoning in *Acta XX Congressus Internationalis Ornithologici IV*. Editor *Lead Poisoning in Waterfowl: procs of an IWRB workshop* (1991). Article on birds and farming in *RSPB Conservation Review*. OIR: damselflies. Research Dept, RSPB, The Lodge, Sandy, Beds SG19 2DL. 01767 680551.

PAINTIN, Anthony Raymond (Tony); *b:* 29 September 1950 in Birmingham; *w:* Pauline. Air traffic control officer. Jersey Bird Recorder 1991-. Co-author of article on birds of Jersey (with M Dryden and T Copp) in *Birdwatcher's Yearbook* 1992. Collator of data for *Jersey Bird Report* 1991-. OIR: flying, piano. 16 Quennevais Gardens, St Brelade, Jersey JE3 8LH. 01534 41928.

PALFERY, John; *b:* 23 December 1947 in Cheltenham, Glos; *w:* Jane. BA Spanish (King's College, London, 1971), MSc Applied Linguistics (Edinburgh, 1990), PGCE 1980. Teacher. Field surveys for NCC Moorland Bird Study in Caithness and Sutherland (Apr-Jul 1987) and Tiree (Apr 1988). Voluntary asst warden Ramsey Island, Aug 1977. Special interests: behaviour (all species, but in the past particularly Black-crowned Sparrow-Lark and White-crowned Black Wheatear); distribution (eg fieldwork for *Atlas of the Breeding Birds of Arabia,* also BTO censuses and surveys); migration (eg fieldwork in Beidaihe, China, Sep-Dec 1987). Contributed notes on desert larks and wheatears to *BWP*; behaviour notes to *British Birds*; articles and notes on behaviour, distribution and identification to *Sandgrouse*; contributions on distribution, migration and birding areas in *Forktail* and *OBC Bulletin*. Photographs published in *British Birds* and *Birding World*. OIR: general natural history, art, reading, walking, travel. 7 Dunard House, 123 Grange Loan, Edinburgh EH9 2EA. 0131 667 0919.

PALMER, Kenneth Howard (Ken); *b:* 3 April 1930 in Beckenham, Kent; *w:* Gillian. BSc Chemical Engineering (Imperial College, London, 1954). Computer systems manager (oil industry), retired. Hampshire Records Committee 1957-60. Chairman London Nat Hist Soc Research Committee 1977-87. Special interests: bird vocalisations, organising surveys (BTO 10km square steward 1976-), 'local patch' work (thirty-year study). Surveys: Dartford Warblers in New Forest 1954-62; waders at Dibden Bay, Hants 1954-62; breeding Grey Wagtails in London area 1979-81; breeding birds in major London woodlands 1985-87. Talks on bird-related topics to natural history societies and other groups since 1955. Leader of field trips for London NHS and National Trust since 1976. Much time spent in USA (inc living there for twenty months 1965-67). Author *Checklist of the Birds of Petts Wood* (1978). Papers based on surveys in *London Bird Report*. Part-editor *Hampshire Bird Report* 1957-59. OIR: use of computers for natural history data (inc site information), classical music, genealogy, cosmology. 55 Clarendon Way, Chislehurst, Kent BR7 6RG. 01689 822646.

PALMER, Malcolm John; *b:* 25 March 1939 in Doncaster, Yorks. Operations Director of Calandra Holidays since 1992. Secretary of Reculver, then Ashford Ringing Groups between 1972 and 1989. Founder-member and Committee Huddersfield Birdwatchers' Club 1966-70. Chairman Ashford Birdwatchers' Club from inception c1986 for three years. Adult education lecturer in ornithology for some fifteen years until 1986. Special interests: migration, conservation and education, esp in Mediterranean region. Several short papers, and a longer one on

Greenfinch movements, in Reculver RG report for 1974. Edited Ashford RG report and contributed paper on House Martin movements. Author *Birdwatching Guide to the Costa Blanca* (1992). Regular 'Nature Trail' column in *Costa Blanca News*. Lectures locally to Spanish and English groups. Travelled fairly widely in Europe, Africa and North America. OIR: athletics coach (some very capable athletes), music lover, all-round sports fan, reasonable linguist (teacher of Spanish in spare time). Calle Javea, 43, 03130 Santa Pola, Alicante, Spain. +34 6 5411310.

PALMER, Stephen Michael; *b:* 24 September 1952 in Hemel Hempstead, Herts; *w:* Carolyn. Air traffic control officer. Business Manager *North-East Scotland Bird Report* 1980 and 1981. Special interest: 'local patch' work inc Common Birds Census farmland plot in Wiltshire since 1984. Committee Wiltshire Ornithological Society 1985-92. Editor *Hobby* (annual WOS publication) 1989-91. Articles in above publications; also *Salisbury Plain Site Dossier* (MOD publication, 1990). Editor of book *Wiltshire Birds* (1991). OIR: moths (esp Microlepidoptera), hoverflies. 137 Lightfoot Lane, Fulwood, Preston, Lancs PR4 0AH. 01772 861570.

PANNELL, Caroline Mary; *b:* 28 January 1955 in Worthing, W Sussex; *h:* Christopher McCrudden. BA Natural Sciences (New Hall, Cambridge, 1977), DPhil Taxonomy and Ecology (Botany) (Wadham College, Oxford, 1981). Self-employed biologist. Special ornithological interest: birds as dispersers of seeds. In this connection advises on ornithological studies in the field (eg fruit eating by birds of paradise and cassowaries in New Guinea, by endemic birds on oceanic islands, and by birds in an English woodland). Scientific papers on this subject in eg *Commonwealth Forestry Review, Monographs in Systematic Botany from the Missouri Botanical Garden, Phil Trans Roy Soc (B)*; also chapter in *The Rainforests: a celebration* by Lisa Silcock (1989). OIR: all aspects of natural history (esp plant/animal interactions), walking, travel. 2 Wolvercote Court, Wolvercote Green, Oxford OX2 8AB. 01865 59777.

PARKER, Allan; *b:* 31 August 1941 in Bawtry, South Yorks; *w:* Susan. Maltby Grammar School 1952-58. ARPS 1989. Professional photographer (self-employed). WEA/Sheffield Univ tutor on birds and natural history since 1990; also one-day courses at Potteric Carr NR on bird and natural history photography. Rotherham and District

Ornithological Society: Committee 1980-, President 1984-86, 1990-92. Yorkshire WT representative South Yorkshire Farming and Wildlife Advisory Group during mid 1980s. Special interest: bird photography throughout British Isles, Europe and the USA (esp birds away from the nest with emphasis on birds in action). Photographs in a wide range of publications and in RPS exhibitions. Speaker on ornithological subjects. OIR: aviation photography and aircraft in general, steam locomotives, motor racing. Ashtree House, 51 Kiveton Lane, Todwick, Sheffield S31 0HJ. 01909 770238.

PARKES, Keith; *b:* 17 July 1947 in Barrow in Furness, Cumbria; *w:* Muriel. MSc Biochemistry (Salford, 1974). MRSC 1977. Secretary Walney Bird Observatory since 1965. BTO 'A' ringer since 1965. Special interest: population and nestbox project in south Cumbrian woodland from 1988. Author of chapter in *Bird Observatories in Britain and Ireland* ed by Roger Durman (1976). *Walney Bird Observatory Report*: co-author all issues, editor 1978-91. 176 Harrogate Street, Barrow in Furness, Cumbria LA14 5NA. 01229 824219.

PARKIN, David Thomas; *b:* 29 September 1942 in Sheffield; *p:* Linda Taylor. Newcastle upon Tyne Royal Grammar School 1951-61. BSc Zoology (Univ Coll, Durham 1964), PhD Zoology (Manchester, 1967). Professor of Avian Genetics, Univ Nottingham since 1996. Prev: Reader in Avian Genetics 1990-96; Lecturer in Genetics then Senior Lecturer, Univ Nottingham 1971-79; demonstrator in Zoology, Univ Edinburgh 1967-71. WWT Scientific Advisory Committee 1982-86. RSPB Council 1985-89. BOU: Council 1987-92, Taxonomic Sub-committee 1987-, Records Committee 1987- and Chairman 1994-. Special interests: genetics, evolution, taxonomy, conservation. Editor *Bird Study* 1988-92. Large number of scientific papers, esp on evolutionary genetics of House Sparrows and conservation genetics of birds of prey. Several related broadcasts on national and local radio and TV. Lectures and seminars in UK and overseas to universities, conferences and local bird clubs. 'Finally achieved 400 birds in Britain with the Norfolk Black-throated Thrush in 1994, but the 289 self-found is a much more highly prized total. Best bird in the UK? Red-flanked Bluetail (Tyneside 1960). Best bird ever? Little Blue Heron, near Cape Town in 1992, was the first for the African continent.' OIR: spending time in the dog world with Linda who is a very successful breeder and exhibitor of English Setters; travel and eating out; my two daughters. Dept of Genetics, School of Medicine, Queen's Medical Centre, Nottingham NG7 2UH. 0115 970 9399; fax 0115 970 9906.

PARSONS, Anthony John (Tony); *b:* 3 July 1939 in Lewisham, London; *w:* Patricia. St Dunstan's College 1950-57. BVetMed, MRCVS (Royal Veterinary College, 1963). Veterinary surgeon (esp avian medicine) since 1963. Somerset Ornithological Society: Secretary 1972-85, President 1985-. Natural History Advisor, Kenneth Allsop Memorial Trust 1975-. BTO 'A' ringer since 1968. In charge of Steep Holm Ringing Station 1975-. Committee Chew Valley Ringing Station 1970-. Special interests: migration and distribution of passerines. Occasional papers/notes in *Bird Study, British Birds, Ringing & Migration, Somerset Birds* (annual report). OIR: entomology. Barnfield, Tower Hill Road, Crewkerne, Somerset TA18 8BJ. 01460 73640.

PATERSON, Andrew M (Andy); *b:* 26 March 1943 in Hull, E Yorks. Deputy Head, International School. Founder-member Filey Brigg Ornithological Group 1977-80. Founder-member Iberian Rarities Committee 1984-89. Founder-member and Co-ordinator, Iberian Seabird Group (GIAM) 1988-91, 1994-. Founder-member and Recorder, SEO-Málaga (local group). Special interests: identification (esp plumages of gannets and gulls), seabird migration in Iberia (esp Málaga province). Author *Birds of the Bahamas* (1974), *Birdwatching in Southern Spain* (1987), *Aves Marinas de Málaga y Mar de Alborán* (1990), *Situación de Aves Marinas de Iberia, Baleares y Canarias* (1994). Co-author (with Ernest García) *Where to Watch Birds in Southern Spain, Andalucía, Extremadura and Gibraltar* (1994). Joint editor (with J S Aguilar and X Monbailliu) *Status and Conservation of Seabirds: Proc 2nd Mediterranean Seabird Symposium, Calvià, 1989* (1993). Sole or joint author of several articles on seabirds published in *Ardeola, British Birds* and *Seabird*; also a number of notes in *British Birds*. Member: GIAM, Medmaravis, Seabird Group, SEO, SEO-Málaga. Edificio San Gabriel 2-4°-A, Escritor Adolfo Reyes, 29620 Torremolinos, Spain. +34 (9)5 2389861.

PATTENDEN, Bernard; *b:* 13 April 1929 near Dartford, Kent. Retired clerk. BTO 'A' ringer since 1967. Special interest: migration, with emphasis on ringing *Acrocephalus* warblers. Published a study of these species in *Birds in Cornwall* (annual report) 1976 to 1989, mainly ringing results but also personal views of movements. Contributor to article on the timing of arrivals of Reed and Sedge Warblers at south coast ringing sites during autumn passage in *Ringing & Migration* (1978). OIR: 'enjoying retirement in the Public Library and music on my radiogram.' 17 Wheal Rodney, Gwallon, Marazion, Cornwall TR17 0HL.

PATTERSON, Ian James; *b:* 30 March 1939 in Duns, Berwickshire; *w:* Muriel. BSc Zoology (Aberdeen, 1961), DPhil Zoology (Oxford, 1964), DSc Zoology (Aberdeen, 1984). University Senior Lecturer in Zoology. Special interests: ecology, behaviour. Author *The Shelduck* (1982). Journal articles in eg *Ibis, J Appl Ecol, Ornis Scandinavica, Wildfowl.* 27 Monymusk Terrace, Aberdeen AB1 8NX. 01224 310485.

PATTON, Sarah Jayne; *b:* 8 June 1965 in Rustington, W Sussex; *h:* Peter. Countryside ranger since 1993. Local 10km square steward, co-ordinating surveys. Joint founder and Secretary, Clymping Gap Preservation and Field Recording Society (a group of birdwatchers recording and protecting this area) 1989-. 'Local patch' article in *Birdwatch* (1993). Editor and contributor *Clymping Gap PFRS Annual Report* 1992-. Author of owl species section in *Birds of Sussex* edited by Paul James (1996). Editor *Sussex Bird Report.* OIR: walking, general natural history. Kew Cottage, 21 Church Street, Littlehampton, W Sussex BN17 5EL. 01903 733815.

PAULL, David Edward (Dave); *b:* 21 October 1937 in Yeovil, Somerset. Shoemaker. Several rotational three-year terms on general committees of Somerset Ornithological Society and Somerset TNC. Special interests: owls, warblers, waders, and identification problem groups; seawatching and deserts. Bird-related travel to Spain, Tunisia, Morocco, Cyprus, Israel. Found first breeding Black-tailed Godwits in Somerset, in 1963. Some thirty notes, mainly on behaviour, published in *British Birds.* Wrote section of *Birds of Somerset* (1988), Editorial Board *Somerset Birds* (annual report) 1972-88. Honorary Life Member Somerset Orn Soc 1989. OIR: Lepidoptera, dragonflies, botany, painting wildlife in watercolours, real ale enthusiast. 22 Listers Hill, Ilminster, Somerset TA19 0EL. 01460 55118.

PAYN, William Hale; MBE 1943; FLS; *b:* 13 February 1913 in Somerton, Suffolk. Bird Recorder for Suffolk and editor of *Suffolk Bird Report* 1961-77; also general editor of *Suffolk Natural History* 1964-72. Founder-member of Suffolk WT (1961). Special interests: migration and taxonomy. Author *The Birds of Suffolk* (1962, 2nd ed 1978), *Ornamental Waterfowl* (1957, 5th ed 1986), *Oh Happy Countryman: a Suffolk memoir* (1994). OIR: foreign travel, gardening, shooting (birds). River Close, Ixworth, Suffolk IP31 2HT. 01359 31458.

PEAL, Ronald Edmund Fraser; *b:* 27 August 1917 in London; *w:* Elizabeth. BOC Committee 1969- (Hon Sec 1971-89, Chairman 1989-93). BOU: Council 1981-85, Meetings Committee 1987-93. Organiser, BTO Wryneck

Survey 1964-66. Tetrad organiser for BTO Breeding Atlas 1968-72. Special interests: birds of NW Morocco, history of ornithology, population fluctuations of the Wryneck, urban nesting of the Woodpigeon. Papers published in *Abtracts Int Orn Congress* XV, XX, XXI, *Bird Study, British Birds, Bull BOC, Ibis, London Bird Report, Scottish Birds*. Member: Groupe d'Ornithologie du Maroc Central. OIR: church work, Vice President Rosslyn Park FC, Hon Assistant Worshipful Company of Cordwainers. 2 Chestnut Lane, Sevenoaks, Kent TN13 3AR. 01732 450313.

PEARSON, Bruce Edward; *b:* 20 September 1950 in Newmarket, Suffolk; *w:* Sara Oldfield. BA Fine Art (Leicester Polytechnic, 1973). President Society of Wildlife Artists 1994- (elected to membership 1978). Freelance artist (specialising in natural history and landscape themes) since 1978. Prev: 1975-78 British Antarctic Survey, biological assistant on seabird programme South Georgia. Artist and author *An Artist on Migration* (1991), and (with Robert Burton) *Birdscape* (1991). TV inc writer and presenter of *Birdscape* (Channel 4, 1991). Work exhibited at several galleries in UK (inc one-man exhibitions), also in France, Netherlands and USA. Bird Illustrator of the Year *(British Birds)* 1984 and Wildlife Artist of the Year *(World Magazine)* 1991. OIR: doing things with the family while converting a derelict former public house with stables into a decent home with studio. The Old Plough, Caxton Road, Great Gransden, Sandy, Beds SG19 3BE. 01677 677558.

PEARSON, David John; *b:* 26 January 1941 in Bedford; *w:* Margaret. Leiston Grammar School, Suffolk 1952-59. BA Natural Sciences (Gonville and Caius College, Cambridge, 1962), PhD Biochemistry (Cambridge, 1965). Formerly Lecturer in Biochemistry at Makerere College, Uganda, and at Nairobi University, Kenya. BTO 'A' ringer since 1957. Contract research scientist with RSPB summer 1992 and with BTO spring 1994. Ringing Secretary Dingle Bird Club (Walberswick, Suffolk) 1960-65. Chairman, Ornithological Sub-committee, EANHS 1976-90. Collator of Palearctic records for *East African Bird Report* 1977-90. Vice Chairman, 6th Pan-African Orn Congress, Francistown 1985. Scientific Programme Organiser, 7th Pan-Afr Orn Congr, Nairobi 1988. Special interests: migration, populations and distributions, esp waders and passerines; Palearctic migrants in Africa; the Bearded Tit in Britain; identification; sound recording, esp E Africa. Projects and expeditions: wader ringing on the Wash 1959-62, in Iceland 1972 and in Kenya 1967-89; study of moult in Bearded Tit in Suffolk 1965, 1968-73; Palearctic passerine migrants at Kampala, S Uganda 1965-68; extended ringing study of Yellow Wagtail at

Nairobi 1970-84; atlas-type distribution survey of Palearctic migrants in Kenya 1977-90; co-organiser of Ngulia ringing project, Kenya 1976-96; expeditions to study migrants on Sudan coast, autumns of 1981, 1982, 1984; surveys of migrant ducks and waders in Kenya, and expeditions to count waders at L Turkana, N Kenya, Feb 1988 and Jan 1989. Joint work/expeditions with local ringing groups in Crimea Aug/Sep 1992 and Kazakhstan Aug 1993. Co-author (with P L Britton *et al*) *Birds of East Africa: their distribution, status and habitat* (1980); chapter on migration in Kenya and Uganda in *Bird Migration* ed by E Gwinner (1990); co-author (with D A Zimmerman and D A Turner) *The Birds of Kenya and Northern Tanzania* (1996); author of many of the wader accounts and Palearctic passerine accounts in *Birds of Africa* (1986-). Over forty scientific papers since 1966, mostly in *Bird Study, Ibis, Ringing & Migration, Scopus*. Member: EANHS, WAOS. 'Probably still hold the world record for the number of species recorded in forty-eight hours (494, with Don Turner and Alan Root, Kenya, 29-30 Nov 1986).' 4 Lupin Close, Reydon, Southwold, Suffolk IP18 6NW. 01502 722348

PEART, Roger Harvey; *b:* 6 August 1944 in Rotherham, Yorks; *w:* Catherine. Cert Ed 1968. BEd Education, Mathematics, Divinity (Exeter, 1969). Schoolmaster, Canford School, Wimborne. BTO Dorset Regional Representative 1991-95. BTO 'A' ringer since 1966. Special interests: ringing, BTO Nest Record Scheme, local nestbox study, Spotted Flycatcher, Siskin, waders. Author *Birds of Canford Park* (1991). Editor of ringing report for *Dorset Bird Report* 1991-96. OIR: classical music, cricket, Sheffield Wednesday, church work. 20 Oakley Road, Wimborne Minster, Dorset BH21 1QJ.

PEERS, Martin Frederick; *b:* 19 December 1945 in Birmingham; *w:* Jeannette. MA History (Trinity Hall, Cambridge, 1967), BA Educational Studies (Open Univ, 1977). Teacher (head of history). Bird Recorder Salisbury and District NHS 1977-78 and Brecknock WT 1986-. Executive Committee Wiltshire Ornithological Society 1976-78, of Herefordshire Orn Club 1979-81, and of Welsh Orn Soc 1987-. BTO Regional Representative for Breconshire 1984-91. Ornithological Rep, SENTA (Sennybridge Training Area, MOD) 1986-. Wetland Bird Survey organiser for Powys 1992-. Special interests: identification, recording, birds of Llangorse Lake, conservation. Travel for birds to Bulgaria, France, Spain, Morocco, Cyprus. Author *Birds of Radnorshire and Mid-Powys* (1985) and joint author (with Michael Shrubb) *Birds of Breconshire* (1990); also several chapters in books. Editor *Breconshire Birds* (annual report) 1986-. BBC

Wales radio broadcast with Lionel Kellaway about Nightjars and Woodcock in the Crychan Forest (1992). OIR: dragonflies, walking, reading, musical appreciation, travel, Birmingham City FC. Cyffylog, 2 Aberyscir Road, Cradoc, Brecon, Powys LD3 9PB. 01874 623774.

PEIRSE-DUNCOMBE, Alastair David; Major Retd; *b:* 9 August 1923 in Perth, Scotland; *w:* Daphne. Regular Army, Royal Artillary 1942-61, inc war service in France and Germany 1944-45; in business 1961-68. SOC: Secretary 1969-83 (also Actg Sec briefly 1988/89), Council 1989-94, Management Committee 1988-94, Borders Branch Committee 1989-92. BTO Council 1979-83. RSPB Scottish Committee 1976-80. Fair Isle Observatory Trust: Asst Hon Sec 1977-80, Hon Sec 1980-83. Author of article on SOC in *Birdwatcher's Yearbook* 1982 and chapter about SOC in *Enjoying Ornithology* by R Hickling (1983). Elected Life Member of SOC (together with wife) 1983. Rosebank, Gattonside, Melrose, Roxburghshire TD6 9NL. 0189 682 2176.

PENHALLURICK, Roger David; *b:* 11 August 1940 in Cardiff, Glamorgan; *w:* Pat. BA Geology and Archaelogy (Wales, 1964). Senior Curator, Royal Institution of Cornwall. County organiser for the BTO Breeding Atlas 1970-73, and for the National Rookery Census 1975-76. Participant in annual Heronries Census and various other BTO surveys. Special interest: the history of ornithology in Cornwall and Scilly; editing Jonathan Couch's manuscript 'Cornish Birds' (begun 1829). Author *Birds of the Cornish Coast* (1968), *A Check-list of the Birds of Cornwall and the Isles of Scilly* (1976), *The Birds of Cornwall and the Isles of Scilly* (1978). Notes in *British Birds*, various articles in *Birds in Cornwall* (annual report) inc a history of ornithology in Cornwall up to 1931 (1980 Jubilee issue), and a piece in *The Countryman* on the Cornishness of Choughs (1978). Hon Life Member of Cornwall Birdwatching & Preservation Society. OIR: writing, book illustrating, calligraphy, gardening, listening to classical music, watching a good Western. 10 Treseder's Gardens, Truro, Cornwall TR1 1TR. 01872 79666.

PENNIE, Ian Durance; *b:* 20 March 1916 in Meikle Folla, Aberdeenshire; *w:* Edith. MB, ChB (Aberdeen, 1939); MSc Ecology (Aberdeen, 1967). General medical practitioner, retired. President and Chairman of Council, SOC 1963-66. Hon warden Loch a' Mhuilinn NNR Scourie, NCC/SNH 1988-96. Special interest: Arctic and sub-Arctic ornithology. Numerous private expeditions to Spitsbergen and Lapland. Joint author *Sutherland Birds* (1983). Chapter 'Bird Life of Sutherland' in *The Sutherland Book* (1982), and contributions on Capercaillie and Slavonian Grebe in

Bannerman's *The Birds of the British Isles*. Many papers in *The Scottish Naturalist* and *Scottish Birds*. Occasional articles and notes in *British Birds*. Hon Member SOC. Life Member Norsk Ornitologisk Forening. OIR: bryology, lichenology, gardening. 5 Badcall, Scourie, Lairg, Sutherland IV27 4TH. 01971 502206.

PERCIVAL, Stephen Mark (Steve); *b:* 29 August 1963 in Hauxton, Cambridge; *w:* Tracey. BSc Biology (Durham, 1984), PhD Zoology (Glasgow, 1987). Senior Lecturer in Ecology, Univ Sunderland since 1991. Prev: Senior Research Asst, Dept Biol Sci, Univ Durham (working on wildfowl grazing and vegetation dynamics at Lindisfarne NNR) 1989-91; Owls Project Officer, BTO 1987-89. Member of Wader Study Group team surveying breeding waders of the Hebridean machair 1984, 1985, 1986 (leader), 1987. Joint conference organiser 'Ecology and Conservation of European Owls', Edinburgh 1989. Project (funded by English Nature) 'Habitat requirements of breeding Golden Plover' Apr-Jul 1992. Conference organiser 'Current issues in the conservation and management of Arctic-breeding geese', Sunderland 1993. Major projects: population ecology and habitat management for Greenland population of Barnacle Geese (started 1984); factors affecting the dynamics of the Svalbard-breeding population of Brent Geese of light-bellied race (in collaboration with Danish workers); habitat requirements of Golden Plover and Curlew in northern Pennines. Further special interests: owl population dynamics; ecology of farmland bird communities. Wide range of articles in eg *British Wildlife, Ibis, J Appl Ecol, J Field Ornithol, New Scientist*. OIR: drinking. Ecology Centre, Science Complex, University of Sunderland SR1 3SD. 0191 515 2532.

PERRY, Kenneth William; *b:* 13 August 1946 in Dublin, Ireland; *w:* Dorothy. Postgrad Dip in Environmental Management (Ulster, Coleraine, 1993), MSc Env Mangt (Ulster, Coleraine, 1995). Asst Manager, Bank of Ireland 1965-96. Hon Treas Irish Ornithologists' Club 1965-68. Founder Hon Treas IWC 1968-69. RSPB Northern Ireland Advisory Committee 1983-84. BTO Regional Rep Co Londonderry 1983-85. Committee RSPB Members' Group Coleraine, Co Londonderry 1988-, Chairman/Group Leader 1996-. BTO Membership and Development Committee and BTO Ireland Officer (part-time) 1996-. BTO 'A' ringer since 1981. Lectures widely in Ireland to ornithological groups since 1963. Special interest: bird photography, esp Dipper and terns. Long-term research: Sandwich Tern ecology (begun 1984) at two colonies in NW Co Donegal, inc problems of predation by mink, flooding due to ineffective control of sluice gates, and contamination of marine environment by commercial salmon farming. Author *The Birds of the Inishowen Peninsula* (priv print, 1975), *The Birds and Flowers of the Saltee Islands* with S W Warburton (priv print, 1976), *The Irish Dipper* (priv print, 1986). Several papers on Dipper and tern ecology published in *Irish Birds*. OIR: local community and charity work. 43 Portstewart Road, Coleraine, Co Londonderry BT52 1RW. 01265 42985; fax 01265 328053.

PERRY, Philip; *b:* 24 June 1956 in Croydon, Surrey. BSc Biology (Exeter, 1976), ACA 1982. Company accountant. Committee Nat Hist Soc of Swaziland 1985-88. Co-ordinator, Swaziland Bird Atlas Project 1985-88. ICBP Representative for Swaziland 1986-88. Special interests: bird photography (semi-professional), African birds. Travel for birds in Europe, Asia, SE Asia, N & S America, Africa. Author *Birds of Prey* (1990), *Facts America: Birds* (1992). Article 'The use of gull nests by Eiders' and various notes in *British Birds*. Photographs published in books, also in magazines inc *BBC Wildlife, Bird Life, Bird Watching, Birds*. Bird Photographer of the Year (*British Birds*) 1991. 'On 31.12.88 discovered a new species for the Southern African sub-region while bird-atlasing in the Kalahari Gemsbok National Park: a White-throated Bee-eater, *Merops albicollis*.' OIR: history, reading, gardening. c/o 8 Sea Gate View, Sewerby, Bridlington, N Humbs YO15 1ES. 01262 679178.

PETTY, Stephen John (Steve); *b:* 16 April 1944 in Leicester; *b:* Linda. Third-year Cert of Institute of Wood Science 1965, Foresters Cert (Forestry Commission, 1965), PhD The ecology of the Tawny Owl in the spruce forests of Northumberland and Argyll (Open Univ, 1992). Bird Ecologist, Forestry Commission Research Division since 1981. Prev: forester. Committee Argyll Bird Club 1984-. Special interests: bird ecology, forest birds, forest raptors; study species inc Tawny, Long-eared and Barn Owls, Sparrowhawk, Goshawk. Editor *Argyll Bird Report* 1989-91. Author or joint author of many papers and articles in eg *Bird Study, Ibis, J Raptor Research, J Wildlife Diseases, Quarterly J Forestry, Proc Roy Soc Edinburgh, Ringing & Migration, Scottish Birds*; also various reports, conference proceedings and chapters in books. Member: Raptor Research Foundation, World Working Group on Birds of Prey and Owls. OIR: listening to music, skiing, travel. Forestry Commission Research Division, Woodland Ecology Branch, Northern Research Station, Roslin, Midlothian EH25 9SY. 0131 445 2176.

PHILLIPS, Adrian Alexander Christian; *b:* 11 January 1940 in Exmouth, Devon; *w:* Cassandra. Westminster School. BA Geography (Christ Church,

Oxford, 1962), Dip Town and Country Planning (Univ College London, 1965). Professor of Countryside and Environmental Planning, Univ Wales, Cardiff since 1992; also part-time environmental consultant, Chairman Commission on National Parks and Protected Areas of IUCN, the World Conservation Union. Prev: Director General, Countryside Commission 1981-92. Board member of World Conservation Monitoring Centre since 1993. RSPB: Council member and Chairman of Committee for Wales from 1992. Board member of Green Alliance 1992-. OIR: 'walking, gardening and (unapologetically) cats!' 2 The Old Rectory, Dumbleton, Evesham, Worcs WR11 6TG. 01386 882094.

PHILLIPS, Ian Malcolm; *b:* 18 November 1960 in Darlington, Co Durham. BSc Geology (Newcastle, 1982), PhD Geochemistry (Mineralogy) (Newcastle, 1985). Senior Clay Mineralogist, Core Laboratories (oil service industry). Special interests: seawatching and seabirds, raptors on passage (esp east coast of NE Scotland). Travel inc Turkey and Gibraltar (for passage raptors), Israel, Hong Kong, S Spain, Crete, N America. Pelagics off SW Approaches and off Hong Kong. Compiler seabirds section of *North-East Scotland Bird Report* 1990-95. Producer of *Long Tails*, newsletter for the NE Scotland bird telephone network, 1993-95. Monthly regional round-up of birds in NE Scotland for *Bird Watching* 1993-. In 1993 updated the official list of birds which occur or have occurred in the NE Scotland region. OIR: watching rugby, playing and watching football (Sunderland AFC supporter). 88 Langdykes Drive, Cove Bay, Aberdeen AB12 3HW. 01224 897898.

PHILLIPS, Nicholas John (John); *b:* 29 May 1953 in St Ives, Cornwall; *w:* Viv. BSc Zoology (Newcastle, 1974). Freelance survey ecologist (specialising in ornithology) since 1990. Prev: Conservation Ranger, Milton Keynes Dev Corpn 1985-90; Warden Bardsey Island Bird Observatory 1983-84; Resident Scientific Administrator, Cousin Island Reserve, Seychelles (ICBP) 1981-83; research asst Edward Grey Inst, Univ Oxford 1977-80; Warden Isle of May NNR 1977. Seychelles Bird Records Committee 1992-. BTO 'A' ringer since 1975. Special interests: vagrancy in relation to migration, ringing (esp migrant passerines), seabirds. From 1990 to 1995: summer ringing studies of migrants, Linford Wildfowl Centre, Milton Keynes; winter gull roost enthusiast; researching occurrence of vagrants in Britain. Overseas: Crete Ringing Group expeditions studying and ringing migrants 1974 and 1975; ICBP expedition to Line Islands, Central Pacific (seabird and general ecological studies) 1990. Joint compiler *Crete Ringing Group Report* (1974), 'much quoted in *BWP*'; a large part of *Bardsey Bird Obs Reports* 1984 and 1985; prize-winning entry in *Best Days with British Birds* (1989). Papers published in *Ibis* and *Ringing & Migration*. Occasional radio interviews. OIR: other aspects of natural history, esp dragonflies; participant in Biological Records Centre (Monks Wood) recording scheme; 'World Music'. Yorkleigh Cottage, Pope's Hill, Newnham, Glos GL14 1LD.

PICKERING, Jane; *b:* 3 April 1965 in Rochford, Essex; *p:* Dr Christopher Norris. MA Natural Sciences (Cambridge, 1990), MSc Museum Studies (Leicester, 1991). AMA 1993. Asst Curator of the Zoological Collections, Oxford Univ Museum since 1989. These collections include one of the largest ornithology collections in the country. Special interests: the Dodo, bird collections in museums. Oxford University Museum, Parks Road, Oxford OX1 3PW. 01865 272950; fax 01865 272970.

PIENKOWSKI, Michael William (Mike); *b:* 2 June 1951 in Derby; *w:* Ann. Bemrose Grammar School, Derby. BSc Biological Sciences (East Anglia, 1972), PhD Zoology (Durham, 1980). Head of International Legislation and Funding, RSPB. Prev: Director Life Sciences, JNCC 1991-95; Asst Chief Scientist, NCC 1990-91; Head of Ornithology Branch, NCC 1984-90; Senior Research Associate, Univ Durham 1976-84 (inc bird migration systems); holder of BOU Research Studentship Univ Durham on ecology and behaviour of Ringed and Grey Plovers; self-employed ecologist 1972-73. Council British Ecological Society 1994-95. Executive Board and Standing Committee IWRB 1991-. International Wader Study Group: Editor 1973-82, Vice-Chairman 1982-87, Chairman 1987-92, President 1992-. BOU: Council 1991-, Chairman Ornithological Affairs Committee 1995-. Scientific Advisory Committees of WWT and BTO 1984-91. Hon Fellow in Zoology, Univ Durham 1985. Chairman, European Forum on Nature Conservation and Pastoralism 1994-. Chairman, UK Dependent Territories Conservation Forum 1995-. Chairman of UK Government's group to end the use of gunshot lead in wetlands 1991-95. Chairman of JNCC/RSPB project team to reintroduce Red Kites to England and Scotland 1987-95. Chairman of Sea-Eagle reintroduction team 1988-92. Special interests: developing positive targets for nature conservation and means for monitoring progress towards achievement, inc involvement in the UK National Action Plan under the Convention on Biological Diversity; science-based approach to incorporation of nature conservation in land-use planning; international co-ordination; the involvement of volunteers and the application of their work to conservation; the application of research results and ensuring their dissemination at all levels; the interactions of behaviour, ecology and population dynamics, including human factors; migration systems and ecology; coastal ecology; agriculture/nature interactions; the potential use of key species for handling and promoting more complex conservation issues. Overseas: study of shorebird ecology and migration in Morocco, Iceland and Greenland. Author or co-author of a number of books, the more recent ones specifically on birds including *Vulnerable Concentrations of Birds in the North Sea*, with M L Tasker (1987); *Seabirds in the North Sea*, with M L Tasker *et al* (1987); *Birds, Bogs and Forestry: the peatlands of Caithness and Sutherland*, with D A Stroud *et al* (1987); *The Conservation of International Flyway Populations of Waders*, with N C Davidson (1987); *Protecting Internationally Important Bird Sites*, with D A Stroud and G P Mudge (1990); *Goose Damage and Management Workshop: procs of meeting organised by WWT at Martin Mere*, with M Owen (1991); *Important Bird Areas in the United Kingdom including the Channel Islands and the Isle of Man*, with D E Pritchard *et al* (1992); *Ireland's Internationally Important Bird Sites: a review of sites for the EC Special Protection Area Network*, with L S Way *et al* (1993); *An Atlas of Seabird Distribution in North-West European Waters*, with C J Stone *et al* (1995); *Actions for Biodiversity in the UK*, with D Hill *et al* (1996); *Farming and Birds in Europe*, with D Pain (in press). Editor *Wader Study Group Bulletin* 1973-82, *Ringing & Migration* 1979-84, *J Appl Ecol* 1995-. Author of over one hundred journal papers, articles and published reports (plus popular articles, radio broadcasts etc), mainly on above research and interests. OIR: walking, skiing, natural history, reading. RSPB, The Lodge, Sandy, Beds SG19 2DL. 01767 680551; fax 01767 683211.

PIOTROWSKI, Steven; *b:* 27 June 1951 in Ipswich, Suffolk; *w:* Ann. Civil engineer, Anglian Water. Suffolk Ornithologists' Group: Vice Chairman 1981-85, Chairman 1985-89, Committee 1989-. Suffolk Naturalists' Society: Chairman 1989-93. Landguard Bird Observatory: founder-member 1982, Treasurer 1982-84, Chairman 1994-. BTO 'A' ringer since 1983. Special interests: ringing and migration, wintering wildfowl and waders. Participant in monthly Birds of Estuaries Enquiry counts on Orwell and Alde estuaries since 1980. Principal editor *Easy Birdwatching* (1989). Author *The New Birds of Suffolk* (in press). Editor *Suffolk Birds* (annual report) 1986-93. Many scientific papers, mostly in *Suffolk Birds*. Many appearances on national and local radio and TV. Winner, Best Annual Bird Report 1991 (*British Birds*). OIR: butterflies and dragonflies (co-author *The Butterflies of Suffolk*, 1986). 18 Cobham Road, Ipswich IP3 9JD. 01473 711856.

PITTAM, Sallie Ann; *b:* 4 December 1947 in Birmingham; *h:* Stuart. Swanshurst Grammar School 1959-66. Survey work for Forestry Commission/Forest Enterprise on population ecology and diet of forest species, esp Goshawk, 1983-. Survey work for National Trust, esp raptors, 1992-93. Herefordshire Raptor Hospital run from home since 1979. County adviser under Hawk and Owl Trust's Barn Owl Network, running a small breeding and release scheme and making site visits to advise on land management. Talks given locally on particular species and on rehabilitation work, inc lecturing to veterinary nurses on management of birds in captivity; also fieldwork with school children to raise awareness of raptor conservation issues. Special interest: nursing care of injured raptors, esp treatment requiring physiotherapy and nursing of head-injured birds. Occasional local radio talks. OIR: yoga, hill walking. Fox House, Leinthall Starkes, Ludlow, Shrops SY8 2HP. 01568 770463.

POMEROY, Derek Edmund; *b:* 6 June 1934 in Beckenham, Kent. BA Zoology (Cambridge, 1957), MA 1959, PhD Animal Ecology (Adelaide, 1966). Deputy Director (and Professor) MUIENR (see address) since 1988. Chairman Uganda Branch, East African Wild Life Society 1991-95. Committee EANHS c1977-. Pan African Ornithological Congress Committee 1988-96. Special interests: conservation, biodiversity issues (esp tropical forests and wetlands). Study species inc Grey Crowned Crane and Marabou. Author *Counting Birds* (1992). Co-author (with A D Lewis) *A Bird Atlas for Kenya* (1989) and (with M W Service) *Tropical Ecology* (1992); also chapters in several books eg *African Wildlife: research and management* ed by F I B Kayanja and E Edroma (1991). Author or co-author of many scientific papers in eg *African J Ecol, Biol J Linn Soc, Gibier Faune Sauvage, Proc Pan Afr Orn Congr.* Member: ABC, also see above. Makerere University Institute of Environment and Natural Resources, PO Box 10066, Kampala, Uganda. Home tel +256 41 541681.

POOL, Peter James; *b:* 8 February 1952 in London; *w:* Claire. Electrical design draughtsman. Committee RSPB Vale of White Horse Members' Group 1983-88. Oxfordshire Atlas Survey 1985-88, 10km square steward. Member of ten-strong team of Common Birds Census workers on large farmland plot since 1982, co-ordinator since 1989. Voluntary wardening of Peregrines 1985 and 1986, and Montagu's Harriers 1986. Occasional paid survey work. Special interests: local survey work, farming and birds. Author of species accounts for wagtails, harriers and Short-eared Owl in *Birds of Oxfordshire* ed by J Brucker *et al* (1992). Regular articles in *The Hobby*, annual journal of local RSPB Members' Group. OIR: other wildlife, real ale, cricket, folk and rock music, gardening. 1 North Cottages, Fyfield Wick, Abingdon, Oxon OX13 5ND. 01865 820442.

POOLE, Gregory (Greg); *b:* 26 October 1960 in Bristol. BSc Zoology (Univ College Cardiff, 1983). Freelance wildlife artist (inc work for RSPB, WWT, DoE, *BBC Wildlife* etc). Regular exhibitor and member SWLA. Winner *Natural World* and Artists for Nature Foundation awards 1993. Winner of Wildlife Art Gallery award 1994. Participant in Artists for Nature Foundation project on the Loire estuary 1994. Artist in residence at Nature in Art Museum 1995 and 1996, and at Les Ecrins reserve, French Alps 1996. 31 Burlington Road, Redland, Bristol BS6 6TJ. Tel/fax 0117 974 1775.

PORTEOUS, Malcolm; *b:* 6 March 1936 in Edinburgh. MA History and Music (Edinburgh, 1960), Teacher's Cert (Moray House College, 1960). Primary school head teacher. Group organiser Edinburgh YOC since 1974. Special interest: introducing young people (c2,000 so far) to ornithology and wildlife generally, and involving them in a wide variety of national and local surveys. Leader of YOC expeditions to many parts of Britain, esp E Anglia and Outer Hebrides. Interest in birds of Africa, with travel to Morocco, Kenya, Malawi, Zimbabwe, Botswana, Tanzania. Survey reports and articles published on the birds of the Water of Leith. OIR: oboist and conductor of several amateur orchestras. 3 Hermitage Gardens, Edinburgh EH10 6DL. 0131 447 0539.

PORTER, David Ian; *b:* 28 February 1934. FRCP (London). Dermatologist. BTO Regional Representative Rugby 1992-. Special interests: 'local patch' surveys, ringing. Long-standing participant in BTO's Garden Bird Feeding Survey and Garden Birdwatch. Interest also in African and Indian ornithology. Member: ABC, WAOS. OIR: Macrolepidoptera, photography. 60 Stanley Road, Hillmorton, Rugby, Warks CV21 3UE. 01788 543803.

PORTER, Richard Frank; *b:* 17 October 1943 in London. National College of Food Technology; Brighton Technical College. CBiol, MIBiol (Ecology and Animal Behaviour) 1981. Head of Species Protection, RSPB since 1979. Secondment to BirdLife International as Head of Middle East Division 1993-. Prev RSPB: Regional Officer SE England 1974-79; Technical Officer 1969-74. Also ICBP: Project Officer, Turkey four months each year 1968-72. Past Committee or Council member: Selsey Bill Bird Observatory, Cape Clear Bird Observatory, Surrey Bird Club Records and Surveys Committee 1962-66, BTO 1970-74, Sussex NT Scientific

Committee 1975-79, Secretary Sussex FWAG 1975-79, ICBP Publicity Committee, NCC's Specialist Group on Raptors 1979-85, Secretary Ornithological Society of Turkey, Chairman OSME, British Birds Rarities Committee 1980-84, Beds and Hunts NT 1984-86, Grafham Water Nature Reserve Management Committee, Rare Breeding Birds Panel 1986-91. BOU Records Committee since 1992. Trustee of Children's Tropical Forests UK since 1992. Special interests: conservation, 'local patch' birding, pelagics, Middle East. Over thirty-five trips made to Middle East, with several major expeditions to Turkey and Yemen. Author *Wild Birds and the Law* (1981,86,93), *Birds of Yemen* (in Arabic, 1996). Co-author *Flight Identification of European Raptors* (1974, 3rd ed 1981; transl into seven languages). Co-author (with Peter Holden) *Spotter's Guide to Birds of Prey* (1981); (with Phil Hollom *et al*) *Birds of the Middle East and North Africa* (1988); (with Leo Batten *et al*) *Red Data Birds in Britain* (1990); (with Steen Christensen and Per Shiermacker-Hansen) *Field Guide to the Birds of the Middle East* (1996). Editor *Predatory Birds of Game and Fish* (1985). Featured in film about his ICBP work in Turkey called *Where Two Worlds Meet* (BBC 'World About Us' series 1969). Papers published in *Birding World*, *Birdwatch*, *British Birds*, *Ecos*, *Ibis*, *Sandgrouse*; also in county bird reports and technical publications. Co-editor *Turkish Bird Report* 1966-69 and *Sandgrouse* 1996. Carthy Memorial Prize, Institute of Biology 1981. Member: OSME. OIR: botany, choreography, travel, reading, collecting paintings and stories. 21 Roundhouse Drive, West Perry, Huntingdon, Cambs PE18 0DJ. Office 01767 680551.

POTTS, George Richard (Dick); *b:* 6 December 1939 in Catterick, N Yorks; *w:* Olga. BSc Zoology (Durham, 1962), PhD Population dynamics of the Shag (Durham, 1965), DSc (Durham, 1987). Director General The Game Conservancy Trust and Managing Director Game Conservancy Ltd since 1993. Prev Game Conservancy: Director General Designate and Director of Research 1990-93, Dir of Research 1977-90, Asst Dir of Research 1975-77, Senior Scientific Officer 1968-75. Earlier: Research Associate Univ Durham 1965-67. 'Many and varied Committees of Government and non-Government bodies.' Special interests: effects of agriculture on birds (esp Grey Partridge, studied since c1968), conservation through wise use. Author *The Partridge: pesticides, predation and conservation* (1986). Editor *The Ecology of Temperate Cereal Fields* (1991) and *Proceedings of Perdix VI: the First International Symposium on Partridges, Quails and Francolins* (1992). Over seventy scientific papers in journals eg *J Animal Ecol*, *Nature*. The Game Conservancy Trust, Fordingbridge, Hants SP6 1EF. 01425 652381.

POTTS, Peter Malcolm; *b:* 10 October 1963 in London. BSc Biological Sciences (Portsmouth Polytechnic, 1986). Countryside Ranger for Hampshire CC (based at Titchfield Haven NNR) since 1990. Prev: asst warden Fair Isle Bird Observatory 1988. Hampshire Ornithological Society: Ringing Secretary of Field Studies Management Committee 1989-96. BTO 'A' ringer and trainer since late 1980s. Leading member of Farlington Ringing Group. Special interests: waders in Langstone Harbour, esp aspects of Black-tailed Godwit and Greenshank movements and feeding behaviour (colour-ringing studies); long-term studies into *Acrocephalus* migration through Farlington Marshes LNR reedbed. Founder-member (1994) and Chairman of Solent Shorebird Study Group; also co-ordinator of wader studies (colour-dyeing) on Southampton Water. Common Birds Census (ongoing at Chilling, also ran Farlington Marshes CBC 1980-87). BoEE/WeBS counts (both high and low tide counts) 1975-. Various other counts and surveys. Asst in compiling and editing *Hampshire Bird Report*, also contributor of papers. Member: Wader Study Group. OIR: other natural history, esp moths, butterflies, dragonflies. Solent Court Cottage, Hook Lane, Warsash, Southampton SO31 9HF. 01489 578649.

POWELL, Roger William; *b:* 26 August 1943 in Leicester; *w:* Lorna. BA Fine Art (Durham, 1965), Dip Ed (Newcastle, 1966). Director of Undergraduate Programme, Dept of Visual and Performing Arts, Univ Northumbria. Special interests: bird photography; long-term study of Greenshank populations in Glen Garry area, Inverness-shire (commenced 1974). Expedition organiser (Seafarer): seabird censuses of N Skye islands 1969 and 1987. Leader of expeditions to Finnish Lapland, Norway, southern Spain and France since 1972. Greenshank and other wader research included in *Waders: their breeding, haunts and watchers* by D and M Nethersole-Thompson (1986). Articles on photographing birds in *Birdwatch* and *Wildlife Photographer*. Occasional photographs published in books; also in magazines eg *Bird Watching, Birds, Regulus* (Luxembourg). Public lectures on photographic work and expeditions since 1990. OIR: film theory and history; wine. 30 Embleton Terrace, Longframlington, Morpeth, Northumberland NE65 8JJ. 01665 570449.

PRATER, Anthony John (Tony); *b:* 3 November 1943 in Hitchin, Herts. BSc Zoology (Exeter, 1965), PhD Avian grazing in reedswamps (East Anglia, 1996). RSPB Deputy Wales Officer 1994-. Prev: RSPB Regional Officer (East Anglia) 1986-94; RSPB Reg Off (SE England) 1979-86; BTO Birds of Estuaries Enquiry Officer and later Head of Populations Section

1970-79; RSPB Wader Feeding Project (feasibility study re Morecambe Bay Barrage) 1968-70. Warden Lundy Bird Observatory 1965. Secretary Rye Meads Ringing Group 1965-68. Co-ordinator IWRB international wader counts 1972-77. Wildfowl Trust Scientific Committee 1975-77. Hertfordshire NHS Ornithological Committee c1975-77. Sussex Ornithological Society: Scientific Committee 1979-86, Council 1983-86, Recorder 1984-86. Co-ordinator national breeding Ringed Plover surveys 1974 and 1984. Joint co-ordinator national breeding Wood Warbler survey 1985. Co-ordinator Reed and Sedge Warbler survey in Sussex 1985. Scientific and Conservation Committee Sussex TNC 1979-86 and Norfolk Naturalists' Trust 1992-94. Research and Survey Committee Norfolk Bird Club 1993-94. Records Committee Suffolk Ornithologists' Group 1987-90 and EANHS 1985-94. Special interests: identification, esp waders; reintroduced and feral geese in Norfolk (research to identify impact on reeds in the Broads); habitat management for wildlife. Widely travelled for birds, esp N and S America, Africa, Europe, Australia, Antarctic. Author *Identification and Ageing of Holarctic Waders* (1977), *Estuary Birds of Britain and Ireland* (1981). Co-author (with J Marchant and P Hayman) *Shorebirds* (1986); (with D Taylor and J Wheatley) *Where to Watch Birds in Kent, Surrey and Sussex* (1987). Contributor to many other books inc *Greenshanks* by D and M Nethersole-Thompson (1970), *Enjoying Ornithology* by R Hickling (1983), BTO Breeding Atlas and New Breeding Atlas, *Birdwatcher's Britain* by C Parslow (1983), *Red Data Birds of Britain and Ireland* by L A Batten *et al* (1990), *AA/RSPB Complete Book of British Birds* ed by M Cady and R A Hume (1988). Editor *Wader Study Group Bulletin* 1970-78. Some one hundred articles on the status of birds, feeding ecology and conservation issues in county bird reports, *Bird Study, RSPB Conservation Review*. Member: Wader Study Group. RSPB Wales Office, Bryn Aderyn, The Bank, Newtown, Powys. SY16 2AB. 01686 626678.

PRENDERGAST, Evelyn David Vereker; MBE 1951, DFC 1944; Colonel Retd; *b:* 19 February 1918 in London; *w:* Mary. Wellington College; Royal Military Academy, Woolwich. Chairman Dorset Bird Club 1978-86. Member Military Conservation Groups, Lulworth (1976-) and West Moors (1985-). BTO 'A' ringer since 1973; also ringed in Sudan and Mallorca. Special interest: birds of Africa. Author of *A Checklist of the Birds of the Larkhill Ranges* (1971). Joint author (with J V Boys) *The Birds of Dorset* (1983). Editor *The Adjutant* (journal of the Army Birdwatching Society) 1970-76. Articles on eg Dorset names of birds, decline of the Blackcock in Dorset, Dorset duck decoys in *Proc Dorset Nat Hist and Archaeol Soc* and other publications. OIR: general natural history and country pursuits; dragonflies. Manor House, Bagber, Sturminster Newton, Dorset DT10 2EY. 01258 472621.

PRITCHARD, David Edward (Dave); *b:* 7 October 1958 in Jarrow, Tyne & Wear. BSc Zoology (Durham, 1980), MSc Conservation (Univ College London, 1981). Manager, Planning and Local Government Unit, RSPB since 1990. Prev RSPB: Casework Officer 1986-90; Conservation Planning Asst 1984-86; Research Ecologist 1981-84. Voluntary warden at RSPB Havergate Island and Insh Marshes reserves 1977-78. County recorder Tyne & Wear for RSPB Beached Birds Survey 1975-77. International Hall (London) Expeditions Working Group 1980-81. President Durham Univ Exploration Society 1978-79. Scientific Adviser Oxford Univ Expedition to Nepal 1985. Director and Secretary, Biological Projects International 1985-. Many committees related to post, eg UK representative ICBP European Community Working Group 1984; UK Environmental Law Assocn Nature Conservation Working Group 1991-; Institute of Environmental Assessment Working Group on Ecological Assessment 1991-; RSPB/BirdLife International Important Bird Areas European Programme Management Committee 1992-; County Planning Officers' Special Advisory Group on Nature Conservation 1992-; NGO Conservation Forum for the (UK) Dependent Territories 1991-; Wildlife Link Habitats Group 1986-, Chairman 1991-93, Vice-Chairman 1993-; Government/ NGO Joint Working Group on Ramsar Sites and Special Protection Areas 1985-; IUCN 'Parks for Life' UK Task Force 1995-; BirdLife International delegations to Ramsar and Bonn Conventions. Special interests: legal and policy aspects of site protection and planning in UK, Europe, UK Dependencies (inc Caribbean); Ramsar Convention; high altitude grassland ecology and bird distribution in Indian and Nepalese Himalayas. Joint author (with R Therivel *et al*) *Strategic Environmental Assessment* (1992). Joint editor *Important Bird Areas in the UK including the Channel Islands* (1992). Contributions to other books. Papers and articles published in eg *Birds*, *Ecos*, *Irish Birds*, *The Planner*, *RSPB Conservation Review*. Also many expedition, internal (mainly RSPB) and limited circulation reports. OIR: hill walking. RSPB, The Lodge, Sandy, Beds SG19 2DL. 01767 680551.

PROCTOR, Robert (Bob); *b:* 9 February 1965 in Elgin, Moray. Elgin Academy. Contract research and monitoring, mainly for RSPB, since 1985. BTO Regional Representative Moray and Nairn 1994-. Moray and Nairn

Rarities Committee 1994-. Wetland Bird Survey (prev BoEE) organiser for Lossie Estuary 1985-. Breeding Bird Survey organiser for Moray and Nairn 1994-. BTO 'A' ringer since 1990. Special interests: identification and migration. Articles published in *Birding World*; drawings in *The Birds of Moray and Nairn* by M Cook (1992), *Moray & Nairn Bird Report* (from 1987) and *British Birds*; also photographs. OIR: moth trapping; photography. 94 Reid Street, Bishopmill, Elgin, Moray IV30 2HH. 01343 544874.

PRYS-JONES, [Prŷs-Jones] Robert Parton; *b:* in Denbigh, Clwyd; *w:* Marilyn. BSc Zoology (Nottingham, 1970), DPhil Comparative physiological ecology of two bunting species (Linacre College and Edward Grey Institute, Oxford, 1977). MIBiol. Head of Bird Group, The Natural History Museum, Tring since 1992. Prev: Head of Estuaries Unit, BTO 1987-92; Lecturer in Percy Fitzpatrick Inst of African Ornithol, Univ Cape Town 1982-87; post-doctoral research post at Stirling Univ (avian energetics) 1980-82; post-doctoral research post in Univ Queensland (avian behavioural ecology and biogeography) 1978-80; research into biology of birds at Aldabra Atoll, Indian Ocean 1974-78. Special interest: birds of the Seychelles. Work on birds in many parts of the world from Arctic to tropics. Member of expedition undertaking research on birds and bats on Dominica, West Indies 1978. Over fifty book chapters and research papers on bird biology: journals inc *Biol J Linn Soc, Bull BOC, Ibis, J Appl Ecol, J Zool (Lond)*. Bird Group, The Natural History Museum, Akeman Street, Tring, Herts HP23 6AP. 01442 824181; fax 01442 890693.

PRYTHERCH, Robin James; *b:* 21 October 1939 in Hastings, Sussex. Royal Wanstead School, Snaresbrook, London. Enfield Technical College. Freelance ornithologist, wildlife illustrator and TV producer since 1991. Prev: Researcher and Producer, BBC Natural History Unit 1968-91. Formerly a structural designer. Committee Bristol Naturalists' Soc Ornithological Section in mid 1960s. Committee Somerset Archaeol and NHS Ornithol Section 1867-69. Founder-member and Committee Bristol Ornithological Club from 1967, Chairman 1972-75. Specialist member of BTO Membership and Development Committee 1989-. Committee Chew Valley Ringing Station since 1964 and tutor on its occasional ringing courses. BTO 'A' ringer since 1965. Organised a survey of breeding Sparrowhawk, Buzzard and Kestrel in Avon for Bristol Orn Club 1980-84. Participated in National Wildfowl Counts in 1960s and BTO Heronries Census from 1969. Special interests: birds of prey, long-term study of Buzzard in a 75 sq km plot W of Bristol (commenced 1980). For BBC, worked on some one hundred radio and TV productions, most of which wholly or partially ornithological; involved travel to Argentina, Falklands, USA, France, Holland, Italy, Greece, former Yugoslavia, Israel, Kenya and Australia, as well as many parts of UK. Producer credits inc radio series *The Living World* and *Wildlife*, and for TV inc *Go Birding* (six), *The Natural World* (Wings over the Holy Land), *The Living Isles* (Beneath the Greenwood), *Wildlife for all Seasons, Island of Birds, Reefwatch, Africawatch, Birdwatch* (from many locations in UK and overseas). Many broadcasts on bird subjects on BBC Local Radio and Radios 2 and 4. Illustrations (almost all pen-and-ink) in several books, eg *Birds of Man's World* by Derek Goodwin (1978), *The Private Life of Birds* by Michael Bright (1993), maps for *Where to Watch Birds in Somerset, Avon, Gloucestershire and Wiltshire* by Ken Hall and John Govett (1988, 2nd ed 1995) and numerous illustrations and maps in *Avon Bird Report, BBC Wildlife, British Birds, Bristol Ornithology* and *The Countryman*. Co-reviser (with Bruce and Robert Campbell) of *A Guide to Birds of the Coast* by C A Gibson-Hill (1976); contributed chapters to *Frontiers of Bird Identification* ed by J T R Sharrock (1980) and *Best Days with British Birds* ed by M Ogilvie and S Winter (1989). Wide range of papers and notes in *BBC Wildlife, Bristol Ornithology* and *British Birds*. Compiler (with Mike Everett) of 'News and Comment' feature in *British Birds* 1983-93. Member of Editorial Board of *British Birds* (1988-), also editorial committees of *Bristol Bird Report* (one year in mid 1960s) and *Bristol Ornithology* (1967-). Member: World Working Group on Birds of Prey and Owls, Hawk and Owl Trust. OIR: classical music, helping brother John with Prytherch family history, reading works of C G Jung. 23 Caledonia Place, Clifton, Bristol BS8 4DL. 0117 974 1912.

PURVEUR, Robert Alan John (Rob); *b:* 30 June 1963 in Gloucester; *w:* Anne. Computer programmer. BTO Regional Representative Gloucestershire 1990-. Gloucestershire Ornithological Co-ordinating Committee and Chairman of Surveys Sub-committee 1990-. Organiser: Glos Winter Garden Bird Enquiry, Breeding Bird Survey for Glos, BTO surveys for Glos. Special interest: census work. Editor *Gloucestershire Gannet* (local BTO newsletter). Author of various local survey reports published in *Gloucestershire Bird Report* and local society journals. 31 Elderwood Way, Tuffley, Gloucester GL4 0RB. 01452 546454.

PYMAN, Geoffrey Arthur; MBE 1980; *b:* 24 July 1920 in Maldon, Essex; *w:* Eileen. Principal admin officer, local government, retired. Essex Birdwatching Society: Chairman 1960-64, Chairman of Recording Committee 1971-85, President from 1991. Secretary British Birds Rarities

Committee 1959-61 (member 1959-70) Special interest: distribution. Co-author (with Robert Hudson) *A Guide to the Birds of Essex* (1968). Editor *Essex Bird Report* 1949-70. OIR: butterflies. Treyarnon, The Ridge, Little Baddow, Chelmsford CM3 4RT. 01245 222417.

RADFORD, Allan Philip (Philip); *b:* 9 August 1920 in Burham-on-Sea, Somerset; *w:* Rosemary. Shebbear College. MB, ChB (Bristol, 1944), DCH (London, 1948). Medical practitioner, retired. President Wildlife Sound Recording Society 1993-, past Chairman, Vice Chairman, Hon Treas. Chairman Somerset Archaeological and Nat Hist Soc 1992-. Special interests: bird behaviour, wildlife sound recording, bird photography. Various notes published in *British Birds* since 1955; regular contributor to *Wildlife Sound* (journal of WSRS); past occasional contributor of wildlife articles and photographs to *Country Life, The Countryman, The Field*. Bird sound recordings have been used in film, video, cassette and CD productions; also deposited in British Library of Wildlife Sounds (now National Sound Archive Wildlife Section) since its inception in 1969. Winner of Documentary Class, Wildlife Sound Recording Society Competition, 1982. Winner of Sounds from Nature Class, British Amateur Tape Recording Contest, 1982, 1985, 1993, 1995. OIR: looking at fungi and dragonflies. Crossways Cottage, West Bagborough, Taunton, Somerset TA4 3EG. 01823 432526.

RAFE, Richard William; *b:* 6 September 1954 in London; *w:* Brenda. Hymers College, Hull. BSc Biology (Westfield College, London, 1975), MSc Ecology (Univ Coll of N Wales, 1979), DPhil Species/area relationships in nature conservation (York, 1983). Manager, Suffolk Team, English Nature since 1991. Prev EN: Policy Development Officer 1990-91, Conservation Officer N Yorks 1988-90, Cons Off Humberside 1983-88. Suffolk Ornithologists' Group Council 1991-. Suffolk Ornithological Records Committee 1995-. Editor *Suffolk Bird Report* 1995. Various papers following doctorate, eg 'Birds on reserves: the influence of area and habitat on species richness' in *J Appl Ecol* (1985); also regular contributor to *The Harrier* (Suffolk OG bulletin). OIR: work and family. 196 Raedwald Drive, Bury St Edmunds, Suffolk IP32 7DW. 01284 700456.

RAINE, Barry Alexander; *b:* 27 April 1941 in Leicester; *w:* Barbara. Representative, East Midlands Electricity. Leicestershire & Rutland Ornithological Society: Committee 1971-89, Vice Chairman 1981-84, Chairman 1984-87. Founder of Leicester Young Birdwatchers' Club, also Secretary 1970-90. Adult education tutor relating to ornithology since 1970.

Voluntary warden (Speyside 1959, Rutland Water since 1994). Ringing with BTO 'A' ringer on Scolt Head Island 1960-62. Special interests: migration; sound recording; study species inc Crossbill, Capercaillie, Ptarmigan, Dotterel, terns. Group leader on tours to Spain, France, Romania, Holland. Occasional radio interviews. 55 Cairnsford Road, West Knighton, Leicester LE2 6GG. 0116 288 7219.

RAINES, Reginald John (John); *b:* 12 August 1925 in Ilkeston, Derbys. MRCS, LRCP (St Bartholomews, London 1950). General medical practitioner, retired. Secretary Cambridge Bird Club 1945,46. BOU Council 1963-66. British Birds Rarities Committee 1975-82. Hon President of late Cheshire Ornithological Assocn 1982. Founder-member Liverpool Ornithologists' Club (1953). Special interests: identification, distribution, migration. Also keen photographer with 'possibly unrivalled collection of nearly 30,000 slides, embracing well over 2,500 species of birds.' Extensive experience abroad with over eighty ornithological expeditions across all continents, inc postwar pioneering surveys in Lapland, E Austria, Greece and Turkey; also tour leader to eg Russia, Caribbean, Sri Lanka, Equador and Galapagos, E Africa, India, N America. Regular lecturer to numerous bird clubs, natural history societies and others. One time editor *Cambridge Bird Report*, *Cheshire Bird Report*. Point House, Ferry Lane, Higher Ferry, Chester CH1 6QF. 01244 372787.

RAMSDEN, David Jonathan; *b:* 4 April 1958 in Bristol; *w:* Frances. Conservation Officer Barn Owl Trust since 1990. Warden Lady's Wood Reserve (Devon WT) 1987-. DWT Conservation Advisory Committee (1991-), Council (1995-) and Conservation and Education Planning Group (1996-). JNCC Barn Owl Liaison Group 1989-. DoE Barn Owl Working Group. Co-organiser Devon Barn Owl Survey 1993. BTO 'C' ringer since 1990. Special interest: Barn Owl. Designed Barn Conversion Research Project, carried out fieldwork and produced reports 1990-94. Researched, developed and carried out various methods of release of captive-bred Barn Owls 1984-. Co-author *Barn Owl Re-introduction Report 1986-1988* and second covering 1986-92; also co-author (with Frances Ramsden) *Barn Owls on Site: a guide for developers and planners* (1995). Articles in eg *BBC Wildlife*, *Birdwatcher's Yearbook*, *Devon Birds*, *Devon Life*. Radio broadcast BBC Radio 4. Numerous lectures and talks. OIR: native American teachings and ceremonies. Waterleat, Ashburton, Devon TQ13 7HU. 01364 653026.

RANDS, Michael Russell Wheldon (Mike); *b:* 2 August 1956 in Ipswich, Suffolk; *w:* Gillian. Dartington Hall School 1967-74. BSc Environmental Sciences (East Anglia, 1978), DPhil Influence of habitat on the population ecology of partridges (Edward Grey Institute, Oxford, 1982). Director and Chief Executive, BirdLife International since 1996. Prev: Deputy Director-General and Director of Strategic Planning and Policy, BirdLife International 1993-96; Programme Director ICBP 1989-93; Asst Prog Dir ICBP 1986-89; post-doctoral research ecologist, Game Conservancy Trust 1982-86; research asst GCT 1979-82; field asst Slapton Ley Field Centre 1974-75. OSME: Council 1982-86, Chairman 1987-92. Fauna and Flora Preservation Society: Committee 1986-93, Council 1993-. World Pheasant Association Council 1987-90. BOU Council 1990-95. International Ornithological Congress: Scientific Programme Committee 1990-94, Applied Ornithology Committee 1990-94. Special interests: international conservation, applied ecology, behavioural ecology, population biology. Ornithological survey work in Iceland 1975 and 1977. Ornithologist on University of East Anglia Turkey Expedition documenting autumn raptor migration through Belin Pass 1976. Leader UEA Nepal Expedition (seven months studying birds and mammals of Terai grassland and forest habitats 1978-79). Organiser and joint leader OSME Yemen Expedition 1985. Ornithologist on ICBP Dominica Rainforest Project 1982. Behavioural study of feral Peafowl 1981-82. Leader Chete Safari Area survey, Zimbabwe 1983. Co-editor (with P J Hudson) *Ecology and Management of Gamebirds* (1988). Editor *A Biodiversity Assessment of the Republic of Yemen* (1992). Editorial Board *Bird Study* 1985-89. Editor *Bird Cons Internat* 1990-93. Over forty scientific papers published in a variety of scientific, ornithological and conservation journals; also numerous popular articles. Co-producer of film on ornithology and conservation in Yemen with English and Arabic scripts 1986. 77 Thornton Road, Cambridge CB3 0NR. 01223 277318.

RANFT, Richard Damian; *b:* 6 July 1959 in Frimley Surrey; *p:* Elaine Ireland. BSc Zoology (Univ College, London, 1981); CBiol, MBiol. Curator National Sound Archive Wildlife Section (formerly British Library of Wildlife Sounds) since 1988; Assistant 1984-88. Special interests: sound recording, sound analysis, taxonomy, vocal behaviour. Expeditions to Costa Rica, Peru, Brazil, Colombia, India. Articles in *Bioacoustics*; various cassettes, CD-ROMs and CDs of bird sounds. Member: NBC. British Library National Sound Archive, 29 Exhibition Road, London SW7 2AS. 0171 412 7402.

RANKINE, Callum; *b:* 13 September 1962 in Stirling; *p:* Catherine Smith. BSc Biology and Geography (Derbyshire Coll of Higher Ed, 1989), MSc Ecology (Lancaster, 1990). UK Habitats and Species Officer, WWF-UK since 1996. Prev: Ornithologist, English Nature 1993-96; Site Manager Humber Wildfowl Refuge (EN) 1992-93; habitat surveyor NRA Yorkshire (surveyed N bank of Humber Estuary for birds) Apr-Nov 1991; RSPB Strumpshaw Fen scheme on Bean Goose/Wigeon interactions Jan-Apr 1991. Local co-ordinator (Humber) for various censuses and surveys in 1993. Wetland Bird Survey organiser N Cambs and S Lincs Sep 1993-96. BTO Regional Representative Huntingdonshire 1994-96. Ruddy Duck Survey co-ordinator N Cambs and S Lincs 1994. Special interests: waders, owls, estuaries (inc tidal power stations and the problems they pose for estuary birds), Special Protection Areas and Ramsar sites. Travel for birds in Morocco, Poland and the Canary Islands. Member: Owl Study Group, Wader Study Group. OIR: rock climbing, mountain biking, mammals (esp bats), beetles, martial arts. WWF-UK, Panda House, Weyside Park, Godalming, Surrey GU7 1XR. 01483 426444.

RAYNER, Jeremy Mark Verinder; *b:* 12 April 1953 in London. MA Mathematics, PhD Animal Flight (Cambridge, both 1978). Professor of Zoology Univ Bristol since 1995. Special interests: evolutionary ecology, energetics and biomechanics of flight. Numerous scientific papers in eg *J Exp Biol, J Zool, Phil Trans Roy Soc Lond (B)*. Scientific Medal, Zoological Society of London 1986. OIR: Oriental tribal rugs, riding (history of riding costume). School of Biological Sciences, University of Bristol, Woodland Road, Bristol BS8 1UG. 0117 928 8111.

RAYNOR, Edward Martin (Ted); *b:* 10 November 1943 in Caversham, Berks; *w:* Penny. BSc Econ (London, 1968). Thames Water. Tour leader for Ornitholidays 1965-74, to Shetlands, Austria, former Yugoslavia, Channel Islands, Mallorca. Outdoor Meetings Co-organiser (with wife) Hampshire Ornithological Society 1975-85. Special interests: collecting data for Nest Record Scheme; migration (records for passerines over more than thirty years). Extensive travel for birds on three continents. Occasional contributor to *British Birds*; regular contributor to Sussex, Hampshire and Dorset bird reports. Member: EAOS, NBC, North American Bird Club, OBC. OIR: Lepidoptera, general natural history, botany, walking, music, gardening, painting. Chalkhill, Lees Hill South, Warnborough, Hook, Hants RG29 1RQ. 01256 862541.

REAY, Peter John (Pete); *b:* 15 August 1943 in Bedford. Bedford School. BA Zoology (Cambridge, 1965), MSc Conservation (London, 1966), PhD Biology of sandeels (London, 1972). Lecturer in Biology (part-ornithology). Birds of Estuaries Enquiry count organiser Tamar Estuary 1988-90. Special interests: wintering Avocet and other estuarine birds, esp Tamar and Plym estuaries. Articles in *Devon Birds* and *Caradon Field and Nat Hist Club Annual Report*; also limited circulation reports on Tamar and Exe Avocets. Member: Wader Study Group. Dept of Biological Sciences, University of Plymouth, Plymouth PL4 8AA. 01752 232909; home 01752 559360.

REBANE, Evald Michael (Mick); *b:* 16 August 1952 in Swansea. BSc Geography (London, 1974), RSA Level 2 in Spanish. Consultant ecologist, wildlife tour leader and travel writer since 1994. Prev: RSPB's terrestrial ecologist for the UK (inc provision of information and advice on land management for birds and agricultural ecosystems) 1990-94; Reserves Manager Scottish WT 1982-90; Ecologist Wilts CC (establishment of biological records centre) 1977-79. Special interests: land management; habitat restoration and design for birds; conservation status of birds in Europe. Travel inc Greece, Spain, Portugal, France, Italy, Kenya. Co-author (with J Andrews) *Farming and Wildlife: a practical management handbook* (1994). Formerly resident on Crete and representative of Hellenic Ornithological Society (1994). OIR: wildlife and landscape photography, dragonflies (former recorder for Co Durham), wine and foods of the world, tennis, world music. 3 High Street, Hemingford Abbots, Huntingdon, Cambs PE18 9AH. 01480 300452.

REDMAN, Nigel James; *b:* 4 November 1952 in Taplow, Bucks. Caterham School. Bird tour leader and administrator for Birdquest since 1984. Natural History Editor, Pica Press/Helm Information since 1994. Prev: Asst Bursar Friends' School, Saffron Walden 1979-83; with Hodder & Stoughton publishers 1976-78; articles with Chartered Accountants 1971-75. Ornithological Society of the Middle East: Council 1980-87, Treasurer 1983-87. Oriental Bird Club: one of founders 1984, first Treasurer 1985-88, Council 1985-, Chairman 1991-95. Special interests: identification, distribution, conservation, taxonomy, sound recording; particular interest in Asia. Worldwide travel for birds, esp Europe, Middle East, Asia and Africa. Co-author (with Simon Harrap) *Birdwatching in Britain: a site by site guide* (1987). Papers and articles in eg *Bird Watching, Birding World, Birdwatcher's Yearbook, British Birds, J Bombay Nat Hist Soc*; contributor and member of editorial boards *Forktail, OBC Bulletin, OSME Bulletin,*

Sandgrouse. Photographs and sound recordings published in various places. Regular lecturer to bird clubs throughout Britain. Member: NBC, OBC, OSME. OIR: music, photography. Banks House, Mountfield, Robertsbridge, E Sussex TN32 5JY. 01580 881114; fax 01580 880541.

REDSHAW, Edward John (John); *b:* 19 May 1936 in Peterborough, Cambs; *w:* Joy. Spalding Grammar School 1947-51. Peterborough Tech Coll 1951-53, Civil Eng Tech (ICE) 1971. Senior Engineer, Anglian Water to 1995. Project Manager for Lapwings Consultants (Lincs TNC) 1995-. Founded and maintained Spalding Bird Observatory (as part of Ken Williamson's Inland Observation Points) at Spalding Sugar Beet Factory 1960-63. Warden/Recorder then Hon Reserve Manager, Baston Fen NR (Lincs TNC) 1967-. Gibraltar Point NR Advisory Committee 1974-78. Founder-member and Committee, Lincolnshire Bird Club 1979-81. Winter Wildfowl Counts organiser Lincs and S Humbs 1984/5-1991/2, Peterborough and S Lincs 1996-. Woodwalton Fen Joint Advisory Committee 1984-. Lincs TNC: Council 1969-, Convenor Scientific Policy Committee 1974-78, Conservation Committee 1978-, Wildlife Records Officer SE Lincs 1974-. Council Spalding Gentlemen's Society (administers Ashley Maples collection of mounted British Birds, 820 specimens) since 1970; also compiled catalogue in 1962. Part-time WEA tutor in natural history inc ornithology. Special interests: inland migration (1953-63); population and distribution (1953-63, 1967-); conservation of wetland habitats; study species inc corvids, Snipe, Lapwing. Waterways Bird Survey, R Glen 1979-89, and regular participant in other BTO surveys. Several papers and survey reports published in *Lincolnshire Bird Report* and *Trans Lincs Naturalists' Union*; editor *Conservation Management* (annual, Lincs TNC) since 1979. OIR: non-marine molluscs, dragonflies, botany, mapping, heraldry and genealogy. 7 Fennell Road, Pinchbeck, Spalding, Lincs PE11 3RP. 01775 768227.

REED, John Michael (Mike); *b:* 23 April 1943 in Hertford; *w:* Shirley. Former computer system administrator. BTO 'A' ringer since 1988. Chairman and founder-member Ivel Ringing Group 1990-. Secretary North West Norfolk RG 1990-. Hon warden Stanborough Reedmarsh (Herts and Middx WT reserve) 1980-. Management Committee Lemsford Springs (HMWT reserve) 1991-. Special interest: use of ringing as a monitoring and censusing technique. Long-term study of wintering Green Sandpipers in Herts. Operator of Constant Effort Site at Stanborough Reedmarsh and nestbox scheme in mid Wales (c700 boxes), both since 1988. Expedition to Kuwait (6-27 Nov 1991) to assess impact of oiling on bird life, an

RSPB/ICBP investigation; revisited Mar-May 1995 for Kuwait Environmental Protection Council. Co-author of article on habitat use and site fidelity of Green Sandpipers in *Bird Study* 1992. Editor and contributor *North West Norfolk RG Report 1993*. OIR: general natural history, computing, crosswords. 21 Hardings, Panshanger, Welwyn Garden City, Herts AL7 2EQ. 01707 336351.

REED, Timothy Michael; *b:* 30 August 1954 in Boxmoor, Herts. BA Geography (Cambridge, 1977), DPhil Zoology (Oxford, 1981). Head of Environmental Standards, JNCC since 1991. Prev: Ornithologist, NCC 1990-91; Leader Upland Bird Survey, NCC 1981-85. Special interests: community ecology, niche processes, island landbird ecology, upland waders, turnovers and bird conservation, long-term changes in bird populations. Wide range of scientific papers in eg *Biol Cons, Biol J Linn Soc, J Animal Ecol, J Biogeography*. Member: ASAB, BES, Wader Study Group, George Wright Society (USA). OIR: family life, renovating old houses, warm climates. Highfield House, Fenstanton Road, Hilton, Cambs PE18 9JA. 01480 831464.

REENERS, Roberta (Bobbie); *b:* 13 December ('in a Baby Boom year') in Rochester, New York, USA; *p:* Rod Tuach. BA Child Psychology/Primary Education (Nazareth Coll, Rochester, NY). Publishing consultant. Ireland's organiser for Birdwatch Europe (1987) and national IWC events eg Celebrating Seabirds (1989). Editor *IWC News* since c1983. IWC Council 1983-86. Committee IWC Dublin Central Branch 1982-85 and Wicklow Branch 1986- (PRO and Publicity Officer for both). Special interest: young birdwatchers. Slide shows on feeding garden birds in winter and on wildlife gardening. Commissioning and consulting editor of *The Complete Guide to Ireland's Birds* by Eric Dempsey and Michael O'Clery (1993). Director/Editor *Irish Birdwatching*. Many broadcasts on national and local radio on bird-related subjects. Cronroe, Ashford, Co Wicklow, Ireland. +353 (0)404 40517.

REES, Eileen Catherine; *b:* 24 February 1956 in London. BSc Combined Sciences (Leicester, 1977), PhD Aspects of the migration and movements of individual Bewick's Swans (Bristol, 1988). WWT: Senior Research Officer 1988-, research scientist 1978-88, research asst to Bewick's Swan study 1977-78. Voluntary post of Whooper Swan species co-ordinator for IWRB 1988-95. Swan Specialist Group Co-ordinator for IWRB/IUCN 1995-. Special interests: migration, site selection and reproductive success of swan species, based on life histories of individual birds and by ringing;

interactions between waterfowl and their environment. Fieldwork in Britain and on expeditions to Iceland, Estonia and Arctic Russia. The 1991 expedition to Arctic Russia resulted in a five-year agreement for studying the ecology and behaviour of Bewick's Swans in their breeding range, together with Russian, Dutch and Danish scientists. Numerous scientific papers in eg *Anim Behav, Condor, Ibis, J Appl Ecol, Wildfowl*; also more general articles in *Gloucestershire Bird Report* and *Wildfowl and Wetlands*. Winston Churchill Travelling Fellowship to study Bewick's and Whooper Swans, respectively at their migratory and breeding sites, 1987. Royal Society Grant for an Overseas Study Visit, to study the breeding biology of Bewick's Swans in the Russian Arctic, 1991. Wildfowl & Wetlands Trust, Martin Mere, Burscough, Ormskirk, Lancs L40 0TA. 01704 895181.

REES, Graham Hughes Peregrine; *b:* 9 September 1936 in Llanstadwell, Pembs; *w:* Linda. Civil Servant. BTO Regional Representative Pembrokeshire 1981-96. Chairman Welsh Ornithological Society 1990-93. Member then Secretary Welsh Records Advisory Group 1984-93. Joint County Bird Recorder Pembrokeshire 1984-96. Dyfed WT: Council 1992-96, Management Committee Skokholm and Skomer Reserves 1986-96, Management Committee Marloes Mere Reserve 1989-95, Secretary Pembrokeshire Organising Committee for Ornithological Research 1980-92, Chairman Bird Group 1993-96. Special interests: all aspects of birds of Pembrokeshire 'which I regard as my patch'; seawatching (the problems of identification involved, how to rationalise 'jizz' and ways of communicating it). Travel for birds inc France, Spain, Greece, Turkey, Malta, Libya, Hong Kong. Co-author (with Jack Donovan) *Birds of Pembrokeshire* (1994). Editor *Pembrokeshire Bird Report* 1981-96, *Skokholm and Skomer Bulletin* 1986-94. Part-editor *Hampshire Bird Report* 1963-64. Occasional contributor to *Bird Watching, Birding World, Birdwatcher's Yearbook, British Birds*. Occasional radio broadcasts BBC Wales (Landmark natural history programme). 22 Priory Avenue, Haverfordwest, Pembs SA61 1SQ. 01437 762877.

REVETT, Donald Leslie; *b:* 19 February 1934 in Ipswich, Suffolk; *w:* Pamela. HNC Mech Eng 1957, Elec Eng 1958. Special Projects Manager, WWT since 1995. Prev: Manager WWT Welney Reserve 1982-95; Decoyman, Nacton Decoy 1971-82. Special interest: habitat creation and management. Frequent interviews for local radio, press and TV. Occasional assistance and presentations for national media. OIR: coastal sailing. 37 Briar Hill, Woolpit, Bury St Edmunds, Suffolk IP30 9SD. 01359 242242.

RICHARDS, Alan Jameson; *b:* 5 February 1933 in Coventry. Bablake School, Coventry. Proprietor Aquila Photographics, writer. Prev: Publicity and Publications Manager, Midshires Farmers, Worcester 1970-74. West Midland Bird Club: Secretary 1964-83, Chairman 1984-. Co-organiser of WMBC 10km bird survey (pilot survey for BTO Breeding Atlas). Co-author (with J Lord and D J Munns) *Atlas of Breeding Birds of the West Midlands* (1970) and (with G R Harrison *et al*) *The Birds of the West Midlands* (1982). Author *British Birds: a field guide* (1979), *The Birdwatcher's A-Z* (1980), *Waterside Birds* (1981), *Seabirds* (1982), *Town Birds* (1983), *Woodland Birds* (1984), *Birds of the Tideline: the shorebirds of the northern hemisphere* (1988), *The Pocket Guide to Shorebirds of the Northern Hemisphere* (1989), *Seabirds of the Northern Hemisphere* (1989). Articles in *Bird Watching* and other magazines. RSPB Salzman Prize 1950. OIR: cricket, graphic arts. PO Box 1, Studley, Warks B80 7JG. 01527 852357.

RICHARDSON, Colin Trevor; *b:* 9 May 1949 in Newcastle upon Tyne. Univ Strathclyde, School of Architecture 1967-72. RIBA (Intermediate) 1970. Architect. Director of Hobby Holidays (birdwatching tour agency) and of Hobby Publications since 1990. Bird Recorder for United Arab Emirates 1985-. Secretary Emirates Bird Records Committee 1993-. Founder-member and Bird Co-ordinator Dubai Natural History Group 1985-. Joint co-ordinator of several regional projects inc Important Bird Areas of the Middle East in 1994 and the IWRB South West Asia Waterfowl Census. UAE co-ordinator Atlas of the Breeding Birds of Arabia. Editor/compiler *Emirates Bird Report* 1987-. Compiler of official checklist of birds in the UAE, published by Emirates Bird Records Committee in 1996. Papers, articles and reports in eg *Birding World, Birdwatch, Emirates Bird Report, Oman Bird News, Phoenix, Sandgrouse*; contributor to *Birding World* and *Birdwatch*. Special interests: migration patterns through Arabia; breeding and distribution of all bird species in Arabia, esp UAE (discovered 15 new species for the UAE 1986-96). Member: OSME. PO Box 50394, Dubai, United Arab Emirates. Tel/fax: Dubai +971 4 313378.

RICHFORD, Andrew Stephen; *b:* 19 May 1952 in London; *w:* Josephine. BSc Ecological Science (Edinburgh, 1974), DPhil Ecology of Jackdaws on Skomer Island (Edward Grey Inst, Oxford, 1978). Commissioning editor at Academic Press with special responsibility for Academic Press and T & AD Poyser titles in ornithology and natural history, 1982-. Prev: Alexander Librarian, Edward Grey Institute, Univ Oxford 1980-82; freelance writer and editor for West Palaearctic Birds Ltd 1979-80; various freelance editorial work 1978-79. BOU Council 1996-. Contributor to *BWP* Vols 3 and 4. Author or co-author of papers on Black Vulture in Mallorca in *Ardeola, Oryx, Vulture News*. Member: AOU. Academic Press Ltd, 24-28 Oval Road, London NW1 7DX. 0171 267 4466.

RIDDIFORD, Nicholas John (Nick); *b:* 25 December 1948 in Stroud, Glos; *w:* Elizabeth. Marling Grammar School, Stroud 1960-67. St Paul's Coll of Education, Cheltenham 1967-72. Cert Ed (Bristol, 1971), BEd (Bristol, 1972), MPhil Migration strategies and population fluctuations (Leicester Polytechnic, 1991). Freelance ecological consultant since 1989. Principal investigator of Earthwatch Europe's Project S'Albufera (multidisciplinary research programme monitoring ecological relationships and environmental change) 1989-. Prev: Warden Fair Isle Bird Observatory 1981-89; Warden Dungeness Bird Obs 1974-80; research asst BTO Dec 1973-Feb 1974; asst warden Fair Isle Bird Obs Mar-Nov 1973; trainee at Tour du Valat Biological Station, Camargue, France Jul-Sep 1970, Jul-Sep 1971. Hon Sec Bird Observatories Council 1975-82. BTO: Ringing and Migration Committee 1980-83, migration projects advisor 1992-. BTO 'A' ringer since 1972, sponsor and trainer from 1974. Special interests: migration strategies, population fluctuations and associated displacement/range expansions, seabirds, island avifaunas, identification. Studied birds (and other fauna/flora) throughout Europe (France, Corsica, Italian Alps, former Yugoslavia, Finland, Norway, Sweden, Denmark, Holland, Spain, Balearic Islands, Portugal), Israel, Great Salvage Island, West and South Africa, and Dominica in the Lesser Antilles. Co-author of Dungeness Bird Obs section of *Bird Observatories in Britain and Ireland* ed by Roger Durman (1976). Joint author (with P Findlay) *Seasonal Movements of Summer Migrants* (1981). Author or co-author of over twenty ornithological papers in eg *Alauda, Bird Study, Birding World, British Birds, Ringing & Migration, Scottish Birds, Seabird*. Compiler/editor *Fair Isle Bird Observatory Report* 1981-88; also of numerous other reports eg Seabird Monitoring Scheme, Project S'Albufera annual reports. Lectured on migration and other topics at BTO, SOC and other conferences; lecture tours of NE USA, South Africa, Scandinavia. Migration seminars given at eg Cornell Univ, Univ of the Balearics, Univ Cape Town. Broadcasts on BBC Radio Shetland and occasionally on BBC Radio Scotland, Radios 4 and 5. Member: OSME, Seabird Group. OIR: all aspects of natural history, esp botany and entomology; learning and using modern languages (esp for encouraging young environmentalists from countries bordering the Mediterranean); Fair Isle's culture and history. Schoolton, Fair Isle, Shetland ZE2 9JU. Tel/fax 01595 760250.

RIDDINGTON, Roger; *b:* 13 October 1966 in Spilsby, Lincs; *p:* Wendy Christie. BA Geography (Oxford, 1988), DPhil Dispersal and post-fledging ecology of Great Tits (Oxford, 1992). Warden Fair Isle Bird Observatory since Mar 1994. Prev: Senior Research Associate Univ East Anglia (ecology of wintering Brent Geese) Oct 1992-Feb 1994; seabird warden FIBO 1992. Special interests: identification, migration, seabirds, human impact on birds (esp disturbance), effects of climate on bird behaviour. Co-author of papers in eg *Biol Cons*, *Bird Study*, *Birding World*, *British Birds*, *Ecology*, *Ibis*. OIR: sport, inc cycling and football. Fair Isle Bird Observatory, Fair Isle, Shetland ZE2 9JU. 01595 760258.

RIDDLE, Gordon Stewart; *b:* 2 October 1947 in Kelso, Roxburghshire; *w:* Rosemary. MA Biology and History (Edinburgh, 1969), Cert Sec Ed in Biol and Hist (Moray House Coll of Ed, 1970). Chief Ranger Culzean Country Park (Nat Trust for Scotland) since 1976. SOC Ayrshire Branch: Vice Chairman 1986-89, Chairman 1990-92. RSPB Scottish Advisory Committee 1995-. BTO 'A' ringer since 1980. Special interests: Kestrel (long-term project since 1972 on the Kestrel in Ayrshire), raptors in general, photography. Co-author diurnal raptor section of *Birds in Ayrshire* by R H Hogg (1983). Author *The Kestrel* (1990), *Seasons with the Kestrel* (1992). Papers published in *Scottish Birds*. Member: Hawk and Owl Trust, South Strathclyde Raptor Study Group (Chairman). Winston Churchill Fellowship 1981 (involvement of children in the countryside). OIR: sport, writing, hill walking, Scottish islands, environmental education, music. Swinston, Culzean Country Park, Maybole, Ayrshire KA19 8JX. 01655 760662.

RIGBY, Dominic Joseph; *b:* 14 November 1964 in Blackpool, Lancs. BSc Environmental Studies (Hatfield Polytechnic, 1987). Reserve Manager, Mere Sands Wood Nature Reserve (Lancs WT) since June 1996. Prev: WWT Martin Mere: Education Officer 1995-96, Marsh Warden 1989-95. Wetland Bird Survey count organiser W Lancs 1993-. Special interests: wildfowl ageing, identification and ringing; experienced counter. Long-term inland Shelduck breeding survey (commenced 1990). Several articles on wildfowl in *North West Birder*. Compiler of *Martin Mere Refuge Report* from inception in 1990, also contributor. OIR: moths, music, cinema, football, cricket, environmental politics and education. 88 Elmers Green, Skelmersdale, Lancs WN8 6SE. 01695 732657; work 01704 821809.

RILEY, Stephen John (Steve); *b:* 31 August 1954 in Chorley, Lancs. BA Geography (Liverpool, 1977), PGCE (Lancaster, 1981), Dip Spec Ed 1986. Teacher (children with learning difficulties). Prev: Co-ordinator Sand Dune Conservation Project (Formby Point, Merseyside), Sefton MBC. Council Lancs WT 1991-94. Conservation Officer RSPB Southport and S Ribble 1975-82. Founder and Committee, Southport RSPB Members' Group 1974-82. Warden Ribble Marshes breeding bird communities 1973-82 (responsible for all wardening schemes on S side of estuary). Wildfowl and wader counts co-ordinator S Ribble 1973-81. Special interests: long-term study of Willow Tits in mosslands of SW Lancs/N Merseyside (commenced 1974); studies of bird and plant communities in sand dunes in SW Lancs 1978-83, 1988-; identification, esp birds of prey and waders (foreign studies and large photo bank built up). Particular interest in tropical rainforest species with long expeditions to Caribbean (four), Venezuela, India/Nepal, Central America, East and Southern Africa (five), Indonesia, Australia. Also travel throughout W Palearctic and N America, inc migration studies at Bosphorus and Cape May (New Jersey). Leader of private expeditions to Kenya. Leader of bird tours to Trinidad and Tobago, Mallorca, Arctic Norway; also of many trips in UK, inc Cairngorms and Norfolk. Author *Guide to Birds and Birdwatching in the Southport Area* (1981). A number of short notes in *British Birds*; numerous articles in regional journals and bird reports. Editor *North West Birder* 1992-94. Several published photographic studies of African and Neotropical species published in eg *British Birds, Lancs Bird Report, National Geographic*. Member: NBC, OBC. OIR: botany, mammals, butterflies, dragonflies, writing, music (guitar), drawing, hill walking, cricket, basketball, conservation and ecology in general, vegetarian cooking. 25 Abbots Way, Formby, Merseyside L37 6DR. 01704 870726

RIVERS, Stuart Leslie; *b:* 11 September 1962 in Reigate, Surrey. Caterham School, Surrey 1974-81. BSc Biochemistry (Dundee, 1985), PhD Biochemistry (Dundee, 1990). Biochemist (research). Fife Bird Club: founder-member 1985, Chairman 1991-. Special interests: birds in Fife (and Scotland); identification, esp waders and buntings. Author *A Check-list of the Birds of Mainland Fife* (2nd ed 1994). Member: ABA. OIR: real ale, listening to blues/rock music. Flat 2, 2nd Floor, 10 Waverley Park, Edinburgh EH8 8EU. 0131 661 2661; work 0131 650 5353.

ROBB, Henry; *b:* 21 August 1933 in Glasgow. Merchiston Castle School, Edinburgh. BA History (Worcester College, Oxford), LLB (Glasgow). Solicitor, retired. BTO Council 1976-79, 1983-86. Chairman Tay Ringing

Group 1975-85. SOC Council 1973-79, 1980-83. Chairman SOC Stirling Branch 1980-83. BTO Regional Representative Central Region 1976-78. Chairman Isle of May Bird Observatory and Field Station Trust since 1990. Local organiser BTO Breeding Atlas 1969-72. BTO 'A' ringer since 1973. Special interests: ringing and migration, nestbox studies, Pied Flycatcher, Redstart, Tawny Owl. OIR: archaeology, opera, local history. 27 Victoria Place, Stirling FK8 2QT. 01786 473618.

ROBERTS, Anthony Howard Norman; *b:* 15 November 1938 in Woodford Green, Essex; *w:* Vivian (Dr). BSc Chemical Engineering (Leeds, 1961), BA, MA Medical Sciences (Cambridge, 1969), MA, BM, BCh (Oxford, 1970, 1972), FRCS 1976. Plastic and Hand Surgeon, Director of the Oxford Regional Burn Unit. BTO 'A' ringer since 1978 and trainer. Secretary of County Durham Ringing Group 1978-80 and of Aylesbury Vale RG 1991-, member of Wash Wader Ringing Group 1976-. Chairman Durham Bird Club 1979-80. Expedition ornithologist: British Schools Exploring Society (Lapland 1976, also second in command), Brathay Society (Faeroes 1980), Rio Mazan (Ecuador, 1986), Senegal (1992). Contributor to *A Guide to Ageing and Sexing Australian Bush Birds* by K Rogers *et al* (3rd ed 1993). Articles in Australian journals on ageing and sexing birds. OIR: sport, travel, photography. The Old House, Whitchurch, Bucks HP22 4JX. 01296 641232.

ROBERTS, Peter John; *b:* 10 July 1951 in London. MSc Ecology (Kent, 1990). MIBiol 1988. Freelance wildlife/birding tour leader since 1976. Freelance consultant since 1987 (inc regional breeding bird surveys, environmental impact assessments, museum displays). Posts: Warden Aldabra Research Station, Seychelles 1986; NCC Warden Ham Street Woods 1984-85 and Stodmarsh 1983; Warden Bardsey Bird Observatory and Field Centre 1976-82. Committee Bardsey BOFC 1983-86. Committee Sandwich Bay Bird Obs 1968-72, Secretary 1970-72. BTO 'B' ringer since 1971. Special interests: ringing and migration studies, identification, seabird studies, island zoogeography, wildlife photography. Worldwide travel for birds and wildlife (esp Africa, Europe, N America). Four-year study of Chough ecology. Three years research into invertebrate biomass in relation to woodland bird feeding (MSc thesis). Author *African Wildlife* (1989), *The Birds of Bardsey* (1985). Editor *Sandwich Bay Bird Obs Rept* 1968-72; author and contributor *Bardsey Bird Obs Ann Rept* 1976-82. Scientific papers and notes in eg *Biol Cons, Bird Study, British Birds*. Photographs in eg *Country Life*.

Member: ABA. OIR: larger mammals (inc whale watching), snorkelling (esp on coral reefs). Flat 3, Eyhorne Cottage, Hollingbourne, Kent ME17 1UY. Tel/fax: 01622 880319.

ROBERTS, Thomas Jones (Tom); Sitara-i-Imtiaz (Star of Service) from Govt of Pakistan 1993; *b:* 2 September 1924 in Bangor, Gwynedd; *w:* Frances. Rugby School. MA Agric Econ (Cambridge, 1948), MSA Agric Econ (British Columbia, 1950), PhD Biological Sciences (Cambridge, 1993). Founding Governor of WWF Pakistan. Member of Punjab Wildlife Management Board 1970-77 and of Sind WMB 1979-84. Proprietor of cotton business in Pakistan, retired. Employed by FAO as Project Director 1973-80, establishing a Vertebrate Pest Control Centre in Pakistan, which included investigating bird damage to crops. Executive Committee ICBP 1982-86. RSPB Wales Committee 1987-90. Special interest: birds of Pakistan. Travelled very extensively in Far East. Co-editor *Encyclopedia of Indian Natural History* (1988). Author *The Birds of Pakistan* (Vol 1 1991, Vol 2 1992). Fellow of Linnean Society, member of OBC since foundation. OIR: general natural history, photography. Cae Gors, Rhoscefnhir, Pentraeth, Anglesey, Gwynedd LL75 8YU. 01248 450242.

ROBERTSON, Iain Stewart; *b:* 25 November 1949 in Tunbridge Wells, Kent. Milne's Institute, Fochabers, Moray. Freelance bird tour leader, author and editor since 1981. Prev: Warden Fair Isle Bird Observatory 1978-80; Warden Portland Bird Obs 1975-78; asst warden Fair Isle Bird Obs, 1970-71; asst warden RSPB Fetlar 1968-69, 1972. Shetland Ringing Group 1981-86. Seabird monitoring for SOTEAG 1981,85,86. Founder Shetland Bird Club, Secretary 1973-74, Committee 1973-74, 1981-86, 1996-. British Birds Rarities Committee 1985-90. Member of launch committee and editorial team of African Bird Club 1992-. Special interests: birds of Africa, Malagasy, Thailand, Western Palearctic. Travel for birds in thirty-five countries in all continents since 1968. Papers and short notes, esp on identification and distribution, in *British Birds, Bull BOC, Malimbus, Nat Hist Bull Siam Soc, OBC Bulletin, Sandgrouse, Scopus, Scottish Birds*. Editor *Breeding Birds of Europe* by Pforr and Limbrunner (1981), *Birds of the Mediterranean and Alps* by Lars Jonsson (1982). Compiler *Shetland Bird Report* 1973, editor 1984. Chapter on birds in *The Natural History of Shetland* by Berry and Johnston (1980). Member: ABC, OBC, OSME, WAOS. OIR: grousing. Laurelbank, Exnaboe, Virkie, Shetland ZE3 9JS. 01950 460782.

ROBERTSON, Keith David; *b:* 1 October 1951 in Coventry, Warks; *w:* Wendy. BA Chemistry (York, 1973), DPhil Biochemistry (York, 1978). Senior Ranger, Worsbrough Country Park, Barnsley 1983-92. Prev: Ranger, Howell Wood CP near Barnsley 1978-83. Special interest: survey work. BTO Common Birds Census 1979-83; survey of breeding birds of Worsbrough CP 1985 and 1987; plus BTO surveys inc atlas work, Pilot Census Project, Farmland Buntings, Rookeries Census, Breeding Bird Survey. Author of booklet *Flora and Fauna of Worsbrough Country Park* (1996). Contributor, illustrator and editor *Worsbrough Country Park Bird Report* 1984-92. OIR: photography, other natural history (esp flora, fungi and moths). Southfield, Main Road, Roughton, Woodhall Spa, Lincs LN10 6YJ. 01507 522844.

ROBINSON, Martin Colgate; *b:* 13 August 1948 in Iford, Lewes, E Sussex; *w:* Judy. Bradfield College. BA German (Sheffield, 1970). RSPB Warden Killiecrankie since 1982 (also responsible for Loch of Kinnordy and Fowlsheugh); previously Fetlar, Elmley, Arne, Aylesbeare, Loch Garten, Leighton Moss and Morecambe Bay. RSPB contract warden: Fetlar 1973,74; Coquet Island 1972; Bempton 1971. Council Ornithological Soc of Turkey 1975-77. Tutor for adult education evening classes: Ambleside, Kendal, Lancaster, Morecambe 1979-81. Leader, Highland Field Studies courses 1987. Founder Perthshire Black Grouse Study Group 1990. Tayside Raptor Study Group 1991-. Perth and Kinross Records Committee 1993-. Special interests: upland birds (esp Black Grouse), owls (esp Snowy), raptors, woodland species, wetlands. Widely travelled in Europe, Near and Middle East, Africa, India and Nepal. Published papers on breeding Snowy Owls (*British Birds*) and survey of Black Grouse (*Scottish Birds*). Broadcast on Black Grouse (Radio Scotland). OIR: botany (esp bryophytes), entomology, photography, drawing, music. Balrobbie Farm, Killiecrankie, Pitlochry, Perthshire PH16 5LJ. 01796 473200.

ROBINSON, Peter John; *b:* 26 February 1939 in Frien Barnet, North London; *w:* Susan. Fellow Inst Professional Investigators 1984, Principal 1987-89, Hon Life Member from 1989. Grad Member Inst of Fire Engineers 1972. Self-employed ornithologist and writer since 1990. Contracted by English Nature and Isles of Scilly Environmental Trust from 1992 to survey seabird productivity and distribution in the Isles of Scilly. Prev: Senior RSPB Investigations Officer 1974-90, responsible for the Society's investigation and prosecution activities under conservation legislation. English Nature voluntary warden Isles of Scilly since 1990. Founder-member and Secretary Isles of Scilly Seabird Group 1991. BTO

'C' ringer since 1992. Special interests: world bird trade and associated administrative and enforcement issues, egg identification, species' breeding and distribution surveys, seabird breeding biology, removal of mammalian predators from seabird colonies. BTO Nest Record Scheme participant 1960-. Song Thrush study on Isles of Scilly since 1990. Widely travelled for birds in Europe, Africa (also ringed in W and E Africa), Middle East, Central America, USA. Author *Bird Detective* (1981). Editor *Isles of Scilly Bird Report* 1990-. Various reports eg 'Falconry in Britain' commissioned by League Against Cruel Sports (1991), 'Breeding Seabirds in the Isles of Scilly' for English Nature (1992/94). Articles on conservation law and legal status of species, eg 'The Legal Status of Diurnal Birds of Prey in Africa' in *Raptors in the Modern World* by World Working Group on Birds of Prey (1989); also member of Group 1980-90. OIR: writing, people, computers, photography, American football. Riviera House, Parade, St Mary's, Isles of Scilly TR21 0LP. 01720 23057.

ROBINSON, Roy William; *b:* 27 February 1946 in Welwyn Garden City, Herts; *w:* Raye. City & Guilds (Technicians Course Part 2) 1962-67. Partner in Bird Information Service (Birdline and *Birding World* magazine) since 20 May 1987. Graphics Editor and Data Manager *Birding World* since 1987. Proprietor (and originator) of Birdline Aug 1986-May 1987. Proprietor Birdtech since 1990. Prev: Warden Norfolk Ornithologists' Association at Walsey Hills Information Centre and Migration Watchpoint 1980-86. Special interests: visible migration, computers. Competed in Manx Motor Cycle Grand Prix 1968 and 1971. 33 Blackbird Close, Bradwell, Great Yarmouth, Norfolk NR31 8RT. 01493 600966; fax 01493 442445.

ROCK, Peter; *b:* 27 September 1951 in Tidworth, Wilts. BA Fine Art (Newcastle, 1975), Cert Ed, ATD (Bristol, 1977). Teacher, Head of Creative Arts, Badminton School, Bristol. BTO 'A' ringer since 1979 and sponsor. Member of Chew Valley Ringing Station. EURING co-ordinator for colour-marking of large gulls since 1990. Special interest: urban Lesser Black-backed and Herring Gulls in Bristol. Several expeditions to Portugal, Spain and Morocco to find Bristol-ringed gulls; bird ringing and atlasing in several countries, esp Portugal (over twenty visits). Article in *BBC Wildlife* on urban gulls. Scientific adviser for various TV films inc *Herrag the Gull* (BBC 1987), *Seabird City* (RSPB 1988), *Seagull Story* (BBC 1989), *Nature Detectives* (BBC 1993). Several radio interviews, mainly for BBC *Natural History Programme*. OIR: good friends, good food and good wine. 59 Concorde Drive, Bristol BS10 6PX. 0117 907 8041.

RODERICK, Hywel Wyn; *b:* 6 June 1954 in Aberystwyth, Ceredigion. Ardwyn Grammar School, Aberystwyth. HNC Applied Biology (Aberystwyth Coll of FE, 1974), BA Science (Open Univ, 1984). Plant Pathologist, Inst of Grassland and Environmental Research, Aberystwyth. Council Welsh Ornithological Society 1988-. Hon warden Dyfed WT reserves at Old Warren Hill and Coed Penglanowen 1976-88, 1992-. Special interests: Chough ecology, waterfowl in Cardigan Bay, history of local avifauna. Editor *Ceredigion Bird Report* 1984-. Author or co-author of articles in *Bird Watching, Ceredigion Bird Report, Nature in Wales.* 32 Prospect Street, Aberystwyth SY23 1JJ. 01970 617681.

RODWELL, Stephen Philip; *b:* 18 August 1966 in Princes Risborough, Bucks. BSc Forestry (Univ Coll North Wales, 1987). Ornithologist. British Antarctic Survey: zoological field asst at Bird Island, South Georgia participating in studies of penguins and albatrosses, also contract staff at HQ Aug 1987-May 1990, Jan-Mar 1993. Wetland Trust: member of team studying migratory birds in Sussex and West Africa (Senegal and Guinea-Bissau) annually 1991-94. Field/research asst Edward Grey Institute and RSPB for periods in 1992 and 1993. Special interests: moult of albatrosses, penguin biology, Palearctic migrants, African ornithology. Member of Italian ringing team on Mediterranean Islands Project and Italian/UK team studying terns on the Ivory Coast (1991). Co-author of papers in *The Auk, Condor, Emu, Ibis, Marine Biol,* and *Seabird.* Member: WAOS. 53 Stratton Road, Princes Risborough, Bucks HP27 9BH. 01844 344246.

ROGERS, Edgar Paul (Paul); *b:* 7 October 1940 in Shelfield, Walsall, W Midlands; *w:* Christine. Queen Mary's Grammar School, Walsall 1952-59. Cert Ed in Chemistry, Physics and Biology (Goldsmith's Coll, London, 1963). MIBiol, CIBiol 1972. Director Shorelands Birdwatching and Wildlife Holidays since 1988. Leader for other birdwatching holidays inc Ornitholidays, Caravan Club, Field Studies Council 1986-91. Lecturer Extra-mural Dept of Surrey Univ in ornithology and natural history 1978-88, and for London Univ Extra-mural Dept in ornithology, nat hist and conservation 1971-78. Leader East Surrey RSPB Members' Group 1983-88. BTO 'C' ringer since 1980. Special interests: migration, photography. Participant in Gwynedd Barn Owl Project organised by CCW, monitoring breeding behaviour and success 1990-. Travel inc most of Europe; also Antarctica, The Gambia, Madagascar, Senegal, Morocco, Zimbabwe, USA (Arizona, Florida, Texas). Travel articles with photographs and site guides in eg *Bird Watching, Birds, Birdwatch.* Address is former home of late Charles Tunnicliffe RA, bird and wildlife artist;

research into Tunnicliffe's life and work has led to several TV appearances and radio broadcasts. OIR: wildlife art, walking, sport (esp squash, cricket), folk music. Shorelands, Malltraeth, Anglesey LL62 5AT. 01407 840396.

ROGERS, Michael John; *b:* 5 October 1932 in Sutton Coldfield, West Midlands. King Edward's School, Birmingham. Metropolitan Police 1958-81. Recorder Sussex Ornithological Society 1978-83. Recorder/Editor, Isles of Scilly (Cornwall Birdwatching & Preservation Society) 1982-90. Hon Secretary, British Birds Rarities Committee 1978-. Founder of Assocn of County Recorders and Editors in 1993 and its Secretary since then. Special interest: rare birds. Compiler of 'Rare Birds in Great Britain', published annually in *British Birds*, commencing with report for 1977. 'Ruddy Shelducks in Britain 1965-79' published in *British Birds* 1982. 2 Churchtown Cottages, Towednack, St Ives, Cornwall TR26 3AZ. 01736 796223.

ROLLIE, Christopher John (Chris); *b:* 10 December 1957 in New Cumnock, Ayrshire; *w:* Catherine. BSc Biology (Stirling, 1980), Cert Ed (Jordanhill Coll, Glasgow, 1981). RSPB Conservation Officer, Dumfries & Galloway since 1991. Supervisor, Habitat Survey of Cumnock & Doon Valley District 1981-82. South Strathclyde Raptor Study Group 1984-. Founder-member and Secretary/Chairman Dumfries & Galloway Raptor Study Group 1990-. Initiated Hen Harrier wing-tagging project in S Scotland 1988. Co-ordinator: Breeding Raven Survey of S Scotland and Northumberland 1989 and 1994; Beached Bird Survey, D & G 1991-; Merlin Survey, SW Scotland 1993-94; Corncrake Survey, SW Scotland 1993. Member Galloway Forest Bird Project 1992-. Special interest: open country raptors and Raven. Various interviews on radio and TV on a number of ornithological items/issues from 1990. Film credit for RSPB film *Skydancer* (Hen Harrier). OIR: hill walking, travelling, Robert Burns. Moorglen, 22 Main Street, St John's Town of Dalry, Kirkcudbrightshire DG7 3UW. 01644 430581.

ROPER, Paul; *b:* 20 June 1964 in Hoddesdon, Herts; *w:* Carol. Manager for Royal Mail. BTO 'A' ringer since 1989. Hon Secretary Rye Meads Ringing Group since 1991. Junior Leader of Norwich YOC Group 1979-81. Special interests: ageing and sexing, moult, changes in colour of soft parts with age, birds and weather, photography, taxidermy. Projects inc colour-ringing study of Water Pipit since 1993; assistance with cannon-netting of Sandwich Terns and with colour-ringing of Chough pulli on Isle of Man. Illustrations published in several issues of *Herts Bird Report* and *Rye Meads RG Report*; also for logos, magazine/leaflet covers. Member: Guild of Taxidermists.

OIR: motorcycling, walking, squash, swimming, abseiling. 3 Dewhurst Old School, Churchgate, Cheshunt, Herts EN8 9WB. 01992 640388.

ROSAIR, David Basil; *b:* 26 June 1948 in Glasgow. Wimbledon College. BSc Biochemistry (St Andrews, 1969). Ornithologist. Director Kentish Bird Tours since 1992. Leader of overseas tours for Wildwings. Kent Ornithological Society: Executive Committee and Recorder in late 1970s. Special interest: identification and study of waders esp ageing, moult, migration and associated environment. Major ongoing project to observe and study all the world's wader species. Related travel to over sixty countries inc expeditions to Japan, Alaska, Ecuador and Paraguay, Argentina, India, Australia, New Zealand. Author *Hamlyn Photographic Guide to the Waders of the World* (photographs assembled by David Cottridge) (1995). Work commenced on new Palearctic wader guide. Articles on wader identification in *Birding World*, *Birdwatch*, *British Birds*. OIR: gardening, music, dining out. Seaview Caravan Park, St Johns Road, Whitstable, Kent CT5 2RY. 01227 794503.

ROSE, Harvey Ernest; *b:* 10 April 1936 in London; *w:* Rita. BSc Mathematics (Leicester, 1958), PhD (Leicester, 1961). University lecturer. County Bird Recorder Avon since 1987. Vice President Bristol Naturalists' Society 1993 and 1994. Local organiser Birds of Estuaries Enquiry/ Wetland Bird Survey 1982-. Special interests: wader studies, migration. Papers on the birds of Clevedon Bay (*Bristol Ornithology*, 1992) and birds of the Avon shore (*Proc Bristol Nat Soc*, 1992); also writer of numerous parts of *Avon Bird Report* from 1985. Member: Australasian Wader Study Group, Wader Study Group. OIR: listening to classical music. 12 Birbeck Road, Bristol BS9 1BD. 0117 968 1638; work 0117 928 7992.

ROSELAAR, Cornelis Simon (Kees); *b:* 16 May 1947 in Hoorn, Netherlands; *p:* Irene Maas. Biology studies at Univ Amsterdam 1966-74; Drs degree 1986. Collection Manager, Information Officer and Associate Scientist of Bird Dept, Zoological Museum, Univ Amsterdam since 1970. Bird Remains Identification Officer, Royal Netherlands Airforce since 1992 (identification of birds to family or species by tiny fragments of down remains). Member, Commissie Dwaalgasten Nederlands Avifauna (CDNA, Dutch Rarities Committee) 1975-83 (Secretary), 1990-. Special interests: bird taxonomy, esp study of geographical variation of Palearctic birds. Ringer at Castricum Ringing Station. Seabird counter at Hondsbosse Zeewering. Author of sections on families, nomenclature, subspecies, plumages, bare parts, moults, measurements, weights, structure, geographical variation, and recognition for each bird species in *BWP* (inc 10th updating volume with additional and split species). Author *Songbirds of Turkey* (1995). Co-author (with D Jones and R W R J Dekker) *The Megapodes* (1995); (with H Shirihai) geographical variation and taxonomic notes in *The Birds of Israel* by H Shirihai (1996); (with M Engelmoer) *Geographical Variation of Holarctic Waders* (in press). Numerous papers published in eg *Ardea*, *Beaufortia* (on subspecies of Knot), *Dutch Birding*, *Ringing & Migration*, *Wader Study Group Bull*, *Watervogels* and conference procs. Member: Dutch Birding Assocn, Nederlandse Ornithologische Unie, OSME. Wrangel/Alaskan breeding Knot *Calidris canutus roselaari* named after C S Roselaar by P S Tomkovich (Moscow) in 1990. Zoölogisch Museum der Universteit van Amsterdam, Bird Dept, Postbox 94766, 1090 GT Amsterdam (visitors' address: Mauritskade 61). +31 20 5255423; home +31 72 5125423.

ROSSITER, Brian Nicholas (Nick); *b:* 12 January 1944 in Dawlish, Devon; *w:* Anna. BSc Chemistry (Hull, 1965), PhD Chemistry (Hull, 1970). University lecturer in computing science. Committee Northumberland & Tyneside Bird Club 1983-. BTO Regional Representative Northumberland 1984-90. European Breeding Atlas co-ordinator, N Northumberland 1987. BTO Breeding Atlas co-ordinator N Northumberland 1988-92. Northumberland County Breeding Atlas co-ordinator and editor 1987-95. Birds of Estuaries Enquiry count organiser Northumberland 1990-92. County Bird Recorder Northumberland 1990-. Special interests: upland birds, gull roosts. Long-term study of Common Gull numbers, movements and breeding in NE England (commenced 1983). Articles published in *Birds in Northumbria* (annual report) on the results of surveys of Buzzard, Mute Swan, Ringed Plover, Cormorant, Green Woodpecker, Lapwing, other waders and Goosander made in Northumberland from 1983-87. Co-editor *Birds in Northumbria* from 1990 issue. OIR: walking, Lepidoptera, opera (esp Wagner). West Barn, Lee Grange, Ordley, Hexham, Northumberland NE46 1SX. 01434 673509.

ROUSE, Andrew Stephen (Andy); *b:* 15 January 1965 in London; *p:* Julia Van Gorkom. BSc Electrical and Electronic Engineering (Plymouth Polytechnic, 1987). Professional wildlife photographer. Main interests: birds of prey, woodpeckers, kingfishers; Schedule 1 photography licence holder for nest photography of these species. Photography-related travel in India, Africa, Alaska, Canadian Arctic, New Zealand. Wide variety of work published in eg *BBC Wildlife*, *Bird Watching*, *Birds*, *Nat Geog*, *Vie Sauvage*; also prints, inc limited editions. Voluntary work for Hawk and Owl Trust inc Barn Owl Survey for Surrey in 1994, and manager of slide library in same year. Brambles, 75 Furze Hill Road, Bordon, Hants GU35 8HB. 01428 712371

ROXBURGH, Richard (Dick); *b:* 8 June 1920 in Catrine, Ayrshire; *w:* Martha. Retired. Co-ordinator/Chairman SW Scotland Raptor Study Group 1980-90. Co-ordinator S Strathclyde Raptor Study Group 1990-. Co-ordinator of Peregrine surveys in SW Scotland 1971, 1981, 1991. Special interests: raptors and other 'hill' birds. Co-author (with M Marquiss and D A Ratcliffe) 'Breeding success and diet of Golden Eagles in southern Scotland in relation to change in land use' in *Biol Cons* 1985. Acknowledged in many papers on SW Scotland raptors, also in books eg Donald Watson's *The Hen Harrier* (1977) and D A Ratcliffe's *The Peregrine Falcon* (1980) and *Bird Life of Mountain and Upland* (1990). RSPB President's Award 1992 for lifetime contribution to bird conservation. OIR: local history, reading, hill walking. Upper Flat, 2 Cornmill Street, Catrine, Ayrshire KA5 6QT. 01290 551384.

RUSSELL, Anastasia (Tasie); *b:* London; *h:* David. Waterperry Horti-cultural School (Diploma); Royal Hort Soc Cert. Part-time in husband's hardy plant nursery. Short contracts: Lower Avon Valley bird survey (NCC 1990); rare birds on heathland SSSIs in Eastern Dorset (EN 1991); Wanderwell Quarry and green corridor (Dorchester) bird surveys (W Dorset DC 1993); Woodlark and Dartford Warbler survey, Turnerspuddle Heath, Bovington Camp (MOD 1993). Secretary Purbeck NHS c1965-67. Portland Bird Observatory Committee 1965-75. Committee Dorset Bird Club (Dorset Nat Hist & Archaeol Soc) 1964-87; Committee and Field Meetings Organiser (New) Dorset Bird Club 1987-92. Bovington Conservation Committee (MOD) 1977-. Hawk & Owl Trust Projects Advisory Committee 1993-95. County co-ordinator National Peregrine Survey 1991. Voluntary warden Morden NNR since early 1980s. Special interests: study of Hobby population in Dorset since 1976 (awarded grant by British Ecol Soc to study status of Hobby in heathland areas of Dorset in 1983); Hen Harrier and Merlin Winter Roost Survey from 1984/85. Member: Hawk & Owl Trust, OBC. OIR: drawing, painting, music, books, pictures, photography, carvings, travel. 33 Bryantspuddle, Dorchester, Dorset DT2 7HT. Tel/fax 01929 471414.

RUTTLEDGE, Robert Francis (Robin, 'Jim' in India); MC 1924, Waztristan; Major Retd; *b:* 11 September 1899 in Carlow, Ireland; *w:* Rose. Marlborough College. ScD (Trinity College Dublin, 1981) the first and only ornithologist to be given this honour. Officer Indian Cavalry, Poona Horse, retired. Commandant, The Governor of Madras Bodyguard 1934-39. President Irish Wildbird Conservancy 1968-72. Sometime Irish representative on Goose Research Panel of IWRB. Founder and Director Saltee Bird Observatory 1950-62. Special interests: migration, distribution, conservation, Greenland White-fronted Goose. Joint author *Birds of Ireland* (1954). Author *A List of the Birds of the Counties of Galway and Mayo* (1950), *Ireland's Birds* (1966), *A List of the Birds of Ireland* (1980), *Birds in Counties Galway and Mayo* (1994). Contributor to *The Handbook of British Birds* (1938-41), *The Birds of Dublin and Wicklow* ed by Clive Hutchinson (1975), and *BWP* Vol 1 (1977). Some two hundred and fifty papers and notes published in Irish and English journals. Editor *Irish Birds* 1953-72. Awarded Bernard Tucker Medal in 1961 for outstanding service in the field investigations of the BTO. 'Together with another man I "fought" the owners of Wexford North Slob severely (but with no words of anger) to let a portion of the North Slob become a reserve for Greenland White-fronted Geese. To this they eventually agreed and the Irish Government designated a part of the Slob as a bird sanctuary.' OIR: pig-sticking; fox hunting; jackal hunting in India 'where I was Master and Huntsman of the Peshawar Vale Hounds and later of the Madras Hounds'; Snipe and Woodcock shooting for some time 'until I eventually gave it up, not wishing to continue killing the birds'; trout fishing. Doon, Newcastle, Greystones, Co Wicklow, Ireland. +353 (0)1 2819237.

SAFFORD, Roger James; *b:* 16 August 1967 in Richmond Surrey. BA Natural Sciences (Cambridge, 1988), PhD Conservation of the forest-living birds of Mauritius (Durrell Inst of Cons and Ecol, Univ Kent, 1994). SE Asia projects co-ordinator, Royal Holloway Institute for Environmental Research, Univ London from Aug 1995. Prev: Mauritian Wildlife Appeal Fund: leader of project on conservation of endemic passerine birds 1989-93. African Waterfowl Census: National Co-ordinator, Mauritius 1990-93. Member IUCN Species Survival Commission since 1991. Jersey Wildlife Preservation Trust: first capture of Madagascar Teal for captive breeding programme (1993). Special interests: all aspects of western Indian Ocean and African natural history and conservation, esp birds. Five years in this area (1988-93), largely in Mauritius (above) but one year total in Madagascar (wildlife surveys of rainforest 1988, and wetlands 1993), three visits to Comoro Islands (rediscovered Anjouan Scops Owl in 1992); also Ethiopia, Seychelles, Réunion and Rodrigues; conservation and management of wetlands, esp in Vietnam. Papers in various journals, mainly on Indian Ocean and African faunistics and conservation. Founder-member

ABC (1994) and of Working Group on Birds in the Madagascar Region (1992). OIR: all natural history (esp mammals), sport, mountaineering and trekking, photography. 16 Berwyn Road, Richmond, Surrey TW10 5BS. 0181 876 5179.

SALAMAN, Paul George William; *b:* 27 January 1971 in Australia. Raynes Park High School 1984-89. BSc Environmental Biology (Anglia Polytechnic Univ, 1994). Voluntary warden Dungeness RSPB Reserve Jul-Aug 1987. Committee Surrey Bird Club and Records Committee London NHS 1989-93, and Bird Recorder for Surrey-in-London. Committee Cambridge Bird Club 1991-94. President Cambridge Student Birders (student section of CBC) 1991-93. Assisted in organisation of first National Student Bird Race (1992). Special interests: bird censuses and surveys; ringing (UK and Colombia); sound recording (Colombia and Australia); forest falcons in SW Colombia (doctoral research 1995-98). Leader of three ornithological/ conservation expeditions to SW Colombia 1991-93. Discovered the Chocó Vireo (*Vireo masteri*) new to science (*Ibis*, 1996), also five new species for Colombia and many range and altitude extensions, and rediscovered Tumaco Seedeater there in 1994 after eighty-two years 'lost'. Co-author of papers in eg *Cotinga, Ibis, World Pheasant Assocn J.* Pen-and-ink illustrations published in various annual reports (eg *Fair Isle Bird Obs Report*) and magazines (eg *British Birds*); also exhibited in Mall Galleries, London 1987 and 1988. Expeditions to Colombia presented in several magazines (eg *Reader's Digest*), national newspapers and local radio. Lectures to: Prince Bernhard at BP Conservation Expedition Award (1992), BOC, Royal Geog Soc, EGI (Univ Oxford). Young Ornithologist of the Year (Senior Section) 1988. Winner first international BP Conservation Expedition Award by BirdLife International and Fauna and Flora Pres Soc. Lecture winner at EGI student conference 1993. Member: NBC. Wrote conservation proposal for, and initiated implementation of, Río Ñambi Community Nature Reserve (1992). 28 Oakway, West Wimbledon, London SW20 9JE. 0181 542 8741.

SALMON, David Gregory; *b:* 29 August 1954 in Bushey, Herts. Senior Development Officer, WWT since 1995. Prev WWT: Development Officer 1993-95; Fundraising Officer 1990-93; Scientific Officer and Organiser, National Wildfowl Counts 1979-89; Asst Sci Off 1973-79; Clerical Officer 1971-73. Special interest: wildfowl. Co-author (with M Owen and G L Atkinson-Willes) *Wildfowl in Great Britain* (2nd ed 1986). Editor and co-author *Wildfowl and Wader Counts* 1980-89. Author or co-author of numerous papers on wildfowl distribution and numbers in eg *Biol Cons,*

Bird Study, *British Birds*, *Proc Linn Soc*, *Wildfowl*. OIR: choral singing, theatre, railways. c/o WWT, Slimbridge, Gloucester GL2 7BT. 01453 890333.

SANDILANDS, Gary James; *b:* 11 June 1955 in Stockport, Cheshire; *w:* Gillian. BSc 1977, MSc 1978, PhD 1983 Engineering Materials (Newcastle). CEng 1988. Materials testing engineer. Montgomeryshire WT: Chairman Llanidloes Local Group 1992- Voluntary warden Llyn Mawr Reserve 1991-. Special interests: identification, photography, survey work. Participant in pilot census for BTO Breeding Atlas; also Whooper Swan, Nightjar, winter wildfowl counts since 1991. Overseas birding inc USA (Texas), Sweden, Netherlands, Japan. OIR: 'Barbra Streisand, Manchester United and "pints" - and not necessarily in that order.' Pen-y-Coppi, Carno, Powys SY17 5JP. 01686 420388.

SANKEY, Jack; *b:* 17 September 1931 in Croft, Lancs (now Ches). Newton-le-Willows Grammar School. Trained as mechanical engineer at Leigh, Wigan and Liverpool Colleges. Draughtsman 1954-65. Teacher 1965-86. County Bird Recorder Shropshire 1984-90. YOC Leader at Wm Brookes School, Much Wenlock 1969-85. Extra-mural ornithological classes and field meetings for Univ Birmingham and Bridgnorth College. Slide/talks to local clubs and societies. Committee for Shropshire breeding bird atlas project 1985-90. County co-ordinator for several BTO surveys. Special interest: Shropshire species, especially the recording of breeding status. Co-author (with Graham Harrison) *Where to Watch Birds in the West Midlands* (1987). Contributor to *An Atlas of the Breeding Birds of Shropshire* by P Deans *et al* (1992). Several articles for eg *Birdwatcher's Yearbook*, *British Birds*, *The Countryman*, *Shropshire Bird Report*, *Shropshire Wildlife*. Black-and-white sketches published in Shropshire literature inc *Atlas of the Breeding Birds of Shropshire* (above) and various natural history reports. Occasional interviews for local radio. OIR: formerly Lancs champion race walker, now rugby league spectator (Wigan supporter), theatre and cinema, sketching, rambling and camping, evenings with friends at the local. 11 Mardol Terrace, Much Wenlock, Shrops TF13 6BH. 01952 727761.

SAUNDERS, David Raymond; *b:* 13 December 1937 in Nailsworth, Glos; *w:* Shirley. Stroud Boys Technical School; Stroud Tech Coll. Director Dyfed Wildlife Trust since 1976. First Warden (for West Wales Field Society, later Dyfed WT) of the Skomer Island NNR 1960-66. Organiser of the first national seabird census, Operation Seafarer, for the Seabird Group 1968-71. Special interests: seabirds, writing. Author *Seabirds* (1971),

A Guide to the Birds of Wales (1974), *Birdwatching* (1975), *RSPB Guide to British Birds* (1975, over 200,000 copies sold), *A Brief Guide to the Birds of Pembrokeshire* (1976), *Where to Watch Birds in Wales* (1987, 2nd ed 1992), *Rare Birds of the British Isles* (1991). Co-author (with Stanley Cramp and W R P Bourne) *The Seabirds of Britain and Ireland* (1974). Editor *The Nature of West Wales* (1986). Paper, 'Blackburnian Warbler: new to the Western Palearctic' in *British Birds* 1992; also numerous popular articles since 1962. OIR: polar, maritime and military history (editor of *The Gallipolian* for the Gallipoli Association). Woosung, Pointfields, Hakin, Milford Haven, Pembrokeshire SA73 3EB. 01646 692316; office 01437 765462; fax 767163.

SCHOFIELD, Peter; *b:* 4 July 1933 in Leeds; *w:* Jacqueline. MA Natural Sciences, Economics (Emmanuel College, Cambridge, 1957). Environmental consultant since 1993. Prev: Director of Resources, Countryside Council for Wales 1990-92. Earlier Nature Conservancy Council: Reorganisation Unit Wales 1989-90; Regional Officer, South England 1976-89; Deputy to Director, Wales 1973-76; Asst to Director of Conservation, Wales 1968-73. Founder and Hon Sec Mid Cheshire Ornithological Society 1964-68. Hon Warden T A Coward Memorial Reserve, Marbury, Cheshire 1966-68. Council Cheshire Conservation Trust 1964-68. Cheshire Bird Recording Committee 1966-68. President Cambrian Ornithological Society 1973-75, 1991-94. Council RSPB Wales 1974-76. Hon Member Newbury District Ornithologcal Club 1976-96. Council and Scientific Committee, Bardsey Bird and Field Observatory 1972-88. Council Welsh Ornithological Society 1992-96. Council Member and Chairman, Gwynedd Conservation Committee of North Wales Wildlife Trust 1992-95. Eurosite: Chairman of Management Plan Working Group 1989-92, Vice President 1989-96. Chairman North Wales WT 1996. Council, Royal Society for Nature Conservation 1996. Special interests: birds and islands, birds and rivers, birds and estuaries, birds of Central Europe (Poland, Czech and Slovak Republics, Hungary), conservation of bird habitats, management of bird reserves. Travel for birds to Brazil, Peru, USA, New Zealand, Japan, W and Central Europe, Scandinavia, Seychelles. Expedition to Lista, Norway for bird migration 1955. Author *The 'Magpie' Book of British Birds* (1978). Joint author (with Kenneth Williamson *et al*) *Wildlife in Britain* (1976), and (with Pat Morris *et al*) *The Natural History of the British Isles* (1979). Articles in eg *Bird Study, Country Life*; bulletins on islands, rivers, nature reserves and local area studies. Broadcasts on *Living World* and *Wildlife* for BBC. Churchill Fellow 1991. Member: Seabird Group. Interests include the structure, performance and development of voluntary conservation and ornithological bodies. OIR: landscape painting, rugby football, hill walking. Llwyn Onn, Tal y Bont, Bangor, Gwynedd LL57 3YH. 01248 353690.

SCOTT, Derek Albert; *b:* 27 June 1944 in Bradford, Yorks; *w:* Joanna. Bradford Grammar School 1955-63. BA Zoology (St John's College, Oxford, 1966), DPhil Breeding biology of the Storm Petrel (Edward Grey Institute, Univ Oxford, 1970). Independent consultant (ornithology, wildlife management, wetland conservation) since 1979. Prev: Advisor on Ornithology to the Iran Department of the Environment 1970-76. Wide range of consultancies primarily for international conservation bodies (eg IWRB, WWF, IUCN); also for UN agencies, national governments (Libya, Oman) and private companies. Special interests: waterbirds and their habitats, seabirds, desert birds, forest birds. Extensive travel worldwide. Over 6,300 species seen. Author *A Preliminary Inventory of Wetlands of International Importance for Waterfowl in West Europe and Northwest Africa* (1980). Co-author (with H M Hamadani and A A Mirhosseyni) *The Birds of Iran* (1975); (with C M Poole) *A Status Overview of Asian Wetlands* (1989); (with C Perennou and T Mundkur) *Asian Waterfowl Census 1987-91* (1994); (with P M Rose) *Waterfowl Population Estimates* (1994). Editor *Managing Wetlands and their Birds* (1982); *A Directory of Asian Wetlands* (1989); *A Directory of Wetlands in Oceania* (1993); *A Directory of Wetlands in the Middle East* (1995). Co-editor (with M Carbonell) *A Directory of Neotropical Wetlands* (1986); (with P Cromarty) *A Directory of Wetlands in New Zealand* (1996). Papers published in eg *Bird Cons Internat, Forktail, Ibis, Sandgrouse, World Pheasant Assocn J*; also numerous unpublished reports. Member: ABC, NBC, OBC, OSME, NBC. Runagate, Far Green, Coaley, Dursley, Glos GL11 5EL. 01453 860062.

SCOTT, Elizabeth Ann (Ann); *b:* 13 July 1944 in Rochester, Kent; *h:* Bob. RSPB Senior Wildlife Adviser since 1993. Prev RSPB: Enquiry Officer 1985-93; Development Officer (HQ) 1981-85; Dev Off (SE England) 1974-77. Leader Medway YOC Group 1971-74. Committee Maidstone RSPB Group early 1970s. RSPB Local Representative Rochester 1972-74. Adult education tutor, Kent and Cambridge 1978-. Leader of foreign bird tours 1981-. Special interests: waders; photography; running training courses in Ghana, Rwanda and Burundi. OIR: gardening, dog walking, writing. 8 Woodlands, St Neots, Cambs PE19 1UE. 01480 214904.

SCOTT, Nicholas (Nick); *b:* 19 December 1952 in Tonbridge, Kent. BSc Botany (Newcastle, 1978), PhD Ecology (Newcastle, 1983). Ecological consultant. Prev: Senior Warden Druridge Bay Nature Reserves

(Northumberland WT) 1984-93 (included directing project creating wetlands after opencast coalmining, leading to 350 acres of bird reserves). Special interests: habitat creation, wetland management (esp for waders). OIR: 'crazy adventures in remote places.' Mote Hills, Elsdon, Northumberland NE19 1AB. 01830 520240.

SCOTT, Philippa; Lady; *b:* 22 November 1918 in Bloemfontein, South Africa; *h:* the late Sir Peter Scott. ARPS 1979. Wildlife photographer. Hon Director, Wildfowl & Wetlands Trust since 1991. Prev: Hon Asst Director WWT 1980-91; Asst Secretary Severn Wildfowl Trust 1947-51. Special interest: wildfowl. Member of 1951 expedition to breeding grounds of Pink-footed Geese on the Thorsaver, Iceland. Member of numerous WWT ringing teams catching Pink-footed Geese in Britain 1949-56. Photographic contributions to WWT publications; also first UK record of Ring-necked Duck in *British Birds* 1955. OIR: foreign travel with wildlife interests, scuba diving and identification of coral fish, walking, music. The New Grounds, Slimbridge, Gloucester GL2 7BS. 01453 890333.

SCOTT, Robert Ernest (Bob); *b:* 11 May 1938 in Carshalton, Surrey; *w:* Ann. AIEEM 1992. Head of Reserves Management, RSPB since 1988. Prev RSPB: Senior Reserves Manager 1984-87; Reserves Manager (England) 1979-83; Senior Warden, Northward Hill Reserve, Kent 1975-79. Earlier: Warden, Dungeness Bird Observatory 1960-70; Warden, RSPB Dungeness Reserve 1960-75; Scientific Asst, Dept Zool, British Museum (Nat Hist) 1956-59. Junior representative London NHS Committee 1950s. Recorder for south London (London NHS) late 1950s. Ornithological correspondent *Folkestone Herald* 1960/70s. BTO Ringing & Migration Committee mid 60s-early 70s. Bird study tutor for WEA and LEAs mid 60s-early 80s. Freelance lecturer on ornithological subjects 1970-. Tour leader (UK and overseas) for various companies 1976-. DoE Wildlife Inspector 1983-. BOU Council 1994-. Special interests: migration, ringing, identification, populations, land management, photography; particular interest in ornithology of Bulgaria and enthusiastic about Africa; enjoyment of social ornithology (eg dining clubs, meetings, conferences). Member of ornithological expeditions inc West Indies, Iran, Ghana, Zululand, Sweden. First publication, a letter in *The Field* 1957 questioning the identification of pipits. Author *The Birdwatcher's Key* (1976, also in Dutch, Swedish, Spanish); *The Birdwatcher's Calendar* (1982); *The Atlas of British Bird Life* (1987). Contributions to books inc *Bird Observatories in Britain and Ireland* ed by Roger Durman (1976), *RSPB Nature Reserves* ed by Nicholas Hammond (1983), BTO Winter Atlas, *Go Birding* by Tony

Soper (1988). Compiler of 'News and Comment' for *British Birds* since 1994. Many articles and other items on a range of ornithological subjects. Member: ABC, Bulgarian Society for the Protection of Birds, LPO, World Bird Club. Participated in training courses in Ghana, Rwanda, Burundi, France, Italy, Bulgaria. Added birds to national lists of Britain, Ireland, Yugoslavia (Montenegro), Bulgaria, Ghana, Canada. OIR: reading (esp adventure novels), bird stamp collecting, watching TV trash, American football, travel. 8 Woodlands, St Neots, Cambs PE19 1UE. 01480 214904.

SEARS, Elizabeth Jane (Jane); *b:* 12 November 1960 in Nottingham; *h:* James Campbell. Nottingham High School for Girls 1971-78. BA Natural Sciences (Girton College, Cambridge, 1982), MA 1986, DPhil A study of Mute Swans in relation to lead poisoning (Oxford, 1987). Head of Data Management Section, RSPB Research Department since 1996. Prev RSPB: Senior Research Biologist (Head of Aquatic Research Team covering estuarine, marine and freshwater research) 1992-96; Research Biologist 1989-92; post-doctoral research asst (monitoring effect of legislation prohibiting use of lead weights on incidence of lead poisoning in, and population dynamics of, Mute Swans) 1986-89. Voluntary warden Ramsey Island Nature Reserve, Jun-Aug 1979. Executive Committee Seabird Group 1993-94. Scientific Advisory Committee WWT 1994-. Chairman IWRB Swan Study Group, UK c1986-89. Special interest: lead poisoning of birds, esp Mute Swan. Developed pioneer technique for measuring birds' body condition using ultrasound. RSPB projects inc study of ornithological value of set-aside, co-ordination of seabird monitoring and Beached Birds Survey, Little Tern population monitoring, Red Kite survey in Spain. Cambridge Icelandic Expedition 1982 (seabird censuses); Dominica Rain Forest Project (inc forest bird censusing, radio tracking). Travel also in India and Nepal, Zimbabwe, Pakistan, Botswana and South Africa, Thailand, Colombia. Joint editor (with P J Bacon) *Proc Third IWRB International Swan Symposium, Oxford, 1989.* Contributor to books inc *Angling and Wildlife in Fresh Waters* ed by P S Maitland and A K Turner (1987), *The Birds of Oxfordshire* ed by J W Brucker et al (1992). Author or co-author of many scientific papers on research topics in eg *Biol Cons, British Birds, British Veterinary J, Environmental Pollution, J Appl Ecol, J Zool (Lond), Seabird, Wildfowl.* Articles published in eg *Birds, The Guardian, Economist, New Scientist, Das Tier, Which?*; also conference procs and reports. Advisor to BBC Natural History Unit and appearances on several regional TV programmes. OIR: sailing, walking, cycling, canoeing. RSPB, The Lodge, Sandy, Beds SG19 2DL. 01767 680551.

SELL, Martin Richard Warren; *b:* 8 May 1939 in Bath; *w:* Judith. Berkhamsted School, Herts 1953-57. BA Modern Languages (Exeter, 1960). Planning Officer British Rail, retired 1993. Monthly wildfowl and wader counts for Theale area, Berks 1983- (member Theale Area Bird Conservation Group). Fieldwork in local tetrads for BTO Breeding Atlas. Reserve Manager, Aston Upthorpe Reserve, Berks 1969-91. Several bird surveys and censuses under contract to Berks, Bucks and Oxon NT since 1993. Chairman Reading Ornithological Club 1985-88. President Reading and District NHS 1982-84. Special interest: bird and natural environment conservation. OIR: general natural history (esp botany), gardening, classical music (inc playing piano), philately, travel abroad. 27 Fernbrook Road, Caversham, Reading RG4 7HG. 01734 471170.

SELLAR, Patrick James; *b:* 19 June 1929 in Aberdeen. BSc Electrical Engineering (Aberdeen, 1950). MIEE, CEng 1959, FRGS 1981. Electrical engineer, retired. Co-founder British Library of Wildlife Sounds (BLOWS) 1969. Chairman Fair Isle Bird Observatory Trust 1990-95. Chairman International Bioacoustics Council 1969-. Chairman Wildlife Sound Recording Society 1993-. Special interest: sound recording. Ornithologist with British North-East Greenland Expedition 1980 and Petermann Peak Expedition 1985. Study of songs of two sympatric chaffinch species on Canary Islands 1984, 1989, 1991. Joint editor *BWP* Vols 5-9 (1985-94) and contributor of sound recordings for sonagrams in Vols 1-9 (1977-94). Articles on bird sound recording and study of bird songs in eg *Behaviour*, *British Birds*. Contributor of sound recordings to radio and many published discs (eg *Bird Song Adventure* 1972), cassettes and CDs. Winner, European Broadcasting Union Wildlife Tape Recording Competition 1970. OIR: sailing, flying, hill walking, opera, tram driving, entomology, photography and the Arctic. 89 Riddlesdown Road, Purley, Surrey CR8 1DH. 0181 660 1512.

SHACKLETON, Keith Hope; *b:* 16 January 1923 in Weybridge, Surrey; *w:* Jacqueline. Oundle School. Hon LLD (Birmingham, 1983). Artist/naturalist. Shipboard naturalist for polar regions and oceanic islands since 1969. Founder-member and Trustee WWT. Past President Royal Society of Marine Artists and Society of Wildlife Artists. Author *Wildlife & Wilderness: an artist's world* and *Ship in the Wilderness* (1986). Exhibitions: RSMA and SWLA annually. TV: BBC series *Animal Magic* 1965-69; Survival Anglia *Animals in Action* 1979-82. 'Master Wildlife Artist' award (Leigh Yawkey Woodson Art Museum, USA 1986). OIR: small boat sailing. Woodley Wood Farm, Woodleigh, Kingsbridge, Devon TQ7 4DR. 01548 550027.

SHAND, Robert (Rab); *b:* 7 September 1955 in Edinburgh; *p:* Alison Scott. City & Guilds Mech Eng (Telford College, 1974). Organiser, Birdline Scotland since 1990. Founder-member Fife Bird Club 1985-, Secretary 1989-. Special interests: identification, migration, Nearctic and Neotropical birds. Travel for birds in Europe, N, S and Central America, Morocco. Articles on migration and foreign birding in *Fife Bird Club Report* and *Fife Bird Club Newsletter*. Member: NBC. OIR: listening to hard rock music, vegetarian cooking (esp Indian food). 33 Liddle Drive, Bo'ness, West Lothian EH51 0PA. 01506 825101.

SHARKEY, Neil; *b:* 1936 in Clonmel, Tipperary, Ireland; *w:* Margaret. IWC: Council 1979-85 and 1989-93, National Secretary 1981-84. IWC Galway Branch: various posts since 1975, inc Chairman and Secretary. Special interest: fostering ornithology in Galway and the west of Ireland generally. Galway organiser BTO New Breeding Atlas. Compiler and editor of quarterly *Galway IWC Newsletter*, and contributor to *Birds of Galway* ed by Tony Whilde (1990). 1 Glenard Crescent, Salthill, Galway, Ireland. +353 (0)91 521554.

SHARPE, David John (Dave); *b:* 25 October 1954 in Douglas, Isle of Man. BDS (Liverpool, 1977). Dentist. Hon Sec Lancaster & District Birdwatching Society 1988-94. BTO Regional Representative N Lancs 1988-. Wilfowl Count co-ordinator N Lancs 1988-. Chairman Heysham NR Management Committee 1990-. BTO ringer since 1989. Special interests: ringing, mainly Mute Swan and Swallow pulli 'and anything else partly feathered'; fieldwork for various BTO, WWT and local surveys; travelling abroad. Member: North West Swan Study Group. OIR: work and Boddingtons Best Bitter. 17 Greenwood Avenue, Bolton-le-Sands, Carnforth, Lancs LA5 8AN. 01524 822492.

SHARROCK, John Timothy Robin (Tim); *b:* 6 December 1937 in Alphington, Devon; *w:* Erika. Maidstone Grammar School, Kent 1949-56. BSc Botany (Southampton, 1959), PhD Ecology (Southampton, 1967). Managing Editor *British Birds* since 1976. Prev: National Organiser BTO/IWC Breeding Bird Atlas Project 1969-76. Earlier: Head of Survey Section, National Institute of Agricultural Engineering 1965-69. Cape Clear Bird Observatory: Recorder 1959-69, Chairman 1970-75 and 1980-85, President 1987-. BOU: Records Committee 1970-90, Secretary 1970-77, Council 1969-72 and 1976-81. Chairman, European Ornithological Atlas Committee 1971-85. BTO Winter Atlas Working Group 1980-85. Council, Systematics Assocn 1975-77. Report Editors' Committee 1970-76. British

Birds Rarities Committee 1969-83. BTO Populations and Surveys Committee 1967-77. Council, Seabird Group 1966-70. Rare Breeding Birds Panel 1973-, Hon Sec 1973-83. Special interests: censuses, surveys, distribution studies, patterns of records, editing and writing. Fieldwork for Waterways Bird Survey and Bedfordshire Tetrad Atlas project. Author *Scarce Migrant Birds in Britain and Ireland* (1974), *The Birdwatchers' Quiz & Puzzle Book* (1975), *The Birdwatchers' Second Quiz & Puzzle Book* (1976), *The 'British Birds' Mystery Photographs Book* (1983). Compiler *The Atlas of Breeding Birds in Britain and Ireland* (1976). Contributor to *The Changing Flora and Fauna of Britain* ed by D L Hawksworth (1974) and *Bird Observatories in Britain and Ireland* ed by Roger Durman (1976). Co-author (with Erika Sharrock) *Rare Birds in Britain and Ireland* (1976); (with Peter Holden) *The RSPB Book of British Birds* (1982); (with J Ferguson-Lees and I Willis) *The Shell Guide to the Birds of Britain and Ireland* (1983); (with Peter Holden) *A First Book of Birds* (1984). Editor and contributor *Birds New to Britain and Ireland* (1982). Editor *The Natural History of Cape Clear Island* (1973). Papers published in eg *Ardeola, Bird Study, British Birds*; over three hundred short contributions to various ornithological journals. Hon Life Member of BTO (1976). Member: Bangkok Bird Club, OBC, Seabird Group. OIR: playing bridge, setting and solving puzzles, watching speedway, dining well. Fountains, Park Lane, Blunham, Bedford MK44 3NJ. Office 01767 640025.

SHAW, Geoffrey (Geoff); *b:* 1 December 1950 in Nottingham; *w:* Lynda. BA Biology (Stirling, 1976). Leading Ranger for Bird Conservation, Forest Enterprise, Galloway Forest Park since 1991. Prev: Senior Ranger, Forestry Commission 1976-91. BTO Regional Representative Kirkcudbright 1983-94. SOC Branch Committees, Stirling 1974-76, Wigtown 1976-81. BTO 'A' ringer since 1973, trainer since 1991. Special interests: raptor and owl ecology (esp Barn Owl, Merlin), forest birds, conifer seed eaters, Dipper. Fieldwork for Waterways Bird Survey 1973-96. Author *Barn Owl Conservation in Forests* (1990). Editor *BTO Owl Study Group Newsletter* 1990-. Papers on study topics published in eg *Bird Study, British Birds, BTO News, Ringing & Migration, Scottish Birds, Scottish Forestry*. Member: Dumfries & Galloway Raptor Study Group, South Strathclyde Raptor Study Group, North Solway Ringing Group. OIR: livestock farming (sheep and cattle). Kirriereoch, Bargrennan, Newton Stewart, Wigtownshire DG8 6TB. 01671 840288.

SHAW, Kenneth Douglas (Ken); *b:* 16 October 1952 in Glasgow; *w:* Kathy (Dr Kathy Evans). BSc Biology (Paisley College of Technology, 1974).

Manager RSPB Vane Farm Reserve since 1995. Prev RSPB: Regional Officer East Scotland 1992-95; Conservation Officer Grampian & Tayside 1987-92; Asst Regional Officer North England 1981-87; Information Officer Scotland 1979-81; species protection warden Lake District 1979. County Bird Recorder Grampian (except Moray) 1987-93. BOU Records Committee 1993-. British Birds Rarities Committee 1994-. Scottish Birds Records Committee 1992-, Chairman 1996-. Director Fair Isle Bird Observatory Trust 1992-95. Member, Grampian Raptor Group 1987-95. Committee, Northumberland and Tyneside Bird Club 1984-87. Special interests: monitoring upland birds, Fife Breeding Bird Atlas, WeBS counter, identification, seawatching. Widely travelled, esp Middle East. Member 1993 OSME expedition to Yemen. Bird tour leader, particularly Europe, N Africa, Middle East. Compiler *North-East Scotland Bird Report* 1988-93. Contributor to *Birding World*, *British Birds*, etc. Media appearances. OIR: cetaceans, sport, real ale, curries and cooking. Vane Farm Nature Centre, by Loch Leven, Kinross KY13 7LX. 01577 862355.

SHAWYER, Colin Roy; *b:* 17 July 1949 in Smallford, St Albans; *w:* Valerie. HNC Applied Biology (Hatfield Polytechnic, 1973), Hon MUniv for research on the Barn Owl (Open Univ, 1990). Consultant Director, The Hawk and Owl Trust since 1989. Wildlife management and research consultant since 1989. National Co-ordinator, Barn Owl Survey of Britain and Ireland 1982-85. Barn Owl Liaison Group of JNCC 1990-96. Barn Owl Advisory Group, Dept of Environment 1992-96. BTO Raptor Research and Surveys Committee 1996. Projects Advisory Committee, The Hawk and Owl Trust 1994-96. Special interests: raptors, bird surveying and behaviour. Author *The Barn Owl in the British Isles* (1987), *The Barn Owl* (1994). Articles published in a wide range of books (eg *Birds in Europe: their conservation status*), journals and magazines (eg *Bird Watching, Nature, New Scientist*). Several TV appearances and radio broadcasts. RSPB Birds and Conservation Awards: Category winner and National winner for 'The most positive contribution overall to the conservation of wild birds and the countryside 1987'. Ford European Conservation Awards: Category and UK winner 1992, for raptor conservation. Member: LIPU, Russian Raptor Link. OIR: restoration of antiques. 15 Butterfield Road, Wheathampstead, Herts AL4 8PX. 01582 832182.

SHEPHERD, Michael (Mike); *b:* 10 February 1963 in St Helens, Merseyside. BSc Zoology (Bristol, 1984), PhD Avian Biology (Nottingham, 1992). Ornithologist, Scottish Natural Heritage since 1993. Prev: project manager BTO 1991-93; research asst, Univ Nottingham 1988-91; research asst, Univ Leicester 1987; project officer, Lancs TNC 1985-87. Special interests: breeding biology (esp Corn Bunting, Tree Pipit), song (esp Corn Bunting, Great Tit), conservation. Papers published in eg *Anim Behav, Ardea, Behavioural Ecol, British Birds, Ibis, J Avian Biol, Ornis Scandinavica, Scottish Birds*. Various reports eg on effect of commercial cockling on waterfowl, impact assessments and bird surveys. OIR: football, golf, hill walking, cycling, skiing, fly fishing, jazz music. 26 Nelson Street, Edinburgh EH3 6LJ. 0131 557 5883.

SHEPPARD, Geoffrey Charles (Geoff); *b:* 25 August 1944 in Bristol, Avon. Secretary SOC West Galloway Branch since 1976. BTO Regional Representative, Wigtown District since 1983. BTO 'A' ringer since 1980. Member North Solway Ringing Group since 1982. Special interests: raptors, waders, migration. Barn Owl population study since 1983. Member: Dumfries and Galloway Raptor Study Group, Wader Study Group. The Roddens, Leswalt, Stranraer, Wigtownshire DG9 0QR. 01776 870685.

SHEPPARD, Joseph Ralph (Ralph); *b:* 2 April 1944 in Londonderry, Northern Ireland; *w:* Liz. BA Natural Sciences (Dublin, 1968), MSc Feeding ecology of Oystercatchers on mussels (Wales, 1972). Environmental consultant since 1978. Prev: Lecturer in Ecology, Bristol Polytechnic 1970-78. Contracts largely related to environmental impact assessments and habitat design, also survey work for eg IWC. Since 1980 has run (with wife) wildlife holidays in Donegal, escorted expedition cruises around Donegal coast, and environmental awareness courses on own farm (where 11.5 acre deciduous woodland planted) for teachers and other groups. National organiser for IWC Winter Wetlands Survey 1984/85 to 1986/87, and Concrake Census 1993. Voluntary work inc Planning Officer for local branch of Irish National Trust, member of National Council 1981-84, 1989-. Member of statutory Wildlife Advisory Council (to Minister for Tourism, Fisheries and Forestry) 1984-87. Member of Irish Wildfowl Committee and its successor the Irish Wildbird Conservancy, on Council 1982-86. Helped to form Donegal Branch of IWC, Chairman 1982-86, 1990-96. Organiser of fieldwork, and/or edited the results, for Donegal contribution to most of the national bird surveys since 1960s, inc first Peregrine survey and the three Atlases. Executive Board of IWRB 1986-96. Special interests: the birds of Donegal (compiling computer database of observations since 1956), taxonomy, global conservation, photography. Foreign travel for birds inc N Korea, central Asia, Canada, most of Europe. Author of *Ireland's Wetland Wealth: the birdlife of the estuaries, lakes,* *coasts, rivers, bogs and turloughs of Ireland* (1993). Contributor to *Wigeon in Ireland* ed by J Harradine (1991). Papers on eg breeding waders of sand dune machair in north-west Ireland and Goosanders breeding in Ireland published in *Irish Birds*. Regular broadcasts on local radio, mostly news interviews but also several programme series. OIR: 'I struggle to occupy the same Donegal niche on matters botanical and entomological, and record plants, dragonflies, butterflies and moths for the relevant organisations.' Carnowen House, Raphoe, Lifford, Co Donegal, Ireland. +353 (0)74 47129.

SHEPPARD, ROBERT (Bob); *b:* 9 November 1946 in Sheffield; *w:* Gail. Primary school head teacher. Regional advisor to The Hawk and Owl Trust since 1989. Lincolnshire Bird Club: founder-member 1979, Chairman 1980-89, Vice President 1990-. Special interests: photography, long-term nestbox study of Tawny and Barn Owls (started 1976). Articles in magazines eg *Bird Watching, The Raptor*. Regular local radio spot and occasional TV documentaries. Illustrated talks on owls and birds of prey to local societies and natural history groups. OIR: gardening. 21 Beech Avenue, Bourne, Lincs PE10 9RR. 01778 424366.

SHIRIHAI, Hadoram; *b:* 2 May 1962 in Israel; *w:* Lilly. High school in Jerusalem (inc three-year field study of Black-winged Stilt and Golden Eagle). Freelance ornithologist, birding tour leader and author since 1989. Prev: full-time field ornithologist at the Nature Reserves Authority and the Society for the Protection of Nature in Israel (SPNI) 1981-88. Job included foundation and management of the International Birdwatching Center in Eilat, annual spring and autumn raptor migration census in Eilat (nine seasons), foundation and management of the ringing station in Eilat, breeding bird surveys, foundation of the Rarities and Distribution Committee for Israeli Birds. Continuing work for SPNI and Eilat Birding Center relates to the Israeli Breeding Atlas and other special projects on nature conservation. Voluntary work: identification consultant *Birding World*, consultant editor *Dutch Birding*, correspondent *British Birds* 'European News' feature, member Western Palearctic List Committee, Israeli correspondent *BWP*. Special interests: taxonomy, identification and migration of Western Palearctic (mainly countries of Middle East and Mediterranean basin) and East African birds, esp warblers and raptors. Research undertaken by ringing, study of skins (in Europe's largest museums), and DNA analysis. Author *The Birds of Israel* (1996), *Macmillan Birder's Guide to European and Middle Eastern Birds* with A Harris and D Christie (1996), *The Genus Sylvia* (in prep). Co-author in the Bird Atlas of Europe project. Over fifty papers in eg *Bull BOC*, *Birding World*, *British Birds*, *Dutch Birding*, *Torgos* (Israel). Discoverer of more than 40 new species for Israel, 10 of them also being new for the Western Palearctic; also discovered a species of shearwater new to science. PO Box 4168, Eilat, 88102 Israel. Tel/fax +972 7 379326.

SHOOTER, Philip; *b:* 13 November 1936 in Clay Cross, Derbyshire; *w:* Lynne. Country Park maintenance. WEA tutor in ornithology 1970-90 and a course director at Losehill Hall Study Centre in same period; also weekend courses for Derbyshire CC. Derbyshire Ornithological Society: founder-member (1954), past member of Committee and Records Committee, also Field Officer for several years. Founder-member Ogston Hide Group (now Ogston Bird Club) in 1968 and its first Chairman. Founder-member Birdholme Wildfowl Reserve Group in 1970. County representative of RSPB in early 1970s. Ornithological Recorder for Matlock Field Club during the period of fieldwork for the first BTO Breeding Atlas. Contributor to BTO Nest Record Scheme 1966-76 and carried out wildfowl counts on a number of N Derbys waters for Wildfowl Trust. Special interests: distribution; breeding populations; study species inc Dipper, Pied Flycatcher, Lapwing, Nightjar. Author *Where to Watch Birds in Derbyshire* (1982, rev ed 1987). OIR: visiting historical buildings. 153 Market Street, Clay Cross, Chesterfield, Derbys S45 9LX. 01246 864985.

SIMMONS, Kenneth Edwin Laurence [Ryder] (Ken); *b:* 29 March 1929 in Kenton, Middlesex; *w:* Marion. Sacred Heart College Droitwich 1941-45, St Mary's College Twickenham 1946-48. Teacher's Cert (London, 1948). MSc Breeding biology of Brown Booby (Bristol, 1967), PhD Breeding biology of Great Crested Grebe (Bristol, 1970). Professional ornithologist 1964-80 (retired for health reasons). Prev: teacher (inc schoolmaster on Ascension Island 1962-64); research associate Univ Florida (nesting studies on Green Turtle, Ascension Island 1963 and 1966). After Bristol, other ornithological research on duck courtship, and later on behaviour and behavioural ecology of West Palearctic birds based in Dept of Psychology, Univ Leicester 1970-80. West Palaearctic Birds Ltd: own time unpaid 1970-73, 1980-94; three-quarter time 1973-75; full-time 1975-80 (SRC grant). Reading Ornithological Club, 1950-61: Committee, joint Recorder, Chairman. Scientific Advisory Committee BTO 1959-61. Founder-member and Committee Bristol Ornithological Club, 1966-70. BOU: 237 papers abstracted for 'Recent Ornithological Publications' in *Ibis* 1956-68; Council and Meetings Committee 1969-73. *British Birds*: Notes/Behaviour Notes Panel since 1968. Bird study topics include ethology, behavioural ecology, taxonomy (inc behaviour characters), courtship, inter-specific territorialism, parental care, parent/young relations (inc brood division), parental anti-predator strategies (esp distraction behaviour), faecal sac removal, feeding behaviour (esp seabird hunting methods and plumage types), food hiding, foot movements, comfort behaviour, head scratching, anting, sunning. Main study species: Great Crested Grebe, Graceful Warbler, Little Ringed Plover, Brown Booby. Fieldwork abroad in Gibraltar, Egypt, Texel, Djerba, Denmark, Ascension Island. Special interests inc seabird studies (esp Brown Booby) and conservation problems (esp feral cat predation) at Ascension Island 1961 to present. Biographer of Edmund Selous, Stanley Cramp. Author *Studies on Great Crested Grebes* (1955), *The Sunning Behaviour of Birds* (1986), *The Great Crested Grebe* (1989). *BWP*: Co-editor (with Stanley Cramp) Vols 1-3 (1977-83), behaviour consultant 1966-69, Editorial Board 1969-94, editor of 'Social Pattern and Behaviour' and 'Voice' sections 1970-81, editor of family summaries 1970-94. Contributions to other books inc *The Birds of the British Isles* Vol 8 (Bannerman, 1959), *A New Dictionary of Birds* (Landsborough Thomson, 1964), *Social Behaviour in Birds and Animals* (Crook, 1970), *Private Lives* (Boswall, 1970), *A Dictionary of Birds* (Campbell and Lack, 1985), *Dictionary of National Biography: Missing Persons* (Nicholls, 1993). Many papers and notes in eg *Ardea*, *Avicultural Magazine*, *Behaviour*, *Bristol Ornithology*, *British Birds*, *Bull BOC*, *Ibis*, *J Zool (Lond)*, *Living Bird*, *Wildfowl*. Leverhulme Fellowship 1964-65. Union Medal, BOU 1979. Member: AOU, Species Survival Commission IUCN/Grebe Specialist Group BirdLife Int. OIR: 'good' music (19th/20th century), collecting CDs, watching TV, biographical studies of Elgar. 66 Romway Road, Leicester LE5 5SB. 0116 273 7614.

SIMMS, Colin; *b:* 15 June 1939 in North Yorks. BA Biology (Keele, 1961). Independent naturalist (self-employed) since 1981. Prev: Keeper of Natural History, The Yorkshire Museum, York 1965-81; Liverpool Museums (vertebrate zoology) 1961-65. Voluntary work inc surveys (mainly avifaunal) since 1967 in co-operation with government agencies in various overseas countries, esp N America, subarctic and Central Asia; some censuses in Britain, inc breeding bird census work in 1972 and wildfowl counts in 1960s and 70s. Contracts with MAFF, MOD, National Parks etc 1980s and 90s. Tutor in avian morphology and other subjects for Northern FE and Art Colleges 1967-81. Tutor in ornithology for WEA and University Extension courses in N Yorks and Northumberland 1967-85. Talks and excursion leader for bird and natural history groups 1959-84. Special interests: biogeography, taxonomy and ecology inter-relations (esp raptors and some waders and passerines); related holarctic travel and expeditions totalling over two years inc all of N America, parts of Greenland, Iceland, N Scandinavia, Siberia and Kamchatka, Central Asia and Middle East, S Europe esp Italy (inc Sicily). Most fieldwork, esp last decade, intrasite upland (inc winter) avifauna; particular species include Merlin, Gyr Falcon, Golden Plover, Black Grouse, some buntings. Contributor to Holarctic Avian Speciation Atlas (HASA). Papers and notes in eg *Bird Study, British Birds, The Naturalist.* Hundreds of bird poems published, some collected as *First* and *Second Books of Birds* (1978 and 1980). Early work, inc consulting and appearing, for TV natural history programmes (Anglia, YTV, BBC North, BBC 2, Tyne-Tees) c1967-80; also radio programmes in UK and occasionally USA and Canada. Cross Fell Cottage, Carrigill, Alston, Cumbria CA9 3EB.

SIMMS, Eric Arthur; DFC 1944, RAF Retd; *b:* 24 August 1921 in Kensington, London; *w:* Thelma. Latymer Upper School, London 1932-39. BA History (Merton College, Oxford) 1945, MA 1946, Dip Ed (Oxford, 1946). Freelance naturalist, broadcaster, lecturer and author since 1967. Prev: senior TV producer and film director on natural history and environmental programmes for Schools TV, BBC 1957-67; resident naturalist BBC and director of wildlife sound recording projects 1950-57. Earlier: Senior English Master, Stratford-upon-Avon High School 1948-50. Lecturer in ornithology for Extra-mural Dept Birmingham Univ 1948-50; same London Univ 1955. West Midland Bird Club Research Committee 1949-50. BTO Research Committee on Visible Migration 1952-55. RSPB Council 1953-63. Member, Dept of Ornithology, Cornell Univ (USA) 1956-. Sound Advisor to *The Countryman* and British Transport Films 1957-61. Advisory Committee on Bird Sanctuaries in the Royal Parks 1972-79. WWF-UK: Advisory Panel 1977-80, Council 1980-86. President Lincolnshire Bird Club 1981-. President of Skylarks Nature Reserve, Holme Pierrepoint, Notts ('first reserve specially designed for physically disabled') 1983-87. Conservation Committee Lincs TNC 1986-88. Warden/Manager South Witham Nature Reserve, S Lincs 1986-. Special interests: (a) wildlife sound recording: introduced tape recorders, parabolic reflectors, short-wave radio links and hydrophones to techniques of natural history sound recording in Britain 1951-57; carried out first BBC sound recording expeditions for animal sounds to the Camargue, Coto Doñana and central Spain, and Switzerland; made first recordings of birds of the high tops in the Grampians; represented BBC for first time at an International Ornithological Congress (Basel 1954) where played tapes and demonstrated new techniques of wildlife sound recording; first to demonstrate links between vocalisations and behaviour; (b) visible migration studies: discovered overland 'Cotswold corridor' autumn migration route (1948); extended study to Severn and Wash in subsequent years; made migration watches in NW London 1951-80 and many other sites in British Isles, Provence and Switzerland; (c) birds of suburbia: twenty-nine year study of bird life at Dollis Hill, NW London 1951-80, probably the longest study of its kind. Also studied birds in N America and E Africa. Author *Bird Migrants* (1952), *The Songs and Calls of British Birds* (1953), *Voices of the Wild* (1957), *Witherby's Sound Guide to British Birds* with Myles North (1958), *Woodland Birds* (1971), *Wildlife in the Royal Parks* (1974), *Live and Let Live* (1975), *Birds of Town and Suburb* (1975), *British Thrushes* (1978), *Birds of Town and Village* (1979), *Wildlife Sounds and their Recording* (1979), *The Public Life of the Street Pigeon* (1979), *A Natural History of Britain and Ireland* (1979), *A Natural History of British Birds* (1983), *British Warblers* (1985), *The Song Thrush* (1989), *British Larks, Pipits and Wagtails* (1992). Contributions to *The BBC Book of the Countryside* ed by Arthur Phillips (1963), *The Natural History of Britain and Ireland* by Heather Angel (1981), *Collins British Birds* by John Gooders (1982), and *The Illustrated Encyclopedia of Birds* ed by Jonathan Elphick (1990). Scientific papers and notes in ornithological journals and county bird reports. Numerous articles in daily press and eg *Bird Notes*, *Birds*, *Birdwatch*, *Birdwatching*, *British Birds*, *Country Life*, *The Tape Recorder*, *Wildlife Sound*. Seven thousand broadcasts on national and local radio, notably started the *Countryside Programme* on BBC in 1952 (broadcast in it from start to finish in 1990, 325 progs without break); presented *Nature Notebook* on BBC World Service 1967-78 (over 500 progs) and weekly natural history contribution on LBC 1977-87 (517); presented a number of radio series illustrated with own recordings, eg *Bird Sounds and their Meanings*, and a group which were the first to relate recorded vocalisations with behaviour, *The Little Ringed Plover*, *The Stone Curlew* and others; presented many radio features, eg *Bee-eaters in Britain*, *The Land of the Griffon*, *The Queen's Visitors* (inc interview with Prince Philip), also school programmes; regular appearances on other series inc *The Naturalist*, *Birds in Britain*, *Naturalists' Notebook*. Produced and presented BBC TV series inc *Man in Nature*, *A Year in the Country* (28 progs), *A Year's Journey* (42 progs); also singles, eg *Wildlife in the Arctic*. OIR: aviation; collecting fossils, geological specimens and Neolithic artefacts; botany; local history; church architecture; drawing; classical music; Vice Chairman Parish Council; JP. 21 Church Street, South Witham, Grantham, Lincs NG33 5PJ. 01572 767251.

SIMPSON, David Matthew (Dave); Captain MN Retd; *b:* 22 December 1942 in Stockton on Tees, Co Durham. Trinity House Navigation School, Hull. Master Mariner 1968. Shipmaster. Special interests: identification and migration, esp birds of the Australasian and Oriental regions. Since 1988 has worked exclusively on New Guinea's 'Fly River', also made numerous birding trips into neighbouring areas inc Wallacia, N Australia, New Britain and the Solomons. Many short articles and reports published in *Sea Swallow* (journal of Royal Naval Birdwatching Society). Member: Papua New Guinea Bird Society. 'Over the past twenty years my main interest in life has been the rainforest birds of the Eastern hemisphere.' OIR: all aspects of natural history, maritime and military history, geography, rugby league. c/o 4 Ruswarp Lane, Whitby, N Yorks YO21 1ND. 01947 602693.

SKILLETER, Morris; MBE (Mil) 1945, CBE (Civil) 1965; *b:* 11 July 1917 in South Shields, Co Durham; *w:* Margaret. LLB (King's College, London, 1950). FCIS 1966. Retired. Past Chairman of Durham WT and Durham Bird Club. Contributions to *Nigerian Field* eg 'Some Notes on Kaduna Birds' (1963) and to *The Birds of Nigeria: an annotated check-list* ed by J H Elgood *et al* (1981, 2nd ed 1994); paper on winter site fidelity of Redstart in N Nigeria in *Malimbus* (1995). Member: WAOS. Lectures and talks on matters of ornithological interest given to various societies, clubs and institutions. 12 Westcliffe Road, Sunderland SR6 9NW. 0191 548 7238.

SKINNER, Neville John; *b:* 28 June 1929 in Lowestoft, Suffolk; *w:* Gladys. BSc Physics (Nottingham, 1950), PhD Physics (London, 1956). FInstP, CPhys. Retired Professor of Physics. Bird Recorder for Botswana 1983-86. Co-ordinator of Nest Record Card Scheme for Botswana 1983-96. Special interest: Afrotropical ornithology, esp analysis of breeding and distributional data. Articles in eg *Ibis* (duetting 1970), *Scopus* (breeding of Red-chested Cuckoo 1978), *Notornis* (wader counts 1981-83), *Babbler* (six-monthly breeding reports etc 1983-96). Co-author (with J H Elgood *et al*) *The Birds of Nigeria: an annotated check-list* (2nd ed 1994). Member: ABC, Botswana Bird Club, WAOS. OIR: genealogy. 60 Gunton Drive, Lowestoft, Suffolk NR32 4QB. 01502 573913.

SLATER, Kenneth Hannah (Ken); *b:* 27 April 1956 in Glasgow; *w:* Alison. Arbroath High School. HND Biological Science (Dundee Inst Tech, 1991), BSc Biotechnology (Dundee Inst Tech, 1993). SNH field officer, Caenlochan NNR 1993-. Prev: RSPB contract biologist Jun-Aug 1992. BTO Regional Representative Angus 1989-. Chairman Scottish WT Arbroath

Group 1984-86. BTO 'A' ringer since 1989. Special interests: riparian birds, esp biology of local populations of Dipper and Grey Wagtail. Article on the Dipper in Angus published in *Angus and Dundee Bird Report 1991*. Appearance in *Wildtrack*, BBC Radio Scotland. Member: Tay Ringing Group, Tayside Raptor Study Group. OIR: landscape photography, reading. 19 Carnegie Street, Arbroath, Angus DD11 1TX. 01241 877073.

SLATER, Peter James Bramwell; *b:* 26 December 1942 in Edinburgh; *w:* Elisabeth. BSc Zoology (Edinburgh, 1964), PhD Animal Behaviour (Edin, 1968), DSc Bird Behaviour (Edin, 1983). FIBiol 1986, FRSE 1991. Professor of Natural History, Univ St Andrews. Trustee Fair Isle Bird Observatory 1963-94, Vice Chairman 1990-94. Scientific Advisory Committee Wildfowl Trust 1978-81. Isle of May Bird Observatory Committee 1985-89. Scottish Committee RSPB 1988-93. Special interest: bird behaviour, esp song. Author or editor of various books on animal behaviour, eg *Bird Song: biological themes and variations* with C K Catchpole (1995). Numerous articles in books and journals inc *Anim Behav, The Auk, Behaviour, Bird Study, Condor, Ethology, Ibis, Wilson Bull,* etc. Asst editor *Scottish Birds* 1965-67, 1991-. Member: AOU, Cooper Orn Soc, Wilson Orn Soc. School of Biological & Medical Sciences, Bute Medical Building, University of St Andrews, St Andrews, Fife KY16 9TS. 01334 463500.

SLATOR, Colin; *b:* 10 October 1951 in Ripon, N Yorks; *w:* Clare. Countryside Ranger, Harrogate BC since 1992. Summer warden for National Trust on Farne Islands Mar-Oct 1973, Apr-Dec 1977; asst coastal warden (Northumberland) Jan-Jun 1979. Founder-member (1973) High Batts Nature Reserve Group, Chairman 1990-95. Harrogate & District Naturalists' Society: Ornithological Recorder and Chairman of Records Committee 1985-88, Bird Rarities Committee 1989-96. Co-ordinator of HBNRG's Wetland Bird Survey work on River Ure 1981-83, 1991-93. WEA tutor in ornithological and related subjects, most winter sessions since 1988. Member of several local reserve management committees. Special interests: identification, migration, photography, habitat management, conservation. Foreign travel inc Holland, France, Austria, Spain, Turkey (Bosphorus), Soviet Central Asia, Soviet Far East and Lake Baikal, Nepal (two five-week trips), Israel, Kenya, N America, Peru. Large collection of slides and books relating to these trips and expeditions. Short items published in *British Birds* and local annual reports; also occasional photograph (eg Brewer's Blackbird in *Birding World*). Compiler of annual bird reports in *Harrogate & District Nat Soc Ann Rept* 1985-88, joint compiler 1990. Member: Dutch Birding Assocn, OSME. OIR: other natural history (esp dragonflies, butterflies and mammals), conservation of habitats, family. 3 St Johns Walk, Kirby Hill, Boroughbridge, N Yorks YO5 9DJ.

SLINN, Denzil John (John); *b:* 27 August 1925 in Stafford; *w:* Diana. BSc Zoology (Queen's Univ Belfast, 1951). MIBiol 1954. Hon Research Fellow, Univ Liverpool (Lecturer in Marine Biology, retired). Special interests: seabirds, inc gulls (esp Herring Gull). Co-author (with J P Cullen) *Birds of the Isle of Man* (1975, rev ed 1983). Articles on above interests in *Journal of the Manx Museum, Peregrine,* and *Proc Isle of Man Nat Hist and Antiquarian Soc.* OIR: photography. Vermont, Station Road, Port Erin, Isle of Man IM9 6AR. 01624 833691. Or Port Erin Marine Laboratory, Isle of Man IM9 6JA. 01624 832027.

SMALLSHIRE, David (Dave); *b:* 19 August 1951 in Wolverhampton; *w:* Judith. Wednesfield Grammar School 1962-69, Wulfrun College of FE 1969-70. Senior Consultant (Ecologist), ADAS since 1970 (inc co-ordinator for England of bird monitoring in ESAs). West Midland Bird Club: Research Committee 1974-; Hon Warden Belvide Bird Reserve 1977-83; Editorial/Records Committee 1976-83; Staffordshire Branch Committee 1974-83, Secretary 1976-79. Council, Bardsey Bird and Field Observatory 1976-80. Leicestershire and Rutland Orn Soc: Committee 1984-86, Convenor Scientific and Conservation Sub-committee 1985-86, Outings Committee 1985-86. Devon Birdwatching & Preservation Society: Council 1989-92, Chairman Future Development Committee 1989-, Editorial Committee and Records Committee 1989-. BTO/Wader Study Group: organiser Inland Wader Enquiry 1972-74. Birmingham Univ Extra-mural Dept/WEA tutor, evening class on birds, Wolverhampton 1975-79. Field Studies Council: tutor 'Birds in the Landscape' courses 1974-79 at Preston Montford. Special interests: population monitoring, habitat management, wetland birds, identification, migration. Bird-related visits to Zambia and Tanzania, Canada (Ontario), and extensive travel in Europe. Author *Belvide Bird Reserve: a natural history* (1987). Co-author (with Alan Richards) *The Birds of Belvide Reservoir* (1974). Co-editor (with G R Harrison *et al) Birds of the West Midlands* (1982). Editorial Committee *West Midland Bird Report* 1976-83 and *Devon Bird Report* 1989. Joint editor *Devon Bird Report* 1990-. OIR: watching, photographing and recording other wildlife, esp dragonflies and butterflies; reading biological publications; watching too much television. 8 Twindle Beer, Chudleigh, Newton Abbot, Devon TQ13 0JP. 01626 853393.

SMITH, Anne Judith (Judith); *b:* 20 July 1944 in Bury, Greater Manchester; *h:* Edward Smith. Manchester College of Commerce 1962-63. FLA 1974. Retired librarian. County Bird Recorder Greater Manchester 1992-. BTO Regional Representative Manchester 1992-. Committee Manchester Ornithological Society 1992-. Wigan Wildlife Advisory Group 1990- and Greater Manchester WAG 1994-. Formerly Committee, Conservation Officer, Newsletter Editor of Leigh Orn Soc. Special interests: breeding wildfowl and waders; Mute Swan; site conservation; survey work (inc BTO Breeding Bird Survey, Common Birds Census and Waterways Bird Survey). Compiler of annual reports: *The Birds of the Abram Flashes SSSI* 1991-94; *Breeding Mute Swans in Wigan Metropolitan Borough* 1990-95. Also Editor of *Birds in Greater Manchester* (annual report) 1992-. OIR: bats. 12 Edge Green Street, Ashton-in-Makerfield, Wigan, Lancs WN4 8SL. 01942 712615.

SMITH, Arthur Harold Victor (Harold); *b:* 26 April 1923 in London; *w:* Elizabeth. BSc Botany (London, 1944), PhD Geology (London, 1960). Retired scientist (British Coal). BTO Regional Representative SW Yorks 1983-92 (organised BTO surveys locally). Chairman Yorkshire Naturalists' Union Ornithological Section 1985-88. Recorder for Birds, Sorby NHS 1977- (also SNHS representative on local conservation bodies, eg Moorland and Woodlands Advisory Group of Sheffield Council). Special interests: population studies (BTO Common Birds Census woodland and moorland plots since 1977); computerisation of bird records (to improve quality of bird recording locally with particular reference to site recording and the use of BTO habitat/land-use codes). Editor of *Birds in the Sheffield Area* (1974). Compiler of bird report in monthly *Sorby Newsletter*. OIR: gardening, natural history, photography. 16 Silverdale Close, Sheffield S11 9JN. 01742 362953.

SMITH, Donald Anthony (Don); *b:* 23 April 1944 in Aberdeen; *w:* Annie. Strathallan School, Perthshire 1958-62. Royal College of Science and Technology, Glasgow 1962-65. FRPS 1979. Managing Director, Perdita Products since 1987. Prev: Managing Director, Nature Photographers Ltd 1982-85. Secretary-General, Assocn of British Nature Photographers 1970-1980. Vice President, International Federation of Wildlife Photography 1977-1980. RSPB Council 1988-92. Photographic consultant to *British Birds* 1981-94. BTO 'A' ringer since 1984. 'Master' banding permit (Canada) 1995-. Special interests: photography and ringing, esp birds of prey in SW Scotland. Discovered the Red Sea Cliff Swallow *Hirundo perdita*, Sudan 1984 (*Ibis*, 1985). Bird Photograph of the Year (*British Birds*) 1979. Member: Clyde Ringing Group. OIR: underwater photography, travel in remote places. Scoretulloch House, Darvel, Ayrshire KA17 0LR. 01560 323331.

SMITH, George Alfred; *b:* 7 July 1932 in Peterborough, Cambs; *p:* Olive Leonard. BVetMed, MRCVS (London, 1959). Veterinarian, retired. Special interests: parrots, systematics, ethology, distribution, the late stages of incubation and hatching (esp in altricial birds), population genetics, extinction. Travelled in Australia, Paraguay, Bolivia, Brazil, Philippines to study parrots in the wild. Author of avicultural books inc *Lovebirds and Related Parrots* (1979). Regular contributor to avicultural journals; also papers on parrots published in *Ibis*. Lectured in UK, Europe, Brazil, N America and Australia. Member: Avicultural Society. OIR: herpetology, gardening (esp alpines), historical research, wandering and wondering (esp in S America). Greenacre, Great North Road, Haddon, Peterborough PE7 3TN. 01733 243725; fax 01733 240233.

SMITH, George Davidson; *b:* 21 September 1959 in Haddington, East Lothian; *w:* Jacqueline. Electrical supervisor. BTO Regional Representative Lothian 1991-. Chairman of Conservation Sub-committee SOC Lothian Branch 1989-94. BTO 'C' ringer since 1992. Special interests: Grey Heron, Siskin, raptors. Co-ordinates monitoring of Buzzard increase in Lothian. Article on influx of Quail in Lothian published in *Lothian Bird Report* 1989. OIR: hill walking, canoeing, photography, youth club leader. 16 Stewart Avenue, Currie, Midlothian EH14 5SD. 0131 449 5366.

SMITH, Kenneth William (Ken); *b:* 30 November 1947 in Woodstock, Oxfordshire. BSc Physics (Imperial College, London, 1969), DPhil Experimental Physics (Sussex, 1972). Head of Aquatic and International Research, RSPB since 1996. Prev RSPB: Senior Research Biologist 1988-96; research biologist 1986-88; contract research biologist 1983-86. Earlier: national survey organiser BTO/RSPB 1981-83. Rare Breeding Birds Panel 1991-. BTO Regional Representative Hertfordshire 1980-90. Herts Bird Club Committee 1980-. BTO Ringing Committee. Herts FWAG Committee 1981-83. President Herts HNS 1996-. Scientific Committee Herts and Middlesex WT. Local organiser of some national and many county bird surveys. BTO 'A' ringer since 1978. Special interests: bird conservation, survey work, use of ringing as a study tool, woodpeckers, Green Sandpiper. Co-author (with C J Mead) *The Hertfordshire Breeding Bird Atlas* (1982). Co-editor *The Breeding Birds of Hertfordshire* (1994).

Over sixty papers and articles published in scientific journals. Member: Wader Study Group. RSPB, The Lodge, Sandy, Beds SG19 2DL. 01767 680551.

SMITH, Mavis Barbara; *b:* 7 February 1956 in Darwen, Lancs; *h:* Francis. Bird recorder and editor of annual report for Darwen area since 1989. Special interest: long-term study of migrants through the Darwen area (commenced 1986). Weekly column on birds for *Darwen Advertiser & News* 1986-90 and monthly contributor to *Bird Watching* since 1986. Founder-member and recorder, Blackburn & District Bird Club 1991. Lectures on birds given to local groups, also guided walks. OIR: voluntary tutor for adults with learning difficulties in English language. 47 Baron Street, Darwen, Lancs BB3 1NP.

SMITH, Peter; *b:* 9 October 1945 in Bedford; *w:* Sandra. Stratton Grammar School, Biggleswade. FRICS 1969. Managing Director, Halifax Property Services London & East Region. Committee Bedfordshire NHS 1964-76, Chairman 1974-76. Responsible for waders section of *Bedfordshire Bird Report* since 1990. Special interests: birds in Bedfordshire, their status and migration; conservation of sites; photography. Widely travelled throughout N America, Ecuador, Galapagos, Argentina, Africa, Europe, Russia, India, Far East, Borneo, Australia, often as expedition leader. Illustrated talks given to local societies. Trustee of Peter Smith Charitable Trust for Nature. OIR: supporting Leighton Buzzard Rugby Club, playing cricket for Aspley Guise CC, captaining local pub quiz team. The Old Rectory, Hills End, Eversholt, Milton Keynes MK17 9DR. 01525 280001.

SMITH, Peter John Strode; Col RM Retd; *b:* 29 August 1927 in Plymouth; *w:* Helen. Hon Secretary and Treasurer, Royal Naval Birdwatching Society 1985-. Collator for annual MOD Bird Count (Naval Establishments) 1990-. Articles published in *Sea Swallow* and *Victorian Ornithological Research Group Journal* (Australia), inc paper on Silver Gull breeding 1965-71 in latter. OIR: entomology. 19 Downlands Way, South Wonston, Winchester, Hants SO21 3HS. 01962 885258.

SMITH, Richard Gordon; *b:* 31 December 1945 in Cardiff, South Glamorgan; *w:* Susan. Cardiff High School. BSc Civil Engineering (Glamorgan Coll of Tech, 1969). CEng, MICE. Regional Quality Manager, Wimpey Construction UK. Glamorgan Bird Club: Chairman 1993/94, Records Committee 1980-96. Member of Welsh Records Advisory Group 1980-91. County Bird Recorder Glamorgan 1980-87. Special interest:

photography. Travel esp N America, N Africa, Middle East (also Europe); related illustrated lectures given. Editor *Glamorgan Bird Report* 1980-84; sub-editor *Mid and South Glamorgan Bird Report* 1985-96. Articles on birds of Florida and Fuerteventura published in *Birding World*. Numerous photographs in eg *Rare Birds of the British Isles* by David Saunders (1991), *Birding World*, *British Birds* and bird reports. 35 Manor Chase, Gwaun Miskin, Pontypridd, Mid Glam CF38 2JD. 01443 205816

SNOOK, Alan Michael (Al); *b:* 13 May 1954 in Southampton; *w:* Julie. Bookseller, specialising in ornithology and general natural history; also freelance cartographic draughtsman. WEA tutor on British birds 1986-88. Hampshire Ornithological Society Management Committee 1992-. Editor *HOS Newsletter* 1992. Cartographic work for *The Birds of Hampshire* by Clark and Eyre (1993); sundry notes for *British Birds*. OIR: 'passion for books'. 16 Emmett Road, Rownhams, Southampton SO1 8JB. 01703 730009.

SNOOK, Reginald Francis (Reg); *b:* 10 October 1938 in Ipswich; *w:* Ann. Artist. Department of the Environment Inspector specialising in birds of prey since 1982. RSPB representative for Suffolk during 1960s. Founder-member Suffolk Ornithologists' Group (1973). Special interests: long-term study of Tawny and Barn Owls since c1964, esp adaptation to man's environment; rehabilitation studies of all British owls (inc wild disabled and injured birds prior to release); liaison with DoE in respect of imported birds (esp parrot-type birds and birds of prey), also identification of birds of prey held in captivity. Numerous articles on birds of prey in journals and magazines using own illustrations. Paintings in collections worldwide (paintings by commission only). OIR: general natural history and environmental pressures on countryside. 5 Manor Road, Ipswich IP4 2UX. 01473 251037.

SNOW, David William; *b:* 30 September 1924 in Windermere, Westmorland; *w:* Barbara. Eton College. DPhil Systematics of Paridae (New College, Oxford, 1953), DSc (Oxford, 1976). Senior Principal Scientific Officer, Natural History Museum 1968-84, retired. Prev: Director of Research BTO 1964-68; Director, Charles Darwin Research Station, Galapagos 1963-64; New York Zoological Society, Residential Naturalist at tropical field station in Trinidad 1957-61; Demonstrator, Edward Grey Institute, Oxford Univ 1949-56. Special interests: ecology, behaviour, systematics, esp Neotropics. Author *A Study of Blackbirds* (1958), *The Web of Adaptation: bird studies in the American tropics* (1976),

The Cotingas (1982). Co-author (with B K Snow) *Birds and Berries* (1988). Co-editor (with C M Perrins) *Concise BWP* (in press). Various papers in ornithological journals eg *The Auk, Condor, Ibis, J für Orn*. Godman-Salvin Medal, BOU 1982; Brewster Medal (with B K Snow), AOU 1972. Member: AOU, Deutsche Ornithologen-Gesellschaft, SEOF. The Old Forge, Wingrave, Aylesbury, Bucks HP22 4PD. 01296 681351.

SNOW, Philip; *b:* 7 September 1947 in Altrincham, Cheshire. Lymm Grammar School 1958-64. Northwich School of Art 1965-67. Birkenhead College of Art 1976-77. BA Illustration (Manchester Polytechnic 1983). Freelance illustrator since 1983. All illustrations for *River Birds* by Lovegrove and Snow (1985), *Collins Field Notebook of British Birds* by Lovegrove and Snow (1986), *Birds of Mull* by Madders and Snow (1987, 3rd ed 1993), *Birdwatching on Anglesey and Lleyn* by V McFarland (1990), *Birds and Forestry* by Avery and Leslie (1990), *Birds of Mid Argyll* by Madders *et al* (1992), *Hebridean Birds and Landscape - a sketchbook* (in prep); joint illustrator of over thirty other books. Regular contributor of pictures to eg *BBC Wildlife, Bird Watching, British Birds*; also overseas magazines. Widely exhibited in London galleries inc Tryon Gallery, South Bank, Barbican, Design Centre, SWLA Mall Galleries; elsewhere inc Royal Academy 'British Art' show in Gulf States, RSPB Birds in Art in Wales Exhibition, Anglesey Heritage Gallery, Royal Cambrian Academy, NCC 'Impressions of Nature' touring exhibition, The Artist/Art in Nature exhibition and book 1996. Collections inc Welsh National Library, Gulf Royal families, RSPB. As much work as possible donated to conservation and other charities. OIR: creation science and the Bible. Pensychnant Nature Centre, Sychnant Pass, Conwy LL32 8BJ. Tel/fax 01492 581139.

SPEAKMAN, John Roger; *b:* 29 November 1958 in Leigh, Lancs; *w:* Mary. BSc Biology and Psychology (Stirling, 1980), PhD Energetics of foraging in wading birds (Stirling, 1984), DSc Animal Energetics (Aberdeen, 1996). Reader in Zoology, Univ Aberdeen since 1995. Prev: Senior Lecturer 1993-95, Lecturer 1989-93. Research: energetics in avian flight, formation flight of geese, predation by birds on bats. Numerous scientific articles in journals inc *American Naturalist, Bird Study, J Exp Biol*; others in eg *Wader Study Group Bulletin*. OIR: photography. Dept of Zoology, University of Aberdeen, Aberdeen AB24 2TZ. 01224 272879; fax 01224 272396.

SPEIGHT, Graham John; *b:* 8 May 1958 in Barnsley, Yorks. Carpenter by trade. Joint organiser and leader of Budget Bird Tours. Barnsley Bird Study Group: Recorder and member of Rarities Committee since 1980. Many extended trips abroad, each of six to ten months, to countries in Asia, Australasia and Latin America (over 5,000 species in 60 countries). Trips include site surveys for conservation bodies, with reports to eg BirdLife International and Asian Wetland Bureau, also to universities and bird societies in the countries. Joint editor *Yorkshire Birding* since its inception in 1992. Editor *Barnsley Area Bird Report* 1986-89 and compiler or part writer in previous four years. Participant in Yorkshire TV programme on twitching in 1988. Member: ABC, Asian Wetland Bureau, OBC (founder-member), OSME. OIR: playing five-a-side football and watching Barnsley FC. 12 Park Grove, Barnsley, S Yorks S70 1PY. 01226 282408.

SPENCE, Ian Miller; *b:* 8 January 1950 in Singapore. BA Psychology (Liverpool, 1977), MSc Educational Psychology (Sheffield, 1986). Principal educational psychologist. Committee Leigh Ornithological Society 1979-85. Leigh area recorder for Manchester breeding atlas survey 1979-84. Member, Clwyd Bird Recording Group, Hon Sec 1993-95. Clwyd Co-ordinator for Wales Raptor Study Group 1992-. BTO Ringing Committee 1994-. Council North Wales WT. BTO 'A' ringer since 1982. Special interests: all aspects of ringing (esp training of ringers), breeding studies, migration, moult, special studies of Common Snipe and Lesser Black-backed Gull, ringing in Italy and Senegal. Co-author *Breeding Birds in Greater Manchester* (1984). Article on gull ringing in *Gull Study Group Bulletin* (1981); author or co-author of papers in *Ringing & Migration* and *Welsh Birds*. Editor of ringing reports in *Clwyd Bird Report* 1989 and 1990. Co-editor *Clwyd Bird Report* 1990. Has produced own annual ringing report since 1982. Member: Seabird Group, Wader Study Group. OIR: listening to classical music and jazz, eating good vegetarian food, discussing current issues, assisting conservation of wildlife generally. 11 Tan y Bryn, Pwllglas, Ruthin, Clwyd LL15 2PJ.

SPENCE, Robert John Mouat (Ian); *b:* 23 December 1937 in Stroma, Caithness. Baker. Committee Shetland Bird Club since 1985. Winter wildfowl counts and regular contributor to *Shetland Bird Report* since 1974. Monthly Beached Bird Surveys 1980-. OIR: bowls, badminton, fishing, photography, sailing. Sunnyside, Uyeasound, Unst, Shetland ZE2 9DL. 01957 755231.

STAFFORD, John; *b:* 1 May 1921 in Sutton, Surrey; *w:* Patricia. King's College London and Westminster Hospital School 1939-45. LRCP, MRCS 1945, MRCGP 1966. Retired doctor. RSPB: Council 1956-66, Chairman Educational & General Purposes Committee 1965-66. President Sussex

Ornithological Society 1962-66. Founder and President Shoreham and District Ornithological Society 1953-96. BTO 'A' ringer 1954-70. Special interests: migration, ringing (started first ringing station in Sussex in 1953). Member of Eric Hosking's party to Spain to photograph Lammergeier 1958, also to Bulgaria 1960. Articles on wintering Blackcaps in British Isles (1956) and Nightjar Survey (1962) published in *Bird Study*. Wrote introduction to *The Birds of Shoreham* by John Newnham (1988). Broadcast with Bruce Campbell and Maxwell Knight on BBC *Naturalist's Notebook*, and later with James Fisher. OIR: wooden scale models, dolls houses, models for local museum. 9 Mill Hill, Shoreham-by-Sea, W Sussex BN43 5TG. 01273 452545.

STAFFORD, John; *b:* 11 June 1929 in Leigh, Lancs; *w:* Lily. Leigh Grammar School. MA Mathematics (St John's College, Cambridge, 1955). FBCS 1968, FSS 1973. Chartered Information Systems Practitioner 1995. Research consultant; retired university lecturer. Isle of Wight County Bird Recorder 1953-. BTO: National Organiser Census of Heronries 1957-71, IOW representative 1954-92 (local organiser of many surveys). RSPB: IOW representative 1955-78. WWT: IOW representative since 1954 (inc local organiser of Wildfowl Counts etc). Seabird Group: IOW organiser 'Operation Seafarer' 1969. IOW Nat Hist and Archaeol Soc: Council from 1953, President 1975-78, Vice Pres 1963-75 and 1978-, Chairman Computing and Recording Committee, member of various other committees. Hampshire and IOW Naturalists' Trust: Chairman IOW Area Board 1975-78. IOW County Council: Countryside Advisory Panel 1972-78, Environmental Advisory Panel 1990-94. Farming and Wildlife Advisory Group, IOW Committee since 1990. Ran series of joint University/WEA courses on Isle of Wight birds, 1982-90. Council member of National Federation for Biological Recording from 1993. Special interests: IOW birds, heronries, seabird colonies, use of computers in ornithological and other biological recording, population dynamics (in c1960 worked on computer simulation of dynamics of heronries and rookeries). Editor *Isle of Wight Birds* (annual report) since 1984, and of earlier annual reports in *Proc IOW Nat Hist and Archaeol Soc* since 1953; also many articles, census and survey accounts in these reports. Series of heronry papers in *Bird Study* in 1950s to 70s, notably 'The Heron Population of England and Wales, 1928-1970' in Vol 18, 1971. Radio broadcast on national heronries census in 'Birds of Britain' series (BBC, 1960). OIR: collecting bird stamps, genealogy, French wines, watching cricket (Vice Pres Brighstone CC). Westering, Moor Lane, Brighstone, Newport, Isle of Wight PO30 4DL. 01983 740280.

STANDLEY, Peter Edward; *b:* 26 July 1931 in Walton-on-Naze, Essex; *w:* Dorothea. Government Service, retired. Recorder Reading Ornithological Club 1965-83, 1990-. County Recorder Berkshire 1966-. Special interests: habitat conservation, esp where used by locally scarce species. Joint editor (with N J Bucknell *et al*) *The Birds of Berkshire* (1996). Editor *Reading Ornithological Club Annual Report* 1965-73. Joint editor annual *Berks and Oxon Bird Report* 1966-73. Editor *Birds of Berkshire* (annual report) 1974-. Contributor of articles to county bird reports. Siskins, 7 Llanvair Drive, South Ascot, Berks SL5 9HS. 01344 23502.

STEAD, Philip John; *b:* 9 July 1930 in Middlesbrough; *w:* Anne. HND Structural Engineering (Constantine Tech Coll, 1951). CEng, MIStructE 1956. Sales executive, steel fabricator. Recorder for VC65 (W half of N Riding of Yorkshire) 1963-72. Member of Yorkshire and Durham & Northumberland Records Committees 1963-72, and of Hertfordshire Records Committee 1986-94. Chairman Teesmouth Bird Club 1961-63. Special interests: identification, waders and seabirds. Travel for birds in Austria, Canary Islands, Greece, India, Kenya, Spain, Sweden, USA. Author 'The Birds of Tees-side' in *Trans Nat Hist Soc of Northumberland and Durham* (1964) and *The Birds of Tees-side 1962-67* (1969). Illustrated *The House Sparrow* by J D Summers-Smith (1963). Participant in two-part BBC radio broadcast on migration, spring and autumn 1959. Various short items in *British Birds* and paper in *Ardeola* on birds seen in Andalucía in May 1958. OIR: natural history (esp Lepidoptera and Odonata), botany (esp orchids), aircraft (esp associated with WW2, Korean War, Vietnam), military history and battlefields. 14 Arretine Close, St Albans, Herts AL3 4JL. 01727 866904.

STEBBING-ALLEN, George; *b:* 15 February 1942 in Camelsdale, W Sussex; *w:* Lin. The Mercers' and Haberdashers' Aske's Schools 1952-59. Author and lecturer. Founder and first leader of West London RSPB Members' Group 1970 and of South East Herts Group 1971-75. Worked closely with Trevor Gunton of RSPB to develop Members' Group movement. From 1979, lecturer to clubs and societies on bird-related topics. Special interests: taxonomy (esp in relation to field identification techniques); factors affecting the distribution of birds worldwide (eg plate tectonics, evolutionary biology, island biology); international bird protection and conservation issues (eg deforestation, pollution); eco-tourism; hummingbirds (ongoing study of

Hermits and their parallel adaptation with flowers). Active field ornithologist since 1968, esp concerned with study of bird movements according to habitat and season. Study countries inc New Zealand, Jamaica, Costa Rica. Author *A Diversity of Birds* (1994). Founder-member NBC. OIR: music, esp Renaissance polyphony and the operas of Verdi. 123 Chiltern Park Avenue, Berkhamsted, Herts HP4 1EZ. 01442 384941; fax 01442 384942; mobile 0410 401813.

STENTIFORD, Michael (Mike); *b:* 17 August 1935 in Exeter, Devon; *w:* Hilary. Countryside Interpretation Officer, Planning & Environment Committee, States of Jersey since 1992. RSPB Group Leader and Representative, Jersey Members' Group 1976-92. Author *The Birdwatcher's Jersey* (1987); co-author (with Beth Lloyd and Sue Hardy) *Island Walks* (1991). Twice-monthly article 'Nature Notes' for *Jersey Evening Post*; various articles on natural history for Jersey Tourism publications. Ornithological adviser to the Channel Television series *Wildabout Jersey* (1989). Regular contributor to BBC Radio Jersey. RSPB President's Award 1991. OIR: walking. Naparima Cottage, La Commune, Victoria Village, Trinity, Jersey JE3 5HS. 01534 861114.

STEVENTON, David John; *b:* 21 March 1949 in Stoke-on-Trent, Staffs; *w:* Jean. Oundle School. BA Natural Sciences (Cambridge, 1970); Dip in Management Studies (Portsmouth Polytechnic, 1978). Cheshire and Wirral Ornithological Society: Vice Chairman 1990-93, Chairman 1994-. BTO 'A' ringer since 1967. Special interest: seabirds. Series of expeditions to Shiant Islands 1970-89. Secretary Shiants Auk Ringing Group 1972-. Articles on various species published in *Cambridgeshire Bird Report*, *Hampshire Bird Report*, *Ringing & Migration*, *Seabird Group Report*. Technical editor *Cheshire and Wirral Bird Report* 1986-. Member: Seabird Group, Wader Study Group. OIR: music, theatre, decorating, cooking. Welland House, 207 Hurdsfield Road, Macclesfield, Cheshire SK10 2PX. 01625 421936.

STEWART, Andrew (Andy); *b:* 15 May 1965 in Burnley, Lancs; *w:* Jacqueline. Community nurse for people with learning disabilities (RNMH). 'I am a volunteer who reads Darvic leg rings on Pink-footed Geese for the WWT. I carry out this task every weekend from 6 September until mid April the following year and also use every day of my six weeks annual leave to pursue this obsession. I have been locating marked Pinkfeet since December 1987 and read on average between 400 and 500 Darvic rings per winter. My search for Pinkfeet takes me from the mosses in Lancashire in autumn to Dumfries in winter, and finally to the Grampian region in spring prior to the birds' return to their breeding grounds in Iceland and Greenland. In addition to my ring reading work, or "Darvic twitching" as I call it, I have participated in a number of catches in both England and Scotland where Pinkfeet have been caught for marking purposes. In spring 1991 I participated in a WWT expedition to southern Iceland to assist in the study of behaviour of grey geese prior to breeding.' Co-author of paper 'Winter movements and site-fidelity of Pink-footed Geese ringed in Britain, with particular emphasis on those marked in Lancashire' in *Bird Study* (1994), and JNCC report 'Survival estimates of Pink-footed Geese 1987-1991' (1995). OIR: collecting books on the history of the US Eighth Air Force, playing Scottish bagpipes. 8 Bowes Close, The Beeches, Tottington, Bury, Lancs BL8 1UA. 0161 762 9774.

STEWART, Peter Francis; *b:* 10 October 1938 in Plymouth, Devon; *w:* Julie. Retired RAF (Sergeant Electronic Engineer). Cyprus Ornithological Society: Secretary 1961, 1967-69, Ringing Officer 1967-69, Rarities Committee 1983-. Committee Severn Estuary Gull Group 1990-. BTO 'A' ringer since 1960. Special interests: Cyprus ornithology, Mediterranean seabirds, long-term ringing and study of wintering gulls (esp Lesser Black-backed and Herring) at landfill sites in Glos, Hereford and Worcs (begun 1984). Co-author (with S Christensen) *Check List of the Birds of Cyprus* (1971) and (with P R Flint) *The Birds of Cyprus: an annotated check-list* (1983, 2nd ed 1992). Contributor to *BWP* Vols 1-8 and to various other publications eg *The Cyprus Magazine*, *Bulletins* and *Reports* of the Cyprus Orn Soc and *Bulletin of the Severn Estuary Gull Group*, of which also editor. Member: as above, also North Cyprus Society for the Protection of Birds. OIR: photography, family history research. 10 Digby Road, Evesham, Worcs WR11 6BW. 01386 48091.

STEWART-SMITH, John; *b:* 6 March 1932 in Ireland; *w:* Jenifer. RAF Cranwell and Bristol Univ. RAF pilot, retired. Founder-Chairman Emirates Natural History Group, Abu Dhabi 1971-77. Originated United Arab Emirates Checklist 1970. Organised IUCN Survey of Arabian Gulf 1973. Assisted International Falconry Convention, Abu Dhabi 1973. IWRB Arabian Correspondent 1970-77. Special interests: photography, migration and navigation. Extensive travel in Saudi Arabia, UAE, Oman, Gibraltar, Libya, Sudan, Ethiopia, Kenya, Hong Kong, Brunei, Singapore, Equador, Cyprus, Spain, Lebanon, Malta,

Iceland, Canada, USA. Conservation and bird news broadcast on Abu Dhabi Radio. Occasional notes for *British Birds* and other publications. Personal library of c15,000 35mm slides of birds of above countries (contact: Roundhouse Publishing Services, PO Box 140, Oxford OX2 7QD), many used in publications eg *Wildlife of Arabia* by Professors Talhouk and Büttiker (1981). OIR: gliding, sailing, writing, staying off committees. 24 Carneton Close, Crantock, Newquay, Cornwall TR8 5RY. Tel/fax 01637 830546.

STIRRUP, Simon Andrew; *b:* 23 February 1961 in Birkenhead, Merseyside. BSc Zoology (Durham, 1982). Project leader with computer software house. Cataloguer of bird specimens in Merseyside County Museum Dec 1982 to Mar 1983. RSPB species protection warden (Montagu's Harrier) Apr-Jul 1983. Secretary Cambridge Bird Club 1984-89. Secretary Oriental Bird Club 1990-93, Council 1989-. Special interests: birds of Oriental region, esp China. Member of Cambridge Ornithological Expedition to China 1985 and China Cranewatch Expedition 1986. In UK, very interested in birds of central Cumbria. One of four authors of annual satirical magazine *Not BB* 1986-90. OIR: photography, badminton, music, walking, travel. 19 Gainsborough Close, Cambridge CB4 1SY. 01223 426060.

STOCKER, Leslie Robert (Les); MBE 1992; *b:* 31 January 1943 in Oxford; *w:* Sue. Emanuel School, London 1954-59. Author and wildlife care consultant. Chairman, St Tiggywinkles, The Wildlife Hospital Trust 1978-. Special interest: medical care and rehabilitation of wild birds. Author *Code of Practice for the Rescue, Treatment, Rehabilitation and Release of Sick and Injured Wildlife* (1991), *The Complete Garden Bird* (1991). Foreign correspondent for *Wildlife Rehabilitation Today* (USA). Wildlife phone correspondent for London Broadcasting. Member: International Wildlife Rehabilitation Council (USA), National Wildlife Rehabilitators Association (USA), European Wildlife Rehabilitation Association (founder, 1990). OIR: photography, palaeontology. Wildlife Hospital, Aston Road, Haddenham, Bucks HP17 8AF. 01844 292292.

STODDART, Andrew Michael (Andy); *b:* 7 July 1963 in Bradford, W Yorks. MA Spanish and French (Cambridge, 1984). Planning Manager, Norfolk and Waveney Training and Enterprise Council. RSPB species protection warden Mar-Jun 1985. British Birds Rarities Committee 1993-. Norfolk Bird Records Committee 1993-. Special interests: migration and identification (esp passerines), birds of Palearctic region. Identification papers for *Birding World*. Asst editor *Norfolk Bird Report* 1990-92. OIR: travel, current affairs. 43 Gilman Road, Norwich NR3 4JB. 01603 485761.

STONE, Carolyn Judith; *b:* 8 March 1963 in Bristol; *h:* Tim Barton. BSc 1983, MSc 1985, PhD 1986 Marine Biology (Univ College Swansea). Biological oceanographer with the Seabirds at Sea Team, JNCC 1990-95. Special interests: seabird distribution offshore in north-west European waters; relationship between this distribution and oceanographic factors, eg depth. Papers on these interests published in *Bird Study*; also JNCC atlas and reports on distribution of seabirds at sea around Skomer and Skokholm islands, 1992 and 1993, and the use of trawlers as a food source by Lesser Black-backed Gulls in the Celtic Sea. OIR: sailing and boating; walking; playing piano, clarinet and guitar; wood carving; pottery; visiting Pembrokeshire. 16 Nether Blackhall, Inverurie, Aberdeenshire AB51 4EW.

STONE, David Arthur (Dave); *b:* 19 April 1945 in Edinburgh; *w:* Rosemary. BSc Agriculture (London, 1967), MPhil Soil Science (Nottingham, 1978). Research leader (plant nutrition). BTO 'A' ringer since 1962. Founder and organiser Hampshire Avon Swan Study 1974-. Ringing Secretary Brandon Ringing Group 1974-. Special interests: Mute Swan, population dynamics and conflict with man, Constant Effort Site ringing. Articles published in eg *Ringing & Migration*. OIR: local and community affairs, entomological recording (esp Carabid beetles), gardening. Overbury, Wolverton, Stratford-on-Avon, Warks CV37 0HG. 01789 731488.

STONE, Norman Haslock Francis; *b:* 21 November 1928 in Harold Wood, Essex. ALA 1960. Retired librarian. BTO Regional Representative N Bucks 1978-87. British Ornithologists' Club Committee 1986-90, 1995-. Buckinghamshire Bird Club Committee 1980-83. Special interests: evolution/ecological isolation. Travel in E and W Africa. Co-author of articles in *Buckinghamshire Bird Report* and contributor to *The Birds of Buckinghamshire* ed by P Lack and D Ferguson (1993). Member: WAOS. OIR: natural history, music, art. 64 Trinity Road, Old Wolverton, Milton Keynes MK12 5PB. 01908 318955.

STONEHOUSE, Bernard; *b:* 1 May 1926 in Kingston upon Hull; *w:* Sally. BSc Zoology (Univ College, London, 1953), MA 1959, DPhil Penguin

Biology (Merton College, Oxford, 1960). Senior Associate, Scott Polar Research Institute, Univ Cambridge (research on impacts of tourism in polar regions). Consultant in polar ecology and management since 1990. Prev: Chairman, Postgrad School of Environmental Science, Univ Bradford 1974-82; Senior Lecturer and Reader in Zoology, Univ Canterbury (New Zealand) 1960-69; demonstrator, Dept of Zoological Field Studies, Univ Oxford 1957-60; biologist, South Georgia 1953-55; meteorologist/biologist/pilot, Falkland Island Dependencies Survey 1946-50. BOU Council 1975. Special interests: biology of penguins and other Antarctic birds, biology of seabirds. Leader BOU Centenary Expedition to Ascension Island 1957-59. Many research papers, books, reports and broadcasts. Queen's Polar Medal with Antarctic clasp 1953. Union Medal, BOU 1971; Vocey Trophy for Antarctic Conservation, New Zealand Antarctic Society 1975. OIR: cruising as guest lecturer and researcher aboard Arctic and Antarctic tourist ships. 43 Commercial End, Swaffham Bulbeck, Cambridge CB5 0ND. 01223 812402.

STRANGEMAN, Peter Jack; *b:* 15 March 1944 in Cuckfield, Sussex; *w:* Pamela. Land surveyor. Research Committee London Natural History Society (Ornithology Section) 1970-91. Co-ordinator in the London area for surveys of House Martin (1974) and Cormorant (1979/80, 1984/85, 1985/86). Committee, Central Royal Parks Wildlife Group 1988-90. Wildfowl counter at Barn Elms Reservoirs, Greater London for over 25 years to 1990/91. Wetland Bird Survey counter for part of Portsmouth Harbour since 1991. Participant in BTO surveys inc Common Birds Census 1965-71. Special interests: urban ornithology and birds of wetlands, esp reservoirs; migration and movements; all sightings of Kestrels kept since 1957. Author of chapter 'Birds in Fulham' in *A History of Fulham to 1965* ed by P D Whitting (1970), several papers in *London Bird Report* and occasional notes in *British Birds*. OIR: Fulham football supporter, member of Letter Box Study Group, general natural history. 22 Andrew Crescent, Waterlooville, Hants PO7 6BE. 01705 254758.

STRATTON, Vivian Alfred (Viv); *b:* 8 August 1946 in St Ives, Cornwall; *w:* Annette. HNC Construction (Cornwall College, 1969). Manager of Construction at Cornwall College. Asst Conservation Officer, Cornwall Birdwatching and Preservation Society 1989-94. Tutor for the Natural History Certificate course at Cornwall College 1981-85. Long-term study of seabirds at St Ives Island since 1956 (esp identification of petrels, shearwaters, skuas, gulls). 'I introduced Peter Harrison, Steve Madge and

Vic Tucker to seabirds, and also to the beautiful West Cornwall valleys.' Chartered 'Scillonian 3' annually since 1986 for pelagic trips into Western Approaches looking for rare seabirds. Since mid 1970s studied intensively the migration of passerines (esp warblers, chats, flycatchers, buntings). Had earlier found Porthgwarra (1957), Cot Valley and Nanquindo (1959), now recognised as of major importance for migrants, particularly of American and Asian origin. Studies over twenty years of effect of monofilament nets on seabirds, inc large reduction in numbers of wintering divers, grebes, sea ducks and auks in W Cornwall. Carried out in-depth survey of West Penwith Moorlands 1960-65, 1970-73, 1980-83, which was instrumental in obtaining ESA status for them. Several studies of wintering harriers, Merlins and owls, and summer studies of Nightjars. Involved from 1990 in conservation and protection of environmentally sensitive areas in Poland through the Jeagellonian University in Krakow, with surveys of eg Aquatic, Barred and River Warblers, Great Snipe, Lesser Spotted Eagle, shrikes and storks. Many contributions to *Birds in Cornwall* (annual report), also some work for Radio Cornwall. 2 Alexandra Row, St Ives, Cornwall TR26 1EH. 01736 796487.

STRICKLAND, Robert Vincent (Bob); *b:* in Dublin. Managing director (medical equipment supply company). Founder of IWC Liffey Valley Branch (1985), Chairman (1988-90), Secretary (1991-96). IWC Council (1990) and Executive Committee (1988). Special interests: bird photography, leading overseas bird tours, Neotropical birds (visits to Venezuela, Costa Rica, Mexico, Ecuador, Galapagos). Author of bird information articles in local press, eg *Liffey Valley News*. Occasional broadcast on local radio. Bird photographs published, also shown in local and national exhibitions. OIR: symphonic music and opera enthusiast. 14 Lucan Heights, Lucan, Co Dublin, Ireland. +353 (0)1 6280758.

SULLIVAN, Matthew Stephen; *b:* 12 February 1964 in Woking, Surrey; *w:* Ann. BSc Zoology (Manchester, 1985), DPhil Ornithology (Oxford, 1991). University lecturer in behavioural ecology since 1993. Prev: Post-doctoral Fellow, Univ Sheffield 1991-93 researching sexual selection in Zebra Finches. Special interests: avian and insect behavioural ecology. Articles published in eg *Anim Behav, Ethology, J World Pheasant Assocn, J Zool.* OIR: contemporary music, natural history, wine. Dept of Biological Sciences, Manchester Metropolitan University, Manchester M1 5GD. 0161 247 1164.

SULTANA, Joe; *b:* 11 November 1939 in Gozo, Malta; *w:* Lucy. Lyceum Gozo 1952-56, St Michael's Teachers Training College 1958-60. Principal Environment Officer, Nature Conservation Areas in the Maltese Islands since 1994. Prev: Environment Manager 1993-94; Conservation Officer, Environment Dept 1981-92; Manager, Field Studies Centre 1977-80. Earlier: Government School Teacher 1961-76. Malta Ornithological Society: Asst Sec 1966, Secretary 1967-75, President 1976-87, Council Member 1988-93. Co-founder of MOS Bird Ringing Scheme with help of BTO in 1965, Ringing Officer of the Scheme since 1968. BirdLife International (prev ICBP): Chairman of Maltese National Section 1984-92; ex-officio member of European Section 1983-84; Chairman of European Executive Committee 1985-92; World Council Member. Special interests: migration in central Mediterranean, the (few) breeding birds of Malta, Mediterranean seabirds, general bird identification, travel and photography. Senior author *Bird Studies on Filfla* (1970), *Guide to the Birds of Malta* (1975), *l-Aghsafar* (1976), *A New Guide to the Birds of Malta* (1982). Co-author *Localities with Conservation Values in the Maltese Islands* (1987). Co-editor *Red Data Book for the Maltese Islands* (1989). Editor *Bird's Eye View* 1981-. Editor *Medmaravis News* 1990-. Scientific Committee *Gli Uccelli d'Italia* 1988-. Editorial Board *Il-Merill* 1979-; also regular contributor as author or co-author on Maltese ornithology, moult and breeding biology of some species, and ringing records. Co-author of papers on seabirds in Medmaravis Publications. Member: BirdLife Malta; Council, Mediterranean Marine Bird Assocn (Medmaravis). Hon Member, Hungarian Orn Soc. 3 Sciberras Flats, Fleur-de-Lys Junction, Fleur-de-Lys BKR 02, Malta. +356 440278; fax +356 225665.

SUMMERS-SMITH, James Denis (Denis); *b:* 25 October 1920 in Glasgow; *w:* Margaret. BSc Metallurgy (Glasgow, 1947), PhD Physics (Reading, 1953). CEng 1968, FIMechE 1989. Mechanical engineering consultant (esp tribology). BOU Publications Committee 1955-60. BTO Scientific Advisory Committee 1958-62. Founder-member Teesmouth Bird Club (1961). Special interest: genus *Passer*. Author *The House Sparrow* (1963), *The Sparrows* (1988), *In Search of Sparrows* (1992), *The Tree Sparrow* (1995). Co-editor (with J Pinowski) *Granivorous Birds in the Agricultural Landscape* (Warsaw, 1990). Some twenty-five papers on sparrows published in eg *Bird Study, British Birds, Bull BOC, Ibis, J für Orn, Ostrich*. Body and Sparrow Prize, BTO 1989; Stamford Raffles Award, The London Zoological Society 1992.

OIR: computing, travel, wine. Merlewood, The Avenue, Guisborough, Cleveland TS14 8EE. 01287 632449.

SUTCLIFFE, Stephen John (Steve); *b:* 9 July 1946 in Halifax, Yorks; *w:* Anna. Trained accountant. Warden, Skomer Island NNR 1986-94. Prev: Hon Warden, St Margaret's Island 1964-92. Hon Secretary BTO 1993-97. Various ornithological and conservation committees prior to moving to Skomer. Special interests: migration ringing, seabird studies (esp *Larus* gulls), Magpie colonisation and breeding success, Oystercatcher survival, Short-eared Owl breeding success and dispersal, long-term study (since 1965) of Cormorant dispersal, bird population fluctuations generally. Numerous papers and articles in Welsh journals and bulletins; gull paper in *Bird Study*; review of *Larus* gull populations in W Wales for CCW. Member: Seabird Group, Wader Study Group. OIR: golf. Mullock Cottages, Marloes, Haverfordwest, Pembrokeshire SA62 3QT. 01646 636754.

SUTHERLAND, Martin Philip; *b:* 27 September 1954 in Broadstairs, Kent; *w:* Jill. AIEEM 1992. Freelance ecologist, principally involved in organising and conducting ornithological surveys and assessing likely development impacts. Leader of overseas birdwatching tours since 1980, mostly for Cygnus Wildlife. Prev: Warden Bardsey Bird Observatory 1983; woodland bird surveys for Sussex WT and RSPB 1982-83; asst bird observatory warden 1976-80 ie Calf of Man, Fair Isle, Manomet (Massachusetts, USA), Bardsey; also summer warden Sandwich Bay NR; field asst for ITE on Eider surveys in E Lothian and Puffin research on Isle of May and St Kilda 1975. Records Committee Kent Ornithological Society 1978-80 and 1991-96. Special interests: migration, habitat communities, bird song and adaptability. Tours led to European countries, northern India, widespread USA, Peru and Argentina; also travel for birds to Botswana, Zimbabwe, Ethiopia, Morocco, Canaries, Madeira and Azores. Articles in eg *Bird Observer of Eastern Massachusetts* ('Ground nesting and related behaviour of Common Nighthawks in Massachusetts'), *Kent Bird Report* and *Sussex Bird Report*. OIR: all aspects of natural history, keeping and attempting to breed tropical fish (esp South American catfish of the genus *Corydoras*). 92 Pierremont Avenue, Broadstairs, Kent CT10 1NT. 01843 603378.

SUTTON, John Trevor; *b:* 17 May 1950 in Manchester; *w:* Ruth. BA Music and Education (Durham and Open Univ, 1975). Deputy head teacher. BTO Regional Representative Greater Manchester 1981-85. BTO Winter Atlas local co-ordinator. Regional co-ordinator for Greater Manchester Atlas. BTO 'C' ringer since 1983. Special interests: ringing, photography. Extensive travel in W Palearctic. Joint author (with P K Holland and I M Spence) *Breeding Birds in Greater Manchester* (1984), also illustrations for this and for *Birds in Greater Manchester* and *Birds in Huddersfield* (annual reports). Exhibition of watercolour paintings BTO Conference 1986. Radio Manchester studio phone-ins and natural history programme 1982-84. Database conversion for BTO's BirdRing program. OIR: music and art, juggling. 'Computing is a vice'. 2 Manor Mills Cottages, Meltham, Huddersfield HD7 3AU.

SVENSSON, Lars Gunnar Georg; *b:* 30 March 1941 in Sweden; *p:* Lena Rahoult. DGI (Grafiska Institutet, Stockholm, 1964). Publishing editor and graphic designer. Editor *Vår Fågelvärld* 1971-74. Short-term ringer and warden at Capri Bird Observatory 1961, 1966 and Ottenby Bird Observatory 1961-65, Board member Swedish Ornithological Society (SOF) 1971-77. Founder Swedish Rarities Committee (1972) and Chairman 1972-87. Member SOF Nomenclature Committee 1974-83. Tour leader and lecturer. Special interests: identification, ageing and sexing in the hand, migration, taxonomy, nomenclature, bird sound recording. *Identification Guide to European Passerines* (author/artist/publisher, 1970, 4th ed 1992); *The Hamlyn Guide to the Birds of Britain & Europe* (co-author/b&w drawings, 1970, original ed rewritten in 1986, latest ed 1992); *Photographic Guide to the Birds of Britain & Europe* (co-author/b&w drawings, 1988); *Collins Guide to the Birds of Britain and Europe* (co-author Swedish ed, b&w drawings, 1980); *Sveriges fåglar* (*The Birds of Sweden*, checklist, editor 1978); *Bestämningsguide för vissa tättingar* (*Identification Guide to some Passerines*, author/artist/publisher 1964); *Soviet Birds* (recordist, tape cassette with leaflet 1984); *Fågelsång i Sverige* (*Birdsong in Sweden*, recordist and author, CD, book and tape cassette 1990); *Fågellokaler i Sverige* (*Where to Watch Birds in Sweden*, co-author, editor, map designer 1972, 4th ed 1985). Articles on identification (with own illustrations) *Birding, Birding World, Limicola, Vår Fågelvärld*. Honorary Ringer of the BTO 1985. Letterstedtska Författarpriset (authorship award) 1994. Member: Swedish Ornithological Society. Research in major museum collections in Denmark, England, Russia, Sweden, USA. OIR: wine, golf. Sturegatan 60, S-114 36 Stockholm, Sweden. +46 (0)8 6632655.

SWANN, Robert Lockhart (Bob); *b:* 28 December 1950 in Glasgow; *w:* Dora. MA Geography (Aberdeen, 1974). Principal Teacher of Geography, Tain Royal Academy. Aberdeen University Bird Club: founder-member 1972, Secretary 1972/73, President 1973/74. Chairman SOC Inverness Branch 1980-85. BTO Regional Representative Small Isles 1983-, Inverness-shire 1984-90. Secretary Highland Ringing Group 1986-. Executive Committee Highland Raptor Study Group 1983-. SOC Council 1995-. BTO 'A' ringer since 1970. Special interests: long-term monitoring of seabirds (ringing, counting, assessing productivity) at Isle of Canna 1971- and North Sutor, E Ross 1980- (both studies part of JNCC Seabird Monitoring Programme); wader and wildfowl studies (ringing, counts) in the Moray Firth 1977-; raptor studies, esp Buzzard and owls 1975-. Over twenty papers published in eg *Bird Study, Ibis, Ringing & Migration, Scottish Birds, Seabird*. BTO Tucker Medal 1993, for major contribution to ornithological knowledge in a variety of fields (first Scot to be awarded the medal). 14 St Vincent Road, Tain, Ross-shire IV19 1JR. 01862 894329.

SWEET, George Ernest; *b:* 20 November 1909 in London; *w:* Audrey (deceased). Artist. Recorders' Committee Avon Ornithological Group and Committee *Avon Bird Report*. Special interests: raptors, behaviour, Europe and Near East. Contributor to *BWP* (text). Consultant *Red Data Birds in Britain* (1990). Illustration of Honey Buzzard in *Ibis*. Co-author (with S M Taylor) of account of N Somerset in *Birds of Somerset* by Palmer and Balance (1968). 30 Cornwallis Crescent, Clifton, Bristol BS8 4PH.

SYKES, Thelma Kathryn; *b:* Heckmondwike, Yorks. BA English Language and Literature (Durham, 1962). Computer programmer/systems analyst with Inland Revenue to 1990. Artist and writer. Involved with Deeside Naturalists' Society in creation of Connahs Quay Reserve on Dee Estuary. Compiled, wrote, illustrated and published biennial reports on this reserve for years 1977-84. Illustrator for *Birdwatcher's Yearbook* 1985-96. Co-illustrator *Population Trends in British Breeding Birds* by J Marchant *et al* (1993), BTO New Breeding Atlas and *Atlas of European Breeding Birds* (in prep). *BBC Wildlife* Special Award for Nature Writing 1988. Member of Founding Committee of Northern Exhibition of Wildlife Art 1994-. Blue Neb Studios, 18 Newcroft, Saughall, Chester CH1 6EL.

TALLACK, Robert Edward (Bob); *b:* 20 May 1939 in London; *w:* Kathleen. King Edward VI Grammar School Macclesfield 1950-57. Self-employed fabric retailer. Gower Ornithological Society: Secretary 1970-78, Records Committee 1971-, Chairman 1978-79. Founder-member Welsh Ornithological Society (1988). Participant in national and local surveys since 1969; organiser of W Glamorgan counts for several BTO single-species breeding surveys since 1975; carried out a woodland Common Birds Census since 1977. Co-author (with D K Thomas and D M Hanford) *An Atlas of Breeding Birds in West Glamorgan* (1992). Editor *Gower Birds* (annual report) 1985, 1986; also contributor of several articles. OIR: reading, listening to music (esp classical or trad jazz). 1 Woodside Close, Killay, Swansea SA2 7EB. 01792 204031.

TASKER, Mark Lindley; *b:* 29 November 1955. BSc Zoology (Durham, 1977). Head of Seabirds and Cetaceans Branch, JNCC since 1991. Prev: Marine Ornithologist, NCC 1987-91; field asst in Antarctic, Univ California, Irvine 1988; Leader, Seabirds at Sea Team, NCC 1983-87; Orkney Seabird Monitoring Officer, NCC 1983; member, SAST, NCC 1979-83; summer warden, Isle of May 1979; research officer, Humber Estuary, Univ Hull 1978-79; research asst, Walney Island, Univ Oxford 1973. Executive Committee Seabird Group 1983-. Executive Committee Pacific Seabird Group 1985-. Business Manager *North-East Scotland Bird Report* 1985-95 and of *Birds of North-East Scotland* by S T Buckland *et al* (1991). Special interests: seabird ornithology worldwide, conservation of all birds, Scotland, islands, travel. Co-author (with Lloyd and Partridge) *The Status of Seabirds in Britain and Ireland* (1991). Senior author or co-author of many books and reports deriving from the Seabirds at Sea Project. Author, senior author or co-author of many scientific papers in eg *The Auk*, *Ibis*, *Neth J Sea Res*, *Seabird*. Contributor of sections in several multi-author books. Editor *North-East Scotland Bird Report* for several years in 1980s, also of *Seabird Group Newsletter* 1985-. Member: Colonial Waterbird Society, Netherlands Seabird Group, Pacific Seabird Group, Seabird Group, Wader Study Group. OIR: building dry stone walls, skiing, hill walking, cycling, reading, collecting books, photography, gardening. Drumshalloch Croft, Banchory, Kincardineshire AB31 5QB. 01330 823165. Or Seabirds and Cetaceans Branch, JNCC, Dunnet House, 7 Thistle Place, Aberdeen AB10 1UZ. 01224 655701; fax 01224 621488.

TATE, Peter; *b:* 5 February 1926 in Great Holland, Essex; *w:* Anne. Blundells School Tiverton. Retired member of London Stock Exchange. Part-time bird tour leader 1979-89. Treasurer BOC 1962-74. Chairman Stocker's Lake (reserve) Management Committee, Herts and Middx TNC c1982-90. Special interests: migration, swallows, nightjars, warblers. Author *East Anglia and its Birds* (1977), *A Century of Bird Books* (1979, 2nd ed 1985), *Swallows* (1981), *Birds, Men and Books* (1986), *The Swallow* (1986), *The Nightjar* (1989). Articles for *Birdwatcher's Yearbook* 1981 and 1986. Member: AOU, Gibraltar Ornithological and Nat Hist Soc, Southern African Orn Soc. OIR: twitching aircraft types not previously come across. Half Acre, Rooks Hill, Rickmansworth, Herts WD3 4HZ. 01923 773863.

TATNER, Paul; *b:* 17 August 1955 in Haslemere, Surrey; *w:* Dr Mary Tatner. BSc Zoology (Manchester, 1976), PhD (Manchester, 1980). Lecturer in Ecology and Behaviour, Univ Paisley since Dec 1987. Prev: research asst Stirling Univ 1982-87; research asst Manchester Museum 1980-81 (on bird gallery). Chairman Manchester Univ Bird Club 1979. BTO 'A' ringer since 1979. Special interests: Magpie ecology in the urban area (doctoral research); energetics of birds (ie measurement of free-living energy expenditure using the doubly labelled water technique: inc Robin, Dipper, Wheatear). British Ecol Soc Travelling Fellowship (1986) to study the energetics of breeding in tropical birds (Malaysia). Papers, mainly on research topics, in eg *Anim Behav, The Auk, Bird Study, Ibis, J Theor Biol, J Zool, The Naturalist, Ringing & Migration, Surrey Bird Report*; also book and conf proc contributions. OIR: two children, downhill skiing, wind surfing. 8 Burnside Terrace, Easwald Bank, Kilbarchan, Renfrew-shire PA10 2EY. Or Dept of Biological Sciences, University of Paisley, Paisley PA1 2BE. 0141 848 3129; fax 0141 848 3116.

TAYLOR, Antony M (Tony); *b:* 3 May 1948 in London; *w:* Ann. BA Zoology (Univ College, Oxford, 1971), MSc Zoology (Newcastle, 1978), PGCE (West London Inst of Higher Ed, 1977). Biology teacher. Prev: junior research associate, Research Unit on the Rehabilitation of Oiled Seabirds (Univ Newcastle) 1971-75. Asst warden RSPB Loch Garten Reserve 1967. Asst warden Fair Isle Bird Observatory 1976. BTO 'A' ringer since 1976. Ringing Secretary Lundy 1979-. Special interests: ringing (esp migrants, Reed Bunting); breeding ecology and behaviour of Guillemots (MSc thesis; 1972-75, 1978 breeding seasons spent on Farne Islands and Lundy); breeding geese (expeditions to Central Iceland 1966, 1969 and Spitsbergen 1968). Articles published in *British Birds* and *Ibis* (Guillemot moult). Compiler of Lundy Field Society ringing reports (1979-) and LFS bird reports (1985-). Occasional line drawings and photographs in eg *British Birds*. OIR: sailing, rowing, music. 26 High Street, Spetisbury, Blandford, Dorset DT11 9DJ. 01258 857336.

TAYLOR, Donald William (Don); *b:* 2 October 1938 in Hornsey, London; *p:* Patricia Pringle. Teacher's Cert (Handicraft) Loughborough College, 1961, (Design & Technology) Goldsmith's College, Univ London 1968. Retired schoolmaster. Tutor for WEA evening classes 'Birdwatching for Beginners' 1970-76. Chairman Kent Ornithological Society Editorial and Records Committee 1981-. Bird tour leader for several operators 1967-90. Special interest: to see all the wader species of the world. Travel inc USA, Galapagos, The Gambia and Senegal, Botswana, Kenya, Morocco, Israel, E Austria, Mallorca, SW Spain, Pyrenees, Canary Islands, Nepal, and widely in S America. Author and illustrator (drawings and photographs) *Birdwatching in Kent* (1985). Author *Birding in Kent* (1996). Co-author (with Jeffery Wheatley and Tony Prater) *Where to Watch Birds in Kent, Surrey & Sussex* (1987, 2nd ed 1991). Contributor to *Best Days with British Birds* (1989). Co-editor (with D L Davenport) *Birds of Kent* (1981, 2nd ed 1984). Editor *Kent Bird Report* 1969-80. Illustrated lectures given on birdwatching in Kent and abroad. OIR: thematic stamp collecting: 'Birds of the World'; former county basketball player and club cricketer. 1 Rose Cottages, Old Loose Hill, Loose, Maidstone, Kent ME15 0BN. 01622 745641.

TAYLOR, Maurice Percival (Moss); *b:* 2 August 1943 in Bexleyheath, Kent; *w:* Fran. Chigwell School. MB, BS (Royal Free Hospital Medical School, London, 1967), MRCS, LRCP 1968, DRCOG 1969. Full-time birder. Prev: General medical practitioner (retired). BTO: Regional Representative Norfolk 1978-91, 1995-, Council 1979-85, Hon Sec 1982-84, Treasurer 1985. Council Norfolk Naturalists' Trust 1987-92. Council Norfolk & Norwich Naturalists' Society 1990-93. BTO 'A' ringer since 1961 and founder of Sheringham Ringing Group 1974. Special interests: migration along N Norfolk coast (inc collection and publication of both ringing and visible migration data), birding trips abroad (inc leader of tours to The Gambia). Author *The Birds of Sheringham* (1987). Articles published in eg *Birdwatch*, *BTO News*, *Norfolk Bird Report*, *Ringing & Migration*. Editor of ringing report in *Norfolk Bird Report* 1979-87. Regular lecturer on all aspects of ornithology. BTO Jubilee Medal 1988. Member: ABA, ABC. OIR: dragonflies. 4 Heath Road, Sheringham, Norfolk NR26 8JH. 01263 823637.

TAYLOR, William Graham (Bill); *b:* 8 May 1949 in Glasgow; *w:* Pamela. School computing and a/v technician. Research asst RSPB Hen Harrier Survey Apr-Jul 1989. BTO Regional Representative East Inverness & Speyside 1990-94. BTO 'A' ringer since 1985. Secretary of ringing partnership with Brian Etheridge. Operator of Constant Effort Site and large nestbox scheme. Special interests: Crested Tit (esp designs of nest sites to encourage breeding in young commercial plantations), ringing wildfowl and waders with Highland Ringing Group, monitoring breeding raptors, photography. Royal Air Force Ornithological Society expeditions: Masirah Island, Oman 1979; Uists, Western Isles 1981; Cyprus 1982; Mingulay, W Isles 1985; Belize 1986; Brunei 1988. Others: RAF Kinloss Bird Club, Belize 1987; Highland RG, Flannans, W Isles 1988; Army Birdwatching Society, Belize 1989. Joint author of papers on breeding Dunlin in *Wader Study Group Bulletin* and Crested Tit in *Forestry*. OIR: general photography. 22 Forbeshill, Forres, Morayshire IV36 0JL. 01309 673099.

TEMPLE LANG, John Keller; *b:* 14 December 1936 in Ireland; *w:* Léan. Trinity College Dublin: BA (Mod) 1957, LLB 1958, MA 1961, LLD 1980. Solicitor 1958, Barrister 1986. Director, Directorate General for Competition, European Commission, Brussels. Professor, Trinity College Dublin. Studied wildlife conservation in the USA, Canada, Europe and Ghana. Involved in all major wildlife conservation developments in Ireland since 1964 and largely responsible for many of them. Drew up detailed recommendations for comprehensive legislation based on the laws of countries throughout the world, which were agreed by all Irish national sporting and conservation bodies and form the basis of the Irish Wildlife Act 1976. Actively involved in fieldwork for the BTO Breeding Atlas 1968-72, and Belgian Atlas 1974-78. Organised Irish National Trust's pioneering case to protect the North Bull Island bird sanctuary in 1972-73. Secretary, Irish Society for the Protection of Birds 1959-61, 1964-67. Chairman, Irish Ornithologists' Club 1966-67. Member, Irish Wildfowl Committee 1967. Irish Wildbird Conservancy: Secretary 1968-72, Chairman 1972-74. Irish National Section ICBP: Secretary 1965-73, 1977-80; Chairman 1980-89. BTO Council 1971-75. An Taisce National Trust for Ireland: Nature Conservation Committee 1966-70, Executive and Council 1970-73. Legal Adviser, Irish Hawking Club. Hon member, British Falconers Club. Organiser, Irish Peregrine Falcon Survey 1967-73. Chairman, European Continental Section, ICBP 1980-84. Co-secretary, Standing Committee on Applied Ornithology, International Ornithological Congress 1986-. Articles on bird and nature conservation and species in eg *Biol Cons, British Birds, European Law Review, Le Gerfaut, Irish Bird Report* (on Peregrine Falcon Survey), *Irish Naturalists' Journal* and *Sandgrouse*; also in *Promise and Performance* ed by J Blackwell (1983), *Environment and Development in Ireland* by J Feehan (1992),

Peatlands, Economy and Conservation by M Schouten (1990), Riverine Forests in Europe ed by C Imboden (1987), and introduction to *Conservation of Lowland Dry Grassland Birds in Europe* by P Goriup *et al* (1991). Organiser, ICBP World Seabird Conference 1982. Involved in drafting the European Directive on Wild Bird Conservation. Member of steering committee for Grimmett and Jones, *Important Bird Areas in Europe* (1989). Since 1964 lectured extensively on wildlife conservation. Avenue Chateau de Walzin 12(6), B-1180 Brussels, Belgium. +32 (0)2 3451949.

THELWELL, David Alan; *b:* 31 March 1950 in Birkenhead, Merseyside. Freelance wildlife illustrator since 1989. Local organiser of BTO Breeding Atlas, Hampshire Ornithological Society Atlas and WWF surveys in Romsey area. Artwork organiser HOS Book Committee 1991-93. Special interests: field sketching, travel for birds. Illustrations in eg *Bird Watching, Bird Life, British Birds, BTO News, The Countryman, Hampshire Bird Report*; also local and national papers. Illustrations for many books inc both BTO Breeding Atlases and Winter Atlas, *Atlas of Birds of the Western Palearctic* (1982), *A Dictionary of Birds* (1985), *Birds of Prey of the World* (1990), *An Illustrated Encyclopedia of Birds* (1990), etc. OIR: walking, travel, cooking, family, moths and butterflies. Heronsmead, Timsbury, Romsey, Hants SO51 0NE. 01794 368238.

THOM, Valerie MacLaren; *b:* 24 January 1929 in Tynemouth, Northumberland. BSc Agriculture (Edinburgh, 1949). Asst warden Fair Isle Bird Observatory 1955. Wildfowl Count organiser for Scotland 1963-70. RSPB Scottish Committee, BTO Council, Secretary of State for Scotland's Advisory Committee on Birds (all in 1970s). Secretary and Chairman Ornithological Section, Perthshire Society of Natural Science 1965-72. SOC: Council 1967-70, President 1978-81, Hon President 1986. Fair Isle Observatory Trust: Trustee and Director 1970-93, Hon Sec 1986-92. Author *Birds in Scotland* (1986), *Scottish Birds* (1994). Author or co-author several papers on wintering ducks and geese in Scotland in *Scottish Birds* and *Wildfowl*. Editor *Scottish Birds* and *Scottish Bird News* 1982-87. OIR: wildlife conservation, photography, travel, reading. 19 Braeside Gardens, Perth PH1 1DB. 01738 623508.

THOMAS, David Hugh; *b:* 7 May 1943 in Nairobi, Kenya. BSc Zoology (Sheffield, 1966), MSc Ecology (Aberdeen, 1967), PhD Role of adrenal steroid hormones in avian osmoregulation (Hull, 1973). Senior Lecturer in Zoology (see address). Special interests: behavioural and physiological adaptations of birds to extreme environments, esp deserts (research on sandgrouse and phasianids in Moroccan Sahara, Negev, Namib and Sonoran Deserts) and marine habitats (research on penguins in southern Africa, and on shearwaters in UK), and related interests in bustards; biology and ecological energetics of sandgrouse; physiological function and control of avian salt and water balance (function of bird kidneys, salt glands and intestine studied in co-operative research projects at Univs Copenhagen, Hull, Arizona, Beersheva, and Port Elizabeth). Research articles in eg *Bull BOC*, *Ibis*, *J Comparative Zool*, *J Zool*, *Ostrich*, *Pflügers Archiv*. OIR: photography of biological subjects (inc birds), travel, botany and gardening, walking, squash. School of Pure & Applied Biology, University of Wales at Cardiff, PO Box 915, Cardiff CF1 3TL. 01222 874303.

THOMAS, David Vaughan (Vaughan); *b:* 10 June 1949 in Royston, Herts; *w:* Jane. BEd, MA. Headmaster. Gwent Ornithological Society: Committee 1985-86, Secretary 1986-91, Chairman 1991-. BTO 'A' ringer since 1987. Senior member of Llangorse and Goldcliff Ringing Groups since 1985. Special interests: migration, breeding biology, habitat conservation. OIR: reading, local history, gardening. The Sycamore, Tabernacle Lane, Llanvaches, Newport NP6 3BL. 01633 400953.

THOMAS, Derek Keith; *b:* 26 October 1941 in Chorley, Lancs; *w:* Pranee. BSc 1963, PhD 1966 Mathematics (London), DIC (1966), PhD Zoology (Wales, 1981). Senior Lecturer in Mathematics, Univ Wales, Swansea. RSPB Committee for Wales since mid 1970s. Chairman RSPB West Glamorgan Members' Group 1972-82. Chairman Glamorgan WT 1985-88. Past Chairman Gower Ornithological Society. BTO Ringing and Migration Committee 1980-83, Membership and Development Committee 1994-. BTO Regional Development Officer for Mid, South and West Glamorgan 1994-. BTO Council 1995-. Membership Secretary Welsh Ornithological Society 1993-. BTO 'A' ringer since 1976 and member of Sponsors Panel. Special interests: feeding ecology of marshland passerines (esp Reed, Sedge and Cetti's Warblers and Reed Bunting); territoriality and feeding ecology of Rock Pipit; House Sparrow; moult. Author *An Atlas of Breeding Birds in West Glamorgan* (1992). Co-author (with H E Grenfell) *A Guide to Gower Birds* (1992). Editor *Gower Birds* (annual report) 1980-85. Papers published in eg *Bird Study* and *Ringing & Migration*. Many radio and TV broadcasts on birds and conservation. Laburnum Cottage, Manselfield Road, Murton, Swansea SA3 3AR. 01792 232623.

THOMAS, Timothy Michael (Tim); MBE 1991; *b:* 14 May 1953 in Hastings, E Sussex; *w:* Laura Hanlon. Hastings Grammar School 1964-72. Senior Scientific Officer, RSPCA (with special responsibility for rehabilitation of wild animals inc birds) since 1981. Prev: Asst Warden Mallydams Wood nature reserve 1973-81. Secretary British Wildlife Rehabilitation Council 1987-. Special interests: rehabilitation of birds (esp the cleaning, treatment and release of oiled birds). Work mainly in UK, involving many oiling disasters, but advises worldwide (eg provision of advice and treatment of oiled birds in Ireland and Saudi Arabia). Regular contributor to national and international conferences on oiled wildlife. Editor *British Wildlife Rehabilitation Council Proceedings* 1991, joint editor 1989. Papers published on effects of oil on wildlife, etc. Lord Erskine Award, Oct 1991 (RSPCA award for the rescue of birds affected by the Gulf oil spill). OIR: walking, cabinet making, scuba diving, travel. 23 Park Terrace West, Horsham, W Sussex RH12 1HY. 01403 267255.

THOMPSON, Desmond Bruin Angus (Des); *b:* 27 January 1958 in Inverness; *w:* Dawn. BSc Biology (Paisley College, 1979), PhD Flocking behaviour of gulls and plovers (Nottingham, 1984). Head of Uplands and Peatlands Branch, Scottish Natural Heritage since 1992. Prev: Head of Uplands Branch GB, NCC 1985-91; Research Fellow, Univ Liverpool (song dialects of Corn Buntings) 1984-85; Demonstrator, Univ Nottingham 1983-84. Special interests: montane, peatland and moorland birds; upland conservation; tundra and Arctic birds. Co-author (with C J Barnard) *Gulls and Plovers: ecology and behaviour of mixed species feeding groups* (1985); (with Colin Baxter) *Scotland - land of mountains* (1995); (with I Byrkjedal) *Golden and Grey Plovers: birds of tundra* (in prep). Co-editor (with M B Usher) *Ecological Change in the Uplands* (1988); (with M B Usher and A J Hester) *Heaths and Moorland: cultural landscapes* (1995). Over seventy scientific papers in journals inc *American Naturalist, Anim Behav, Biol Cons, Ibis, J Appl Ecol, Ornis Scandinavica, Wildfowl*. Joint winner of BES annual prize for best student lecture, 1982. Leverhulme Research Fellow, 1987. Hon Fellow, Univ Edinburgh. Visiting scholar to Norwegian Institute for Nature Research in 1991. Co-ordinator of BirdLife International Forum on Conservation of Tundra and Moorland Birds 1993-94. Elected to Board of International Centre of Alpine Environments in 1995. Son of late Desmond and Maimie Nethersole-Thompson. OIR: landscape photography, history of Antarctic Exploration, Celtic FC, 'family preoccupations!'. Scottish

Natural Heritage, Research and Advisory Services Directorate, 2 Anderson Place, Edinburgh EH6 5NP. 0131 466 2419.

THOMPSON, Paul Michael; *b:* 1 September 1959 in Chesterfield, Derbys. BA Philosophy, Politics and Economics (Oxford, 1980), MA Development Economics (Sussex, 1981), PhD Geography and Planning (Middlesex Polytechnic, 1990). Senior Research Officer, Flood Hazard Research Centre. Co-founder Madagascar Environmental Research Group (MERG) 1988. Special interests - 1. Oriental region: particularly Bangladesh since 1986 (winter wildfowl and wader counts), also helped in lowland forest surveys in Peninsular Thailand (1987, 1988) and birding in India, Nepal, Burma, Malaysia; 2. Madagascar: secretary/co-leader of three expeditions to survey little known protected areas, Zahamena Réserve Integrale Naturelle in 1985 (one of ICBP expedition award winners, expedition film won BBC Mick Burke Award), Manongarivo Special Reserve in 1987-88 (RGS Shell Environmental Paper), and Ambatovaky Special Reserve 1990 (also produced colour booklet on birds distributed free to schools in Madagascar). Member of student expeditions to Iceland (Oxford Univ, 1980, waders) and Morocco (Univ London, 1983, seawatching). Papers published in *Bird Cons Internat* and *Forktail*; also ICBP and MERG expedition/survey reports. Member: OBC. Middlesex University, Queensway, Enfield EN3 4SF. 0181 362 5359.

THOMSON, Kelvin; *b:* 28 October 1968 in Stirling. HNC Chemistry (Falkirk Coll of Tech, 1990). Scientist, United Distillers. Leader RSPB Tayside Members' Group 1991-. Special interests: breeding success of raptors, esp Hen Harrier, Merlin (with Tayside Raptor Study Group); counts and surveys of geese (extensive work on Islay with RSPB Warden, Loch Gruinart); supporting fieldwork for other species inc Barn Owl, Corncrake, breeding waders. BTO 'C' ringer since 1994. Active member of Tay Ringing Group, esp cannon netting of passage terns and waders. OIR: badminton, hill walking, cycling. 22 Grampian Avenue, Auchterarder, Perthshire PH3 1NY. 01764 664243.

THORPE, John Peter; *b:* 29 April 1951 in Isleworth, Middlesex; *w:* Ann. BSc Zoology (St Andrews, 1973), PhD Zoology and Genetics (Wales, 1977). Reader in Biology, Univ Liverpool since 1991. Prev: Senior Lecturer 1989; Lecturer 1979. Occasional voluntary warden at Calf of Man Bird Observatory. Special interests: speciation and genetics of birds, migration, behaviour, roosting behaviour and feeding ecology of Hen Harrier, seabirds. Articles on Hen Harrier, Peregrine, Goldcrest, Wheatear,

Fieldfare, Jay in *British Birds, Peregrine, Ringing & Migration*. Editor *Zoological Journal of the Linnean Society* and *Marine Biology*, both from 1995. Radio broadcast on roosting Hen Harriers. Member: Hawk and Owl Trust. Elected Fellow of Linnean Society in 1980, Council from 1992. OIR: restoring antique furniture, clocks and watches; Chairman Isle of Man Victorian Society. Dept of Environmental and Evolutionary Biology, University of Liverpool, Port Erin Marine Laboratory, Port Erin, Isle of Man IM9 6JA. 01624 832027.

THURGATE, Hugh Cedric; *b:* 12 January 1963 in Durham. BSc Ecological Science (Edinburgh, 1985). National Trust Head Warden South Down Area, Co Down since 1994. Prev: NT Asst Warden Murlough NNR 1990-93; RSPB contract warden at various reserves in GB 1987-90. BTO Wetland Bird Survey co-ordinator for Dundrum Inner Bay and Dundrum Bay, Co Down 1992-. BTO 'C' ringer since 1994. North Down Ringing Group 1992-. Special interests: bird song, migration, monitoring bird populations. NCC Whimbrel behavioural study fieldwork, Orkney 1983. Member of Operation Aetos, eight-month study of raptors in the Vicos-Aoos National Park in Pindos Mountains NW Greece 1986. National Dotterel Survey fieldwork in Glen Cova, Angus 1987. National atlas fieldwork in Upper Glenfeshie, Inverness-shire 1988 and Mourne Mountains 1990. National and local atlas fieldwork, Suffolk 1989. National Wildfowl Counts 1987-93. Birds of Estuaries Enquiry counts 1989-93. Member of Opération Rapace, two-month study of raptor migration across Bab-el-Mandeb straits, Djibouti Oct 1987. Wetland Trust bird ringing expedition to Djoudj National Park, Senegal Feb 1992. National Corncrake census, Rathmelton, Co Donegal 1993. Hooded Crow productivity study, Murlough NNR 1991-. Bird ringing in The Gambia on European Science Foundation project. Interviews on Radio 4 *Natural History Programme* and BBC Scotland and BBC2 *Countryfile* programme; work for Grampian TV and RSPB film *For Love of Birds* - all during period as Operation Osprey warden at Loch Garten 1988. OIR: natural history in general (esp butterfly ecology), Nordic skiing, mountaineering, horse riding, rugby union, marathon running, weight training, slide photography, world travel. 10 Ardilea Road, Clough, Downpatrick, Co Down BT30 8SL. 01396 751247.

TIDMAN, Roger; *b:* 17 May 1947 in Cambridge; *p:* Irene Breeze. Cambridgeshire High School for Boys. BSc Opthalmic Optics (Aston, 1970). FBCO 1980, ARPS 1983. Wildlife photographer. BTO Membership and Development Committee 1992-96. Photographic consultant *British*

Birds 1991-93. Travel for photography in China, USA, Canada, Antarctica, Argentina, Kenya, Rwanda, S Africa, Israel, Norway, Spain, Costa Rica. Photographs published regularly in eg *Bird Watching, Bird Life, Birding World, Birds, Birdwatch, British Birds, Country Life*; also in eg *Photographic Guide to the Birds of Britain and Europe* (1988), *Photographic Guide to Birds of the World* (1991) and many other books and periodicals. Winner RSPB/Kodak sponsored 'Birds in Winter' competition 1986. Winner 'Bird Photograph of the Year' (*British Birds*) 1996. 'Proud winner of 2 silver medals whilst at primary school for study of "Bird and Tree" in competition for schools arranged by RSPB.' OIR: watching Norwich City, squash, good pubs, good company. 142 Fakenham Road, Briston, Melton Constable, Norfolk NR24 2DL. 01263 860776.

TIPLING, David John; *b:* 23 July 1965 in Worthing, Sussex. Freelance nature photographer (agency Windrush Photos), writer and lecturer, specialising in birds. Photographic editor for *Kent Bird Report* 1992-. Special interest: photographing Siberian migrant birds. Related expeditions to China. Author *Top British Birding Spots* (1996). Articles published in eg *Bird Watching, Birding World, Birds, Birdwatch, British Birds*. Hundreds of photographs reproduced worldwide in books, magazines, journals and other media. OIR: skiing, motor racing, golf, eating Indian and Chinese food, and 'a good pint of Guinness'. 99 Noah's Ark, Kemsing, Sevenoaks, Kent TN15 6PD. 01732 763486; fax 01732 763285.

TITCOMBE, Colin Ralph Thomas; *b:* 23 August 1944 in Caldicot, Gwent; *w:* Glenys. Portwall Secondary Modern School. Naturalist (consultant and lecturer). Fieldwork for Birds of Estuaries Enquiry 1969-75, BTO Breeding Atlas 1971-72, RSPB Beached Bird Survey 1979-83. Tutor for courses on birds for Univ Wales Cardiff Extra Mural Dept 1983-85. Special interests: avian ecology and history, birds in relation to afforestation. Overseas travel for birds in Balearics, Iberia, Malta, Scandinavia, Switzerland, Turkey, West Indies, Kenya; also tour leader. Author or co-author of articles for *Gwent Bird Report*. Occasional radio broadcasts. OIR: collecting books on natural history, general wildlife study, local history, gardening. Brockwells Farm, Caerwent, Newport, Gwent NP6 4AJ. 01291 421098.

TODD, Ralph Ronald; *b:* 30 October 1950 in Ipswich, Suffolk; *w:* Brenda. Head of Accommodation Planning and Development, BBC World Service. Founder and Leader RSPB Bexley Members' Group 1978-86. RSPB Local

Representative SE London/NW Kent 1986-. RSPB Council 1988-93, Chairman Education and Membership Committee 1991-93. Council Kent TNC 1992-. Special interests: identification for beginners and local environment appreciation; leading bird tours and holidays; collating bird records for London Borough of Bexley; wildlife photography. Travel inc Antarctica, Falklands, Argentina, Galapagos, China, Romania, Kenya, Egypt, The Gambia, USA and Europe. 'Speyside in Scotland remains favourite retreat.' OIR: following international athletics and Ipswich Town FC. 9 Horsham Road, Bexleyheath, Kent DA6 7HU. 01322 528335.

TOMLINSON, Christopher Graham (Tommo); *b:* 19 November 1954 in Burnley Lancs; *w:* Lorraine. Ormskirk Grammar School. Asst Curator WWT, Martin Mere since 1987. Prev WWT: Marsh Warden 1977-87, Warden 1976-77. BTO 'C' ringer (waterfowl) since 1987. Responsible for ringing of swans, geese and ducks at Martin Mere. Special interests: identification, behaviour and migration, habitat development for waterfowl and all fauna and flora, hide design and construction, drawing and photographing birds. Expedition to Iceland in spring 1989 to study Pink-footed Geese on breeding grounds. Involved with several radio and TV programmes. OIR: family, fell walking, sport. 58 Orrell Lane, Burscough, Ormskirk, Lancs L40 0SQ. 01704 894499.

TOMLINSON, David Howard; *b:* 24 January 1950 in Bromley, Kent; *w:* Janet. Professional freelance writer on wildlife; runs Gourmet Birds holidays. Prev: staff of *Country Life* 1973-91. Special interests: photography and writing. Author *African Wildlife in Art* (1991), *Ducks* (1996). Joint author (with Bill Oddie) *The Big Bird Race* (1984) and (with Clive Finlayson) *The Birds of Spain and Portugal* (1993). Numerous articles; regular contributor to all the major birding magazines, as well as general magazines and newspapers. Recipient of RSNC Gold Medal for fundraising on behalf of the British Wildlife Appeal, 1990. Instigator of 'Big-Day Birding' in the UK; founded the County Birdrace competition in 1986. OIR: tennis, squash, shooting, riding, English springer spaniels, wine and travel. Windrush, Coles Lane, Brasted, Westerham, Kent TN16 1NN. 01959 563627; fax 01959 562906.

TOOMER, Derek Keith; *b:* 8 February 1946 in Weston-super-Mare, Somerset; *w:* Janice. BSc Botany (Bristol, 1968), PhD Fungal Physiology (Nottingham, 1972). Membership Development Officer, BTO since 1996. Prev: Research Officer, BTO 1991-96. Leader South Bedfordshire RSPB Members' Group 1973-84. Special interests: wintering waders, garden birds, foreign birding and photography. Lectures given on bird topics. OIR: passion for worldwide travel. BTO, The Nunnery, Thetford, Norfolk IP24 2PU. 01842 750050.

TOYNE, Elliott Paul (Paul); *b:* 21 July 1967 in Hammersmith, London. BSc Science and the Environment (DeMontfort, 1988), PhD Ecology of Northern Goshawk (Imperial College, London, 1994). Conservation Officer (International Species) WWF-UK since 1996. Prev: Project leader of Northern Goshawk survey of Forest Enterprise woodland in Wales 1992-96. Special interests: raptor ecology, Neotropical parrot ecology. Leader of Anglo-Ecuadorian expeditions to Podocarpus National Park, southern Ecuador during 1990-94. Interests there include national park management, environmental impact assessment of eg gold mining and colonisation, wildlife sound recording and the collection and identification of Lepidoptera. Parrot work published in eg *Bird Cons Internat, Bull BOC, Cotinga, Ornitologia Neotropical, Papageien*. Sound recordings deposited at the National Sound Archive, London. Scientific adviser for two TV documentaries: *Parrots in Peril* (1994) and *Spirit of the Wildwood* (1995). Member: Corporación Ornitológica del Ecuador, NBC, Raptor Research Foundation. c/o 2 Cypress Road, Newport, Isle of Wight PO30 1EX. Tel/fax 01983 524224.

TREEN, Robert Leslie (Bob); *b:* 19 February 1925 in Dalton-in-Furness, Cumbria; *w:* Winifred. Retired. Organiser of Birds of Estuaries Enquiry/Wetland Bird Survey for Duddon Estuary since 1969; also Low Tide Count organiser and co-ordinator of many other surveys (eg Ringed Plover, Shelduck) on Duddon. Special interest: waders. Member: Wader Study Group. 5 Rydal Close, Dalton-in-Furness, Cumbria LA15 8QU. 01229 464789.

TRELEAVEN, Richard Barrie (Dick); *b:* 16 July 1920 in Lewisham, London; *w:* Margery (deceased). Dulwich College 1932-36. Seven years Army, serving in Burma (16th Punjab Regt Indian Army). Family clothing business in Launceston until 1981. Committee Cornwall Birdwatching and Preservation Society in 1950s, and for nine years Committee of British Falconers' Club. Founder-member Society of Wildlife Artists 1965. Special interest: long-term study of the Peregrine in N Cornwall (commenced 1951). Author of *Peregrine, the Private Life of the Peregrine Falcon* (1977), *Peregrine Watching* (in prep). Published 'Notes on the Peregrine in Cornwall' in *British Birds*, the first British ornithological paper to record the decline in the Peregrine population. Various papers on Peregrine and raptor problems in *Country Life, The Falconers' Journal, Zeitschrift für Tierpsychologie* ('High and low intensity hunting in raptors' 1980), and publications of the Hawk and Owl Trust inc 'Eleven year study of the population, distribution, and breeding success of the Peregrine on a stretch of the North Cornwall coast' in *The Raptor* 1995. Forty years reviewing books on birds of prey for leading journals. Exhibited annually with SWLA in London. TV appearances in *The Shadow of the Falcon* (BBC 1974), *Secrets of the Coast* (ITV 1982), *Winged Assassins, Birdscape* (Ch4 1991); consultant for *Skyraider* (BBC 1991). Gave Bernard Tucker Memorial Lecture, Oxford 1977. OIR: fly fishing, reading, writing short stories. Blue Wings, 21 Tiny Meadows, South Petherwin, Launceston, Cornwall PL15 7JD. 01566 773756.

TRIGGS, Paul; *b:* 18 November 1955 in Lyneham, Wilts; *w:* Debra. Accountant. BTO 'A' ringer since 1995. Merseyside Ringing Group: Secretary 1988-89, Treasurer 1990-94. Member Clwyd Bird Recording Group (responsible for compilation of *Clwyd Bird Report*) 1993-. Special interests: study of migration and population numbers through ringing; breeding biology of Buzzard, Pied Flycatcher, Swallow. Participant in expeditions: Shetland Islands 1975, Outer Hebrides 1981, Islands of Bernaray and Mingulay 1985, Belize 1986 and 1987, Cyprus 1995. Also spent 15 months in Belize 1985-86 (active member of Belize Audubon Society) and six months in Falkland Islands 1983. Contributor to Army Birdwatching Society and Royal Air Force Ornithological Society reports on birds of Falklands. Talks given on ornithology-related subjects to local birdwatching groups. OIR: most sports, travel, gardening, photography. 4 Coed Terfyn, Pen y Mynydd, Chester CH4 0XB. 01248 548627; work 01244 280800.

TRODD, Paul; *b:* 4 October 1955 in Hillingdon, Middlesex; *w:* Pat. BTEC HNC Mech & Prod Eng 1991. British Gas TransCo Engineer. Prev Royal and Merchant Navies 1972-77. Bedfordshire Bird Recorder 1987-91. Hon warden Dunstable Sewage Works 1992-. Scientific Committee Beds NHS 1987-92. Committee Bedfordshire Bird Club 1993-. Special interests: breeding birds and migration (esp in Beds), waders. In 1970s travelled widely in navy, studying birds in Europe, Africa, West Indies, Middle East; ample opportunities to study seabirds, also raptor movements at Gibraltar. Co-author (with B Clews and A Heryet) *Where to Watch Birds in Bedfordshire, Berkshire, Buckinghamshire, Hertfordshire & Oxfordshire* (1987, 2nd ed 1995); (with D Kramer) *The Birds of Bedfordshire* (1992); (with R A Dazley) *An Atlas of the Breeding Birds of Bedfordshire 1988-92*

(1994). Articles published in *Bedfordshire Naturalist* (inc six bird reports 1986-91), *Bird Life*, *Bird Watching*, *British Birds*, *Sea Swallow*. Occasional work with BBC local radio. Leader of local bird trips and lecturer on history of Bedfordshire birds. 'Addicted to 24 hour sponsored bird races for charity and lay claim to have been the first birder to have seen 100 species in a day in Bedfordshire.' OIR: gardening, reading (large collection of bird books and journals), life-long Queen's Park Rangers supporter. 186 West Street, Dunstable, Beds LU6 1NX. 01582 603067.

TROLLOPE, Jeffrey (Jeff); *b:* 4 March 1928 in Acton, Middlesex; *w:* Sarah. FIScT 1978. Corporation of London Animal Health Inspector, with special duties for the identification of imported avian species on behalf of HM Customs and Excise (CITES) and MAFF, 1976 until retirement in 1993. Prev: ethological studies on avian and primate species Univ London 1965-76; animal air travel company manager and adviser on avian and primate species 1956-65; RSPCA 1954-56; Zoological Society of London 1949-54. Visiting lecturer on birds, Biological Science Dept, Paddington College 1974-78. Special interests: breeding biology and behaviour; Emberizidae, Fringillidae, Estrildidae, Ploceidae, Turnicidae, Columbidae. Photographic and observation trips to Kenya, Tanzania, Zimbabwe, Botswana, Zambia, Senegal, The Gambia, Canada, USA and Europe. Author *Seed-eating Birds* (1992). Articles in eg *Avicultural Magazine*, also illustrations. Member: Avicultural Society. Awarded nine medals by Avicultural Society for the first-time aviary breeding of foreign bird species in UK. OIR: hill walking, gardening. 37 Station Road, Hounslow, Middx TW3 2AP.

TRUNKFIELD, Gordon Christopher; *b:* 13 August 1957 in Manchester. BA Fine Art Painting (Norwich School of Art, 1979). Graphics Technician, Tameside Coll of Tech. Bird Illustrator of the Year (*British Birds*) 1990. Artwork published in magazines eg *Birding World*, *British Birds* and books eg BTO New Breeding Atlas and *The Birds of Berkshire* by P E Standley *et al* (1996). Exhibited at European Bird Art Exhibition, Dublin 1993. 1 High Bank Avenue, Stalybridge, Cheshire SK15 2SW. 0161 338 3513.

TUCKER, John; *b:* 25 July 1946 in Leeds, Yorkshire. BSc Biology (York, 1979), MSc Conservation (Univ College, London, 1980). Head of Conservation, Shropshire WT. Vice Chairman Zambian Ornithological Society 1970-76 and founding editor of its newsletter 1971-73. Conservation Committee Shropshire Ornithological Society 1994-. Special interest: the application of information for conservation. Co-author (with P Deans *et al*)

An Atlas of the Breeding Birds of Shropshire (1992). Senior editor *Hartlebury Common, a Social and Natural History* (1986). Numerous short bird notes in *Bull Zambian Orn Soc* 1970-76, and subsequently several bird and general ecological papers in eg *Arboricultural Journal, British Birds, Bull BOC*. Originator (with Shrops OS) of TETRAD, computer program to map and process data, within UK counties, at the tetrad level. Co-director (with Peter Tucker) of 'birdBASE' computerised database of European birds, 1990-92. OIR: photography, historical ecology and post-glacial history generally. 13 Brook Road, Pontesbury, Shrops SY5 0QZ. 01743 790486; work 01743 241691; fax 01743 366671.

TUCKER, Nigel Allen; *b:* 21 September 1948 in Bristol. Freelance wildlife sound recordist and sound technician, BBC Natural History Unit 1984-96. Prev: partner and tour leader, Wingspan Birdwatching Tours 1981-84. Committee Bristol Ornithological Club 1981-83. Special interests: identification, distribution, taxonomy, photography and sound recording. Sound recording trips to Israel, Tunisia, USA, Canada, Pakistan, Kenya, Tanzania, Madagascar, E Russia, Kazakhstan, New Zealand, Fiji, Hong Kong, Australia. Broadcast sound on TV programmes eg *Land of the Eagle, The Trials of Life,* and series The Natural World (BBC2) and Wildlife on One (BBC1). LPs and cassettes compiled and produced inc *Your Favourite Bird Songs* and *A Sound Guide to Waders in Britain* for BBC; also for *BBC Wildlife Magazine* and other publishers. 8 Julius Road, Bishopston, Bristol BS7 8EU. 0117 949 6561.

TUCKER, Victor Roy (Vic); *b:* 14 August 1945 in Plymouth, Devon; *w:* Sylvia. Committee Plymouth RSPB Members' Group since 1987. Adjudicator for rarity records published by both Cornwall and Devon Birdwatching & Preservation Societies. Ecology officer for reserves owned and managed by Devon BWPS since 1990. Special interests: identification and migration studies, esp seabirds. Member of 1970 Oxford Univ expedition to Afghanistan and Kashmir, studying migration routes via Himalayas. Visits to various European countries, inc E Europe, as co-leader of ornithological trips for specialist tour company. Author *Birds of Plymouth: a city avifauna spanning years 1950-1994* (1995). Co-author (with D Norman) *Where to Watch Birds in Devon & Cornwall* (1984, 2nd ed 1991). Worked extensively and closely with Peter Harrison on preparation of his book *Seabirds* 1982-83. Articles published in eg *Birding World* and *Devon Birds*, notes in *British Birds*. OIR: Lepidoptera, esp habitat requirements of butterflies. Periglis, 4 Clovelly View, Turnchapel, Plymouth PL9 9SY. 01752 401096.

TURNER, Angela Kathleen; *b:* 25 December 1954 in London. BSc Zoology with Botany (Royal Holloway College, London, 1976), PhD Ornithology (Stirling, 1981). Managing Editor of *Animal Behaviour*. Special interest: behaviour and ecology of hirundines. PhD on foraging behaviour of Barn Swallows and Sand Martins, 1977-80. Post-doctoral research on behaviour and ecology of hirundines and swiftlets in Venezuela and Malaysia, 1981/82. Related papers in scientific journals inc *Anim Behav*, *Bird Study*, *Ibis*, *J Animal Ecol*; articles and news items in popular magazines and papers inc *BBC Wildlife*, *Birds*, *British Birds*, *The Guardian*. Author of *A Handbook to the Swallows and Martins of the World* (1989) and *The Swallow* (1994). Chapters or sections in books inc *The Illustrated Encyclopedia of Birds* ed by C M Perrins (1990), *The Cambridge Encyclopedia of Ornithology* ed by M Brooke and T Birkhead (1991) and the BTO New Breeding Atlas. Dept of Life Science, University of Nottingham, Nottingham NG7 2RD. 0115 951 3249.

TURNER, Robert (Rob); *b:* 13 February 1949 in Lewisham, London; *w:* Angela. St Joseph's Academy, Blackheath, London; Stockwell College of Education, Bromley, Kent. Teacher at local junior school in Devizes. Committee Wiltshire Ornithological Society 1976-. County Bird Recorder 1982-. BTO Regional Representative W Wilts 1980-92. BTO 'A' ringer since 1981. Special interests: ringing (inc Constant Effort Site), local atlas work. MOD Imber Conservation Group: sub-group leader for ringing. Founder-member of West Wiltshire Ringing Group in 1988, also member Chew Valley Ringing Station since 1980. Compiler of county bird report for publication in *Hobby* (journal of Wilts OS) since 1982. Contributor to *Wiltshire Birds* ed by Stephen Palmer (1991). OIR: playing badminton, following football (Chelsea FC) and cricket (Kent), making scale model aircraft. 14 Ethendun, Bratton, Westbury, Wilts BA13 4RX. 01380 830862.

TURTON, John Michael (Mick); *b:* 4 February 1957 in Barnsley, Yorks; *w:* Kathleen. Barnsley College of Technology 1975-77. Joiner. Asst countryside ranger, Anglers Country Park since 1993. Barnsley Bird Study Group: various posts since formation in 1970 inc Recorder, Records Panel, Secretary, Chairman. Voluntary warden Wath Ings nature reserve from 1974. Illustrated lectures given to local bird and natural history groups since 1980. Special interests: birds of Palearctic and Oriental regions, photography. Travel to over 35 countries in Europe and Asia, inc five-month trip to Thailand, India and Nepal 1981/82, four months Thailand, Malaysia 1983/84, seven months Taiwan, Hong Kong, Philippines, Sabah,

China, Tibet, Inner Mongolia 1985/86; also visits to N and S America. Co-leader of birding trips to China and India. Involved since 1992 in setting up and editing *Yorkshire Birding* (quarterly). Line drawings and short notes on identification published in that magazine, also in *Birding World* and *British Birds*. Drawings and short articles regularly in *Barnsley Area Bird Report* since 1978. Several photographs published in various magazines. Appeared in Yorkshire TV programme on twitching, 1989. Member: OBC. 150 Everill Gate Lane, Broomhill, Wombwell, Barnsley, S Yorks S73 0YJ. 01226 755422.

TUTT, Derek; *b:* 1 April 1940 in Gillingham, Kent; *w:* Zena. Proprietor of Barn Owl Travel (founded 1973); organiser and leader of all holidays. Voluntary warden with NCC for several years up to 1974. Special interests: migration, roosting, identification. Short articles published in *Birds*, *Country-side*. Had own monthly programme on BBC Radio Kent for several years in 1970s and also hosted a programme with local wardens. Received special award for contribution and commitment to environmentally sensitive tourism from Aylesford Newsprint and Kent County Council 1995. OIR: most other aspects of natural history, esp butterflies; advanced driving. 21 Heron Close, Lower Halstow, Sittingbourne, Kent ME9 7EF. 01795 844464.

TYLER, Stephanie Joy; *b:* 6 April 1944 in Ingleton, Yorks; *h:* Lindsay. BA Natural Sciences and Zoology (Cambridge, 1965), PhD Animal Behaviour (Cambridge, 1968). Conservation Officer RSPB Wales 1984-95. Prev: Conservation/Development Officer Gwent WT 1979-84. BTO: Ringing Committee 1987-91, Research and Surveys Committee, Council 1978-83, Regional Representative Gwent 1988-. RSPB Wales Advisory Committee 1980-84. Gwent Ornithological Society: Committee 1981-. Gwent Breeding Atlas organiser 1981-85. Committee Ethiopian Wildlife and Nat Hist Soc 1973-76. Secretary Dee Estuary Conservation Group 1993-95. Secretary Severn Estuary Conservation Group 1993-. BTO 'A' ringer since 1965. Special interests: ecology and conservation of rivers and river birds worldwide (esp dippers, wagtails and other species of mountain rivers), general interest in wildlife conservation worldwide, ringing, nest recording. Sabbatical to Nepal to look at river birds 1990-91; trips to NW Argentina and S Bolivia to study Rufous-throated Dipper 1993; three-and-a-half years in Ethiopia, one in Tanzania, six months in Kenya. Joint author (with Stephen Ormerod) *The Dippers* (1994); (with Jerry Lewis *et al*) *The Gwent Atlas of Breeding Birds* (1987). Author or joint author of book chapters/contributions eg BTO Winter Atlas, New Breeding Atlas,

Birds as Monitors of Environmental Change ed by R W Furness and J J D Greenwood (1993), *The Value of Birds* by ICBP (1987). Numerous papers on aspects of ecology of Dipper and Grey Wagtail between 1971 and 1994, published in eg *Bird Study, Environmental Pollution, Freshwater Biol, Ibis, J Appl Ecol, J Zool, Oecologia, Ringing & Migration,* and county bird reports. Other papers on Mountain Wagtail in Ethiopia in *Scopus*; on various other African birds in *Bull BOC* and *Scopus*; on Goosander, Ring Ouzel and birds of reeds and waders in Wales in *Welsh Bird Report*. Editor *The Dipper* (Gwent OS newsletter) 1981-. Editor *Walia* (EWNHS journal) and *Newsletter* 1974-75. Various articles and broadcasts on wildlife, esp birds, in a range of magazines and other media. Member: ABC, Botswana Field Soc, EANHS, Ethiopian Wildlife and NHS, Kalahari Soc, OBC, OSME. OIR: walking/travelling and botanising in remote places, conservation management, listening to music. Yew Tree Cottage, Lone Lane, Penallt, Gwent NP5 4AJ. 01600 712610; work 01686 626678.

UNDERHILL-DAY, John Christopher; *b:* 9 October 1943 in Fulmer, Bucks; *w:* Jackie. BSc Biology, PhD Breeding biology of Marsh and Montagu's Harriers. FRICS 1980, MIBiol 1991. RSPB Senior Site Manager, Dorset since 1996. Prev RSPB: Senior Warden, Haweswater 1988-96; Principal Reserves Officer/Head Land Agent 1985-88; Deputy Reserves Officer 1973-85; Asst Reserves Manager 1971-73; Warden, Coombes Valley 1970-71. Chairman Cumbria Bird Club 1995. Special interests: raptors (esp harriers), bitterns, upland/heathland birds, population and behavioural studies. Papers on status of British and European bitterns, behaviour and status of Marsh and Montagu's Harriers, and various species surveys published in *Ardea, Bird Study, British Birds, J Appl Ecol* and county bird reports; numerous articles in eg *Birds, Country Life, The Living Countryside*. Contributor to BTO Winter Atlas, New Breeding Atlas and *Red Data Birds in Britain* (1990). OIR: plants and plant communities, photography, books, travel, music. Syldata, Arne, Wareham, Dorset BH20 5BJ.

UNSWORTH, David John; *b:* 1 May 1964 in Eastleigh, Hants. Cert in Environmental Studies (Southampton, 1996). Civil Servant (Marine Safety Agency). Wetland Bird Survey (WeBS) local organiser for Langstone Harbour, Portsmouth Harbour, Southampton Water, Beaulieu Estuary and NW Solent 1988-. WeBS counter in Langstone Harbour 1979-, and Bealieu Estuary 1988-. WeBS low tide count organiser/participant for Langstone and Portsmouth Harbours and Southampton Water 1990-. Secretary of Solent Shorebird Study Group 1994-. Records Committee and production of *Hampshire Bird Report* 1986-. Voluntary warden at North Solent NNR 1995-. Numerous local and national surveys since 1979. Special interest: shorebird ecology in the Solent. Results of various surveys published in *HBR*. Member: Wader Study Group. 142 Malmesbury Road, Shirley, Southampton SO15 5FQ. 01703 232467.

UNWIN, Brian; *b:* 21 May 1945 in Horden, Co Durham; *w:* Jennifer. A J Dawson Grammar School, Wingate, Co Durham. Journalist. Founded Durham Bird Club in 1975, Committee to 1984, Recorder 1975-80. Led initiative which resulted in establishment of Whitburn Bird Observatory in 1971. From 1969 led campaign to save Barmston Ponds (subsidence pools), one of which survived and became LNR in 1993. This campaign also resulted in setting up of WWT centre at Washington; member of appeals committee for this centre in mid 1970s. RSPB representative for Sunderland late 1960s/early 70s and organised outings for YOC members. Instrumental in establishment of Scientific Advisory Committee for Castle Eden Dene LNR which has since become an NNR. On Council of Durham County Conservation Trust 1970-73, serving as Editor. Committee Sunderland NHS in late 1960s. Special interest: migration on NE coast. Overseas travel inc Israel (studies of raptor passage spring 1981, autumn 1988), voyage on RN ice patrol ship from Uruguay to Antarctic peninsula, returning to Falklands (Dec 1981 to Jan 1982), Sri Lanka (tour leader 1984), USA, Canada, Morocco. Numerous articles about birds and birdwatching published since 1963. Joining Press Assocn (now PA News Ltd) in 1984 led to steady flow of stories to newspapers, radio and TV nationwide and occasionally further afield. Columns: 'Wildlife Watch' in *Newcastle Journal* (fortnightly then monthly, 1982-90); 'Birdwatch' in *Northern Echo* (weekly, 1986-); 'Birds' in *Daily Telegraph* northern editions (mainly monthly, 1987-92); also regular articles in *Bird Watching* (late 1980s/90s). Compiler of records at Whitburn Bird Obs since 1990 and involved in production of *Birds in Durham* (annual report) 1972-84. 'Freelance of the Year' in North East Press Awards 1987. Ongoing effort to make own seaside garden more attractive to migrants arriving on S Tyneside coast (73 species since 1989, not counting flyovers). OIR: supporting Sunderland FC; cinema and theatre-going and eating out; listening to music; dog walking. 16 Shearwater, Whitburn, Sunderland SR6 7SF. 0191 529 5012; fax 0191 529 5022.

UTTLEY, Brian; *b:* 17 December 1947 in Huntingdonshire. Reading Ornithological Club: Committee c1986-, Conservation Officer 1988-. Chairman Theale Area Bird Conservation Group c1988-, and of Friends of

Lavell's Lake Conservation Area c1990-. Organiser of all work parties (sixty a year) for these groups, mainly wetland around gravel pits. Special interest: 'committed local patch worker, on a daily basis for most of the year.' 65 Omers Rise, Burghfield Common, Reading RG7 3HH. 01734 832894.

VAN DEN BERG, Arnoud Bernard; *b:* 15 June 1952 in the Netherlands; *p:* Cecilia Bosman. Drs Biology (Free Univ, Amsterdam, 1980). Ornithologist. Editor (and founder) *Dutch Birding* 1979-. Dutch Rarities Committee 1980-92 (Chairman 1990-92). Associate of Laboratory of Ornithology, Library of Natural Sounds, Cornell Univ (USA) 1983-94. Ringer at Van Lennep Ringing Station (Neth) 1985-94. Member of (Dutch) Guild of Nature Photographers and Foto Natura agency 1986-. Board of Netherlands Ornithologists' Club 1989-92 and Dutch Birding Assocn 1989-. Editorial associate *Vogels* 1990-92, 1994-95. Bird tour leader for Limosa Birdwatching Holidays 1990-. Advisor for *Limicola* (Ger) 1992-. Identification consultant for *Birding World* 1988-. Taxonomic sub-committee Commissie Dwaalgasten Nederlandse Avifauna 1995-. Expeditions and field research inc India (also Afghanistan, Pakistan and Nepal) studying *Gyps* vultures; Latin America, inc collecting sound recordings of birds (vocalisations of c150 species recorded on tape for first time, in 1980-81); Indian Ocean, inc studying seabirds; Turkey, photographer biologist for wader and waterfowl project; Netherlands, ornithological aspects of harbour developments at IJmuiden; Morocco, Slender-billed Curlew survey (inc taking first-ever colour photographs of the species); SE Asia (Sumatra, Java, Bali, Malaysia, Thailand) collecting sound recordings of birds; Saudi Arabia, monitoring effects of oil spills on birds of the Arabian Gulf. Special interests: identification, photography and sound recording. Author *List of Dutch Bird Species* (priv print, many editions 1987-94), *Checklist of Birds of the Netherlands* (priv print, 5 editions 1994-96), *Where to Watch Birds in Holland, Belgium & Northern France* (1996). Co-author *De Belangrijkste Vogelgebieden van Europa* (largely by John Gooders, 1989), *Vogels Nieuw in Nederland* (1990), *Parels van de Oriënt* (1993), *Birdwatching: a Nature Company guide* (Australia, 1996). Also editor and (co-)translator of several standard ornithological books into Dutch. Over three hundred papers and notes in some sixty ornithological journals and magazines inc *Ardea, Birdwatch, British Birds, Dutch Birding, Limicola, Limosa, Vogels*. Some two thousand photographs in books and periodical publications, and over twenty-five sound recordings on cassette, disc and CD, mostly in USA. Duinlustparkweg 98, 2082 EG Santpoort-Zuid, Netherlands. +31 (0)23 5378024; fax +31 (0)23 5376749.

VARTY, Clive Geoffrey; *b:* 11 September 1931 in Ambleside, Westmorland. Retired paper merchant. Leeds Birdwatchers' Club: Committee 1971-80, President 1973-75. Yorkshire WT: Council 1976-84, Vice Pres 1980-84, Hon Sec 1983-84, Hon Life Vice Pres 1988-. Yorkshire Naturalists' Union, Ornithological Section: Committee 1980-84, Protection of Birds Committee 1979-93 (Sec 1979-84). YNU Executive Committee 1980-84. Special interest: raptor studies. Editor *Yorkshire Naturalists' Union: Protection of Birds Committee Centenary Year 1891-1991* (1991). Infrequent contributor of papers and articles on ornithology to YNU journal *The Naturalist* and *YNU Bulletin*. Member: Hawk and Owl Trust. Ongoing study of biographical works on ornithology and natural history. OIR: collecting antiquarian and secondhand books. 26 Craggwood Road, Horsforth, Leeds LS18 4PB. 0113 258 7627.

VAUGHAN, Richard; *b:* 9 July 1927 in Maidenhead, Berks; *w:* Margaret. PhD History (Cambridge, 1955). Professor of History at Universities of Hull and Groningen, Holland, 1965-89. Special interest: photography. Author *Gulls in Britain* (1972), *Birds of the Yorkshire Coast* (1974), *Arctic Summer, Birds in North Norway* (1979), *In Search of Arctic Birds* (1992). Author of 54 articles in *Country Life* illustrated with own photographs, published 1952-86; other articles in eg *Bird Watching*, *Birdwatch*, *British Birds*. Papers in eg *Ibis*, *Rivista Italiana di Ornitologia*. Photographs published in many books and periodicals. Bradwell, Sparkhayes Lane, Porlock, Minehead, Somerset TA24 8NE. 01643 862936.

VERNON, John Douglas Rae (Rae); *b:* 19 November 1929 in Cardiff. BSc Zoology (Univ Wales Cardiff, 1951). Advisory Entomologist in Min of Agriculture (ADAS) 1954-88, now retired. Joint correspondent (with M Thévenot) for Morocco for *BWP*. Joint organiser (with B L Sage) of BTO National Survey of Rookeries 1975. Special interests: food, feeding habitat and distribution studies of Black-headed and Common Gulls; rookeries; birds of Morocco. Papers on gulls and rookeries in *Bird Study*; on ornithological visits to Tunisia and Morocco in *Alauda*; review of fifty years of ornithology in NW Africa 1930-80 in *Bull BOC* (1980). Species text on Common Gull in BTO Winter Atlas. *The Birds of Morocco: BOU check-list* (with M Thévenot *et al*) (in prep). Member: ABC, OSME. OIR: conservation issues, botany, travel, walking. 16 Orchid Meadow, Pwllmeyric, Chepstow, Gwent NP6 6HP. 01291 626008.

VERON, Paul Kendell; *b:* 14 August 1959 in Guernsey; *w:* Rosie. BSc Geography (Univ Wales Swansea, 1980), PGCE (Exeter, 1981). Chief Executive, Guernsey Post Office. Guernsey Rare Birds Committee 1994-96. Channel Islands ringer from 1976. Special interests: ringing, migration, seabird populations, movements and mortality, travel. Editor *Important Bird Areas in the Channel Islands* (1996). Papers published in *Bardsey Bird Observatory Annual Report, Guernsey Bird Ringing Report, Ringing & Migration, La Société Guernesiaise Trans.* Author of *Vale Marais Report* Nos 1-5 (1971-92); co-author of *Bailiwick of Guernsey Ringing Report* Nos 1-3 (1974-81). Several broadcasts on local ornithology on BBC local radio. OIR: worldwide travel. Ty Coed, Rue du Closel, Vale, Guernsey GY3 5AR. 01481 49661.

VILLAGE, Andrew (Andy); The Revd Dr; *b:* 20 May 1954 in Shipston-on-Stour, Warwickshire; *w:* Liz. Stamford School. BSc Zoology (Durham, 1975), PhD Ecology of Kestrels (Edinburgh, 1980), BA Theological Studies (Trinity College, Bristol, 1992). Clergyman in the Church of England. Prev: Senior Scientific Officer, Institute of Terrestrial Ecology, Monks Wood, Huntingdon 1980-89; Higher Scientific Officer, ITE, Edinburgh 1979-80. Projects Advisory Committee, Hawk and Owl Trust since 1993. Special interests: ecology and behaviour, population ecology of raptors (esp Kestrel, Short-eared and Long-eared Owls), Lapwing in farmland in winter. Author *The Kestrel* (1990), *Falcons* (1992). Articles, mainly on Kestrel and owls, in eg *Anim Behav, The Auk, Bird Study, J Animal Ecol, Ornis Scandinavica, J Zool, Ringing & Migration.* The Rectory, 3 High Street, Middleton Cheney, Banbury OX17 2PB. 01295 710254.

VINE, Anthony Edward (Tony); *b:* 23 October 1929 in Swaffham, Norfolk. King's School Ely. RAF as meteorologist 1947-50. Cambridge Tech College. Agriculture, also wildlife consultant. Committee Cambridge Bird Club over twenty years 1950s-70s, Vice President since 1979. BTO Regional Representative Cambs 1950s-70s. Suffolk Records Committee 1970s-80s. Founder-member Cambridgeshire WT. Fieldwork for BTO Breeding Atlas. Long-term counts of all heronries in Fenland drainage basin from late 1940s (when W B Alexander was National Organiser): some 500 nests at approx 36 heronries each year. Natural history lecturer for WEA and local authorities in Cambs and Norfolk since 1960s. Special interests: distribution, migration. 'Advent of present rarity mass hysteria has killed my activities.' One or two papers eg on Curlew Sandpiper/Little Stint migration, and notes eg on Canada Geese, published *British Birds* in 1950s. Editor *Cambridgeshire Bird Report* 1951 and joint editor in other years.

OIR: badgers and bats, underground Britain, industrial archaeology. Cromer Lodge, Wereham, King's Lynn, Norfolk PE33 9BA. 01366 500248.

VINICOMBE, Keith Edgar; *b:* 29 October 1953 in Bristol. Queen Elizabeth's Hospital School. BA Geography (Univ Wales, Swansea, 1975). Civil Servant. Prev: Bird survey work in Gwynedd Apr 1976-Apr 1977. Committee Bristol Ornithological Club 1979-81. British Birds Rarities Committee 1982-91. BOU Records Committee 1991-. Hon birdwatching warden at Chew Valley Lake and member of CVL Conservation Committee since c1980. Special interests: birding at Chew Valley Lake and identification. Author *The Macmillan Field Guide to Bird Identification* illus by A Harris and L Tucker (1989, pbk 1993) and *Rare Birds of Britain and Ireland* (in prep). Many articles, papers and notes in various magazines, mainly *British Birds*. Editorial Board *Avon Bird Report* 1979-81. Identification Notes Panel *British Birds* 1991-. OIR: football (Bristol City FC) and music (inc Beatles, Dylan). 11 Kennington Avenue, Bishopston, Bristol BS7 9EU. 0117 975 4758.

VITTERY, Alan; *b:* 11 November 1943 in Middlesbrough; *w:* Bronwen. Public Servant, retired. Diplomatic Service 1964-79, serving in Bulgaria, The Gambia, Turkey, Pakistan, Ethiopia and Mozambique. Senior Executive Officer/Principal in NCC 1979-90 (Head of Site Safeguard Policy Branch and Head of Public Affairs). Co-founder Ornithological Society of Turkey (now OSME) 1968, Council 1969-73, 1978-84. Committee East Sutherland Bird Group 1992-95, Chairman 1996-. Bird Recorder Sutherland 1993/94. Special interests: migration, raptors, waders, seawatching. Studying and compiling checklists of birds of the Ionian Islands, Greece. Co-author *Notes on the Birds of The Gambia* (1966), *A Check List of the Birds of Addis Ababa* (1975). Contributor to *The Bird-watchers' Book* (1974) and *BWP* (raptors and warbler movements). Editor *Check List of the Birds of Turkey* (1971). Editor *Orn Soc of Turkey Bird Report* 1968/69, co-editor 1966/67, 1970-73. Regular contributor to *World of Birds* magazine 1970-73. Two papers on Ethiopia in *Scopus* (1978 and 1983), one in *Forktail* on Pakistan (1995); also articles in *Birdwatch*. Member: OBC, OSME. OIR: butterflies, sport, classical music (esp Shostakovitch). Elmag Croft, 164 West Clyne, Brora, Sutherland KW9 6NH. 01408 621827.

VOOUS, Karel Hendrik; Officer, Order of the Golden Ark (Netherlands) 1981; Officer, Order Oranje Nassau (Netherlands) 1991; Professor; *b:* 23 June 1920 in Amsterdam, Netherlands; *p:* Hendrika (Henny) Luiting. MA

Biology (Univ Amsterdam, 1945), PhD Thesis: 'On the history of the distribution of the genus *Dendrocopos*' (Univ Amsterdam, 1947). Professor of Zoogeography (from 1963 Systematic and Geographic Zoology), Free University, Amsterdam 1955-75 (retired through ill health). Assistant Curator through to Deputy Director, Zoological Museum, Univ Amsterdam 1939-63. Memberships and offices: Council for Nature Conservation; Chairman, Committee for Fauna Preservation; Netherlands Avifauna Committee 1957-79; Permanent Executive Committee of the International Ornithological Congress; International Ornithological Committee; Standing Committee for Ornithological Nomenclature; Standing Committee for the Co-ordination of Seabird Research; ICBP (Netherlands Section); World Group for the Conservation of Birds of Prey; Advisory Committee of the President of the WWF (Netherlands Appeal); Chairman, Netherlands Committee for European Conservation Year 1970; Hon Secretary-General, XV International Ornithological Congress (The Hague, 1970); Hon Secretary, Nederlandse Ornithologische Vereniging 1946-56; Council, Nederlandse Ornithologische Unie 1957-68; Hon President, 12th International Conference of International Bird Census Committee (IBCC) and European Ornithological Atlas Committee (EOAC) (Netherlands, 1992); Hon President, XXI International Ornithological Congress (Vienna, 1994). Honours: Corresponding Member Schweizerische Ornithologische Gesellschaft (1951), BOU (1971), Deutsche Ornithologen-Gesellschaft (1968); Hon Member Royal Naval Birdwatching Society (1959), Australian Seabird Group (1971), Société Ornithologique de France (1972), Sociedad Española de Ornitología (1973), Netherlands Society for the Protection of Birds (1974), Club van Nederlandse Vogelkundigen (1995); Hon Fellow AOU (1969), BOU (1984); Foreign Member Royal Belgian Academy for Arts and Sciences (1969). Special interests: systematics, nomenclature, zoogeography, seabirds, birds of prey, owls, international conservation. Author *Vogels van de Nederlandse Antillen* (1955, English ed 1963), *Atlas van de Europese Vogels* (1969, also English ed), *Die Vogelwelt Europas* (1961), *Owls of the Northern Hemisphere* (1988), *In de Ban van Vogels* (1995). Co-editor *BWP* Vols 1-9 (1977-94). Over 350 papers etc in journals and conference proceedings in sixteen countries. These include 'List of Recent Holarctic Bird Species' first published in parts (*Ibis* Vol 115, 1973 and Vol 199, 1977) then reprinted, with a foreword, as a separate publication under the same title by Academic press for the BOU in 1977. Member of Editorial Board of *Ardea* and Editor for over 30 years; also Editorial Board of *Limosa*. BOU Gold Medal 1975. v.d. Duyn v. Maasdamlaan 28, 1272 EM, Huizen NH, Netherlands.

WAGSTAFF, William Huard (Will); *b:* 28 April 1960 in Cardiff, South Glamorgan; *w:* Margaret. BSc Biology and Geology (Cambridge Coll of Arts and Tech, 1981). Conservation Officer, Isles of Scilly Environmental Trust; Asst Heritage Coast Officer for Isles of Scilly since 1989. Prev: self-employed wildlife tour guide on Isles of Scilly 1985-89. Occasional leader of birding tours to The Gambia and Falkland Islands. Bird Recorder Isles of Scilly and Secretary Scilly Rarities Panel 1987-. Treasurer Scilly Trail and Hide Fund 1988-. BTO Regional Representative Isles of Scilly 1993-. Special interests: study of migrants passing through Isles of Scilly and breeding seabirds on the islands; African birding. Author of many articles about birdwatching on Scilly since 1985 in *Bird Watching, Birdwatch* and local magazines; on own rarities in *British Birds*; review of the year for *Isles of Scilly Bird Report* since 1988 and systematic list for same 1988-94. Frequently interviewed about the islands' bird life on local and national radio (also World Service) and TV; acted as wildlife consultant for many TV programmes made on the islands. 'I am probably best known for the walks I lead around the islands during the summer and the weekly slideshows that I give during the season. This means I am talking to on average 3500 people per year. The way many birders know me is because I do the nightly log call and organise slideshows etc for the birders and make sure the CB system is up and running and also make sure the Bird News boards are ready for use each day and are being used. Otherwise I have been lucky to find some of the rarities that turn up here and have become known as a result of their publication. I am also the voice behind the Birdline Isles of Scilly which covers all the recent sightings on the islands.' Article on this in *Birdwatcher's Yearbook* 1997. Member: Isles of Scilly Seabird Group. OIR: reading, badminton, cricket, travel. 42 Sally Port, St Mary's, Isles of Scilly TR21 0JE. 01720 422212.

WAINE, Jason Carthew; *b:* 31 October 1949 in Wolverton, Bucks; *w:* Rosemary. BVetMed (Royal Veterinary College, London Univ, 1973), MRCVS 1973. Veterinary surgeon, general practice. Special interests: long-term project studying the gross pathology, diseases and causes of death in wild birds; the structure and pathology of the avian skull; treatment of injured or diseased wild birds, esp wildfowl. Articles published in annual reports of Fair Isle and Gibraltar Point Bird Observatories. Chapters on autopsy techniques and diseases of the head and neck in wildfowl in BSAVA's *Manual of Raptors, Pigeons and Waterfowl* (1996). Member: Assocn of Avian Veterinarians, British Small Animal Veterinary Assocn, British Veterinary Assocn, Wildlife

Disease Assocn. OIR: rugby union, palaeontology, walking, reading, wildlife gardening. 250 Birchfield Road, Redditch, Worcs B97 4LZ. 01527 542834. Surgery: 97 Mount Pleasant, Redditch, Worcs B97 4JD. 01527 550111; fax 01527 550217.

WALBRIDGE, Grahame; *b:* 16 January 1956 in Portland, Dorset; *w:* Sumalee. Weymouth Grammar School. Operating bird information lines Birding Southwest (since Aug 1991) and Rare Bird News (since Apr 1992). Prev: Civil Servant 1977-93. British Birds Rarities Committee 1992-. Special interests: identification, taxonomy, migration. Author of identification papers in *Birding World* and *British Birds*, collaborator on many more in latter. Founder-member OBC, member OSME. OIR: watching sport; music; all aspects of natural history and conservation. 16 Haylands, Portland, Dorset DT5 2JZ. 01305 860098.

WALDON, John; *b:* 21 May 1951 in Weston-super-Mare, Somerset; *w:* Fiona. Weston-super-Mare Grammar School. Dip Ad (Gloucestershire College of Art, 1974). RSPB Regional Officer SW England since 1994. Prev RSPB: Senior Conservation Officer 1986-94; Asst Regional Officer SW 1982-86. Counter for Wetland Bird Survey. Special interests: conservation of estuary birds and Stone Curlew. Frequent interviews and press articles on conservation issues. Active, in personal capacity, in preparation of case for protection of internationally important wetlands in British Columbia, Canada. Bradleigh, Aboveway, Exminster, Exeter, Devon EX6 8DT. 01392 833310.

WALKDEN, Paul; *b:* 3 November 1952 in Huddersfield, Yorkshire; *w:* Suzanne. Agricultural sales manager. WWT Council 1989-95. Gloucestershire Ornithological Co-ordinating Committee: Secretary 1988-93, Surveys Sub-committee Secretary 1989-93. Dursley Birdwatching & Preservation Society: Committee member and Trustee 1988-. Member of Severn Vale Ringing Group 1989-. Special interest: Mute Swan (three-year study in local 10km square). Bibliography of Sir Peter Scott in *Sir Peter Scott at 80: a retrospective* ed by Jonathan Bennington (1989); another, updated, in *The Art of Peter Scott: images from a lifetime* by Philippa Scott (1992). Biography of Sir Peter Scott in *Dictionary of National Biography*, Supp Vol: 1986-90 (in prep). Contributor to *Forty Years on, a celebration of Gloucestershire wildlife* ed by Maurice Bullen (1993). Articles published in eg *Gloucestershire Bird Report* and *Wildfowl and Wetlands*. OIR: general natural history, collecting wildlife books and wildlife art. 32 Oakfield Way, Sharpness, Glos GL13 9UU. 01453 811029.

WALKER, David Glaister; *b:* 15 October 1955 in North Shields, Northumberland; *w:* Wendy. Roving conservation officer, Western Isles, RSPB 1993-94. Prev RSPB: research asst, Argyll 1992; warden, Geltsdale 1990-91; species protection team leader (Sea Eagle), Hebrides 1989; roving conservation officer, Borders 1988; senior species protection warden, Cumbria 1979-85. Earlier: asst warden, Farne Islands, National Trust 1978. Species co-ordinator for Golden Eagle and Goshawk, Cumbria Raptor Study Group from inception in 1992; also member of Argyll Raptor Study Group. Special interests: diurnal behaviour and juvenile dependency of Golden Eagle and Goshawk. Author *The Lakeland Eagles* (1991). Papers on Golden Eagle published in *Ibis*. Member: as above, also World Working Group on Birds of Prey. Illustrated talks given. 5 Naddlegate, Burnbank, Penrith, Cumbria CA10 2RL. 01931 713361.

WALKER, Frank; BEM 1970; *b:* 21 July 1924 in London. Educated in RAF. Aero Space Systems Operator, retired. Special interests: identification, migration, status and distribution. Founded Hong Kong Birdwatching Society with A St G Walton in 1957. Founder of Royal Air Force Ornithological Society in 1965 (now Hon Life Member). BTO 'A' ringer 1953-83 and worked with various ringing groups in UK and overseas. Many foreign trips between 1955 and 1981, inc Cyprus, Middle East, Far East. Notes on Oman published by OSME. In 1982 commenced a series of eleven-month round the world trips plus numerous visits to eg Mediterranean Basin, N America, Australia, New Zealand, Hawaii, Fiji, Spain, N Africa; notes published by RAFOS under title *Ramblings of a Vagrant* (1967-96). Seabird counts from Cape St Vincent, Portugal Nov 1992-Mar 1996. 67 Stonedale, Sutton Hill, Telford, Shrops TF7 4AL. 01952 586957.

WALLACE, Donald Ian Mackenzie (Ian); *b:* 14 December 1933 in Great Yarmouth, Norfolk; *w:* Wendy. BA Economics and Law (Cambridge, 1954). Marketing and general management. Loretto School Ornithological Society, Editor 1954. Cambridge Bird Club, President/Editor 1956-57. Ornithological Section of London NHS, Editor 1959-60. Between 1963 and 1970: St Agnes Bird Observatory, Chairman; BTO Scientific Advisory Committee; RSPB Council; BOU Council. British Birds Rarities Committee: member 1960s, Chairman 1972-76. Flamborough Ornithological Group, founder-member and Chairman 1972-91. Founder-member Society of Wildlife Artists. Special interests: difficult identification; distribution and status; 'local patch' work; 'joyful birdwatching, especially seawatching and falls.' Population studies of Regent's Park, London

(1951-65); Nanyuki and Lake Nakuru, Kenya (1952-54); Lagos, Nigeria (1968-71); Holme upon Spalding Moor, Yorks (1979-85); Needwood Forest, Staffs (1985-). Expeditions: St Kilda, Canada (1956), Arctic Norway and Finland (1957), Spain (1960-61), Lebanon, Syria and particularly Jordan (1963, 1965, 1966), Northern Nigeria (1971), Baluchistan (1972), Nova Scotia (1975, 1978), Siberia and Mongolia (1980). Author *Discover Birds* (1979), *Birdwatching in the Seventies* (1981), *Birdwatching* (1982), *Marvels and Mysteries of Bird Life* (1984), *Birds of Prey of Britain and Europe* (1983). Editor *British Birds* 1972-76. Editor (Field characters) and artist *BWP* 1976-93, *Concise BWP* (1994-). Illustrator and contributor, various titles 1959-; art editor 1994-. Columnist for *Bird Watching* 1986-. Occasional contributor to BBC and ITV 1950-. Sound recordist for BBC of Leach's and Storm Petrels (1956). Mount Pleasant Farm, Main Road, Anslow, Burton-on-Trent, Staffs DE13 9QE. 01283 812364.

WALLACE, Michael Frederick; *b:* 12 July 1943 in London; *w:* Gwen. ARICS 1972. Chartered Surveyor. Voluntary wardening on Skomer Island and Little Tern Colony at Gronant, N Wales in 1980s. Shropshire Ornithological Society: Excursion Secretary 1978-83, Secretary 1991-. Shrops WT: Hon Land Agent 1992-, Council and Exec Committee 1992-. Co-ordinator of fieldwork in part of Shrops for county atlas 1985-90. Special interests: relationship between species of birds and habitats; counter for Wetland Bird Survey on three meres in N Shrops (1980-) and BTO Waterways Bird Survey on River Severn, Shrops (1991-); waterbirds, corvids, Buzzard. Author of several species accounts for *An Atlas of the Breeding Birds of Shropshire* by P Deans *et al* (1992). Contributor to *Birdwatcher's Britain* ed by John Parslow (1983). OIR: walking in the countryside, organic gardening, reading, bee-keeping. 75 Larkhill Road, Copthorne, Shrewsbury, Shrops SY3 8XJ. 01743 369035.

WALLEN, Michael Sean (Mike); *b:* 26 April 1965 in High Wycombe, Bucks. Public Service. Committee Buckinghamshire Bird Club 1989-. Voluntary wardening on Skomer Island each year since 1985, inc censusing of Lesser Black-backed Gulls in May. Special interests: gulls (identification, movements/fluctuations), migration, photography. Editor *Buckinghamshire Bird Report* since 1989; sketches and photographs in same. Photographs also published in *Birding World*, *British Birds* and *The Birds of Buckinghamshire* ed by Lack and Ferguson (1993). OIR: walking, running, eating out and socialising. Silver Birches, Valley Road, Hughenden Valley, High Wycombe, Bucks HP14 4LD. 01378 311270.

WALSH, James Frank (Frank); *b:* 2 September 1937 in Derby; *w:* Brenda. BSc Zoology (Liverpool, 1962), PhD Medical Entomology (Salford, 1984). MIBiol 1969, CBiol 1991. Entomologist (medical). Asst Editor of *Lancashire Bird Report* 1990-, and of *Malimbus* 1993 and 1994. Member of BirdLife International Specialist Group on Storks, Ibises and Spoonbills. Special interests: West African and Ugandan ornithology, African storks. Over fifty papers and notes on African birds, mostly in *Malimbus* but also in *Bull BOC, Ibis, J für Orn, Ostrich, Scopus, Tauraco.* Ornithologist resident in West Africa 1965-90. Collaborating with R A Cheke in preparation of the Togo volume in 'BOU Check-list' series. Member: ABC, EAWS, SAOS, WAOS. OIR: other natural history (esp hippopotamus and saturniid moths of Africa), book collecting. 80 Arundel Road, Lytham St Annes, Lancs FY8 1BN. 01253 737765; fax 01253 796080.

WALTER, Michael Frank; *b:* 16 January 1949 in Ilford, Essex; *w:* Marion. Chigwell School 1960-67. BSc Zoology and Botany (Durham, 1970). Warden RSPB Blean Woods since 1982. Prev RSPB: Warden Fore Wood 1976-82; asst warden Wolves Wood, Church Wood (Hedgerley), Ynys-Hir, Leighton Moss, Coombes Valley 1972-76. Earlier: Warden Farne Islands, National Trust 1970-71. Committee Canterbury RSPB Members' Group 1987-. BTO 10km square steward 1992-. Special interest: woodland birds. Chapter on lowland deciduous woodland in *RSPB Nature Reserves* ed by N Hammond (1983). OIR: walking, cycling. 11 Garden Close, Rough Common, Canterbury, Kent CT2 9BP. 01227 462491.

WALTERS, Michael Patrick; *b:* 5 November 1942 in Portrush, N Ireland. Natural History Museum, Tring since 1970, Curator of Egg Collecton since 1972. Ornithological representative on International Council for Crypto-zoology 1992-. Special interests: eggs (Museum has largest collection in the world); extinct birds. Author *The Complete Birds of the World* (1980, illus ed 1981) and *Eyewitness Handbook: Birds Eggs* (1994). Co-author (with Alan Knox) *Extinct and Endangered Birds in the Collections of the Natural History Museum* (1994). Articles and notes published in eg *British Birds, Bull BOC, Emu, J Bombay Nat Hist Soc, Notornis, Sandgrouse.* Member: OBC, OSME. OIR: music (esp Gilbert and Sullivan), amateur actor, collecting 78rpm gramophone records (esp opera and light opera). The Natural History Museum, Dept of Zoology, Bird Group, Akeman Street, Tring, Herts HP23 6AP. 01442 824181; fax 01442 890693.

WALTERS DAVIES, Peter; *b:* 1 July 1928 in Aberystwyth, Cardiganshire; *w:* Margaret. BSc Zoology inc Agricultural Zoology (Univ College of

Wales, Aberystwyth, 1954). Jesus College, Univ Oxford 1954-57: postgraduate research with Edward Grey Institute of Field Ornithology. BTO 'A' ringer since 1955. Biological consultant, Wildlife Surveys (Wales) since 1989. Prev: Nature Conservancy/NCC Regional Officer for South Wales, then Scientific Development Officer (Wales) with special responsibility for the Red Kite in Wales, 1957-86. Various committees inc Joint Chairman NCC/RSPB Red Kite Committee (to 1987), member JNCC Red Kite Project Team (to 1989), member CCW/RSPB Kite Group (1988-93). Secretary Welsh Ornithological Society 1988-92. CCW licence for Red Kite manipulation in Wales 1992-. Dyfed WT: Chairman North Ceredigion Conservation Committee 1989-, Conservation and Management Committee 1993-. Chairman and area representative, Welsh Kite Watchers Group 1994-. Trustee, The Welsh Kite Trust 1996-. Special interests: species conservation and management in Wales; liaison with landowners. Joint author (with P E Davis) of Red Kite paper in *British Birds*. OIR: fishing, woodwork. Alltgoy, Caemelyn, Abersytwyth, Dyfed SY23 2HA. 01970 615418.

WANLESS, Sarah; *b:* 23 April 1951 in Scarborough, Yorkshire; *p:* Michael Harris. Scarborough High School for Girls 1962-69. BSc Zoology (Aberdeen, 1974), PhD Aspects of population dynamics and breeding ecology of the Gannet on Ailsa Craig (Aberdeen, 1979). Visiting post-doctoral researcher at NERC Institute of Terrestrial Ecology, Banchory since 1991. Prev: post-doctoral research asst Univ Glasgow 1990-91; contract work for NCC 1980-88; research asst Univ Durham 1977-80. NCC summer warden Isle of May 1983-87. Organiser of North Atlantic Gannet Survey 1984-85 and 1994-95. Committee Seabird Group 1990-. Special interests: seabirds (esp auks, shags and sulids), population monitoring, radio telemetry, diving behaviour. Work concentrated mainly in Scotland; spent 1989-90 and 1994-95 seasons at Bird Island, South Georgia. Published work on a wide range of topics related to seabirds in ornithological and ecological journals eg *Condor, Ibis, J Zool, Polar Biol*. Editorial Board *Scottish Birds* 1987-89. Editor *Seabird* 1990-. OIR: classical music, travel (esp to islands), wildlife art. NERC Institute of Terrestrial Ecology, Hill of Brathens, Banchory, Kincardineshire AB31 4BY. 01330 823434.

WARBURTON, Anthony Barry (Tony); *b:* 23 July 1935 in Sale, Cheshire; *p:* Jenny Thurston. Burnage Grammar School, Manchester. Director, World Owl Trust (prev British Owl Breeding and Release Scheme) since 1972. Hon Manager Eskmeals Dunes Nature Reserve (Cumbria WT)

1972-. Council Cumbria WT 1985-88. Hon Sec West Cumberland Field Society 1970-73. Member of DoE Barn Owl Working Group 1991-. Co-ordinated Peregrine wardening in W Cumbria throughout 1970s and 80s. Special interest: owls. Countrywide lecturer on owls and general conservation subjects 1975-93. Co-author (with D S Bunn and R D S Wilson) *The Barn Owl* (1982). Owl-related articles in *Animals, British Birds, International Zoo Year Book*; others in eg *Birds Illustrated, World of Birds*. Presenter of various ITV series inc *Nature Trail*, also regular panellist on TV series eg *Looks Natural* (BBC) and *Amoeba to Zebra* (ITV). Member: Federation of Zoological Gardens, Hawk & Owl Trust. OIR: fell walking, sport, reading. World Owl Trust, The Owl Centre, Muncaster Castle, Ravenglass, Cumbria CA18 1RQ. 01229 717393.

WARD, Eric; *b:* 18 November 1919 in Warrington, Cheshire; *w:* Margaret. BA Geography (Sheffield, 1947). Schoolmaster, retired. Founder-member East Lancashire Ornithologists' Club (1955). Founder-member and Chairman, Rossendale Ornithologists' Club (1976). Bird Recorder Rossendale 1983-96. Carried out BTO Common Birds Census on 100ha plot in upland Lancashire 1968-95. Author *Rossendale Birds* (priv print, 1988). Editor *Rossendale OC Annual Report* 1983-96. OIR: fell walking. Highcroft, 63 Booth Road, Waterfoot, Rossendale, Lancs BB4 9BP. 01706 213304.

WARD, Philip Arthur (Phil); *b:* 19 June 1963 in South Shields, Co Durham. Harton Comprehensive School 1974-79, Hebburn Technical College 1980. Countryside Ranger Elan Estate, Welsh Water since 1992. Prev: contract wardening for English Nature and RSPB 1989-92; also for Gateshead Council 1986-88. Chairman of local group of Radnorshire WT 1993-95. Leader of birdwatching weekends for various organisations inc bird clubs, RSPB members' groups and wildlife trusts. BTO 'C' ringer since 1988, active in Radnorshire and occasionally abroad (eg Portugal). Member: Welsh Kite Watchers Group. OIR: sports (esp running and cycling), wide range of musical interests (inc playing guitars), keen amateur entomologist. Elan Valley Visitor Centre, Rhayader, Powys LD6 5HP. 01597 810880.

WARDEN, David; *b:* 1933 in Birmingham. BVMS (Glasgow, 1957), MRCVS 1957. Veterinary surgeon. Special interests: continuing Reed Warbler study begun in 1974; numbers and distribution of birds of prey. Contributions to BTO Nest Record Scheme over forty years. Occasional papers to local bird reports and notes to *British Birds*. Member: ABC. Centaur, Ham Lane, Bishop Sutton, Bristol BS18 4TZ. 01275 332321.

WARHAM, John; *b:* 11 October 1919 in Halifax, Yorks; *w:* Audrey ('Pat'). King Edward VI Grammar School, Retford, Notts. BSc Zoology (Durham, 1965), MSc Ornithology (Durham, 1968), PhD Ornithology (Canterbury, NZ, 1973), DSc (Durham, 1985). FRPS 1957. Teaching at Univ Canterbury, NZ 1966-85, Reader in Zoology from 1977. Secretary, Zoology Section of Australia & NZ Assocn for the Advancement of Science, Christchurch 1968. Council NZ Ecological Society 1967-75, President 1977. Senior member International Ornithological Committee of the International Ornithological Congresses from 1986. Special interest: since 1975 solely Procellariiformes: all aspects of their biology (also a bibliography with over 11,800 fully keyworded citations (see Internet address below). Biologist, Australian National Antarctic Expedition (Macquarie I) 1959-61. Led Univ Canterbury Zoology expeditions to The Snares, Campbell and Antipodes Islands 1967-70. Author *Bird Watcher's Delight* (1951), *The Technique of Bird Photography* (1966, 4th ed 1983), *The Technique of Wildlife Cinematography* (1966), *The Petrels: their ecology and breeding systems* (1990), *The Petrels: their physiology, behaviour and conservation* (1996). Co-author (with D L and V N Serventy) *The Handbook of Australian Sea-birds* (Sydney, 1971). Also contributions to other books eg 'The Crested Penguins' in *The Biology of Penguins* ed by B Stonehouse (1975). Numerous scientific papers in eg *Ardea, The Auk, British Birds, Bull BOC, Condor, Emu, Ibis, Notornis, Scottish Birds, Sea Swallow*; also very many popular articles. Exhibition 'Wild Australia' (resulting from nine years wildlife photography) hung at Kodak Melbourne and Sydney, and Qantas Gallery London. *Look* film with Peter Scott in Macquarie Island for BBC TV c1962. Frank M Chapman Awards (AOU) 1973, 1996; Prince and Princess of Wales Science Award (Royal Soc NZ) 1988; Claude McCarthy Fellowship 1988; Serventy Medal (RAOU) 1992. Dept of Zoology, University of Canterbury, Private Bag 4800, Christchurch, New Zealand. +64 (0)3 3667001; fax +64 (0)3 3642024; Internet http://www.canterbury.ac.nz/zool/jw.htm.

WARR, F E (Effie); *b:* 8 March 1938 in Southgate, Middlesex; *h:* John. Librarian, Rothschild and Ornithological Libraries at Natural History Museum, Tring since 1989. Prev: short-term posts and freelance research in natural history in between periods of residence abroad 1964-89; scientific asst in Bird Section of British Museum (Natural History) 1955-64, 1968. Secretary OSME 1983-88. Special interests: Middle East and history of ornithology. Co-author (with Graham Bundy) of Arabian Gulf checklist in *Sandgrouse* 1980. Member: OSME, WAOS. 6 Mansion Drive, Tring, Herts HP23 5BD. 01442 822108.

WARREN, Michael John (Mike); *b:* 26 October 1938 in Wolverhampton, West Midlands; *w:* Kathryne (Kate). NDD Illustration Special (College of Art, Wolverhampton 1958). SWLA 1972. Professional artist, specialising in paintings of birds, since 1972. President Nottinghamshire Birdwatchers 1995-. Founder-member Society for Wildlife Art for the Nation (1985). Formerly Committee West Midland Bird Club, Treasurer SWLA, duck counter. Travel for birds inc Europe, USA, the Pacific and Africa. Work exhibited in UK, Canada, USA, Luxembourg; also in exhibitions following Artists for Nature Foundation (ANF) expeditions to The Netherlands (1992), Poland (1993), Spain (1995), Ireland (1995). Several one-man exhibitions at eg Moorland Gallery and Barbican Arts Centre, London; Carl Battaglia Gallery, New York; Wildlife Art Gallery, Lavenham. Postage stamp designs for British Post Office (waterbirds, 1980) and Republic of Marshall Islands (native and migratory birds, 1990-92). Conservation stamp designs for National Audubon Society (USA) 1984-96; other commissions inc 50 paintings of N American wildfowl. Artist/author *Shorelines* (1984). Illustrator *Where the Wildgoose Flies* by Joyce Pope (1995). Work included in *20th Century Wildlife Artists* (1986), also in ANF books, eg *Artists for Nature in Extremadura* (Wildlife Art Gallery, Lavenham, 1995). The Laurels, The Green, Winthorpe, Notts NG24 2NR. 01636 73554.

WARREN, Robert Bennett (Bob); *b:* 4 February 1919 in Harold Wood, Essex; *w:* Dorothy. ACII 1948. Insurance. Essex Birdwatching Society: Records Committee 1950-72 (Chairman several years), Vice President 1971. Recorder Suffolk Ornithologists' Group 1979-85. Vice Pres Suffolk Naturalists' Society 1989. Suffolk Bird Recorder (appointment of Suff Nat Soc) 1985-91. Paper 'The severe weather of 1962/63 and its effects on the birds of Essex' in *Essex Bird Report* 1963. OIR: walking and music. 37 Dellwood Avenue, Felixstowe, Suffolk IP11 9HW. 01394 270180.

WARRILOW, Griffith John (Griff); *b:* 3 October 1945 in Leicester; *w:* Julia. Kibworth Beauchamp Grammar School, Leics 1957-64. BSc Geography and Zoology (Univ Wales, Swansea, 1967), Dip Ed (Univ Wales, Cardiff, 1968), MPhil Life Sciences (Leicester Polytechnic, 1981), PhD Geography (Leicester Univ, 1988). Geographer. Part-time tutor in ornithological studies, Dept of Adult Education, Leicester Univ 1974-. Survey co-ordinator for county atlas 1977-84. BTO 'A' ringer since 1973 and trainer 1973-85. Ecological consultant to various landowners 1989-. Special interests: mapping bird distribution patterns (national surveys in GB 1969-72, France 1971, Switzerland 1976, local surveys in Leics and

Rutland 1976-84); bird ringing (1971-); ecological succession and bird community change in a flooded disused gravel working (1974-80); Blue Tit (1980-87): the influence of microclimate on first-egg date in woodland; time of egg laying; incubation pattern and regulation of egg temperature; woodland reserve design; the influence of edge zone on breeding bird populations; species richness of small *versus* large woodland reserves. Travel in Europe, inc leader of groups to Netherlands, France, Mallorca. Author *Atlas of Breeding Birds in Leicestershire and Rutland* (1996). Paper on roosting Reed Buntings in *Ringing & Migration*. Regular reviewer of ornithological atlases in *Journal of University Cartographers*. Occasional illustrator (eg *Birds of Rutland Water*) and official cartographer for that reserve. 'Ringer of first British Little Ringed Plover to be recovered in Africa (1974), finder of latest recorded Red-backed Shrike in GB (Norfolk, Nov 23 1986) and only springtime male Yellow-breasted Bunting to date (Lincs, May 1977).' OIR: French woodland management, French vineyards (esp Alsace), cooking, rail transport (GWR steam, TGV, modern tramway systems), butterflies, cultivating alpine plants (esp gentians). 13 Woodbury Rise, Great Glen, Leics LE8 0ER. 01533 592649.

WATERS, Raymond James (Ray); *b:* 31 October 1952 in Feltham, Middlesex. BSc Ecology (Royal Holloway College, London, 1974), PGCE (Keswick Hall, Norwich, 1977). Birds of Estuaries Enquiry/Wetland Birds Survey National Organiser, BTO 1990-. Wardening for NCC in 1976 and RSPB in 1979. Joint Projects Officer for Suffolk Ornithologists' Group 1985-94. Joint BTO Regional Representative Suffolk 1985-90. Special interest: waders. Joint author *Wildfowl and Wader Counts* 1990-. Member: Wader Study Group. OIR: racquet sports. BTO, The Nunnery, Thetford, Norfolk IP24 2PU. 01842 750050.

WATERS, William Estlin (Estlin); *b:* 6 November 1934 in Toronto, Canada; w: Judith. Cardiff High School for Boys. MB, BS (London, 1958), Dip in Industrial Health (St Andrews, 1965), FFCM 1976, FFPHM 1989. Professor of Community Medicine, Univ Southampton 1976-90, Professorial Fellow 1990-94, Emeritus Professor 1994-. Occasional tutor on ornithological topics, Dept of Adult Education, Univ Southampton. Special interests: migration, esp trans-Mediterranean movements and those observed from the smaller British and Irish islands ('a devotee of Great Saltee, Skokholm, Lundy and all the remote islands in the Hebrides'); seabirds; history of ornithology; 'point and squeeze' photography; formerly interested in recording bird sounds on tape. Travel inc N and S America, Africa, Middle and Far East, Australia, South Georgia, Antarctica and the archipelagos of the Seychelles and Galapagos. Much birdwatching during National Service in Cyprus and Libya (1960-61) and on St Kilda almost continuously May 1961-Sep 1962. Author of papers, mainly on migration and seabirds, published in *British Birds, Ibis, Nature in Wales, Scottish Birds, World of Birds*; also shorter contributions in *The Adjutant, Ardeola, Bird Migration, Cape Clear Bird Observatory Bulletin, Irish Naturalists' Journal, Seabird Bulletin*. Contributor to *Birds of the World* by J Gooders (1970-71) and supplied material for *BWP*. Photographs published in several journals and other publications. Member: ABC, OBC, OSME, WAOS. OIR: collecting old and new books, visiting remote islands. Orchards, Broxmore Park, Sherfield English, Romsey, Hants SO51 6FT. 01794 884254.

WATSON, Adam; *b:* 14 April 1930 in Turriff, Aberdeenshire; *w:* Jenny. BSc Zoology (Aberdeen, 1952), PhD (Aberdeen, 1956), DSc 1967. FRSE 1971, FIBiol 1980, CBiol 1980, Fellow Arctic Inst of N America 1983. Emeritus Scientist. Prev: Senior Principal Officer (Special Merit in Research) Institute of Terrestrial Ecology (also leader of ITE Red Grouse Team) 1971-90; Officer in Charge of Nature Conservancy's Mountain and Moorland Research Station 1966-71; Senior Scientific Officer Nature Conservancy Unit of Grouse and Moorland Ecology 1961-65, Principal SO ditto 1965-66; Senior Research Fellow Univ Aberdeen 1957-60; Asst Lecturer Univ Aberdeen 1953-56; Zoologist on Arctic Inst of N America Baird Expedition to Baffin Island 1953; Carnegie Arctic Scholar 1952-53; demonstrator McGill Univ, Montreal 1952-53. Secretary SOC Aberdeen Branch 1947-50. Special interests: bird population dynamics and behaviour, esp studies on Red Grouse and, to a lesser extent, Ptarmigan, Golden Eagle, Dotterel, Snow Bunting; Arctic birds, esp Snowy Owl; human impact on mountain and moorland birds; bird populations and agriculture, esp Corn Bunting. Editor *Animal Populations in Relation to their Food Supplies* (Brit Ecol Soc Symposium, 1970). Co-author (with D Nethersole-Thompson) *The Cairngorms* (1974, 2nd ed 1981). Numerous scientific papers published in eg *British Birds, Bird Study, Can J Zool, Ibis, J Animal Ecol, J Appl Ecol, J Wildlife Management, Ornis Fennica, Ornis Scandinavica, Scottish Birds*. Nuffield Fellowship to lecture at N American univs 1969; RSE Neill Prize 1986 for outstanding contribution to natural history in Scotland, esp study of Red Grouse; Distinguished Scholar of Univ Virginia 1986. Member: North East Scotland Raptor Study Group. OIR: hill walking; cross-country skiing; mountaineering; studying place names, Gaelic dialect, social and land-use history, and human populations in north-east Highlands; soil erosion on lowland and mountain; natural tree regeneration; lichens; mountain snow patches and climate change. c/o ITE, Hill of Brathens, Glassel, Banchory, Kincardineshire AB31 4BY. 01330 823434.

WATSON, Christopher Richard (Chris); *b:* 21 November 1953 in Sheffield, S Yorks; *w:* Margaret. MIBS 1991. Freelance film and TV sound recordist. Prev: RSPB Film and Video Unit 1985-87. Screen credits inc *The Last Dance of the Caribbean Flamingo* (TV New Zealand, 1992), *Goshawk, Phantom of the Forest* (Survival Anglia, 1993), *Hen Harrier* (RSPB, 1993), *Operation Survival* inc White-tailed Eagle and Corncrake (BBC Scotland Nat Hist Series, 1995/96), *Being There: Estuaries* (BBC Nat Hist Unit, 1996). Member Internat Assocn of Wildlife Film-makers, Wildlife Sound Recording Society. 19 The Riding, Kenton, Newcastle upon Tyne NE3 4LQ. 0191 285 5204.

WATSON, Elizabeth Jill (Jill); *b:* 29 July 1942 in Sheffield, Yorks; *p:* David Duplain. Royal Naval School, Haslemere Surrey. Nursing Cert and Dip, 1962. Credits in science subjects (Open Univ, 1976-80). Part-time writer. Bird Recorder Alderney 1992-. Special interest: writing articles about birds, mainly of Great Britain and Channel Islands. Editor of annual ornithological report for *Alderney Society Bulletin*. Founder-member NBC. OIR: general natural history, gardening, walking, photography. Riduna House, 23 Victoria Street, Alderney GY9 3TA. 01481 822414.

WATSON, Frederick Joseph (Derick); *b:* 11 December 1939 in South Shields, Co Durham; *p:* Barbara Davies. BA Fine Arts (Durham, 1961). Full-time bird artist since 1979. Prev: Senior Lecturer then Course Director for BA in Fine Art Sculpture at Sheffield Polytechnic 1969-79; earlier lecturing posts at Huddersfield Coll of Tech and Manchester Coll of Art & Design. Hon Sec Huddersfield Birdwatchers' Club c1978-80. Organiser (with Robert Gillmor) of bird art exhibits at RSPB Annual Members' Conferences, inc demonstrations of bird painting, since 1977. Bird painting workshops for RSPB, WWT etc. Visiting tutor/guest speaker elsewhere in UK and USA. Leader in 1995 and 1996 for American Assocn for the Advancement of Science groups on wildlife expeditions to Britain and Ireland. Special interests: field sketching, exploration of birds in relation to their habitat through paintings and drawings (esp species in 'non-fieldguide' plumages), seabirds, waders and waterfowl. Many visits, totalling almost five years residence, to W USA since 1979; expedition to Morocco as guest of the British Ambassador, March 1986. Responsible for print production, illustration and design of *Birds in Huddersfield* (annual report) c1977-87; illus in other annual reports (eg Derbyshire, Sheffield), journals and magazines (eg *Bird Life, British Birds*), and books (eg *Atlas of Breeding Birds in Greater Manchester, Birds of the Sheffield Area and Peak Park*). Author and illustrator of articles in eg *Dalesman* and *Mainstream* (magazine of Animal Protection Institute of America). Many one-person and group exhibitions, inc Mall Galleries (UK) and 'Birds in Art' touring exhibition in Sweden and USA. Designated 'Readers' Selection' by *Natural World* magazine for SWLA Exhibition 1992; Artist in Residence, 'Nature in Art' at Wallsworth Hall, Gloucester (Society for Wildlife Art for the Nations) 1992; USA guest tour (Jack Richeson/US Art Gilds) 1994; New Mexico/California tour (New Mexico Artists' Gild) 1995. Notable UK collections inc Bank of Scotland, BTO, Northumbrian Water, RSPB; others in N America (inc Robert Bateman in Canada, Univ California at Davis in USA). Work in many collections worldwide. OIR: general natural history, history, architecture, travel, photography/video, computers (not games), the sea, current affairs, psychology. St Margarets, Brierylaw, St Abbs, Eyemouth, Berwickshire TD14 5PH. Tel/fax 01890 771588.

WATSON, Jane; *b:* 12 May 1968 in Shoreham-by-Sea, Sussex. BSc Zoology (Manchester, 1990). Producer and Photographer, Partridge Films, Bristol 1996. Producer, BBC Scotland, Aberdeen 1995. Producer, RSPB Film & Video Unit 1991-94. Asst warden North Ronaldsay Bird Observatory Jun-Aug 1986; asst warden Bardsey Bird and Field Obs Sep-Nov 1986; research asst Station Biologique de la Tour du Valat, Camargue Apr-Aug 1987; teaching ringing at Long Point Bird Obs, Canada Jun-Sep 1989. Produced film *The Flamingo Triangle* (RSPB, 1993), winner of the Marais Poitvin award at 9th International Ornithological Film Festival at Ménigoute, France (1993), winner of Prix de l'Environnement at Festival de l'Oiseau, Abbeville, France (1994). Programme chairman of 7th International Wildlife Film-makers' Symposium, 1993. c/o 83 Buckingham Road, Shoreham-by-Sea, W Sussex BN43 5UD.

WATTS, David Earp; *b:* 23 December 1912 in Hoylake, Cheshire; *w:* Dorothy. BA Mathematics and Geography (Oxford, 1935), MA 1937. Teacher in Liverpool and South Africa then Headmaster of Kingsmead in Hoylake 1949-1979, retired. Special interest: bird song recording. Several trips of a few months to record song in South Africa in last five decades; recordings of over 360 different southern African species; intended to be available eventually to researchers so multiple, not just single, recordings; able to produce sonagrams. Presentations given at bi-annual seminars of International Bioacoustics Council, eg 'The Larks of South Africa', 'The

White-eyes of South Africa'. Articles in *Wildlife Sound*, illus with sonagrams. Member: SAOS, WSRS. Many lectures with slides and recordings to clubs in UK and SA. OIR: keen church member and active worker; earlier commandant of boys' holiday camps in UK and SA. Allt Alyn, Llanferres, Mold, Clwyd CH7 5TG. 01824 780204.

WEAVER, Peter; *b:* 13 August 1944 in Stamford, Lincs; *w:* Catharine. Stamford School. MA Geography (Cambridge, 1967). Freelance author, teacher, lecturer. Special interest: seabirds, esp Fulmar. Author *The Birdwatcher's Dictionary* (1981). Contributor to *A Dictionary of Birds* by B Campbell and E Lack (1985). Articles in magazines eg *Birds*. Member: Seabird Group. c/o C H Weaver, Queen Elizabeth II High School, Douglas Road, Peel, Isle of Man IM5 1RD.

WEBB, Andrew (Andy); *b:* 26 February 1960 in Lincoln. Marling School, Stroud, Glos. BSc Zoology (Durham, 1982). Data Specialist, Seabirds at Sea Team, JNCC since 1987. Prev NCC: Ornithologist, SAST 1983-87; Ornithologist, Moray Firth Shorebirds 1983; Ornithologist, Uists survey team 1983. BTO Regional Representative Aberdeenshire 1984-89. Birds of Estuaries Enquiry count organiser Aberdeenshire 1984-89. Bird Recorder North-East Scotland 1993-. Special interests: seabirds (distribution studies, marine ecology, identification), survey work, photography. Member of Durham Univ expedition to Morocco 1980 and Cambridge Univ expedition to Beidaihe, China 1985. Other trips to Nepal, China, France, Spain, Turkey, Cyprus. Published work on seabird distribution, biology, wader breeding surveys, identification, local distribution in eg *Biol Cons*, *Bird Study*, *Birding World*, *Ibis*. Editor *North-East Scotland Bird Report* 1990-93. Some photographs published in eg *Birding World*, *British Birds*. Occasional radio and TV. Member: OBC, Seabird Group. OIR: cetaceans, swimming, food and cooking. 4 Morningside Place, Aberdeen AB10 7NG. 01224 312484.

WELCH, Geoffrey Reginald (Geoff); *b:* 9 December 1955 in Birmingham; *w:* Hilary. BSc Zoology and Applied Entomology (Imperial College, London, 1977). Manager Minsmere RSPB Reserve since 1991. Prev RSPB: Senior Warden Nene Washes 1986-91; Warden Fairburn Ings 1980-86; asst warden Minsmere 1978-79; contract warden at North Warren (twice) and Wolves Wood 1977-78. Conservation Management Committee, Suffolk WT 1991-94. Suffolk Ornithological Records Committee 1991-96. OSME: Council 1986- (initially as Publicity Officer, then Joint Hon Sec and Librarian), Chairman 1992-97. Special interests (all undertaken as team with wife): migration (esp birds of prey) and conservation of wildlife habitats, principally in Middle East, predominantly Djibouti and Turkey. Related activities include organising and leading expeditions to Djibouti to search for endemic Djibouti Francolin, carry out survey of Arabian Bustard, count raptors, consult over conservation and research creation, work on national sites inventory. Developed standardised bird recording system and sites and species computer database for collecting and collating information gathered by birdwatchers visiting countries in the Middle East. Publications (jointly with wife) inc three Djibouti expedition reports (priv print), numerous papers on raptor migration (esp Djibouti) in *Sandgrouse* and *OSME Bulletin*; general articles on birdwatching in Djibouti in *Dutch Birding*. Member: OSME. OIR: 'keen interest in moths and dragonflies, home brewing, and frequently lecturing on my various ornithological exploits.' Minsmere Reserve, Westleton, Saxmundham, Suffolk IP17 3BY. 01728 648298; fax 01728 648529.

WELLS, James Henry (Jim); *b:* 27 April 1957 in Lurgan, Co Armagh; *w:* Grace. BA Geography (Queen's Univ Belfast, 1979), Dip Town & Country Planning (Queen's Univ Belfast, 1981). Assistant Public Affairs Manager, National Trust since 1990. Prev: NT Interpretation Manager at Giants Causeway on N Antrim Coast 1989; carried out three research projects in N Ireland for RSPB during 1987 and 1988: survey of breeding waders, impact of waste disposal on nature conservation, wintering wildfowl survey of Lough Neagh. Chairman Northern Ireland Raptor Study Group 1993-. Member Belfast Lough Nature Conservation Committee 1989-. Treasurer Assocn of Lough Neagh Users 1991-. Wetland Bird Survey organiser for Co Antrim (inland sites) 1992- (and previously for National Waterfowl Counts). Formerly on Lagan Valley Regional Park Committee, Mournes Advisory Council, and Executive Committee of Ulster WT. Special interests: nesting raptors and wintering waterfowl. Long-term study (commenced 1977) of nesting success of Peregrine in N Ireland. Joint co-ordinator (with Graham McElwaine) of recording Darvic-ringed Whooper Swans in Ireland. Heavily involved in campaign to protect the remaining areas of wildlife habitat of Belfast Lough. 16 Bridge Road, Lurgan, Co Armagh BT67 9LA. 01762 321837.

WELLS, Michael John (Mike); *b:* 10 October 1960 in Walton-on-Thames, Surrey. Bury Grammar School 1968-79. BA Natural Sciences (Zoology) (Gonville and Caius College, Cambridge, 1982), MA 1987, PhD Ecology and behaviour of Ringed Plovers in the Western Isles, Scotland (Univ Wales, Cardiff, 1991). MIBiol 1991, CBiol 1991, MIEEM 1994. Ornithologist/Ecologist, Nicholas Pearson Associates Ltd, Bath since

1991, Associate since 1995. Univ Michigan contract field ornithologist, Isla Genovesa, Galapagos 1983/84 (9 months). Asst warden, Arundel WWT Centre 1980 (3 months). Special interests: ecology and behaviour of wading birds, esp methods of quantifying energy intake and determining diet in winter, determining breeding success without observer effect in summer; behavioural and morphometric differences between individuals within a species; assessing and monitoring the effects of major developments on inland and coastal bird populations; factors controlling wader distribution on estuaries (undertook counts for Severn Estuary Low Tide Counts Project on behalf of BTO winter 1987/88); re-creation of lowland wet grassland for wading birds on clay soil systems; interactions between birds and windfarm developments. Organiser of project for maximising ornithological value of coastal lagoons in Fete, Ghana 1993. Special study species: Ringed Plover, Darwin's Medium Cactus Ground Finch (in Galapagos Is), Purple Moorhen (incubation behaviour studied for two months in Bharatpur Bird Sanctuary, Rajasthan, India 1981). Papers on Ringed Plover ecology presented at international conferences in France (1985) and Hungary (1992): proceedings published in *Wader Study Group Bulletin*. Contributed material to *Birdlife of Coasts and Estuaries* by P N Ferns (1992). Researched, wrote and delivered public lectures in Cardiff on the plight of seabirds in the Gulf during the Gulf War. Field cameraman for amateur video *Crofting and Conservation* featuring bird life of the Western Isles, presented at the 1985 Western Isles Cultural Festival. Large number of unpublished consultancy reports. Member: Wader Study Group. OIR: music, playing guitar and mandolin; French and Spanish languages and cultures; tennis. 4 Malvern Terrace, Camden Road, Bath BA1 5JT. 01225 319912; work 01225 445548.

WESTON, Michael Ross (Mike); *b:* 3 June 1943 in Staines, Middlesex. Windsor Grammar School 1954-61. MA Modern Languages (Oxford, 1966); also studied at Geneva Univ 1963. Fellow of the College of Preceptors 1990. ARPS 1992. Head of German at the British School in the Netherlands. Special interest: photography (both freelance and agency), mostly in The Netherlands, UK, France and Germany but birds also photographed in a dozen other European countries plus Morocco, Turkey, Canada and USA. Some five hundred photographs and/or illustrated articles in books and magazines in various countries; UK publications inc *Bird Watching, Birds, Birdwatch, British Birds, BTO News*. Exhibitions in Brighton (1981), The Hague (1981, 1992), Oxford (1984) and, as part of the Royal Photographic Society Nature Group exhibitions, at many venues throughout the UK. Broadcast on BBC radio programme *The Living World:*

a visit to Flevoland (1987). OIR: music, esp classical guitar, opera and choral. J v Oldenbarneveltlaan 16b, 2582 NP Den Haag, The Netherlands. +31 (0)70 3558265.

WHEATLEY, Jeffery John (Jeff); *b:* 31 May 1933 in Epsom, Surrey. BSc(Econ) (London School of Economics, 1954). Telecommunications economist. Surrey Bird Club: Chairman of Records Committee 1983-, President 1993-. Bird Recorder Surrey 1983-. Special interests: birds in Surrey, world birding, mountain birds. Travel for birds inc Antarctica, Australia, India, Japan, Soviet Central Asia, various parts of Africa, Europe, North and South America. Named contributor to *Birds in Surrey* ed by Don Parr (1972). Author of Surrey section of *Where to Watch Birds in Kent, Surrey and Sussex* by Don Taylor *et al* (1987, 2nd ed 1991). Editor of *Surrey Bird Report* 1983-93 (asst editor 1971-82); various papers and illustrations published in same. OIR: botany, computing, films, genealogy, poetry, family. 9 Copse Edge, Elstead, Godalming, Surrey GU8 6DJ. 01252 702450.

WHITAKER, James; *b:* 29 May 1935 in Leeds, Yorks; *w:* Margaret. Bookseller and publisher of bird books (propietor of Peregrine Books). Voluntary wardening at Fairburn Ings in 1970s (pre RSPB). Special interests: breeding biology of moorland species; long-term study of Golden Plover (commenced 1965). Treasurer and Trustee of the Jourdain Society national collection of eggs of the Western Palearctic (the Society holds collections of many esteemed ornithologists and provides study facilities). OIR: collecting crested china, motorcycling, collecting books and paintings, long distance walking. 27 Hunger Hills Avenue, Horsforth, Leeds LS18 5JS. 01532 585495.

WHITEHOUSE, Stephen Martin (Steve); *b:* 17 December 1956 in Birmingham; *w:* Helen. Royal Grammar School, Worcester. BSc Biological Sciences (Wolverhampton Polytechnic, 1979). Director, Birdline Midlands Oct 1989-; ornithological consultant for The Foreign Birdwatching Reports and Information Service May 1989-. County Bird Recorder Worcestershire 1987-95. Main Committee West Midland Bird Club 1987-95. Extra-mural studies tutor for Univ Birmingham 1987-92. Warden of Worcs Marsh Warbler population in 1988. Special interests: migration and identification, taxonomy of gulls (esp *argentatus, cachinnans, fuscus* group), status of birds in Worcs, sound recording, distribution and location of bird species in the Neotropics and Asia. Extensive travel abroad, inc leader of group trips, to 35 countries eg Thailand, Malaysia, Costa Rica, Ecuador, Kenya, The

Gambia, Argentina, Antarctica, Venezuela, India and most of Western Palearctic. Over thirty articles on bird finding abroad published 1987-95 in eg *Bird Watching, Birding World, Birdwatch, Birdwatcher's Yearbook*. Co-editor of *West Midland Bird Report* 1984-95. Winner of Wildfowl Trust's National School Competition 1974. Member: ABC, NBC, OBC, OSME. 'Have enjoyed a long British twitching career and am currently in fourth place in the UK 400 Club life list totals (UK/Eire) with 495 species.' OIR: dragonflies, watching soccer, international rugby and cricket. 6 Skipton Crescent, Berkeley Pendesham, Worcester WR4 0LG. 01905 454541.

WHITTLES, Christopher John; *b:* 13 July 1947 in Shrewsbury, Shrops; *w:* Christine. Nat Dip in Agriculture (Shuttleworth College, 1968), Cert Ed (Wolverhampton Technical Teachers College, 1975). Managing Director, Cereal Consultancy Service since 1976; Chairman, C J Wildbird Foods Ltd since 1987. Prev: lecturer in crop production, Northants College of Agriculture 1968-76. BTO: Ringing and Migration Committee 1974-78, Council 1984-87, Hon Sec 1987-90. Founding Chairman Lincolnshire Bird Club 1977-79, Vice President 1979-. Committee Shropshire Ornithological Society 1983-93. Founder-member Birdfood Standards Assocn 1988, Director and Chairman 1991-. BTO 'A' ringer since 1964. Led, or assisted on, all main ringing training courses in Ireland 1969-90; assisted on Gibraltar Point ringing courses 1976-90. Special interest: study of different races of Chaffinch and their occurrence, 1965-. Major nestbox scheme in S Shrops to study Pied Flycatcher, 1978-. Co-author (with P Deans *et al*) *An Atlas of the Breeding Birds of Shropshire* (1992). Articles on bird food safety in eg *Birdwatcher's Yearbook*. 5 Melrose Drive, Shrewsbury SY2 6QS. 01743 246682. C J Wildbird Foods Ltd, The Rea, Upton Magna, Shrewsbury SY4 4UB 01743 709545.

WILCZUR, Jan Peter Paul; *b:* 27 January 1957 in London; *w:* Margaret. BSc Zoology (Imperial College, London, 1980). Freelance illustrator. Extensive travel for birds inc Mediterranean region, India, Thailand, Mexico, USA. Illustrations published in books eg *The Hamlyn Photographic Guide to Birds of the World* ed by A Gosler (1991) and *The Blackcap* by C F Mason (1995); others in preparation inc *Field Guide to the Birds of the Indian Sub-continent* by R Grimmett and C & T Inskipp, *An Identification Guide to the Birds of South-east Asia* by C Robson, *Concise BWP* ed by D Snow and C M Perrins, and *Birds of the Eastern Palearctic* by S Madge and M Brazil. Illustrations in magazines inc *Bird Watching, Birdwatch, British Birds, British Wildlife*; also in annual reports and elsewhere. OIR: fatherhood. 30 Dover House Road, London SW15 5AU. 0181 878 8925.

WILDASH, Philip Cedric Thomas; Major Retd; *b:* 23 August 1916 in Brentford, Middlesex; *w:* Phyllis (deceased 1982). Merchant Taylors' School, London and Northolt. Army and Foreign Office, retired. Co-founder (with W R P Bourne) Cyprus Ornithological Society, Secretary 1956-57. Special interests: identification, taxonomy and distribution. Long periods of residence in Austria, Czechoslovakia, Norway, Germany, Cyprus, Vietnam; frequent visitor to USA and Turkey. Worked with H Elliott McClure as a ringer for Migratory Pathological Survey, Vietnam 1966-67. Author *Birds of South Vietnam* (Tokyo, 1968). Provided information for David Bannerman's *Birds of Cyprus* (1958) and *A Field Guide to the Birds of South-east Asia* by King, Woodcock and Dickinson (1975). Regular articles on ornithological subjects for *Cyprus Mail* (1957) and *Vietnam Guardian* (1966). Talks on birds given to local audiences. OIR: fishing, crosswords. 34 George Street, Woburn, Milton Keynes MK17 9PY. 01525 290318.

WILKINSON, Charles Gary (Gary); *b:* 25 September 1958 in Belfast; *w:* Gayle. Methodist College Grammar School, Belfast. Bank official. Northern Ireland Ornithologists' Club: Hon Treasurer and Field Trip Organiser 1990-. Regular participant in BTO surveys inc Project Barn Owl (and co-ordinator for N Ireland), Heronries Census, Wetland Bird Survey. Special interest: Barn Owl. Editor of *The Harrier* (NIOC newsletter) 1993-96. Article on birdwatching in Northern Ireland in *Birdwatcher's Yearbook* 1996. Member: Northern Ireland Raptor Study Group. OIR: poetry, sport, hill walking, music. The Roost, 139 Windmill Road, Hillsborough, Co Down BT26 6NP. 01846 639254.

WILKINSON, Peter John; *b:* 4 March 1944 in Birkenhead, Cheshire; *w:* Carol. Bedford School. BA Lit Hum (Oxford, 1966), MA 1971. ACIB 1969. Retired bank officer. Project Administrator (part-time) BirdLife International from May 1994. Treasurer BOU 1976-84. Finance Committee ICBP British Section 1986-91. BTO: Ringing Committee 1987-90, Council 1988-90, Treasurer 1991-94. Council Bedfordshire NHS 1994. Special interests: ringing; identification of hybrid partridges and captive-bred hybrid falcons. Expeditions to Spain and Portugal studying fat deposition in trans-Saharan migrants 1964, 1965, 1967. Lac de Grand Lieu expedition for warbler migration 1976. Articles on identification of hybrid partridges in *British Birds* and *BTO News*. OIR: family. 42 Dale Avenue, Wheathampstead, St Albans, Herts AL4 8LS. 01438 832512.

WILKINSON, Roger; *b:* 23 November 1948 in Blackpool, Lancs; *w:* Lynn. BSc Zoology (Southampton, 1971), PhD Auditory temporal resolution in birds (Southampton, 1975). Curator of Birds/Scholarship and Research Co-ordinator, North of England Zoological Society, Chester Zoo since 1983. Prev: Lecturer, Senior Lecturer Bayero Univ, Kano, Nigeria 1977-83; Research Fellow Southampton Univ 1974-77. BirdLife/WPA Pheasant Specialist Group 1993-. Joint Management of Species Committee (overseeing zoo conservation breeding programmes) 1992-. Chairman, European Endangered Species Programme (EEP) Parrot Taxon Advisory Group. Chairman UK Joint Management of Species Group (JMSG) Parrot TAG. Studbook keeper/species co-ordinator for EEP: Palm Cockatoo. Ditto for JMSG: Blue-eyed Cockatoo; West African Crowned Crane; Spectacled Owl. Council Avicultural Society 1990-. World Pheasant Assocn Captive Breeding Advisory Committee 1990-. Special interests: conservation breeding programmes, co-operative breeding in birds, vocal behaviour in birds, Nigerian ornithology. Papers on these and other topics in eg *Anim Behav, Avicultural Magazine, Ibis, Malimbus, Nature*. Member: WAOS, World Pheasant Assocn, World Parrot Trust. 2 Weston Grove, Upton by Chester, Chester CH2 1QJ. 01244 380280 (work hours).

WILKINSON, William Henry Nairn; Sir (Knight Batchelor 1989); *b:* 22 July 1932 in Warminster, Wilts; *w:* Katharine Loudon. Eton College (King's Scholar) 1945-51. BA Classics (Trinity College, Cambridge, 1954), MA 1956. Former merchant banker. Chairman NCC 1983-91. Winter recorder for IWRB wildfowl counts in Turkey 1963-67. BTO: Council from 1992, President from 1993. Ornithological Society of Turkey: Founder-member and Chairman (1967); became OSME, Vice President from 1987. RSPB: Council 1970-77, 1979-83 and from 1993; Hon Treasurer 1972-77, 1981-83; Vice President from 1993. Chairman, West Palaearctic Birds Ltd 1987-95. Council WWT from 1991. Vice President RSNC from 1993. Council Game Conservancy Trust from 1993. President London WT from 1992. Vice President Kent TNC from 1991. Special interest: wildfowl. Papers presented to ornithological conferences; sundry lectures and speeches given on nature conservation generally. Christopher Cadbury Medal (RSNC) 1993. OIR: archaeology, opera and music. **Deceased** (12 April 1996).

WILLIAMS, Gwyn; *b:* 15 April 1956 in Guildford, Surrey; *w:* Audrey. BSc Rural Environment Studies (Wye College, London, 1978). MPhil The impact of land drainage on the birds of the North Kent Marshes and a strategy for future management (London, 1986). Head of Species and Habitats Policy Department, RSPB since 1993. Prev RSPB: Manager Species and Terrestrial Habitats Unit 1991-93; Species Management Officer 1989-91; Conservation Co-ordinator 1987-89; Conservation Planning

Officer (Water and Recreation) 1979-87. Earlier: Higher Scientific Officer, NCC 1978-79; research asst WWT 1974-75. Great Ouse Flood Defence Committee of the National Rivers Authority, representing conservation interests, 1990-. Special interests: inter-relationships between land use, land use change and birds; undertook comparative study of impact of agricultural policy on land use and birds of the Isle of Man (a non-European Union country) and UK (EU member) in 1987. Co-author (with G Lewis) *Rivers and Wildlife Handbook* (1984). Papers and articles published in eg *Biol Cons, Bird Life, Birds, Ecos, RSPB Conservation Review, Wildfowl*. OIR: peat-free gardening, islands, Tuvan stamps. RSPB, The Lodge, Sandy, Beds SG19 2DL. 01767 680551.

WILLIAMS, James Michael; *b:* 13 July 1964 in Gloucester. Marling School, Stroud. BSc Biology (Southampton, 1986), MSc Biological Computation (York, 1988), PhD Habitat matching and cultural change in Chaffinch song (St Andrews, 1992). Environmental Data Specialist, SNH since 1993. Prev: Data Systems Manager, JNCC Seabirds at Sea Team 1991-93. Created integrated European Seabirds at Sea Database, used in production of *Seabird Concentrations in the North Sea: an atlas of vulnerability to oil pollution* (co-author with I C Carter *et al*, 1993). Special interests: sound recording and analysis methods (see PhD). Papers published in *Bioacoustics, Ibis, J Theor Biol*; also conference procs. OIR: Scottish country dancing, photography (esp close-ups of flowers), natural history and conservation. 12 Rintoul Place, Stockbridge, Edinburgh EH3 5JF. 0131 343 2956.

WILLIAMSON, Richard Leopold Calvert; *b:* 1 August 1935 in Barnstaple, Devon; *w:* Anne. Site Manager, Kingley Vale NNR 1963-95. Prev: Warden of Blakeney Point Reserve 1963 and of Winterton Dunes NNR 1962. Continuous Common Birds Census plots operated at Kingley Vale since 1963 and at West Dean Wood since 1974. Author: *The Great Yew Forest: the natural history of Kingley Vale NNR* (1978). Joint author (with K Williamson) of 'The Bird Community of Yew Woodland at Kingley Vale' in *British Birds* 1973. Various newspaper and magazine articles; also bird and natural history columns in *Portsmouth Evening News* and *West Sussex Observer* since 1963. OIR: driving and restoring vintage cars, classical music, writing novels and bird poems, travel. Keepers, West Dean Wood, Chichester, W Sussex PO18 0RU. 01243 535286.

WILLIS, Heather Anne; *b:* 27 November 1946 in Wokingham, Berks. Customer Service Agent (Traffic), Eurotunnel, Folkestone, Kent. Leader of field trips for RSPB Canterbury Members' Group since 1987. Natural history slide lecturer for clubs and societies in Kent area. Special interests: natural history photography, overseas travel on birding expeditions (eg China, Argentina, Venezuela), lone back-packing (eg two months in Lapland), seawatching, waders. Photographs published in eg *Birding World*, *Birdwatch*, *Camera Weekly*. British list 400, World list 2,475 (October 1996). 'I would like to encourage more women to become involved in ornithology.' Article on this topic published in *Birdwatcher's Yearbook* 1997. OIR: photographing butterflies, moths and other insects; collecting old glass jelly moulds and prints by the Victorian artist Louis Wain. 63 Clements Road, Ramsgate, Kent CT12 6UF. 01843 585932.

WILLIS, Ian Robert; *b:* 18 March 1944 in Hexham, Northumberland; *w:* Diane. Lewes Grammar School, Sussex. Nat Dip in Art & Design (Brighton College of Art, 1964); Art Teachers' Cert 1965. Full-time wildlife artist since 1967. Special interests: raptors, owls, waders, identification, migration, distribution, photography. Travelled extensively throughout British Isles and continental Europe; also Morocco, Egypt, Israel, Russia and eastern Siberia, Kenya, Venezuela, USA (Ariz, New Mex) in expeditions of up to six months. 'With three colleagues conducted first complete autumn census of migration of soaring birds (storks, raptors) over Bosphorous in 1966.' Wetland population studies (summer and winter) in Turkey 1966-75. More recent enthusiasm for tropical Africa and N and S America. Major works fully illustrated inc *Flight Identification of European Raptors* by R F Porter *et al* (1974, 3rd ed 1981), *Birds of Prey of Britain and Europe* by D I M Wallace (1983), *The Shell Guide to the Birds of Britain and Ireland* by James Ferguson-Lees *et al* (1983, and expanded German language ed 1987), *Owls of Europe* by Heimo Mikkola (1983), *Birds of the Middle East and North Africa* by P A D Hollom *et al* (1988). Sole illustrator but mainly line drawings *Birds of Prey* by Leslie Brown (1976), *The Barn Owl* by D S Bunn *et al* (1982), *Red Data Birds in Britain* by L A Batten *et al* (1990), *The Ruff* by Johan G van Rhijn (1991), *The Birds of the Strait of Gibraltar* by Clive Finlayson (1991); also all line drawings in *Birds of Africa* Vols 2-4 (1986-92), *Birds Encyclopedia* ed by C M Perrins and A L A Middleton (1985). All raptors in *BWP* Vol 2 and illustrations in many other works inc *Rare Birds of Britain and Ireland* by J N Dymond *et al* (1989), *Field Guide to the Birds of Kenya and Northern Tanzania* by Dale A Zimmerman *et al* (1996), *Handbook of the Birds of the World* ed by J del Hoyo *et al* (Spain, 1994 *et seq*). Co-author and illustrator of raptor migration and identification papers in *British Birds* and *Ibis*; also popular illustrated articles for newsletters and magazines. Several one-man shows in UK and many mixed exhibitions throughout UK, also in Canada, USA,

South Africa and Kenya. OIR: Lepidoptera; botany; reading archaeology, history and novels; watching films, TV plays and documentaries; visiting art galleries and historical buildings; listening to classical music and jazz; gardening. 20 Albert Street, Dalbeattie, Kirkcudbrightshire DG5 4JP. 01556 611158.

WILSON, Christopher John (Chris); *b:* 9 July 1946 in Sevenoaks, Kent (Irish citizen since 1987); *w:* Ann. Warden Wexford Wildfowl Reserve since 1991. Founder-member IWC Tipperary Branch (1984), Chairman (1987-90). Organised BTO/IWC Autumn Annual Conference 1987. Council IWC 1988, 1989. Cape Clear Bird Observatory: Friends Sec 1982-84, Ringing Sec 1984-93. Organiser of fieldwork in Ireland for BTO Winter Atlas (1983/84). Employed by IWC and BTO as Irish organiser of fieldwork for European Breeding Atlas (1987/88). BTO 'A' ringer since 1980 and sponsor since 1989. Secretary Tipperary Ringing Group 1981-91. Special interests: survey work, inc atlas and single species; ringing, esp training and communication (organiser of five Storm Petrel ringing expeditions to Cape Clear Island and member of Greenland White-fronted Goose Cannon-Netting Team). Ran Constant Effort Site at Ballagh, Co Tipperary 1983-92; commenced another in Wexford in 1993. Editor *Tipperary Birds* (annual report) 1986-90. Editor *Irish Ringers Bulletin* 1994-. Author *Ireland's European Breeding Atlas Results* (priv print, 1989). Co-editor *High Skies, Low Lands: an anthology of the Wexford Slobs and Harbour* (1996). OIR: all natural history (esp butterflies and moths), swimming, photography. Wexford Wildfowl Reserve, North Slob, Wexford, Co Wexford, Ireland. +353 (0)53 23129; fax +353 (0)53 24785.

WILSON, James Jasper (Jim); *b:* 11 April 1960 in Cobh, Co Cork, Ireland; *w:* Ann. Fellow of the Academy of Medical Laboratory Sciences, 1985. IWC Council member three years, Vice Chairman one year, Chairman 1993-96. IWC Cork Branch Committee member for several years, Chairman two years. Irish organiser of BTO/IWC Garden Bird Enquiry 1991-94. Founder and organiser of IWC Winter Bird Feeding Survey 1989-95. Manager (voluntary) of IWC Cuskinny Marsh Nature Reserve since its establish-ment in 1991. Special interests: gulls, garden birds, education, conservation, photography. Editor/compiler Cork County Bird Report 1983-87. Co-author (with John Coveney *et al*) of IWC's *Conservation Strategy for Birds in Ireland* (1993), and (with Don Conroy) *Birdlife in Ireland* (1994). OIR: playing guitar, listening to music, studying all aspects of natural history of local area (esp butterflies and moths). Blanan, Rushbrooke, Cobh, Co Cork, Ireland. +353 (0)21 812716.

WILSON, John; BEM 1991; *b:* 1 October 1935 in Warton, Lancs; *w:* Barbara. Hon MSc (Lancaster, 1989). Senior Warden Leighton Moss RSPB Reserve since 1964. Chairman and co-founder Lancaster and District Birdwatching Society (1959). Member of several reserve management committees. Special interests: conservation management, migration, Bittern, Bearded Tit, Coot, waders, African birds. Travel inc Europe, Africa, Asia, N & S America, Australia. Author *Birds of Morecambe Bay* (2nd ed 1988). Papers published in eg *Bird Study*, *British Birds*. Churchill Fellowship to study Bittern populations in Hungary and Poland 1979. Myers Farm, Silverdale, Carnforth, Lancs LA5 0SW. 01524 701601.

WILSON, Kevin Michael; *b:* 21 March 1966 in Farnham, Surrey. Nat Dip in Countryside Recreation (Merrist Wood Coll of Agric and Hortic, 1987-89). Nature Reserve Warden, Gibraltar Point NNR and Bird Observatory since 1994. Prev: Asst Warden at Gib Point and in Pembrokeshire Coast National Park. Committee Lincolnshire Bird Club 1991-. Lincs Rarities Committee 1992-. Tutor for Nottingham Univ residential courses on bird topics and for Lincs TNC day courses. Special interests: gulls, esp identification and racial separation. Travel for birds inc Spain, Corsica, Turkey, The Gambia, Denmark, Morocco, USA (California, Florida, Ohio), Sri Lanka. Author *Gibraltar Point Bird and Wildlife Report* 1990-95. Contributor *Lincolnshire Bird Report* 1990-93. Nature reports on Lincolnshire radio since 1991. OIR: bats, dragonflies, butterflies, moths, plants, music, football. 3 Aylmer Avenue, Gibraltar Road, Skegness, Lincs PE24 4ST. 01754 765505; work 01754 762677.

WILSON, Richard Trevor; *b:* 4 September 1938 in Ossett, Yorks; *w:* Mary. Nat Dip in Agric (Royal Agric Soc of Eng, 1960), PhD Ecology and biology of the Hamerkop (CNAA, Wolverhampton, 1986), DSc 1990. CBiol, FIBiol 1985. Consultant in international agriculture, natural resources and the environment. Chairman, Scientific Programme, Eighth Pan-African Ornithological Congress, 1990-92. Vice Chairman, Ethiopian Wildlife and NHS 1984-88. Special interests: Hamerkop, owls, Corvidae, African birds, photography. Editor *Proc 8th Pan-African Orn Cong* (1993). Over thirty papers and articles in eg *African J Ecol*, *Ibis*, *Revue de Zoologie Africaine*. Member: Ethiopian Wildlife and NHS, Gambian Orn Soc, Linnean Society (Fellow), WAOS. OIR: classical music, practical conservation of rare breeds of domestic livestock. Bartridge House, Umberleigh, N Devon EX37 9AS. 01769 60244; fax 01769 60601.

WINKLER, Hans Christoph; *b:* 22 April 1945 in Vienna, Austria; *w:* Christiane. PhD Biology of the Syrian Woodpecker (Vienna, 1971), Habilitation (Vienna, 1980). Professor of Zoology at Konrad Lorenz Institute for Comparative Behavioural Research, Austrian Academy of Sciences, Vienna since 1985. Prev: American Museum of Natural History, Dept of Ornithology 1973-74; Inst for Comp Behav Research, Vienna 1969-72. International Ornithological Committee from 1991. Research Committee, Deutsche Ornithologen-Gesellschaft (DOG) from 1994. Scientific Board, Neusiedlersee-Seewinkel National Park 1993-. Special interests: woodpeckers, bustards, fish-eating birds, population monitoring, conservation, behaviour, ecology. Projects carried out in central Europe, S, SW & W Asia, S America. Co-author (with D A Christie and D Nurney) *Woodpeckers: a guide to the woodpeckers, piculets and wrynecks of the world* (1995). Articles published in journals inc *Behavioural Ecol and Sociobiol, Bull Amer NHS, Ibis, J für Orn, Oecologia, Wilson Bull, Z für Tierpsychol.* Member: BirdLife Austria, DOG, OSME. Konrad Lorenz Institut für Vergleichende Verhaltensforschung, Österreichische Akademie der Wissenschaften, Savoyenstrasse 1A, A-1160 Wien, Austria. +43 1 4863315.

WINTER, Stuart; *b:* 18 January 1956 in Hackney, London; *w:* Anne. Journalist. Hon Sec Bedfordshire Bird Club 1993-95. Special interests: identification, N American birds. Travel for birds in Europe and USA. Editor of 'Clubwatch' in *Birdwatch* magazine. Author of 'Strictly for the Birds' ('first weekly newspaper column for birdwatchers') *Daily Star* since 1995. Member: ABA. OIR: supporting Tottenham Hotspur FC. 13 Saffron Close, Luton, Beds LU2 7GF. 01582 25406.

WISEMAN, Edward James (Ed); *b:* 5 June 1936 in Portsmouth, Hants; *w:* Wendy. Asst warden Fair Isle Bird Observatory 1964, 1965. Warden Keyhaven/Lymington Reserve (North West Solent), Hants CC and Hants & Isle of Wight WT since 1966. Warden Farlington Marsh, Hants & IoW WT winter 1971/72. Records and Publications Committee, Hampshire Ornithological Society 1958-. County Bird Recorder Hampshire 1983-92. Special interests: breeding bird studies, esp estuary and heathland birds; birds of prey. OIR: good music (eg Elgar, Handel), cricket (following Hampshire CCC). Normandy Farmhouse, Normandy Lane, Lymington, Hants SO41 8AE. 01590 675906.

WITHERICK, Michael Edward (Mike); *b:* 17 September 1936 in Woodford, Essex; *w:* Penny. BA Geography (Birmingham, 1958), PhD

Geography (Birmingham, 1963). Educational consultant, freelance lecturer and author. Visiting Fellow Univ Southampton. Bird tour leader, Ornitholidays 1992-. County co-ordinator for Hampshire of BTO Register of Ornithological Sites 1973-77. RSPB Council and Chairman of Conservation Committee 1983-86, 1989-93. Member of Inland Waterways Amenity Advisory Council 1993-95. Special interests: habitat and species conservation, environmental education, British county and local avifaunas. OIR: wine. Redlands, North Road, Dibden Purlieu, Southampton SO45 4RF. 01703 848657.

WOLF, James Charles Godwin (Jim); *b:* 24 August 1928 in Watford, Herts; *w:* Marjorie. Retired. Administrator BTO 1983-93. Hon Life Member of BTO, awarded for being driving force in taking BTO to the National Centre for Ornithology. Fellow Zoological Society of London. OIR: fishing, golf, photography. Tailor's Cottage, 59 High Street, Ixworth, Bury St Edmunds, Suffolk IP31 2HN. 01359 231688.

WOLFENDEN, Ian Howard; *b:* 7 May 1955 in Liverpool; *w:* Joan. Waterloo Grammar School. HNC Chemistry (Liverpool Polytechnic), Cert in Clinical Chemistry (Liverpool Polytechnic, 1977). Senior medical laboratory scientific officer in biochemistry in hospital pathological laboratory. BTO 'A' ringer since 1980. Wader counter for BTO. Member of Altcar Rifle Range Conservation Group, representing ornithology, since 1986. Special interests: study of birds of the Crosby-Hightown dunes and Alt Estuary on Merseyside, involving ringing and counting; long-term collection of breeding data (commenced 1978) for Skylark, Meadow Pipit, Reed Bunting, Linnet, Cuckoo, Stonechat, Whitethroat, Willow and Sedge Warblers; using ringing to study migration, adult and pulli survival; colour-ringing Skylark pulli and adults since 1980 to study their biology; studied breeding birds of Seaforth Dock Pools until area became a nature reserve; study of garden birds (esp Greenfinch) through ringing and observation. Articles on these studies published in *South West Lancashire Ringing Group Report* and *Lapwing* (magazine of Lancashire WT). Illustrated talk on Skylark study given at Ringers Conference; also illustrated talks and ringing demonstrations to local groups. OIR: general natural history, wildlife gardening, photography, practical habitat management and conservation. 35 Hartdale Road, Thornton, Liverpool L23 1TA. 0151 931 1232.

WOOD, Andrew Graham (Andy); *b:* 19 November 1958 in Harrogate, N Yorks; *w:* Carol. Harrogate Granby High School. BSc Zoology (Durham,

(1980), PhD Time and energy budgets of the Grey Plover at Teesmouth (Durham, 1984). Assoc Member Brit Computer Soc 1989. Database Administrator, British Antarctic Survey since 1989. Prev: Offshore Biological Programme Database Manager, BAS 1984-89. BTO 'A' ringer since 1984. Member of Wicken Fen Ringing Group. Special interest: application of computer technology to the management and analysis of ornithological and other biological data. Member of numerous ornithological expeditions to Shiant Islands (Outer Hebrides), Foula (Shetland), N France and N Norway; species studied split equally between waders and seabirds. BAS work involves regular visits to 'some of the more ornithologically interesting parts of Antarctica'. Scientific papers on waders, albatrosses and other biological topics published in eg *Antarctic Science, Bird Study, Ibis, J Field Ornithol, Ornis Scandinavica, Polar Biology*. OIR: photography, organic gardening, drawing, woodwork. Westwood, 3 West Street, Over, Cambridge CB4 5PL. 01954 202136.

WOOD, Derek Norman; *b:* 1 March 1932 in London; *w:* Glenys. Retired. Bird Keeper (1953-78) then Head Keeper of Birds (1978-91) Zoological Society of London. Member of Brent Research Group, IWRB, co-ordinating colour-ringed Brent Goose sightings in UK since 1974. Special interests: monitoring of Brent Geese wintering in the UK; raptor ecology (captive breeding projects including first breeding of Andean Condors in the UK; also field experience of 120 raptor species worldwide). Co-author (with wife, Glenys, under pseudonym Glenys and Derek Lloyd) *Birds of Prey* (1969, many editions in several languages). 36 Whitehouse Road, South Woodham Ferrers, Chelmsford CM3 5PF. 01245 322417.

WOOD, John Brian; *b:* 21 May 1946 in Harrogate, Yorks; *w:* Astrid. BSc Forestry (Univ College of North Wales, Bangor, 1970), MSc Ecology (Durham, 1972), PhD Zoology (Aberdeen, 1976). Senior Lecturer in Biology and Conservation, Univ College London 1976-91, 1993-. National Parks Development Adviser and acting Director of National Parks, Turks & Caicos Islands 1991-93. Chairman of Bird Exploration Fund, British Museum, Tring 1988-90. Special interests: conservation, migration. Scientific studies/research contracts undertaken in Afghanistan and Kashmir, Nigeria, France (Tour du Valat), Tunisia (Ichkeul and Kelbia), Saudi Arabia, Somalia, Mallorca (S'Albufera), Turks & Caicos Is. Scientific papers in eg *Bull BOC, Ibis, J Zool (Lond), Ringing & Migration, Scopus*; also contributions to various books. Editorial Board *Bird Study* 1986-89. OIR: dinghy sailing. Dept of Biology, Darwin Building, University College London, Gower Street, London WC1E 6BT. 0171 387 7050; fax 0171 380 7096.

WOODCOCK, Martin Wedgwood; *b:* 14 January 1935 in Sidcup, Kent; *w:* Barbara. Hon Secretary BOC 1965-69. Committee, Kent Ornithological Society 1981-91. Chairman, African Bird Club 1994-. Special interests: identification and distribution of Asian and African birds, painting, sound recording. Extensive travel in these areas, inc six months in Thailand and Malaysia in 1966 and four months in Africa in 1983, researching for illustrations. Author *A Handguide to the Birds of Britain and Europe* (1978). Illustrator *A Field Guide to the Birds of South-East Asia* by Ben King and E C Dickinson (1975), *The Birds of Oman* by Michael Gallagher (1978), *Collins Gem Guide to the Birds of Britain and Europe* by Richard Perry (1980), *The Cotingas* by David Snow (1982), *Estrildid Finches of the World* by Derek Goodwin (1982), *The Birds of Africa* Vol 1 (joint illustrator, 1982), Vols 2-4 (1986-92), *New Holland Pocket Guide to Birds* by Jim Flegg (1989). Author and illustrator *Collins Handguide to the Birds of the Indian Sub-Continent* (1980), *The Hornbills* by Alan Kemp (1995), *Pittas, Broadbills and Asities* by Frank Lambert (1996). Contributor of text and illustrations to various other books. Notes published in *British Birds*. Paintings exhibited in London (annually at the Mall Galleries) and the provinces, in Africa and at the Leigh Yawkey Woodson 'Birds in Art' exhibition in the USA and subsequently in Beijing, China. Bird Illustrator of the Year (*British Birds*) 1983. Member: ABC, OBC, SWLA. OIR: choral singing and classical music. The Fives, Elderden Farm, Staplehurst, Kent TN12 0RN. 01622 843252.

WOODHEAD, Mark Andrew; *b:* 21 December 1954 in Nottingham; *w:* Wendy. Bedford Modern School. BSc Physiology (King's College London, 1976), MB, BS (King's College Hospital Medical School, 1979), DM 1988, FRCP 1996. Doctor of medicine. BTO 'A' ringer since 1972 and trainer. Hersham Ringing Group 1972-79, 1987-92. Member of Bedfordshire Goose Study Group. Ringing expedition to Mallorca (Albufera) 1983; Rio Mazan expedition, Ecuador 1985; ringing expedition to Senegal 1991. OIR: watercolour painting. Ivy Cottage, 327 Oldfield Road, Altrincham, Cheshire WA14 4QT. 0161 929 0595.

WOODS, Richard Duncan; *b:* 14 March 1962 in Bangor, Co Down; *w:* Laureen. Sullivan Upper School, Holywood 1973-80. Birdwatching optical equipment retailer; property developer. Committee Northern Ireland Ornithologists' Club 1984-89, Secretary 1984 and 1985. Founding member and Chairman Northern Ireland Birdwatchers' Association (founded in 1991 with main purpose to publish *Northern Ireland Bird Report*). Co-leader of two Queen's Univ extra-mural birdwatching trips to

Mallorca 1986 and 1992. Organised the first pelagic trips off the W Donegal coast in August 1987 and 1988. *Northern Ireland Bird Report*: asst editor (NIOC) 1980-81, Editor (NIBA) 1991-. OIR: food (restaurants and home cooking). Churchfield, 3 Bangor Road, Holywood, Co Down BT18 0NT. 01232 428272.

WOODS, Robin Wilfrid; *b:* 20 October 1936 in Croydon, Surrey; *w:* Anne. BSc Psychology (Univ College of Swansea, Wales, 1970), PGCE (UCW, 1971), Dip Ed Psyc (UCW, 1974). Psychologist, retired. Participant in BTO Common Birds Census 1964-84 at two sites in Wiltshire and Devon; counted wildfowl and waders on Teign estuary for Birds of Estuaries Enquiry; contributed to BTO Atlas surveys 1988 and 1991. Initiated and co-ordinated data collection 1984-93 for Breeding Birds Survey of the Falkland Islands Trust (in Stanley) and Falkland Islands Foundation in UK (linked since 1991 as Falklands Conservation); collated and analysed data for compiling *Atlas of Falkland Islands Breeding Birds* (due 1996). Special interests: all aspects of Falkland Islands birds from 1956, esp identification and distribution of passerines, shorebirds and seabirds; photography, sound recording and ringing (inc two annual cohorts of 3,000 fledgling Black-browed Albatrosses, jointly with others, on West Point Island 1962, 1963). One-man expedition in 1983 to study passerines in tussac grass using modified Common Birds Census methods and examining the effects of introduced mammalian predators. With Royal Navy personnel, carried out preliminary ecological study of Motley Island, East Falkland in Jan 1995. Author *The Birds of the Falkland Islands* (1975), *Falkland Islands Birds* (1982), *Guide to Birds of the Falkland Islands* (1988); co-edited and revised with Anne Woods *Birds of Vanuata* by H L Bregulla (1992). Scientific papers in eg *British Antarctic Survey Bull* (with W L N Tickell), *Bull BOC, Ibis*. Trustee of Falklands Conservation since 1994. OIR: horticulture, botany, entomology (Lepidoptera), reading detective stories. 68 Aller Park Road, Newton Abbot, Devon TQ12 4NQ. 01626 68935.

WOOLFALL, Steven John (Steve); *b:* 29 August 1960 in Birkenhead, Merseyside; *w:* Lindsey. Birkenhead School. BSc Ecology (Lancaster, 1981). AMA 1986. Keeper of Natural History, Grosvenor Museum, Chester since 1991. Prev: BTO Regional Officer 1988-91; Trainee Museum Asst then Asst Keeper (Birds), Liverpool Museum 1983-88. Leader Wirral RSPB Members' Group 1986-88, 1996-. Cheshire Bird Report Rarities Panel 1985-88. BTO Membership & Development Committee 1988-91. BTO Regional Representative Wirral 1987-88, 1991-93. Wirral Waderwatch Beach Patrol Warden 1986-88. Part-time tutor in ornithology Univ Liverpool 1985-87. Special interests: waders and wildfowl, history of ornithology (species and people). Author of Meadow Pipit account in BTO New Breeding Atlas; also BTO report *A Review of the Birds of the Wyre Estuary in Relation to the Proposed Tidal Barrage* (1991). Papers published in *Archives of Natural History* and *British Birds*; also general articles in eg *Bird Watching, BTO News, RSPB* local newsletters. Compiler and editor of records for divers to storks and skuas to auks in *Cheshire Bird Report* 1985-88. Member: Biology Curators' Group. OIR: bats, cricket, films, real ale, science fiction, writing. 85 Ridgemere Road, Pensby, Wirral, Merseyside L61 8RR. 0151 648 6007.

WORDSWORTH, Philip Bright; *b:* 31 October 1934 in Barnsley, S Yorks; *w:* Barbara. Queen Elizabeth Grammar School, Wakefield. Taxi proprietor. Founder-member and Chairman of Yorkshire WT reserve at Wath Ings from 1976, Committee member since 1985. Secretary Barnsley and District Bird Study Group 1969-80; also recorder and editor of its reports in the early years. Gave illustrated talks using own cine film in 1960s-70s. BTO 'A' ringer 1966-86. Special interest: the Swift. Bird-related travel to the Camargue, Coto Doñana, Turkey, West Africa, Israel. OIR: gardening. Danecote, 7 Kensington Road, Barnsley, S Yorks S75 2TX. 01226 282940.

WREN, Graham John; *b:* 1 September 1936 in Cumnor, Berks. Southfield Grammar School. Agriculture. ARPS (Nature Category) 1983. Summer warden on Farne Islands and voluntary warden on various RSPB reserves in 1970s. Committee West Oxfordshire Field Club 1969-76, 1988-. Special interest: changes in nesting habitats and their effect on breeding populations. Member of trio to launch successful nestbox scheme in W Oxfordshire in mid 1970s for Kestrels and Tawny Owls due to losses through Dutch Elm disease; also artificial nests for House Martins and Tree Sparrows. Long-term project (commenced 1964) to photograph breeding habitats and nests of regular breeding birds, resulting in comprehensive slide collection. Travel for photographing birds to USA, Kenya, The Gambia and extensively in Scandinavia. Slides deposited with Oxford Scientific Films since 1978, resulting in a number being published in books, journals, magazines and videos. Several items on photographic expeditions on BBC Radio Oxford. Freelance leader of wildlife safaris in Britain and Scandinavia. Lectures on ornithological pursuits given to wide variety of audiences. OIR: jazz, motor racing, local history (esp old photographs). 99 Eynsham Road, Botley, Oxford OX2 9BY. 01865 862703.

WRIGHT, Colin Edward; *b:* 25 January 1938 in London; *w:* Patricia. Retired police officer. BTO Regional Representative Shropshire 1967-93. County Bird Recorder Shropshire 1972-83. Vice President Shropshire Ornithological Society 1985-. Fieldwork for county breeding bird atlas 1985-90. Special interests: waterbirds (counter for BTO Waterways Bird Survey 1984-93), garden birds, computerisation of county bird records. Joint author (with P Deans *et al*) *An Atlas of the Breeding Birds of Shropshire* (1992). OIR: hill walking, classical music. 6 St Annes Road, Collegefields, Shrewsbury SY3 6AU. 01743 350372.

WRIGHT, Jack; *b:* 15 December 1918 in Sheffield, Yorks; *w:* Betty. Sheffield College of Arts and Crafts. Royal College of Art (Associate 1948). Principal Lecturer, Head of School of Painting, Manchester Polytechnic, retired 1978. Warden on River Avon, Somerley Estate, Ringwood 1962-68. BTO 'A' ringer since 1969. Ringing in New Forest 1950s-60s, also tending and recording results of fifty nestboxes. 'Common Buzzard (pullus) ringed New Forest on 27 June 1962 found in pole trap La Malmaison area on 28 September 1962, the first recovery abroad of British Buzzard.' Founder-member Christchurch Harbour Ornithological Group (1956). Wildfowl counter Fordingbridge to Bickton (Hants) in 1960s; Slapton Ley (Devon) 1982-85; counts for BTO and WWT on Hayle Estuary (Cornwall) 1989-. County co-ordinator in Cornwall for BTO and WWT monthly counts for estuarine and inland waters 1991-93. Leader of birdwatching holidays and field meetings in Devon and Cornwall 1980-95. Special interests: migration and identification. Extensive travel in Europe; also Morocco, Oman, Sri Lanka. Bird paintings and woodcarvings in exhibitions in The Royal Academy, provincial and local galleries. OIR: walking and gardening. Anchor Cottage, Chapel Street, Marazion, Cornwall TR17 0AE. 01736 710099.

WRIGHT, Robert Malcolm (Malcolm); *b:* 18 September 1939 in Kingswinford, Staffs; *w:* Rosemary. King Edward VI Grammar School, Stourbridge, Worcs. ACIS 1962, AACCA 1964. Site Manager Breckland Heath NNRs and Chippenham Fen NNR (English Nature) since 1985. Prev: Reserve Warden, Caerlaverock NNR 1979-85; Warden Fing-ringhoe Wick Nature Reserve, Essex 1975-78; Warden Calf of Man Bird Observatory 1968-74; asst warden Bardsey Bird & Field Observatory 1966/67. Suffolk Ornithological Records Commmittee 1985-95, Chairman 1992/93. BTO 'A' ringer since 1966. Member of Solway Ringing Group 1979-85 and Lackford RG 1992-. Special interests: ringing and migration. Ringing expedition to Mount Kupe, Cameroon

1992. Author of 'Island' in *Birdwatcher's Year* by L A Batten *et al* (1973), also chapter on Calf of Man in *Bird Observatories in Britain and Ireland* ed by Roger Durman (1976). OIR: travelling, gardening, sport and family. Ridgeway, Fen Road, Pakenham, Bury St Edmunds, Suffolk IP31 2LT. 01359 230579.

WYATT, John Henry; JP 1979; *b:* 14 March 1938 in India; *p:* Maureen Southgate. Clifton College, Bristol 1952-56. Dip in Public Admin (Univ Coll of Rhodesia and Nyasaland, 1962). Sole Proprietor/Managing Director of Waxwing Associates since 1988. Prev: Deputy Director of Development, BTO 1988; various posts, inc Acting Asst Secretary, in HM Overseas Civil Service in Northern Rhodesia/Zambia 1959-71 (compiled records of birds for several districts 1969-71, being responsible for projects resulting from Kafue Gorge Hydroelectric Scheme, eg preservation of bird feeding and roosting areas and migration stop-off points); Keeper (Birds of Prey and Parrots) London Zoo 1958-59; honorary game ranger, Northern Rhodesia/Zambia 1963-71. Public speaker on ornithological and other wildlife subjects 1965-. Adult education lecturer in several counties 1983-. Special interests: photography, bird sounds, tour leading. Regular contributor to *Bird Watching* since 1988. Co-author, co-producer and publisher of *Teach Yourself Bird Sounds* cassette series 1992-. Member: ABC. OIR: classical music, theatre, food and wine, entomology, flower and mammal photography, the Roman Empire, travel and exploration. Little Okeford, Christchurch Road, Tring, Herts HP23 4EF. 01442 823356.

YOUNG, Barbara Scott; *b:* Perth, Scotland. MA Classics (Edinburgh, 1970). Post-graduate studies in Business School, Strathclyde Univ 1970-71. Dip Inst Health Services Management 1974. Chief Executive, RSPB since 1991. Prev: District General Manager, Paddington and North Kensington (became Parkside) Health Authority 1985-91. Hon DUniv (Stirling, 1995). OIR: cinema. RSPB, The Lodge, Sandy, Beds SG19 2DL. 01767 680551.

YOUNG, Robert Andrew (Rob); *b:* 22 June 1960 in Mill Hill, London; *w:* June. Computer consultant. Bird Recorder Hertfordshire 1991-. Herts Rare Birds Panel 1991-. Committee Hertfordshire Bird Club 1990-, Scientific Sub-committee 1994-. Bird Recorder Tring Reservoirs and wildfowl counter there; also joint founder and Chairman of Friends of Tring Reservoirs. Special interests: migration, gulls and ducks. Travel to Israel, West Africa, USA and China. Author *The Birds of Tring Reservoirs* (1996) and articles published in *Herts Bird Report*. Falcon House, 28 Tring Road, Long Marston, Herts HP23 4QL. 01296 668100.